ADVANCES IN FAMILY PSYCHIATRY

Advances in Family Psychiatry

Volume I

Edited by

JOHN G. HOWELLS

INTERNATIONAL UNIVERSITIES PRESS, INC.
New York

Library of Congress Cataloging in Publication Data

Main entry under title:

Advances in family psychiatry.

Bibliography: p.
Includes index.
1. Mentally ill—Family relationships. 2. Family.
3. Family psychotherapy. I. Howells, John G.
[DNLM: 1. Family therapy. WM430.5.F2 A244]
RC455.4.F3A37 616.8'915 78-13895
ISBN 0-8236-0097-1

Manufactured in the United States of America

Contents

VECTOR THERAPY

Preface

Family psychiatry is not family therapy, but as one American family therapist put it ". . . the field of family therapy is to be considered a branch of the broader discipline of family psychiatry." Both are represented in this volume. Family psychiatry, with its fulcrum in the United Kingdom, is broad in scope, and its core idea is that the family is the unit throughout clinical practice—for psychopathology, diagnosis, and treatment. Family therapy, with its fulcrum in the United States, is a narrower approach, but of considerable size, with an emphasis on treatment. This book covers all aspects of family psychiatry—theory, family psychopathology, family diagnosis, family symptomatology, family psychotherapy, and vector therapy.

The literature of family psychiatry grows so rapidly that the clinician in the field is hard-pressed to keep pace with it, let alone assess it. This book offers significant articles from the extensive recent literature on family psychiatry, assiduously collected at the Institute of Family Psychiatry. The collection has been carefully assessed for what is innovative in the field and worthy of inclusion. This volume does not pretend to be a textbook; it covers growing points only.

Perusal of the literature will show that growth in the various aspects of family psychiatry is uneven. Therapy has a vast literature, as indeed has the field of the family in relation to schizophrenia. Theory, psychopathology, and diagnosis are poorly covered; here the compiler was hard-pressed to find useful contributions, although for that very reason perhaps they are all the more valuable for being rare. We have sought to restore balance by a clinical emphasis throughout the field. In the section on psychotherapy, care has been taken to provide a representative illustrative sample from the large offering.

The overall selection has been culled from the international literature. Authors represent Australia, Canada, Czechoslovakia, Holland, Iraq, the United Kingdom, and the United States. The authors are invariably distinguished members of the fraternity of family clinicians.

Theoretical Aspects

Contributions to the theory of family psychiatry, in marked contrast to those on practice, are few. Innovation calls for exceptional people, and in any field such people are a minority. The future of family psychiatry depends on the few.

The first two chapters, on family myths and on areas of concern, are constructively critical, vigorous, and salutary. These are followed by three informative chapters on the classification of families, variant family forms, and an overview of developments in one country.

The attitude of this chapter is rightly critical. The author discusses nine contemporary myths about family functioning. He especially warns that the influences of the clinician's own family may affect his judgments; this is a timely and important reminder.

The Family as a System: Fact or Fantasy?

DAVID S. FREEMAN

A myth is an idea, notion, or assumption that is accepted as fact without any empirical evidence to support it. Usually it is a distortion of reality. At this stage in the development of knowledge about how family systems operate, there appear to be many more assumptions and/or myths about family behavior than empirical facts. I think this is so because the family is one of those systems that we, as researchers, practitioners, and/or theoreticians, are so identified with that it becomes difficult to separate our personal point of view from what actually exists when one views the family objectively.

We all come out of family systems and have strong feelings about how families should behave. Our own personal experience with families tends to serve as a frame of reference for analyzing other people's families. I have found in my own clinical work and in teaching family behavior that it is difficult to see other people's families as functional or healthy if they significantly differ from our own. Another way of putting it is that the more closely other people's families resemble our own, the more likely we are to see those families as functional. Occasionally, the opposite point

---

David S. Freeman, D.S.W., is Assistant Professor, School of Social Work, University of British Columbia, British Columbia, Canada.

Reprinted from *Comprehensive Psychiatry*, vol. 17, no. 6, November/December 1976, by permission of Grune & Stratton, Inc. and the author.

of view prevails—the more different the family is from our own, the more functional it must be. This is also a reactive position. These biases present theoretical and practical problems for dealing with families objectively. Practically, we are more likely to treat families as problematic when their structure and function are unique or, at first observation, peculiar. Theoretically, it becomes a sticky problem because many of our frameworks and scales of measurement for "functional families" do not take in the unique or unusual family structure. When we do encounter families that are so different from our own, we often put them aside with the statement that they provide examples to support the idea that families in today's world are disintegrating. A more optimistic point of view would see these families as illustrations of the great variety of families that can be developed to get the job done.

This paper will detail nine of the most outstanding myths that seem to influence our understanding of family behavior. Each myth will be defined, and some evidence will be provided to illustrate why they are myths.

Myth 1. Family Structure Is Nuclear Rather than Extended

This is one of the more important myths. How we define the structure of the family is significant because it influences whom we see as being important to the family and whom we include in family treatment. For many years now, North America seems to have viewed the family as a two-generational unit. The work of Parsons and Bales (1955) has strongly influenced such a view. Their studies indicate that in an advanced, technologic, industrial society, the most viable and flexible family system is the nuclear one. They describe the nuclear family system as a family made up of parents and children who do not have strong ties to extended kin and can at a moment's notice move where the labor market demands new labor. Since Parsons and Bales's initial work, many articles have appeared stating that the extended family is dead and that the nuclear family is the major family structure in North America. We have gone so far in this direction that family units that have close and significant ties with their extended families have begun to seem more dysfunctional and inappropriate in today's world than those families that have cut their ties with the extended family (Feldman and Scherz, 1967).

One outcome of this myth is that, in our work with families that lack resources, we tend to look outside the family system to find resources rather than explore all the possible extended family relationships that might be able to provide the necessary emotional, social, and economic resources to the family. This position is analogous to the intrapsychic position for understanding individual behavior. For example, in working with someone who does not have significant resources within himself to deal with his difficulties, we find it very difficult to move outside of the individual framework to rally resources that are natural to him, i.e., parents, brothers, sisters. When our framework moves from intrapsychic to intrafamilial, we are then able to do that. However, we have stopped at nuclear, intrafamilial and have not looked at what resources are natural to the family outside of this unit. If we were to discard this myth of the family structure as being nuclear then our treatment strategies, theoretical frameworks, and research designs would include the impact of the extended family on the nuclear family.

Three research studies have dealt with this issue of whether family structure is nuclear or extended. A major study (Leichter and Mitchell, 1967) conducted by Leichter at the Jewish Family Service of New York dealt with the issue of kinship values in casework interviews. The agency workers were mainly first- and second-generation Americans, whereas the clients were newly arrived Jewish immigrants from Eastern Europe. One finding was that many of the families who came in for service valued becoming more involved with their extended families. The families saw their relationships with their extended families as being helpful and supportive to a greater degree than did the workers in the agency.

The second study that questions this myth was conducted by H. Irving (1972) in the Toronto Family Service Agency. His basic goal was to discover who young families turn to when they need help. His findings, quite revealing, showed that young families turn to members of the extended family first, either a father or a mother, brother, sister, or some other relative. Next they seem to turn to neighbors and/or other extrafamilial figures, i.e., social agencies. Irving's findings were consistent with Leichter and Mitchell's in showing that young families continue to see the extended family as very viable for providing help and support when they are experiencing difficulties.

A third study, conducted in London by the National Society for the Prevention of Cruelty to Children, revealed that mothers-in-law play a significant role in their children's marital difficulties. This study showed that extended family members are involved when nuclear families are in a state of crisis (Moore, 1974). The study implies that one's framework for conceptualizing and working with families should include an understanding of the impact and involvement of extended family kin on the nuclear family.

The question one must ask is not whether the family in North America is nuclear or extended, but rather what roles do various members within a family constellation play to facilitate and at times handicap how a particular family unit operates. If we have a very limited concept of family structure, i.e. two-generational families, we tend not to ask questions about extended family and consequently are not aware of the natural resources that are available to family units.

What is crucial about looking at the role of the extended family is not the physical proximity of the family members to one another, but rather the emotional impact that family members have on each other. The old notion of extended family had to do with people living under one roof. Here are just a few of the questions that might be asked to begin to get a sense of what role extended family members play in the operating of the nuclear family: Who are the most important people in your life? Who can get you upset the quickest? Who do you turn to first for help? Who in the family do you spend the most time talking about? Who has had the most impact on your own development?

Myth 2. Families Are Closed Systems

The notion that the family is a closed system rather than an open one seems to be part of our belief system. Having given questionnaires to students learning to become family therapists, I have found that the great majority think that the family is a closed system. Many of the early studies on family behavior were done on schizophrenogenic families. Studies by Bowen (1960), Lidz (1960), Jackson (1960), and Weakland (1960) were all conducted on families that were experiencing very serious emotional problems. These families were operating under a high degree of anxiety and, at first sighting, appeared to be fending off change and closing themselves off from new inputs of information and knowledge from outside. Very few studies have been done on normal families—families that are not experiencing undue or extreme anxiety. I believe it is risky to use studies on dysfunctional families to describe the natural processes that normal families experience.

General systems research has demonstrated that it is impossible for a living system to be closed, that, in fact, the very life of a system is dependent upon its openness (von Bertalanffy, 1973). The issue is not whether a living system is open or closed, but the degree to which the system is open to allow sufficient information and data into its boundaries to facilitate continued growth and development over time. It is hard to imagine any system, particularly a family system, being closed. There are no firm boundaries around the family system. What makes one family system different from another is the arrangement of roles, values, and norms that the family observes to get its own job done as a family. Each family has a unique arrangement of its parts to the whole. It has its own role distribution governing how spouses, parents, and children position themselves in relation to each other. The family has its own normative set-up, what is acceptable and unacceptable behavior within the family and in the outside world. And each family has values, a network of "oughts" and "shoulds" about intra- and extrafamilial behavior. These are the factors that determine a family's boundary.

However, this boundary is permeable to inputs of new information. It does not necessarily follow that all information gets into the family, since part of the norm, value, and role structures of the family might exclude more than they include. Nevertheless, some information does come in. Each member of the family is a provider of new information. How people in the family serve as providers of new information to expand and extend the boundary tells us about the degree of boundary openness. The dichotomy between open and closed tends to obscure the major issue of how a family grows and develops over time. Basic questions that discourage us from seeing the family as resistant to change over time address the following issues: (1) how anxiety affects the family's ability to process new information; (2) who in the family is responsible for bringing in, interpreting, and transmitting new information; (3) what the codification system of the family is for making sense out of certain symbols; and (4) what type of information a particular family needs to continue to learn about itself and its environment. One has only to work with anxious families to discover that when the anxiety lessens, the family's ability to experiment and learn about itself increases.

This theoretical position has implications for how the therapist positions himself in relation to the family. If the therapist takes the position that the family system is a closed system, he will tend to see himself as the one most responsible for opening it up and will tend to do things for the family to achieve this. On the other hand, if the therapist takes the position that the family naturally wants to change and is basically an open system, he will try to tap those resources within the family. As the amount of anxiety in the family decreases, the family will begin to make its own moves at its own time.

MYTH 3. FAMILIES RESIST CHANGE AND TRY TO MAINTAIN THE STATUS QUO

This myth implies a homeostatic model of family stability. Most of the writing on family behavior tends to be influenced by the homeostatic model, one that suggests that families are reactive systems, fend off change, have few mechanisms to help them to grow and change over time. It is unusual to find an article in family literature that discusses the proactive elements within a family. Proaction is different from reaction in that it ". . . is used to designate an action that is not initiated by the confronting external situation, but spontaneously from within. An action of this sort is likely to be a part of a serial program, one that is guided by some directional force, which, in turn, may be subsidiary to a more comprehensive aim. As a rule, proaction is not merely homeostatic . . . if successful, a proaction may be said to be superstatic inasmuch as it results in the acquisition or production of something new . . ." (Murray and Kluckhohn, 1953, pp. 10-11).

This conceptualization of families as proactive significantly affects one's theoretical and therapeutic work. Speer (1970) stressed the need for a theoretical framework to deal with family change over time. He stated that the concept's viability, positive-feedback processes, morphogenesis, and variety are important for providing a more tenable conceptualization of the family system of our society today. The whole concept of change rather than stability needs to be emphasized in our attempts to understand family behavior (Speer, 1970). Most of the literature deals with the family's attempts to maintain stability rather than recognizing that in a rapidly changing society it is the families that can deal with change that can provide the best insights into the functional aspects of family behavior. Quoting Speer (1970), ". . . we need new concepts of family growth, self-evolution and restructuring. . . . Families need to be constructively responsive to change, able to change with change, and capable of learning to learn to give up obsolescent constraints. . . . One of the challenges confronting parents today is teaching children to be able to cope with unthought of and, as a result, unprogrammable situational and environmental changes" (p. 274). Speer is making a case for a morphogenic model of family behavior. In other words, we have to begin to see deviation-amplifying processes as essential for family growth and development rather than view these as dysfunctional. A status quo model would see positive feedback and/or deviation-amplifying feedback processes as a disservice to family stability, whereas a morphogenic model (a model beyond the homeostatic) would highlight and emphasize the growth-producing and sustaining processes that develop out of deviation-amplifying processes. An example of this point of view is found in Selye's research (1974), where he makes a strong case for the functional or healthy aspects of stress. He takes the position that life without stress is death.

It is not stress itself that needs to be analyzed, but the degree of stress any particular system can accommodate in order to thrive. Stress is a given and serves as a propeller in moving a system into action. In the old homeostatic model, stress is seen as a deviant, as an undesirable, something for the system to fend off. In a morphogenic systems model, stress is seen as an important variable for moving a system into action.

MYTH 4. THE FAMILY IS BREAKING UP—DISINTEGRATING

This myth ties in with myth 3. If we have a homeostatic model of family, then family change is seen as a disruption, as evidence of family breakdown. However, if we have an open system concept that also allows for a degree of change over time, we view what is happening to the family today as a response to what is going on in the larger society. The family, of course, is changing because the needs of society have changed. In the past, the family's jobs or functions were tied in with the socioeconomic structure. The family was relied upon to prepare its members to serve in the economic structure of the time. The family of 1975 no longer has this function. Society has taken over through various institutions—school, the military, etc.—to prepare its members for the job market. The primary role of the family today is to meet the emotional needs of its members. If we use a turn-of-the-century model of family stability to analyze the family of 1975, the family of 1975 would end up on the short end of the stick. However, if we recognize that the family is serving a new function and that people's options for meeting needs have changed, then our model for viewing family must also change.

The latest census statistics indicate that people are getting married and divorced at a higher rate than ever before. Statistics also indicate that people are remarrying at as high a rate as they are divorcing. What is the meaning of these statistics? In the past, it was untenable and unfeasible for many people to divorce. Today, the process is much easier, and one can guess that in the future the process will be even easier. The result is that people are divorcing and remarrying more frequently. This may be the product of an increase in one's awareness about what is best for self. The feminist movement has probably had an impact here. It has sent the message out quite strongly to all women that they have needs of their own, and if those needs are not being met through the traditional structure, they then have the right to search out and discover other ways of meeting them. The census statistics indicate that people continue to see marriage as a valid and useful institution for meeting their needs. How the family system should be organized in order to meet individual needs is, however, another question. The high divorce rate could be an indication of this struggle toward reorienting the family system to meet individual rather than economic needs.

One might say that, because the family is no longer a viable unit, married people are deciding not to have any children. On the other hand, one could interpret young people's decision not to have children as resting in their awareness of other needs and satisfactions in life; the decision is not necessarily an attack on the family unit as such.

Myth 5. The Most Stable Relationship Is a Two-Party Relationship

Most people assume that the most common relationship is the two-party one. Early research by Bowen (1966) has indicated that the most stable relationship is the triad (p. 356). This is an intriguing idea because it serves to broaden one's focal point regarding the unit of attention. If one can sit back and observe two people in interaction, one would soon see that two people tend to talk about a third. The outsider serves as the stabilizing element for the two insiders. The triangle serves to stabilize relationships between professional groups and/or between agencies, as well as individuals. Bowen gives a clear definition of how triangles operate. "The basic building block of any emotional system is the triangle. When emotional tension in a two-person system exceeds a certain level, it triangles a third person, permitting the tension to shift about within the triangle. Any two in the original triangle can add a new triangle. An emotional system is composed of a series of interlocking triangles. The emotional-tension system can shift to any of the old preestablished circuits. It is a clinical fact that the original two-person system will resolve itself automatically when contained within the three-person systems, one of whom remains emotionally detached." The concept of triangle is important in that it helps us to defocus on the two-party system and refocus on the significant three-party systems. In my own clinical work, I have seen the triangle operate dramatically between professional groups. Examples of this occurred frequently in my earlier work in psychiatric hospital settings. The usual triangle was between the medical doctor, the nurse, and the social worker. Initially the basic two-party system, the "in" group, might be the nurse and the doctor, with the social worker on the outside. Time spent together between the nurse and the doctor included talking about the social worker on the ward. They would say things like, "We really don't need a social worker on the ward, he just gets in the way with his crazy ideas." The doctor might say that, "The social worker is just mucking up what's going on in the ward treatment plan." Or the nurse might say to the doctor that "The social worker tends to get overinvolved or underinvolved with the patients." In any case, the two have stabilized their relationship by having a scapegoat. This can work out quite well until one or the other feels so much tension between them that talking about the social worker no longer serves to reduce it. When this happens, one or the other will make a move to the social worker. The nurse might move to the social worker who, being on the outside, is waiting for an opportunity to get on the inside. The nurse will say something negative about the doctor, at which point the social worker will be more than willing to become involved. This places the nurse and the social worker in the "in" position and the doctor in the "out" position. Now, this could go on for a period of time until the nurse and the social worker experience so much tension in the relationship that talking about the doctor does not stabilize it. Then one or the other will make a move to the doctor. In this case, it might be the social worker. He might say something negative about the nurse. The doctor, being on the outside and not wanting to stay on the outside, would agree with the statement, and around they go—the social worker and the doctor now talking about the nurse.

The basic difficulty in operating in triangles is that people talk about each other and do not talk about what's happening within the dyadic relationship. This helps stabilize the relationship, but no new learning occurs. Family systems contain the most intense triangles.

J. Haley (1969) provides a beautiful example of how a schizophrenic child who is expert in setting up and negotiating triangles in his home begins to set up the same sort of situations on the ward when he is hospitalized. One of my assumptions is that triangles that become established within the family are acted out in similar ways in other systems the family members are involved in. By keeping the triangle concept in mind, one can begin to intervene in triangles as a way of changing family systems.

Myth 6. There Are Facts for What Goes on within Personal Relationships

This is a myth that many family members cherish. When there is conflict within the family, family members try to figure out who is right and who is wrong. The harder they try to prove rightness and wrongness, the more the conflict accelerates. Very few people have been trained to become aware of process. One way to understand the use of conflict or the attempt to prove right and wrong is to see it as a way of defining process and how people position themselves in relation to each other. One of the most helpful procedures for working with families in therapy is to stay tuned in to the process and not get caught up in the content that people present. It is a common occurrence for families to come in with a story and try to get the therapist to figure out who is right and who is wrong, or to get the therapist to take sides on some aspect of the story. If someone *can* convince the therapist that his picture of the story is correct, then the therapist has entered the triangle, and, in fact, everyone in the family, including the therapist, becomes the loser. In looking at process, the therapist should be tuning in to how individual members within the family use conflict as a way of keeping emotional distance. There are many different types of conflict, i.e., sledge-hammer conflict and vicious-circle conflict, which are illustrations of nonproductive conflict, that is, conflict that keeps relationships pretty much the way they are. There is also functional conflict, which involves the renegotiation and reorganization of relationships. When one family member begins to make a move or change something that's important to him, other members of the family begin to become somewhat uncomfortable and conflict occurs. In dealing with this type of conflict, one has to become aware of the processes that are going on within the family. Which member in the family is most comfortable with change? How is he positioning himself in the family to deal with that change? What are the other family members doing in response to that change? The issues (content) are not as important as how (process) these issues are dealt with.

Myth 7. You Can Learn and/or Know Someone through the Eyes of Another

Many of us learn about other people, not through direct contact with them, but by talking to someone else about them. Most of us who have done individual work can appreciate this problem. One member of the family comes in to tell us about the problems or the difficulties he or she is having with other members of the family. Many times we never get to see those other members of the family and begin to make assumptions and assessments about the whole family through the eyes of one member. If we're fortunate enough then to see the rest of the family or to see the member who was talked about, we discover quite quickly that the person is not at all the way he or she was described. In fact, it becomes even more complicated than that. When we see two individuals together, each seems different from when we saw him or her alone. And then, when we bring the whole family together, all those individuals seem different from when we saw them in dyads. In order to understand people, we have to see them in the context in which their behavior is taking place. Each of us has a vested interest in seeing other people in a certain way. When someone describes someone else to us, is he really describing that person or is he in fact describing his own need to see that person in a particular way? If we take the latter position and discard the myth that we can learn about someone else through the eyes of another, then we will begin to ask that person questions that encourage defining what is going on in him rather than spending time talking about others. This helps us to work with individuals in terms of self-development and cuts down on the person's using the time to ventilate about others and, in a way, making it more difficult to learn about self. This myth relates to how the triangle operates. If a person comes in to describe someone else and we become party to that, then the two of us are in oneness against the other, no matter how neutral we try to be.

Many members of nuclear families feel they know members of the extended family quite well, but after checking out whether what they feel is correct or accurate, find this is not in actuality so. These legends or myths that we have about our extended family members serve as barriers that prevent us from learning about changes that have taken place in our extended family or discovering new resources that might be available.

Myth 8. One Family Member Is the "Sick One"

It is hard to imagine a family in which one member is hurting and other members are not experiencing hurt as well. The other side of this myth is that in order for one member of the family to be seen as dysfunctional, sick, or bad, other members of the family must be seen as functional, healthy, and good. Whenever a family has a member who is seen as a problem, he or she is being evaluated alongside those "healthy" family members. The point I am trying to make is that in order for a family to have a serious problem, other members of the family have to be doing things to help maintain, support, and/or encourage that behavior. Dysfunctional behavior can be seen as serving a certain role within the family. In order for that behavior or that role to be carried out, reciprocal processes must be occurring. One family that was defining its role structure told me that the identified problem was the warmonger in the family, while the mother was seen as the mediator. It was an eye-opener to this family to discover that in order to have a warmonger, one had to have warriors, and to have a mediator, one had to have people who needed to be mediated.

Exploding this myth removes the focus from intrapsychic difficulties and places it on the network of social relationships that help to maintain, stabilize, and/or change a particular problem. Thus, we begin to look at the family as a system, rather than looking at an individual member as being the sole carrier of a problem.

It becomes important to see behavior, then, in terms of role structures and to give the family an opportunity to define the reciprocal aspect of each role within the family. A way of assessing how other members of the family are involved in the dysfunctional behavior of a particular member is to ask the family members how much time they spend thinking, worrying, and talking about the particular problem. If a family spends a good deal (over 50 percent) of their time thinking, talking, and worrying about a particular problem, and by some magic that problem were to disappear, a void then would be present in the family. And that void could become more of a problem than the problem that brought the family in for help. Before a family can afford to give up a particular problem, something else, some other meaningful way of having the family use its time, must be found.

Myth 9. The "Problem" Member of the Family Is the One Who Needs Help

This myth implies that when a family comes in with a defined problem, the center of attention should be the problem carrier. Bowen (1966) has done some very interesting work and writing about the role of the underfunctioner within the family. He takes the position that in order for someone to be an underfunctioner, someone must be an overfunctioner. In fact, the overfunctioner is frequently more anxious and more of a problem than the underfunctioner (p. 351). For example, a family complains that one member of the family is not carrying his responsibilities. It might be as simple as parents' saying that a child is not taking care of his room, that he leaves messes behind. If the complaining member is asked how long he can wait before he picks up after the child, he usually responds, "Not very long." I had one father tell me that he was convinced that his son could never pick up his litter, so within a matter of seconds he would pick up all the child's toys and clothes and what have you. When the child was asked why he wasn't taking better care of his possessions he said, "Well, I know my father is going to do it, and he doesn't give me a chance to pick the stuff up myself." This is a simple example of how the overfunctioner dovetails with the underfunctioner to keep the underfunctioner underfunctioning.

One might consider working more with the overfunctioner or the "healthy members of the family" before one gets involved with the underfunctioner or the problems in the family. If the overfunctioner is the more anxious one, he will take over as a way of dealing with his own anxiety. Until that problem is dealt with, the underfunctioner is not going to be given enough room, opportunity, or time to experience new behaviors.

This myth has real implications for the health delivery system. Most of our services are designed to help the underfunctioners become better functioners without recognizing that there are other members within the family system or the community at large that are feeding in to keep the underfunctioner down. At this point in my clinical work, I zero in much more with those members of the family who are not seen as the problem. I have found that when I am able to alleviate the anxiety of those members of the family who find it necessary to take over for other members of the family, the others begin to move upward.

References

Bowen, M. (1960), A family concept of schizophrenia. In: *The Etiology of Schizophrenia*, Part VI, ed. D. D. Jackson. New York: Basic Books, pp. 346-372.

——— (1966), The use of family theory in clinical practice. *Compr. Psychiat.*, 7:351-356.

Feldman, F. & Scherz, F. (1967), *Family Social Welfare: Helping Troubled Families*. New York: Atherton.

Haley, J. (1969), *The Power Tactics of Jesus Christ*. New York: Grossman.

Irving, H. H. (1972), *The Family Myth*. Toronto: Copp Clark.

Jackson, D. D.(1960), A critique of the literature on the genetics of schizophrenia. In: *The Etiology of Schizophrenia*, Part I, ed. D. D. Jackson. New York: Basic Books, pp. 37-87.

Leichter, H. J. & Mitchell, W. E. (1967), *Kinship and Casework*. New York: Russell Sage Foundation.

Lidz, F. (1960), Schizophrenia, human integration and the role of the family. In: *The Etiology of Schizophrenia*, Part VI, ed. D. D. Jackson. New York: Basic Books, pp. 323-345.

Moore, J. (1974), Mother-in-law's no joke. *Vancouver Sun*, April 12, p. 30.

Murray H. A. & Kluckhohn, C. (1953), *Personality: In Nature Society and Culture*. New York: Knopf.

Parsons, T. & Bales, R. F. (1955), *Family, Socialization and Interaction*. Glencoe, Ill.: Free Press.

Selye, H. (1974), *Stress Without Distress*. Toronto: McClelland & Stewart.

Speer, D. C. (1970), Family Systems: Morphostasis and morphogenesis, or is homeostasis enough? *Fam. Proc.*, 9. 259-278.

von Bertalanffy, L. (1973), *General Systems Theory*. New York: George Braziller.

Weakland, J. (1960), The "double-blind" hypothesis of schizophrenia and three-party interaction. In: *The Etiology of Schizophrenia*, Part VI, ed. D. D. Jackson. New York: Basic Books, pp. 373-388.

Following naturally from the first chapter, we have here a thoughtful analysis of four areas of concern in our understanding of families. The author emphasizes our need to be more productive in the theoretical field and makes some useful recommendations.

Contemporary Concerns

AXEL RUSSELL

The questions and problems fall into four major areas: theoretical questions; clinical and practical problems; training, political, and economic concerns; and research and methodological issues.

Theoretical Questions

Not enough theory building is going on. Integrative development of formal theoretical bases leading to construction of more systematic approaches in the treatment of disturbed families is not impressive. Can we avoid dogmatization or premature calcification?

Foley (1974) juxtaposed Framo's and Boszormenyi-Nagy's position—derived mainly from psychoanalysis and systems theory—with Beels and Ferber's (1969) integrationist stance, as they are trying to move beyond a communication viewpoint. Haley held, however, that no compromise was possible "since the frames of reference are totally different." Learning theory and personality theory still seem to be out in left field. Whether lasting bridges can be built between psychodynamic, systems theory, and learning theories in the practice of family therapy very much remains to be seen.

Axel Russel,, M.D., was formerly Medical Director of the Psychiatric Section of the Oxford Mental Health Centre. He is now Psychiatric Consultant at the Oxford Regional Centre, P.O. Box 773, Woodstock, Ontario, N4S 7X9.

Reprinted by permission from the *Journal of Marriage and Family Counseling*, vol. 2, no. 3, 1976.

Family therapy's increasing acceptance and growth; the claims made for its usefulness; the shifts in emphasis, focus, orientation, and techniques; and its expanding application to a spectrum of clinical entities still do not enable us to predict whether or not it will ultimately fulfill the expectations raised. As with other innovative approaches, it has also become a fad and bandwagon for some, first tried uncritically, later abandoned or rejected a priori. Some critics have noted that its conceptual wilderness led to methods of intervention which depended as much on the personality and the theoretical orientation of the intervenors as it did on other factors.

The single universal comprehensive theory of behavior, which could serve as an iron-clad rationale for intervention into the family system, therefore still evades us, as does an acceptable theory linking family process and the growth of individual family members' personalities. It would clearly be useful to narrow the gaps between the very divergent theories about human behavior by unifying efforts. Are there as many kinds of family therapy as there are individual therapists? Elsa First's recent discussion (1975) of related topics provides a useful polemic, from a psychoanalytic viewpoint, of the "not so convincing solutions of family therapy."

Clinical and Practical Problems

We need universally acceptable definitions of how the normal family functions, of indications and counterindications of functioning, in order to delineate pathology and to guide our interventions. There has been a dearth of work since Zuk and Wynne ten years ago. In our training network (S. W. Ontario) we use a working definition, recalling David Olson's formulations, that "any intervention focusing on the family system rather than the persons in it merits the name of family therapy" (Foley, 1974, p. 3).

Much continues to be said about the applicability of systems theory (von Bertalanffy probably would no longer recognize his creation). As a metatheory it enables us to unify disparate theory elements into a megatheory which will encompass them in a heuristic way. However, a clinically practical system needs to be developed first before it can be plugged into the general systems theory. Unmodified, general systems theory cannot provide the conceptual basis for therapeutic interventions. In fact, when one asks where is the locus or fulcrum of effective intervention, other models suggest specific strategies which appear to offer more suitable options. Clinical procedures based on learning theory need the same integration.

Haley (1975) has suggested that because of "unsettling effects" innovative family therapy procedures are likely to have on "the offerings of Mental Health Clinics" it should be avoided altogether unless "required changes" can be made. He warned that family therapy procedures should not be offered in such a clinic setting because changes in causal theory, diagnosis, therapeutic techniques, and clinical training are required before this can be done successfully. Maintaining harmony among the disoriented staff is vitally important. It is not easy to achieve, as radical changes in administrative and other procedures, in the professional hierarchy, in the ecological and the support systems, in one's own inner and outer world picture, are involved. It appears that the "Holy Trinity of the Mental Health Profession," i.e., the Holy Ghost/Son/Father = Social Worker/Psychologist/Psychiatrist, which "dwells usually in a Community Mental Health Clinic" must be allowed to adjust to the "unthinkable," i.e., become a really multidisciplinary team (Coles, 1974). The current status hierarchy remains the largest obstacle. Existing taboos will have to go. Either trust will be established and a real multidisciplinary team formed or the program will be sabotaged. If team formation is achieved, it delivers comprehensive services to larger numbers of varied people and shows better outcomes.

Foley (1974) recently differentiated major theorists and theories, providing an overview and analysis of basic concepts in the field. Yet Epstein and Levin (1973) believe that not nearly as much difference exists between the therapist categories generally suggested because existing differences seem to be based largely on the personal style and technique of the therapists concerned rather than on any really major differences in theoretical assumptions.

All family therapists continue to emphasize the need to change the family system by altering its interactional processes and largely agree that the primary purpose of working with a family as a group is to improve its functioning as a unit. The overview of "Family Therapy up to 1970" (Group for the Advancement of Psychiatry, 1970) stated that family therapists generally still take either an intrapsychic, an interactional or systems, or an in-between position.

Families generally prefer to perceive their problems in terms of negotiation or conciliation rather than in terms of psychopathology. They learn techniques of negotiating on more concrete issues, which they can generalize to more complicated areas in their lives, and then take over control using these new coping mechanisms to mutual advantage. Such efforts need maximization.

Training, Political, and Economic Concerns

In view of the already noted disruptive consequences for a traditional health delivery system, Framo (1975) questions ". . . whether it is better for family therapy to exist in a setting of competing viewpoints or mixed models" or "if we should not do what psychoanalysis did, which entailed setting up its own institutes and standards" which had "dire consequences for that movement" now trying to stage a comeback. He sees the "validity of arguments on both sides" and has no answer to that question. My answer is neither black nor white; it depends on local conditions. Training in working with families is carried on in many "Family" and "Life Education" institutions in our major cities. It is important to differentiate family therapy from mere counseling. The line is too often ignored.

Emily Mudd (in a personal communication, 1975) provided a historical note that, when she started out, family and marital counselors were constrained by lawyers because the latter considered "counseling" to be their sole domain. In Canada, too few family therapy schools yet exist (Montreal's McGill and Hamilton's McMaster Universities stand out) (Levin and Cleghorn, 1973). Family therapy is usually practiced in clinical settings that use other, more traditional, treatment modalities, or is carried on in private-practice settings or via a small regional network of service delivery centers of all types. Because established professional groups continue to resist change, their stance being largely passive/aggressive, the creation of institutes would seem to be a desirable step. The resistance to change is understandable in dynamic and "systems" terms, but needs to be overcome. Jean Paul Sartre thought change came always as cataclysm. Even if true, as professional change-agents, we should find less destructive ways of bringing it about. Satir's (1972), Whitaker's (personal communication), Minuchin's (1975), or Caplan's (1970) recent pragmatic contributions did not deal specifically with such issues. We have to.

We need to evolve specific training programs for family (or marital) therapists that go beyond the general training program for psychotherapists per se, and beyond the family therapy training models as used at present. Framo (1975) reflected that "whilst student pressure forces some departments of social work to give courses on family therapy," in some schools only "few doctoral programs in clinical psychology (now) offer such a course." Do others? What option will other health disciplines take? It surely ought to be included in psychiatric residency programs, and so on. When it was, this often represented only a gesture, the program being terminated when the "full implication of its use from the system's viewpoint was operationally felt," i.e., when its effect began to seep through. This was a common experience. The dearth of teaching of family dynamics in the training schedule of family medicine practitioners was interpreted by Haley (1975) also as reflecting such a resistance to change.

Sigal et al. (1973) and Spector-Postner et al. (1971) developed a procedure to predict outcome by "fitting" therapists and certain family constellations together.

One can readily agree with Ferber and Mendelsohn (1969) that outcome remains difficult to evaluate because "no-one seems to have the same notions" about outcome, or "refers to the same kinds of treatment." A study of computer printouts of 99 outcome studies carried out over the ten-year period of 1964-1974 (NIMH, 1974) shows that, owing to lack of definitions or standardization, the results cannot be compared usefully. Other, similar methodological problems abound (Spector-Postner et al., 1971). "Problem-solving games" have been found heuristically valuable in the investigation of such problems (Epstein and Santa-Barbara, 1975).

It is assumed that the more experienced a family therapist is, the more likely he is to be flexible and shift his "approach" if the family in treatment remains unchanged. Do we know which therapist is likely to have the honesty, flexibility, self-knowledge, and so on to change his approach and his strategies appropriately (Ackerman, 1971)?

Therapists need a constant testing and maintaining of clinical skills, and often need further training, upgrading of performance, increase of self-knowledge, and encouragement from colleagues to look at themselves and what they are doing. A dogmatic commitment to only one treatment modality or style is insufficient, occasionally even antitherapeutic. We need to master whatever armamentarium of clinical techniques and forms of intervention are required to meet the many needs of each "unique" family system, combining the use of different "models" and resisting dogmatically asserted, usually unsubstantiated, claims for the efficacy of only this or that model, or style, or this or that "school" of family therapy! The history of psychiatric therapies in general, and of psychotherapy in particular, suggests that such temptations be resisted. We need to warn "beginning" family therapists that, because of the differences in style, sensitivity, personality, and the sheer clinical skills displayed, one simply cannot "just" imitate one of the pioneering masters. Family therapists still come from various backgrounds and experience, with varying skills, different theoretical orientations, and having varied degrees of sophistication, training, and education. I agree with often sounded warnings that excitement, turbulence, motivation, spontaneity, or charisma alone are not enough. I understand the lure of viewing the family approach "as a philosophy and orientation to the human condition," and not just as a technique or form of therapy. Some have argued that many of the newer approaches similarly are not therapy but "an existential experience in living." This is arguable, but a potentially dangerous view. The need to separate and yet to relate and be intimate will remain a fact of life and a source of eternal conflict, requiring ongoing compromises.

It is a truism that one can learn to do family therapy only by doing it, and being supervised while doing it. But I question some procedures used. Should a trainee be forced to listen exclusively to signals from a "bug" in his ear instead of to the family? Other extreme training procedures noted involved the "trainer" rushing in every few minutes, yelling something at the trainee and/or the family, and then rushing out again. Communication patterns used by some therapists can be as disruptive, masked, oblique, indirect, and bizarre as those operating in the most pathological families. The use of such dubious means cannot be justified. How to prevent such practices and failure? The ethical problem remains (means vs. ends). Such matters appear to be somewhat neglected by clinical investigators.

Many sensible and tried teaching methods, now part of our training repertoire, demonstrate usefully the differences between what we actually do, how we perceive our in-therapy behavior, and how we report it. Yet, after being supervised and supervising, after watching trainers and trainees and various therapists for years in various settings and situations, I agree that there is clearly no "right" way of doing family therapy. Ferber et al. (1972) are refreshingly humorous in their description of the tribal behavior of family therapists.

Family therapists now appear even more pragmatic and problem-oriented than before. Reputedly, earlier therapists were too obsessed with therapeutic methods, with diagnoses, or nosological categories. Later therapists are said not to care enough about those matters.

Some have alleged that in family therapy there is a "lack of attention to ethnic and subcultural differences found in families, and to economic issues" (Foley and Dyer, 1974). What about funding problems? Paraprofessionals and relationships with such groups? The silence of the profession on social issues generally has also been criticized by some, felt to be wise, even essential, by others. What is it to be?

Research and Methodological Issues

It is a good time to look hard at the effectiveness of our approaches, at the changes as well as the problems that family therapy has brought, now that it approaches majority.

Apart from effects, we need to study the side effects and spin-offs of family therapy also. If symptoms are seen to be adaptive, what "side effects" does the removal of maladaptive patterns have on the other family members, not just the identified patient? A lack in payoff obviously maintains resistance to change. Social systems clearly are subject to evolutionary change. How can systems-influence in a given culture be used more to heal families?

Strictly controlled systematic studies using sound criteria and established evaluative methodology are only possible if a standardized approach to the study of families is developed. The effectiveness of its interventions must be compared with the effectiveness of other treatment modalities, physical or psychotherapeutic.

Summary and Recommendations

We need:

(1) Comprehensive theory building and conceptualizing to deal with theoretical inconsistencies and divergent theories about human behavior in general to better understand family processes. This integration should sharpen techniques of intervention. Research should concentrate on the "how," "when," and "why" of interventions, but should use appropriate supervision. We need to systematize and categorize approaches without dogmatization. Personality-theory development from a family-process point of view needs encouraging. As the absence of a unifying schema has delayed progress, further efforts to integrate Caplan's crisis theory and Erikson's developmental theory with Piaget's learning theory are needed. A clinically practical system to plug into general systems theory

needs development. Scrutiny of the theory and outcome ends of the interactional processes in between is needed, as is evaluation of recent treatment modifications and creative strategies.

(2) More attention to ethnic, subcultural, and economic, as well as general social issues. Funding issues need examination.

(3) Redefinitions of normality and pathology, hence family therapy and its limits; focus on a family's strength rather than its weaknesses; indications and counterindications, transference effects, and side effects, and also a clearer role-delineation within the health delivery field.

(4) Evaluation of the effectiveness of selection, training, and assessment as well as the evolving techniques, procedures, patterns, and styles of therapists. Family behavior needs categorization. Cross-matching of family needs with therapist's style needs exploration. We need to monitor results and compare existing models critically (Winter, 1971).

(5) To search for reinforcement contingencies, individual and system strategies that will accelerate the slow change rate (Sager and Kaplan, 1972). How many of us are working in the prevention field?

(6) To evaluate goal and objective-setting and the use of therapeutic contracts. The relationship of family therapy to counseling needs redefinition.

(7) Mandatory supervision (peer group? licensing? et cetera) to ensure minimal competence and maintenance of standards; re-examination of supervision techniques; avoidance of gimmicky and dubious ploys, tricks, and practices. Ethics and the value systems of all participants need examination. After licensing, "What?" indeed! We must be less naïve and understand, organize, and use power politics appropriately.

(8) Early identification of family systems impervious to change in order to avoid frustration and failure on both sides. Needed are follow-up studies on dropouts, disposition, and fate of therapeutic failures, hard-core, and special-trauma families. We need to work more with multiple family groups; within extended family networks, ecological groups and neighborhoods; with self-help groups transculturally; in ghettos and with social support systems; using and expanding innovative approaches (Singer-Magdoff, 1975; Pattison-Mansell et al., 1975). Framo's (1975) use of individual couples as "assistant therapists" in groups, or the use of a "social systems clinician" (Greenblatt, 1975) are examples. Behavior modification, marathons for families, and so forth are not even now widely tried in Canada and should be. Canada is a wave behind our southern neighbor

in this also. Some work has been attempted in northern Canada with native families via a revived organizational, social/tribal network. Reports are scanty. More consumer and community participation is essential. Family therapy delivery needs careful planning to become more effective in the future.

(9) Trainees/generalists sufficiently competent either to be able to treat families themselves or, if not, sufficiently knowledgeable to refer such families to a therapist-resource using such an approach within their delivery system. This would increase mutual respect either way and avoid the regrettable polarization among therapists. Both might learn to tolerate professional "differences."

(10) To diminish ideological polarization and the opposition of the intuiting, tender-minded, macrofocused "clinician" with the hard-data, statistically-minded, microfocused "scientist." We need both types in order to achieve a suitable Hegelian synthesis in the family therapy field. The entire approach to the family needs standardization in a multidisciplinary comprehensive way, enabling investigations to be done in a strictly controlled, scientific—yet humanitarian—way, using established methodology and meaningful statistical analysis.

It will remain an easier task to express such concerns than to solve them. However, I believe that the approaches suggested would bring nearer desired resolution in the problematic areas outlined.

References

Ackerman, N. W. (1971), The growing edge of family therapy. *Fam. Proc.*, 10:143-156.

Beels, C. C. & Ferber, A. (1969), A family therapy, a view. *Fam. Proc.*, 8:280-332.

Bowen, M. (1967), The family as the unity of study and treatment. *Amer. J. Orthopsychiat.*, 33:4-60.

Caplan, G. (1970), *The Theory and Practice of Mental Health Consultation*. New York: Basic Books.

Coles, E. M. (1974), The holy trinity of the mental health professions. *Canada's Ment. Health*, 22:7-9.

Epstein, N. B. & Levin, S. (1973), Training for family therapy within a faculty of medicine. *Canadian Psychiat. Assn. J.*, 18:203-208.

——— & Santa-Barbara, J. (1975), Conflict behavior in clinical couples: Interpersonal perceptions and stable outcomes. *Fam. Proc.*, 14:51-56.

——— ——— & Napier, A. (1972), *The Book of Family Therapy*. New York: Science House.

Ferber, A. & Mendelsohn, M. (1969), Training for family therapy. *Fam. Proc.*, 8:25-31.
First, E. (1975), Family therapy: The new wave in psychiatry. Review of recent books by Minuchin, Haley, & Hoffman, Watziawick, et al. *New York Review of Books*, Feb. 20, pp. 8-9, 37-38.
Foley, V. D. (1974), *An Introduction to Family Therapy*. New York: Grune & Stratton.
——— & Dyer, W. W. (1974), Timing in family therapy: The "when", "how", and "why" of intervention. *Fam. Coord.*, 4:373-381.
Framo, J. L. (1975), My families; my family. *J. Marriage & Fam. Counseling*, 1:15-28.
Greenblatt, M. (1975), The role of the community mental health worker. In: *Comprehensive Textbook of Psychiatry, Vol. 2*, A. M. Freedman, H. I. Kaplan, & B. J. Sadock. Baltimore: Williams & Wilkins. pp. 2350-2354.
Group for the Advancement of Psychiatry (1970), *The Field of Family Therapy Formulated by the Committee on the Family*, 7.
Haley, J. (1975), Why a mental health clinic should avoid family therapy. *J. Marriage & Fam. Counseling*, 1:2-13.
Kaplan, H. (1974), *The new sex therapy*. New York: Brunner & Mazel.
Levin, S. & Cleghorn, J. (1973), Training for family therapists by setting instructional objectives. *Amer. J. Orthopsychiat.*, 43:439-446.
Minuchin, S. (1975), *Families and Family Therapy*. Cambridge: Harvard University Press.
NIMH (1974), Computer print-out. References of family therapy outcome studies, 1964-1974. Washington, D.C.: U.S. Department of HEW.
Pattison-Mansell, E., Defrancisco, D., Wood, P., Frazier, H., & Crowder, J. (1975), A psychosocial kinship model for family therapy. *Amer. J. Psychiat.*, 132:1246-1251.
Sager, C. J. & Kaplan, H. S., eds. (1972), *Progress in Group and Family Therapy*. New York: Brunner/Mazel.
Satir, V. (1972), *Peoplemaking*. Palo Alto: Science & Behavior Books.
Sigal, J. J., Guttman, H. S., Chagoya, L., & Lasry, J. C. (1973), Predictability of family therapists' behavior. *Canadian Psychiat. Assn. J.*, 18:199-202.
Singer-Magdoff, L. (1975), Demonstration of "Save of Marriage" (SAM) telephone service, American Association of Marriage and Family Counselors Annual Meeting, Toronto. November.
Spector-Postner, R., Guttman, H. A., Sigal, J. J., Epstein, N. B., & Rakoff, V. (1971), Process and outcome in conjoining family therapy. *Fam. Proc.*, 10:451-473.
Winter, W. (1971), Family therapy, research and theory. In: *Current Topics in Clinical and Community Psychology, Vol. 3*, ed. C. Spielberger. New York: Academic Press, pp. 95-121.

For many years there has been controversy over the value of family classifications. The author reviews the relevant literature. Existing family schemata are considered in five main groupings. From the literature, the author extracts, in a tentative way, six family types.

On the Classification of Families

LAWRENCE FISHER

From the beginning of family therapy as a relatively distinct clinical approach, many have expressed the need for a useful and meaningful family typology. Several typologies have emerged over the course of the twenty years between the mid-50's and the mid-70's, and, as the title indicates, this article is a progress report, a review of these existing classification schemas.

Two strategic points need to be made at the outset. First, we shall focus on family classification as opposed to family diagnosis. The term *diagnosis* implies, to some extent, a distinction between sickness and health, or between normalcy and pathology. Such distinctions are particularly blurred in the field of family and couple therapy, and the single most discriminating characteristic between health and disease is often whether or not a family or couple has sought professional assistance. Clearly, what is needed is a system(s) of family classification and not an addition to the perennial controversy over what constitutes pathology. Second, it is apparent that families have been classified and pigeonholed on the basis of a plethora of variables, and the resulting literature spreads

Lawrence Fisher, Ph.D., is Assistant Professor of Psychiatry and Psychology, University of Rochester School of Medicine and Dentistry, Rochester, New York.

Reprinted from *The Archives of General Psychiatry*, vol. 34, April, 1977.

Rodney Shapiro, Ph.D., John Strauss, M.D., and Mary Anna Ham provided helpful comments and critical review.

across a broad range of scientific questions and academic disciplines. Clearly, any single review could not be all-inclusive. With this in mind, I shall focus on those writings that are specifically geared toward creating a classification schema as opposed to those that do so indirectly or with an ancillary focus.

Systems of Classification

Strauss (1973) has proposed a useful grouping of approaches to the diagnosis of individual patients that may be helpful as we review the rather complex field of family classification. The "topological diagnostic model" creates discrete categories of disorder, which implies some degree of mutual exclusiveness of causation as well as intervention techniques. The "dimensional model" does not categorize, but instead attempts to locate individuals along one or more predetermined dimensions. There are no discrete groups; instead, there is an emphasis on relationships among dimensions and on positioning individuals at some point within multidimensional space. Last, is the "mixed model" in which broad categories of disorder are identified and dimensions are specified within each. It may be helpful to keep these models in mind as each schema is reviewed. These models may provide a general frame of reference for reviewing systems of family classification.

Describing and comparing a large number of schemas of family classification requires some degree of organization and classification of the schemas themselves. Hill and Hansen (1960) have proposed a five-point outline of conceptual approaches to the family that includes the interactional, structural, situational, institutional, and developmental frameworks. Using this as a starting point, five major groups or approaches to classification have been selected, based on a review of the existing literatures. (1) "Style of Adaptation" incorporates the family's approach to the world, its pattern of handling stress, and its characteristic tendencies for dealing with crisis. It may involve broad family reactions or it may, on the other hand, relate to behaviors of individual members within the family context. (2) "Developmental Stage" characterizes some approach to denote a family developmental level. Some aspects of the developmental levels of individuals in the family can be used or, alternatively, a broad, more abstract family base level may be established. (3) "Presenting Problem or Diagnosis of the Identified Patient" characterizes a popular approach to family classification, and it has a relatively long history. Typically, the diagnosis or a particular aspect of the individual who brings the family to treatment becomes a criterion for grouping families. (4) "Family Theme or Dimension" is somewhat of a catch-all group. Schemas in this section differentiate families on the basis of some relatively objective dimension such as type of family power allocation, or specific kinds of family structure. (5) "Type of Marital Relationship" is the last of the five approaches to family classification. Since the marital relationship clearly sets the tone of the family's function, a decision has been made by the author to include types of marriages as one approach to the overall problem of family classification.

This five-point organization emerges as one possible logical structure in that each point applies to a major premise underlying the development of the respective schemas. The primary aim of these categories is to facilitate presentation, and while such an organization makes conceptual sense, other equally logical organizational structures could have been proposed.

Style of Adaptation

Three schemas are included in this first category, and all three relate to a classification of families based on an approach to the world or to a style of dealing with stress, either internal or external to the family.

Gehrke and Kirschenbaum (1967) proposed the repressive, delinquent, and suicidal family type. They suggest that children display symptoms when the family communicates a message that the survival of the unit is in some way dependent on them. "Survival myths" are an illusion that each member must maintain a given role to insure family integrity and balance. (1) The repressive family contains the myth that the expression of feelings brings with it the threat of loss of love and possible abandonment, especially if other family members have opposing feelings. Affect is experienced in the children as tension, and they tend to manifest internalized aggressive symptoms. Conflict is never expressed, and everyone must feel the same way about everything. (2) The survival myth in the delinquent family is that one parent cannot survive the sexual-aggressive impulses of the spouse, if expressed openly. The identified patient acts out these impulses to relieve the resulting tension, enabling the spouse to displace impulses and protect the weaker parent. (3) In the suicidal family, the myth states that unless the family remains whole, no member can survive. If one member leaves, destruction of all will occur.

Role boundaries are blurred in these families, and all conflict is eliminated with disqualified interaction and communication.

Richter (1974) described two general kinds of family disturbances: family symptom neurosis and family character neurosis. In the former, a family member drains off family tension by becoming "sick," and, following such an event, a remarkable calm often settles over the family. The scapegoat allows one part of the family to impose its unresolved problem on others, but if the scapegoat becomes "well," the "healthy" person falls victim. The second of Richter's two main categories is the family character neurosis, which occurs when the family as a group creates and maintains distorted perceptions and ideas in an effort to reduce family tension. The family becomes uniform in its adherence to an ideology or point of view so that the illness becomes ego-syntonic with the family. No scapegoat emerges as such, although symptoms may appear in one member when family denial and distortion become too great. There are three subtypes of family character neurosis: (1) The anxiety-neurotic family builds a protective world that keeps out anything that is potentially anxiety-arousing. (2) The paranoid family builds a fortress. Instead of denying anxiety-arousing stimulation, it reconstructs the world and redirects intolerable stress outward toward other groups or individuals. (3) In the hysterical family, a central figure is selected who then assigns artificial roles to each family member in order to escape major family depression. The central figure is a stage manager, and the roles are part of a prescribed play for audiences outside the family.

Reiss (1971a, 1071b, 1971c) contrasts two types of disturbed families, based on a shared "view or explanation of its environment and the patterns or principles that govern its people and events." These family constructs relate to perceptual and cognitive abilities in individual family members and are also apparent in determining how members interact with each other in response to environmental situations: (1) The environment-sensitive family sees the world as enticing, predictable, manageable, and understandable. (2) Consensus-sensitive families see the world as unorganized and threatening. There are no laws or rules for explaining environmental events, and life is seen as outside of one's control.

These three authors, then, typify family classification based on style of adaptation. Richter's distinction between a family symptom neurosis and a family character neurosis may provide the format under which these three schemas may be subsumed. Gehrke and Kirschenbaum's repressive and suicidal families appear to be general family styles and could be categorized under Richter's family-character-neurosis heading. The delinquent family utilizes a clearly identified patient or scapegoat and sounds more appropriate within the family-symptom-neurosis group. In addition, Reiss's consensus-sensitive family designation could be placed within the character neurosis group as well.

Developmental Family Stage

Interest in developmental family stage emerged out of family sociology, and it has only been recently that developmental concepts have been actively incorporated into clinically oriented family work. Glick and his colleague (1955, 1965) have used population-census data to study a number of social and economic variables as they relate to the development of the family over time. Glick has demonstrated that family stages are more useful than age of spouses in understanding and predicting a large number of family parameters. A main emphasis in the field has been a search for appropriate, reliable, and relevant family stage criteria.

Duvall and Hill's report of the National Conference on Family Life (1948) established seven stages, Duvall (1967) revising these seven some twenty years later by broadening the developmental perspective to include Erikson's concept of developmental task. These seven stages appear to be the foundation on which much research has been generated: (1) beginning families; (2) child-bearing families (oldest child 30 months); (3) families with preschool children; (4) families with school children (oldest six to thirteen years); (5) families with teenagers; (6) families as launching centers (first child gone to last child gone); (7) empty nest to retirement; and (8) retirement to death of one spouse.

Both Hill (1964) and Rodgers (1973) assert the need for clarification of the variations that exist in the broad middle range of family life. One approach (Rodgers, 1962) has been to include the age of the youngest child in the family, another, to insert a new stage between Duvall's stages 5 and 6 (Hill, 1964).

Solomon (1973) has proposed one of the few clinically oriented life-stage breakdowns that also includes a developmental-task principle. Like Grunebaum and Bryant (1966), Solomon refers to each stage as posing a life-crisis situation that must be resolved if adaptive growth is to continue. Stage 1—marriage—involves two tasks: ending each spouse's primary gratification with his and her own parents and redirecting these energies into the marriage. Stage 2—birth of first child and child bearing.

This stage requires the solidification of the marriage as well as the establishment of parental roles. A frequent difficulty in this stage is the sacrificing of marital roles for parental roles. Stage 3—individuation of family members. This is the broad midrange of family life in which the task becomes the continual modification of roles and the evolving individuation of each member over time. Stage 4—actual departure of the child. The primary task of this stage is the reworking of parent roles so as to establish a position as parents of adult children. Stage 5—integration of loss. This stage involves the acceptance of social, economic, and physical changes that occur in old age. Solomon has attempted the first steps of an application of family developmental theory to clinical process through his emphasis on the types of pathology that emerge when developmental tasks are not appropriately completed.

Grunebaum and Bryant (1966) have made a similar contribution by suggesting an epigenetic model. Their view is that a breakdown occurs within a family when it is unable to meet the developmental crisis posed by a particular stage within the family life cycle.

The use of a developmental-stage format for the classification of families suggests at least two fundamental views vis-à-vis the nature of family pathology. The first, as evidenced by Haley's (1971) writings as well as by Duvall and other family sociologists, is that family pathology is derived from a combination of life-stage events plus external circumstances. The second view is derived from more clinically oriented work; it suggests that pathology emerges as a function of the construction of the family system itself, and that the developmental stage simply colors its expression or defines the nature of its symptoms.

These two views emphasize somewhat different directions for clinical intervention. The first stresses environmental manipulation as well as involvement with specific family members. The second stresses more of a systems conceptualization of family pathology that leads to an intervention program involving all family members and dealing with the structure of the family unit. While this is clearly not a black-and-white distinction, it does serve to show that one's view of family development and its relationship to other aspects of family life will directly relate to therapeutic strategy.

A review of the several developmental classifications presented above indicates some similarity, with differences being more in emphasis than in actual content. How useful these particular stages are in clinical work is yet to be demonstrated. While most family clinicians incorporate some developmental notions in their approach to families, there have as yet been no demonstrations of how existing family stage formats empirically relate to family pathology.

Initial Problem or Diagnosis of the Identified Patient

As implied by the title, this section focuses on those family classification systems that distinguish among families on the basis of the individual diagnosis, initial problem, or some other aspect of the identified patient.

Serrano et al. (1962) presented a four-point schema based on the function the identified patient serves in keeping the family stabilized: (1) Infantile maladjustment reaction in adolescence. The schizophrenic teenagers in this group serve the function of providing a needy parent with a full-time occupation. The parents tend to hide their lifelong friction, but there are frequent outbursts, usually over tangential matters. The ill child becomes the eventual outlet for the mother, who identifies him as the "sick one," and this process saves other siblings from a similar fate. (2) Childish maladjustment reaction in adolescence. These are arrogant, aggressive, negative, and impulsive adolescents with a penchant for irresponsible behavior leading to guilt and shame in the parents and other adults. Fathers in these families tend to see their sons as intruders, and, by functioning somewhat passively, such fathers are reluctant to assert leadership or authority. The adolescents tend to act out this problem by confronting their father's attitudes and by becoming unlikeable to others. Treatment often includes bringing the father back into the family. (3) Juvenile maladjustment reaction in adolescence. These are anxious and tense adolescents with many somatic complaints and poor school performance. Their fathers are authoritarian and aggressive as a cover for their own feelings of inferiority. The children are seen as rivals, and any challenge or expression of assertiveness on the child's part is met by overreaction; hence the children internalize their hostilities to prevent guilt and reduce the challenge to their father. (4) Preadolescent maladjustment reaction in adolescence. These older adolescents have a relatively acute onset of rebellious and antisocial behavior. The negative behavior tends to reflect an overidentification with the peer group at a time when other youngsters are becoming more individualized. Parents tend to be socially oriented, and they are also passive-aggressive critics. The four types described by Serrano et al. tend to emerge with no general set or model underlying the schema. Hence, these patterns tend to "hold together" on a pragmatic clinical level rather than on a conceptual or theoretical level.

Goldstein et al. (1968) presented a more unified classification system, or at least directed effort at creating a classification system based on family concepts. The referred adolescents and their families were grouped into the following types, based on the behavior of the adolescents themselves: (1) Aggressive antisocial: These are externalizing youngsters who have difficulty restraining impulses, have some degree of inner tension, and tend to act out conflicts. (2) Active family conflict: These are youngsters with inner tension and somatic complaints, but who primarily are disrespectful of parents, are belligerent, defensive, and antagonistic as well. The negative behavior is focused inside the family almost exclusively. (3) Passive-negative: These adolescents do poorly in school, are sullen and somewhat depressed; they are not disruptive, but express undirected, passive hostility and defiance. (4) Withdrawn-socially isolated: These are fearful teenagers who show marked signs of anxiety and tension, who are withdrawn and isolated socially, and who are highly dependent on one or both parents. This four-way grouping is based on two underlying bipolar dimensions: locus of conflict, that is, focus inside the home or outside as well; and overt versus covert activity as expressed in pathology, that is, aggressive acting out as opposed to a passive-negative stance. The authors demonstrated that direct and intrusive forms of social influence by parents are associated with aggressive-antisocial adolescents, whereas rational techniques of control are associated with active family conflict.

The Serrano and Goldstein typologies are descriptions of adolescent behavior rather than styles of family functioning. The adolescents described by these two teams can be combined into two generic clusters. Cluster 1 includes Serrano's juvenile-maladjustment reaction and Goldstein's passive-negative groups. Adolescents in this cluster are described as passive and depressed; they display somatic complaints. They tend to come from constricted families where indirect methods of emotional expression are common; and in at least several cases, the fathers are somewhat dominant and controlling as a cover for their own feelings of inferiority. Cluster 2 includes Serrano's childish-maladjustment reaction and Goldstein's aggressive-antisocial groups. These adolescents are depicted as acting out and irresponsible, and they tend to get into trouble at home, at school, and often with the police. They can be hostile, aggressive, and at times destructive. From description at least, clusters 1 and 2 may reflect the well-known internalizer and externalizer dimensions of personality, respectively. Internalizers direct anxiety back to the self, and, as would be expected, they come from families where acknowledgment of a variety of issues on an overt level is prohibited. Externalizers act out impulses directly and tend to come from families where parental control is reduced or where the family has lost its direction due to overt conflict, usually within the marital dyad. Additional support for this dichotomy comes from the more empirical schemas of Jenkins (1968) and Waring and Ricks (1965).

Beavers et al. (1975) classified adolescent pathology into four groups: healthy, neurotic, behavior disorder, and psychotic. Their clinical and rating-scale data indicated differences between midrange families—that is, families with neurotic and behavioral disorder children—and the extreme groups—that is, healthy and psychotic—as well as differences between the midrange families themselves. In the midrange families (1) separation and individuation is successful; (2) ambivalence, anger, and sexuality are viewed with disdain; (3) an abstract code or morality is adhered to, often personified in a particular person—the grandparent, religious leader; (4) a rigid rule system is adopted that often leads to scapegoating; and (5) the rigidity resulting from the tight-rule system often leads to power struggles between the parents. Neurotic and behavior-disorder families were distinguished in the following ways: (1) Both family types adhere to rigid and authoritarian rules. In the neurotic group, the parents form a coalition to maintain enforcement of family roles in such a way that one spouse is dominant and the other subservient. In the behavior-disorder group the need for adherence to a highly structured family system is the same, but there is no parental coalition to maintain it. (2) The neurotic family uses repression to rid itself of unacceptable feelings and thoughts as prescribed by the moral code. Hence, these impulses are unconscious and are not seen as part of the self. In the behavior-disorder family, denial and projection are used, but frequently such defenses are ineffective and open rule breaking occurs. Hence, the impulses are identified as part of the self, and efforts are placed on their control by internal and external means. (3) Last, neurotic families have few crises and their efforts at maintaining status and power are successful. Behavior-disorder families display frequent crises, and these often serve to maintain equilibrium by pointing to an increased need to control and restrict impulses.

Riskin and Faunce (1970) utilized severity and number of family problems to classify their family sample into five groups. Group A are multiproblem families where several neurotic and psychotic level difficulties ranging from severe psychosis to underachievement in school were present. These families disagree more than they agree; there is a potential for explosiveness; and the tone of the families is one of unfriendliness, chaos, and competition. Group B are "constricted" families with two or three labeled difficulties. Problems are on a neurotic as opposed to a psychotic level, but more than one family member is affected. They are "compulsively clear" and concise, although they cannot stick to a topic for any length of time. The mood is one of depression, and spontaneity is severely reduced. Group C has acting-out or underachieving child-labeled problems. Children appear quiet, sullen, and argumentative. Deeply rooted struggles are covert, clarity of communication is low, and, often, one member is scapegoated. Group D contains families with significant but undiagnosed problems. They are quite diffuse and do not stand out on their own. Group E contains well-functioning, normal families who are clear, rational, affectively expressive, spontaneous, tolerant of differences, humorous, and so on. The significance of this study is not only its establishment of measures for the assessment of family interaction, but its classification system based on what may be termed the degree of pathology as defined by initial problems.

Family Theme or Dimension

The classification schemas presented so far are based on broad, encompassing dimensions that incorporate major thrusts in thinking about families. The schemas presented in this section are very much of a potpourri. They tend to tap major themes that emerge in clinical interviews or to divide families on the basis of a variety of theoretical concepts.

Ackerman (1958; Ackerman and Behrens, 1956) presented one of the first typologically based classification systems. On the basis of extensive clinical data collected on 50 referred families, he developed seven family types: (1) The externally isolated family is isolated and displays a failure of emotional integration into the community, instead tending to redirect energies internally. (2) The externally integrated family, in contrast, displays overactive participation in the community, perhaps due to a failure in internal unity and gratification. (3) The internally unintegrated family is characterized by a split between the parents and an alliance between at least one parent and one child. There is usually a good deal of hostility that maintains the split, and the resulting isolation keeps the inappropriate pairing in operation. (4) The unintended family is characterized by a mutually protective alliance between the parents. Of importance is the satisfaction of parental needs, often at the expense of the children. (5) In the immature family, the immaturity of the marital couple creates a breakdown in the boundaries separating parents and grandparents. Each spouse tries to parentify the other and both remain dependent on their own parents. (6) The deviant family displays marked rebellion against the standards of the community and adopts somewhat deviant goals and values. (7) The disintegrated or regressed family is marked by open conflict, hostility, and lack of integration so that a potential for breakup of the family is great.

Ackerman's system for classifying families is difficult to comment on from a conceptual point of view because each of the seven types appears to tap a somewhat different family dimension. The externally isolated family and the externally integrated family deal with boundary or directional issues, the internally unintegrated family and the disintegrated or regressed family pertain to family organization and structure, and the remaining groups deal with level of parental maturity, egocentrism, and conflict. Although these seven may be a meaningful division of family types, the lack of a useful way to conceptualize and structure them reduces their applicability in theory or model building. Ackerman's main contribution in this early schema was to present relatively clear and concise family types before a clinically based system or structural vocabulary was even developed.

Fallding (1961) interviewed 38 urban Australian families to establish types of adaptive or normal families using the dimension of internal versus external focus. The adaptation family is characterized by each member claiming a broad area of personal life outside of the family. In the identification family, parents at times overfocus their personal interests and energies on the family itself, and a premium is placed on contributing to a positive family atmosphere. The false-identification family falls between these two, and one or both parents have difficulty deciding what role extrafamily activities should play in family life.

Voiland's (1962, Voiland and Buell, 1961) work is significant insofar as it is the only extensive empirical study aimed exclusively at establishing a system of disordered family types that includes prognostic indicators. The schema is based on the nature of psychosocial dysfunction in the family, using highly specific assessment criteria. An individual, socially based dynamic focus, as opposed to an interactional focus, is maintained, and pathology is defined as a breakdown of social functioning as manifested by a failure in fulfilling the requirements demanded by either society or the family.

Four family types were identified: (1) The perfectionistic family is characterized by its high expectations to conform to social rules and mores, and to avoid mistakes at all costs. Prognosis is favorable, especially since the adults assume responsibility and value intervention. (2) The inadequate family is immature and relies on the presence and support of others to maintain internal stability. It anticipates poorly and is unable to be self-reliant in times of even mild distress. Specific problems tend to emerge in financial management, child rearing, and especially in issues to do with pregnancy and family planning. Prognosis is good, and treatment often focuses on training in parental roles and in bolstering certain parts of family structure. (3) The egocentric family seeks the goal of personal status and prestige. Family members become important to each other only insofar as they serve as need gratifiers; they become objects, not people. Friction and hostility dominate and intimacy is lacking, for each acts as a means to an end for the other. Contact with an agency usually is sought by a spouse as a hostile, retaliatory act to the other, or a child will act out the conflict outside the home. Because of the primitiveness of the need-gratification pattern, prognosis is guarded. (4) The unsocial family has difficulties establishing adult relationships and impulses are often acted on directly, leading to psychosis or delinquency. These are chaotic families where responsibility is shunted from one to another, major decisions occur impulsively, work records are poor, and home management is weak. Prognosis is described by Voiland as fair as long as contact is continued. Treatment is often on a crisis basis, with maintenance and support provided as needed to ward off the destructive and chaotic aspects of the family.

Markowitz and Kadis (1964) classified families on the basis of "centeredness" or the person on whom the family revolves. In father-centered families, the father attains major importance and his gratification becomes primary. Similarly, in mother-centered families, the mother assumes the magical quality of the all-giving female, and the maintenance of her position in the family is crucial. In child-centered families, the child and his or her welfare seem to hold the family together and give it status in either the community or the extended family. Last, family-centered families place an overemphasis on family cohesion, and individual needs are often sacrificed for the sake of the larger unit.

Wetheim (1973) made predictions about the response to family treatment on the basis of three dimensions: morphostasis, morphogenesis, and family system. Morphostasis refers to those aspects of family life that produce stability and solidarity, whereas morphogenesis relates to those aspects that permit growth and change within the family system. These concepts are introduced in an effort to broaden systems theory to include growth and change as inherent in family life. Consensual morphostasis refers to a consensually validated distribution of power. Forced morphostasis relates to an enforced power system, not consensually validated. Spontaneous morphogenesis is defined as the family's expected adaptive change in the face of life events; induced morphogenesis refers to a capacity for change when such change is an induced intervention, as in treatment.

The family systems dimension is divided into three types: (1) open family systems are articulated families with a network of subsystems connected by permeable boundaries; (2) closed family systems are rigid settings where rules are dogma and boundaries are not open; and (3) externally open systems operate freely within the environment but communication is minimal within the system. Its opposite, the internally open system, is also described. These three concepts, then, lead to a description of eight theoretical family types. At present, however, there are no clinical or empirical data to support Wertheim's typology, and hence the eight-point typology will not be presented here. The classification system does propose, however, a theoretical model for the prediction of differential response to family treatment in terms of accessibility, duration of treatment, and probable outcome. It deserves concentrated clinical testing, and even if the specifics are not fully supported it should provide the impetus for the development of more elaborate schemas.

Ford and Rarrick (1974) described "family rules" that reflect the overriding life style of the family and the manner in which it approaches the world. Five family rules or styles are described: (1) Children come first. These are somewhat chaotic child-focused families in which both parents have careers, although the wife often sacrifices hers for the children. Children are seen as attempts toward intimacy between the spouses, but this is not successful since only the children can receive the desired emotional closeness. Parental gratification can be received only by becoming childlike and burdening the other spouse. (2) Two against the world. This situation develops when two people view the world with fear and collude together to join hands in mutual defense. (3) Share and share alike. This reflects the family where a true partnership never develops, but instead, the spouses take turns being parent and child. (4) Every man for himself. This occurs in families where the spouses are joined not for emotional reasons but to achieve a goal or complete a task. Lack of trust is common, and individuals use others for what they can get. (5) Until death do us part. This occurs in families where dissolution of the family is sensed, yet that kind of parting is seen only as a consequence of death. So, everyone loves hopefully but pessimistically and the anger and frustration lead to bitterness. Children tend to continue this pattern, and homicide and suicide are common. Because the above rules are unstated, their formulation can be directly related to therapeutic techniques, and Ford and Rarrick suggest that therapy should focus on the constant, explicit restatement of the diffuse, inappropriate rule. Hence, in this case, family classification becomes directly related to treatment technique.

Minuchin (1974) described a bipolar dimension on which to classify families: disengaged versus enmeshed. Enmeshed families turn in on themselves, and the boundaries around members of subsystems of the family become blurred. Disengaged families have rigid boundaries, where contact across subsystems and between people is reduced. These terms can apply as descriptors of entire families or parts of families, and the status of boundary integrity can vary developmentally as well as over the course of treatment.

Some interesting similarities emerge among those schemas reviewed in this section. First, both Voiland and Ackerman refer to uncontrolled, almost chaotic families, called unsocial and disintegrated, respectively. Second, Minuchin's emphasis on the establishment of appropriate boundaries with sufficient permeability and stability is reflected clearly in Ackerman's isolated, integrated, and unintegrated families. Third, Voiland's egocentric and Ackerman's unintended families both reflect the focus on parental need-gratification, often at the expense of the children; whereas their respective inadequate and immature families seem to reflect the constant need for external support in the maintenance of family equilibrium. Fourth, is the similarity among Ackerman's externally isolated, Ford and Rarrick's "two against the world," and Markowitz and Kadis's family-centered families—all of which reflect internally focused families which see the outside world as a threat to their very existence as a unit and which tie family members together in a rigid, unhealthy knot. Last, Markowitz and Kadis's child-centered and Ford and Rarrick's "children come first" families describe situations in which the children assume unusual importance and prominence in the maintenance of family life. So, while each of these authors appears to describe families on the basis of somewhat different dimensions, concepts, or points of view, the descriptions of family types are quite similar in many respects.

Types of Marital Relationships

Although types of marital relatedness have been mentioned in the classification schemas described above, the emphasis was in most cases family-oriented as opposed to couple-focused. The systems reviewed in this section will focus on attempts at classifying marriages alone, without necessary reference to broader family issues. The classification systems included in this section fall into three rough groupings: (1) those based on the dynamics of the individual spouses; (2) those relating to types or patterns of conflict and associated power within the marriage; and (3) those focusing on broad types of "normal" marital relationships.

Individual Dynamics

A small group of authors have described particular patterns of marriage based on the individual dynamics of each spouse. Mittelmann (1944, 1956) described five complementary marital styles based on this individual dynamic model: (1) A spouse is aggressive and dominating to the point of humiliating the partner, whereas the other spouse is passive and submissive. (2) Emotional detachment in one spouse (usually the wife) leads to a craving for support in the other. (3) Intense competition for domination exists between the spouses, yet each is frightened at the prospect of losing the other. (4) Extreme helplessness in one spouse occurs in conjunction with extreme considerateness in the other. The weak partner requires an omnipotent mate, which, when not realized, leads to more depression and neediness. (5) Alternating sequences of helplessness and assertiveness occur in each spouse. As can be seen in this brief summary of five marital types, Mittlemann appears to focus on issues of dominance and need satisfaction.

Pittman and Flomenhauft (1970) described the "dollhouse marriage" in which inadequacy in a spouse is required for the maintenance and stability of the marriage. Attempts at altering this somewhat one-sided relationship may lead to destruction of the marriage, raising the point that structural changes in marital therapy are not always exclusive goals.

Conflict and Power

Conflict and its resolution is often related to marital stress and, hence, marital therapy. With this in mind, two authors have classified couples on the basis of type of conflict or style of handling conflict.

Gehrke and Moxon (1962) described five marital patterns based on the content of the conflict: (1) Masculine-feminine roles, wherein the spouses tend to reverse sex roles, the wife being relatively more masculine and the husband relatively more feminine. Conflict results from the resulting, somewhat ambivalent, stance each spouse takes. (2) Sadomasochistic conflict, in which the male's hostile and negative feelings toward women are expressed through the marriage. Since the wife has a poor view of herself to begin with, she submits to the abuse. (3) Detached, demanding conflict, in which both spouses are immature and require parenting from the other without giving anything in return. (4) Oral dependent conflict, in which both partners require rather primitive need gratification and both are dependent, somewhat helpless people. (5) Neurotic illness conflict, in which the wife displays pervasive and diffuse somatic complaints and appears helpless while the husband dotes in an attempt to fill her every need. He does so out of his own feelings of inadequacy.

Raush et al. (1974) evoked conflict in newlywed couples and described two types of couples. In discordant couples, conflict becomes a battle of wills where, depending on the content of the conflict, one or the other spouse will assume a coercive attacking stance. Disruption and escalation result. Harmonious couples have less heated exchanges where, in one subtype, conflict is easily settled and, in another, the couple tends to avoid the conflict altogether. It should be noted that none of these couples was referred by a clinic and therefore may not demonstrate the more extreme forms of marital distress.

Power has been an important dimension on which couples have been classified. Because it is abstract, power is most often assessed by the observation of conflict and its eventual resolution as well as by patterns of decision making. Hence, power as a dimension for the classification of families and couples needs to be seen as a higher-order variable, conceptualized one step from observable data.

Lederer and Jackson (1968) described three types of power relationships: In the symmetrical relationship, differences between spouse roles are reduced and each has equal power in all areas. The complementary relationship is characterized by the more traditional dominant/nondominant marital pattern. Last, in the parallel relationship, the couple sets up a rather elaborate set of roles that vary between symmetrical and complementary relationships, depending on the context of the decision making.

Zelditch (1964) described eight types of power allocation in families and couples. He suggested that such a classification must take into account Parsons and Bales's (1955) concept of multiple power structures. His view is that it is rather simplistic to believe that all power is exercised according to one hierarchy regardless of content. Different aspects of family functioning call for different power structures and alliances, a view similar to Minuchin's.

If indeed more than one power structure is in operation, then, Zelditch suggests, either decisions are made jointly by the couple or they are made separately by one spouse alone. These marriages are referred to as colleagueship and autonomic, respectively. If, on the other hand, a single power structure is in operation, decisions can be also made jointly or by one partner alone. In the former case, this leads to husband-dominant, equal partnership, or wife-dominant marriages. In the latter case where one partner makes the decision, the results are patriarchal, interchangeable roles, and matriarchal marriages.

Jackson (1959) described four kinds of marital relationships based on power and dominance: (1) A stable-satisfactory relationship occurs when a couple explicitly and overtly reaches agreement about who is in control of specific areas of family life. (2) An unstable-satisfactory relationship is usually temporary and occurs during periods of change when the couple is in the process of working out a definition of the relationship. (3) An unstable-unsatisfactory relationship contains virtually no completed transactions, and, although both parties desire some sense of definition, each maneuvers to control the other and denies the action at the same time. Psychosomatic and hysterical symptoms often result. (4) The stable-unsatisfactory relationship is withdrawn, cold, and distant in an attempt to preclude any issue that might make its instability overt. A united, pseudomutual front is often presented in an effort to avoid potential conflict.

Normal Couples

Cuber and Harroff (1965) undertook an extensive study of nonreferred couples in an effort to determine if social and financial success is related to marital success. Using a detailed open-ended interview technique, the authors established five types of marital relatedness: (1) Conflict habituated: This most frequent type is characterized by well-controlled but rather pervasive conflict that is kept under the surface but emerges in the privacy of the home. Physical violence rarely occurs, and caring is only delivered around periods of crisis. (2) Devitalized: These are couples who share a great deal of sexual and emotional intimacy in the early years of the marriage but who lose their closeness in middle life. Interests are centered outside the family, and the marital relationship is restless but devoid of open conflict. (3) Passive-congenital: This group is characterized by apathy and restlessness but, unlike the devitalized couples, the passive-congenital couples never had the emotional closeness to begin with. The marriage was formed intentionally for a variety of reasons, but there was never any deep caring. (4) Vital: There is in these couples a psychological bond and relatedness that ties their lives together. Disagreements are settled quickly and conflict is avoided. (5) Total: This is something of an idealized group which shares almost all aspects of life in a deep and vital way. It should be kept in mind that these are couples who do not experience sufficient stress in their relationship to consider therapy, separation, or divorce. If one can generalize from Cuber and Harroff's sample, it would appear that the vast majority of successful middle-class people have constricted, conflict-ridden, or zestless marriages. This is a sobering realization in terms of understanding baselines of marital life in American society.

Ryder (1970) established 21 patterns or types of marriages, using a large sample of nonreferred newlywed couples. Five conceptual dimensions were established on the basis of a factor analysis of extensive interview and paper-and-pencil schedules: husband's potency or affectiveness; husband's degree of impulse control; degree of wife's dependency; wife's attitude toward sex; and wife's orientation toward the marriage. Twenty-one marital patterns were identified (because of space limitations, the reader is referred to Ryder's original article for a complete description). Ryder's approach is useful from a methodological point of view in that empirically demonstrable dimensions were converted into scalable, nonreferred marital groups.

A Descriptive Comparison of Family Subtypes

It is apparent that no single family nosology is presently available that will serve to pragmatically unify the various purposes that need to be served. Regardless of how a family schema has been classified, however, and regardless of what dimensions have been used, certain similarities among the descriptions of family types emerge. From a review of all the schemas presented above, six clusters of family types seem to fall together. They were created by comparing the subtypes of each family schema with each other and grouping together those subtypes that, by my understanding of the original authors' description, displayed a reasonable degree of similarity. Table 1 lists each family cluster, the original author, and the specific family subtype involved.

It should be kept in mind that no concept or model underlies these six clusters; they tend to fall together only on a simple, descriptive basis. Each family cluster contains an entire range of psychopathology although, because most of these were derived from samples of referred families, each implies a maladaptive tendency or direction. The descriptions of each cluster are overviews of the several subtypes included. Although each subtype may not fit the overall description totally, sufficient similarities were present to warrant inclusion.

TABLE 1
FAMILY CLUSTERS

1. Constricted Family Types
    1. Gehrke and Kirschenbaum—Repressive
    2. Goldstein et al.—Passive-negative
    3. Serrano et al.—Juvenile maladjustment reaction
    4. Voiland—Perfectionistic

2. Internalized Family Types
    1. Ackerman—Externally isolated
    2. Fallding—Identification
    3. Fold and Rarrick—Two against the world
    4. Gehrke and Kirschenbaum—Suicidal
    5. Jackson—Stable-unsatisfactory
    6. Markowitz and Kadis—Family-centered
    7. Minuchin—Enmeshed
    8. Reiss—Consensus-sensitive
    9. Richter—Family character neurosis

(Continued on next page)

3. Object-Focused Family Types
    1. Child-Focused:
        a. Ford and Rarrick—Children come first
        b. Markowitz and Kadis—Child-centered
    2. Externally Focused
        a. Ackerman—Externally integrated
        b. Cuber and Harroff—Devitalized
        c. Fallding—Adaptation
    3. Self-Focused
        a. Ackerman—Unintended
        b. Ford and Rarrick—Every man for himself
        c. Voiland—Egocentric

4. Impulsive Family Types
    1. Gehrke and Kirschenbaum—Delinquent
    2. Goldstein et al.—Aggressive-antisocial
    3. Serrano et al.—Childish maladjustment reaction

5. Childlike Family Types
    1. Ackerman—Immature
    2. Gehrke and Moxon—Detached, demanding and oral dependent
    3. Voiland—Inadequate

6. Chaotic Family Types
    1. Ackerman—Disintegrated
    2. Voiland—Unsocial
    3. Riskin and Faunce—Group A

Constricted Family Types

These families are characterized by an excessive restriction of a major aspect of family emotional life, such as the expression of anger, negative affect, or ambivalence. Affect is then internalized into anxiety, depression, and somatic complaints. The passive, depressed, internalized child or young adult is often the presenting patient. There may be a concerted effort to protect a "weak" or "ill" family member or family relationship, and adults with particular problems of low self-esteem or past emotional difficulty are often present. Outcome of family treatment is primarily dependent on the degree of constriction. Following some of Wertheim's (1973) views on highly constricted families, the family often looks on intervention with antagonism and resistance so that individual or couple approaches may be more beneficial in the long run. In families with mild to moderate degrees of constriction, a family approach often has favorable results. Such families tolerate the move toward openness and respond to more direct forms of communication and feeling expression.

Internalized Family Types

Such families are inwardly focused and tend to view the world with fear, pessimism, hostility, and as a threat. A constant state of vigilance maintains the boundary between the internal and external world in a rather stable state of defense. The family has a well-defined role structure with strongly held values and powerful sanctions for misbehavior. Although members may stray from the fold, the threat of possible family disintegration and fears of chaos pull them back before complete separation occurs. Family loyalty runs high, and there is often a pseudomutual relationship between the parents. Internalized families view the family therapist cautiously and hesitantly as an outsider and an intruder into the fortress of the family. Prognosis is variable, depending on the thickness of the fortress walls and the therapist's patience and perseverance in tolerating small gains over long periods of time.

Object-Focused Families

These families are characterized by an overemphasis or excessive reliance on the children, the outside community, or the self. (1) In the child-focused subgroup, the children serve in some way as a link between the spouses, maintaining their relationship as a guilt reaction to unacceptable desires for parenting from the other spouse. Often there is competition between the spouses for the children's affection, and life is guided by decisions made ostensibly "because of the children." (2) In the externally focused subgroup, family members turn outside of the family for areas of interest and sources of support. Hypothetically, what is lacking inside is sought outside. (3) Members of the self-focused subgroup stay together to fulfill personal needs, and the emphasis is clearly tipped in favor of self- as opposed to family issues. Family cohesiveness and emotional closeness are low, and people are used for personal purposes, often resulting in explosions of anger and hostility when personal needs go unmet.

The child- and externally focused subgroups demonstrate an inappropriate reliance on other sources for need satisfaction. The emphasis on children or external sources may point to a family system unable to effectively fulfill the needs of its members. The self-focused group may point to a different dynamic insofar as the personal ability to delay gratification and to gain for the self by giving to others is lacking. All three groups point to an overemphasis on one area of gratification, whether it be due to deficiencies in other areas or to certain individual personality dynamics.

The prognosis for object-focused families in family therapy is generally good. The child- and externally focused subgroups display a sufficient degree of internal structure and integration for favorable outcome. Motivation for treatment is primarily dependent on the willingness of the marital pair to renegotiate the marital relationship in terms of commitment and allegiance. One runs the risk of possible separation and divorce in such families because, as the therapist points out the excessive reliance on external sources or on the children, the couple may begin to realize that there is little left of an emotional relationship between them. The prognosis for the self-focused subgroup is more variable, for such individuals may not be able to tolerate sharing the therapist or they may need to first work through a variety of personal issues in individual treatment.

Impulsive Family Types

The majority of these families are characterized by a troublesome adolescent or young adult who displaces his or her parental-based anger onto the community and acts on feelings in a socially undesirable way. Alternatively, many of these adolescents act out the parental conflict or they become the "expressor" for an angry but constricted adult. In any case, the identified patient is brought to treatment by the police, school officials, or exasperated parents who feel helpless to exert functional controls. Family therapy would appear to be a preferred approach to this kind of problem. The acting out against parents or the adolescent's role as a voice for marital or other difficulties implicates other family members and requires their major participation in treatment. Prognosis, however, is probably dependent more on the characteristics of the family than on the presence of acting-out behavior alone.

Childlike Family Types

These are often young families or families where the adults have never thoroughly separated from their family of origin. They are needy, dependent people who rely on their own parents, the community, or other sources for emotional support, decision making, and parenting of their own children. Some are simply immature and frightened, although capable; others are inadequate in ability and aptitude. The presence of major and perhaps destructive emotional ties between first and second generations opens a number of possibilities for family treatment, including single- or multiple-generation sessions. Where the issue is one of inadequacy and not immaturity, however, such couples may need continued "parentlike" assistance from the therapist in the form of long-term supportive work; chances for major improvement leading toward totally independent functioning are slim.

Chaotic Family Types

This somewhat rarer group is composed of poorly structured and decompensating families where chronic psychosis and delinquency are often rampant. There are few rules for anything, reliability of family members is quite low, and family members are constantly leaving and reentering the family. These families are often of low social class where undependability keep adults unemployed and living standards variable. The lack of integration and the marked instability of these families make treatment outcome extremely variable. This is often due to a lack of commitment to the family unit.

Conclusions

Progress in family classification has developed by collecting large amounts of varied data on relatively large samples of families. Then, by a process of theoretical, clinical, or statistical inference, a hypothesis or two has emerged about how families tend to "fall together." At present, however, insufficient data and experience are available to consider establishing a typological classification system as defined by Strauss (1973), one that proposes clearly distinct family types that are mutually exclusive and that assume distinct causes. Although many clinicians have displayed some degree of similarity in their definitions of given family types, we are still at a descriptive level and not sufficiently sophisticated to propose discrete family entities. An alternative, however, is a more thorough adherence to Strauss's dimensional or multidimensional model, which would classify families on the basis of previously specified, well-defined dimensions; and then a determination of the relationships of that classification to a limited number of dependent measures (see Riskin and Faunce, 1970).

The development of a single prominent classification schema, however, may be more restrictive than helpful. I speak here to the nagging uncertainties and inappropriateness of traditional unitary diagnosis to many settings and circumstances. As an addition to the proposal for adopting a dimensional model, we may need to focus on developing several miniclassification schemas rather than aiming for a single classification system. Given kinds of research and clinical endeavors require the inclusion of different family variables, and perhaps no single system should be sought. Our aim may be to focus on narrower, more problem-oriented systems that will display more limited application but that will be based on more solid ground.

The present review, however, demonstrates that family classification on given predefined dimensions can be helpful in both clinical and research efforts. It also points out the fact that certain similarities in types of systems and kinds of families and couples are emerging and that these efforts call for continued study. Coupled with the increasing problems of insurance, record keeping, and governmental needs, research in this area must continue on an accelerated basis.

References

Ackerman, M. W. (1958), *The Psychodynamics of Family Life*. New York: Basic Books.

——— & Behrens, M. L. (1956), A study of family diagnosis. *Amer. J. Orthopsychiat.*, 26:68-78.

Beavers, W. R., Lewis, J., Gossnett, J. T., et al. (1975), Family systems and individual functioning: Mid-range families. Read before the American Psychiatric Association meeting, Anaheim, Calif., May 1975.

Cuber, J. F. & Harroff, P. B. (1965), *The Significant Americans: A Study of Sexual Behavior among the Affluent*. New York: Appleton-Century.

Duvall, E. R. (1967), *Family Development*. Philadelphia: Lippincott.

——— & Hill, R. (1948), *Report of the Committee on the Dynamics of Family Interaction*. Prepared for the National Conference on Family Life, Washington, D.C.

Fallding, H. (1961), The family and the idea of a cardinal role. *Hum. Rel.*, 14:329-350.

Ford, F. R. & Rarrick, J. (1974), Family rules: Family life styles. *Amer. J. Psychiat.*, 44:61-69.

Gehrke, S. & Kirschenbaum, M. (1967), Survival patterns in family conjoint therapy. *Fam. Proc.*, 6:67-80.

——— & Moxon, J. (1962), Diagnostic classification and treatment techniques in marriage counseling. *Fam. Proc.*, 1:253-264.

Glick, P. C. (1955), The life cycle of the family. *Marr. & Fam. Living*, 18:3-9.

——— & Parke, R. (1965), New approaches in studying the life cycle of the family. *Demography*, 2:187-202.

Goldstein, M. J., Judd, L. L., Rodnick, E. H., et al. (1968), A method for studying social influence and coping patterns within families of disturbed adolescents. *J. Nerv. Ment. Dis.*, 147:233-251.

Grunebaum, H. V. & Bryant, C. M. (1966), The theory and practice of the family diagnostic: Theoretical aspects and resident education. *Psychiat. Res. Rep.*, 20:150-162.

Haley, J. (1971), A review of the family therapy field. In: *Changing Families: A Family Therapy Reader*, ed. J. Haley. New York: Grune & Stratton, pp. 1-12.

Hill, R. (1964), Methodological issues in family development research. *Fam. Proc.*, 3:186-205.

——— & Hansen, D. A. (1960), The identification of conceptual frameworks utilized in family study. *Marr. & Fam. Living*, 22:299-312.

Jackson, D. D. (1959), Family interaction, family homeostasis, and some implications for conjoint family psychotherapy. In: *Individual and Family Dynamics*, ed. J. H. Masserman. New York: Grune & Stratton, pp. 122-141.

Jenkins, R. L. (1968), The varieties of children's behavioral problems in family dynamics. *Amer. J. Psychiat.*, 124:1440-1445.

Lederer, W. & Jackson, D. D. (1968), *The Mirages of Marriage*. New York: Norton.

Markowitz, M. & Kadis, A. L. (1964), Parental interaction as a determinant in social growth of the individual in the family. *Internat. J. Soc. Psychiat.*, Congress issue, 10:81-89.

Minuchin, S. (1974), *Families and Family Therapy*. Cambridge: Harvard University Press.

Mittelmann, B. (1944), Complementary neurotic reactions in intimate relationships. *Psychoanal. Quart.*, 13:479-491.

——— (1956), Analysis of reciprocal neurotic patterns in family relationships. In: *Neurotic Interaction in Marriage*, ed. V. W. Eisenstein. New York: Basic Books, pp. 88-100.

Parsons, T. & Bales, R. F. (1955), *Family, Socialization, and Interaction Process*. Glencoe, Ill.: Free Press.

Pittman, F. S. & Flomenhauft, K. (1970), Treating the doll-house marriage. *Fam. Proc.*, 9:143-155.

Raush, H. L., Barry, W. A., Hertel, R. K., et al. (1974), *Communication, Conflict and Marriage*. San Francisco: Jossey-Bass.

Reiss, D. (1971a), Varieties of consensual experience: I. A theory for relating family interaction to individual thinking. *Fam. Proc.*, 10:1-28.

——— (1971b), Varieties of consensual experience: II. Dimensions of a family's experience of its environment. *Fam. Proc.*, 10:28-35.

——— (1971c), Intimacy and problem-solving: An automated procedure for testing a theory of consensual experience in families. *Arch. Gen. Psychiat.*, 25:442-455.

Richter, H. E. (1974), *The Family as Patient*. New York: Farrar, Straus & Giroux.

Riskin, J. & Faunce, E. E. (1970), Family interaction scales: I. Theoretical framework and method. *Arch. Gen. Psychiat.*, 22:504-537.

Rodgers, R. H.(1962), Improvements in the construction and analysis of family life cycle categories. Unpublished thesis, Western Michigan University, Kalamazoo.

——— (1973), *Family Interaction and Transaction: The Developmental Approach*. Englewood Cliffs, N.J.: Prentice-Hall.

Ryder, R.G. (1970), A topography of early marriage. *Fam. Proc.*, 9:385-402.

Serrano, A. C., McDonald, E. C., Goolishian, H. A., et al. (1962), Adolescent maladjustment and family dynamics. *Amer. J. Psychiat.*, 118:897-910.

Solomon, M. A. (1973), A developmental, conceptual premise for family therapy. *Fam. Proc.*, 12:179-196.

Strauss, J. S. (1973), Diagnostic models and the nature of psychiatric disorder. *Arch. Gen. Psychiat.*, 29:445-449.

Voiland, A. L. (1962), *Family Casework Diagnosis*. New York: Columbia University Press.

——— & Buell, B. (1961), A classification of disordered family types. *Soc. Wk.*, 6:3-11.

Waring, M. & Ricks, D. (1965), Family patterns of children who became schizophrenics. *J. Nerv. Ment. Dis.*, 140:351-364.

Wertheim, E. S. (1973), Family unit therapy and the science and typology of family systems. *Fam. Proc.*, 12:361-376.

Zelditch, M. (1964), Family, marriage and kinship. In: *Handbook of Modern Sociology*, ed. R. E. L. Faris. Chicago: Rand-McNally, pp. 680-733.

This chapter discusses the topical issue of variant families. It questions our long-held myths and some of the attributes of the "idealized" traditional nuclear family, and reviews studies on differences between the "idealized" and "variant" families.

Variant Family Forms and Life Styles: Rejection of the Traditional Nuclear Family

BETTY E. COGSWELL

We all live by images that are, in part, myths. The mythical quality of our images of family life stems from two sources. First, the image is idealized and thus never completely attainable; and secondly, the image is partially fictive, thus never exactly representative of reality. Myths are used to guide, judge, and rationalize behavior. Daily life never completely corresponds to the myths one holds; there are only degrees of approximation. The irony is that it is as impossible to live without myths as it is to live with them. Thus, we should not expect to eliminate myths entirely; rather, prevalent myths should be abandoned and replaced with new ones at those points in history when new circumstances and events render too great a breach between approximation and attainment, when actual behavior deviates too far from prevalent myths, and when new views of reality seem more relevant, appropriate, and explanatory for our time.

Betty E. Cogswell, Ph.D., is Assistant Professor in the Department of Family Medicine and Director of the International Programs Office of the Carolina Population Center at the University of North Carolina, Chapel Hill, N.C. 27514.

Reprinted from *The Family Coordinator*, vol. 24, no. 4, October 1975.

The recent emergence of experimental variant family forms suggests that we have arrived at such a point in history. The myth of the idealized nuclear family has become untenable for an undetermined proportion of our society, including both those individuals living in nuclear families and those opting for experimental variant family forms. Some hold to the idealized image but, uncomfortable with the behavior expectations it carries, feel guilty or demeaned by their behavior and actions and in some cases live clandestine second lives. Others speak out against this particular myth and are more candid and open about their own behavioral deviations and more insistent about their aspirations for new family forms, which they feel will correct some of the deficits of the idealized nuclear family. It is this latter group which appears to constitute the membership of experimental variant family forms and life styles depicted in this special issue of *The Family Coordinator*. Unfortunately, this issue does not include the full range of variant family forms and life styles in the United States today. Most notably missing are single-parent families, reconstituted families (second, third, and fourth marriages of previously divorced or widowed partners), retired cohabiting couples, and open marriages, as well as family forms existing outside white middle-class society. Some of these variant family forms are treated elsewhere (Cogswell and Sussman, 1972).

These experimental family forms are recent in origin, for most have only begun to appear within the last decade. By virtue of very short histories, they are in process of development and it is difficult to know how each will proceed to emerge, evolve, and perhaps become institutionalized. As these developmental processes continue, however, new myths about family life are likely to unfold. Myths are most often enigmatic, but the myth of the idealized nuclear family is far better developed and distinguishable than new emerging myths associated with experimental variant family forms, which are still extremely vague and ill defined.

Before proceeding further, it is important to indicate how the term "variant family form" has been used. Some authors use the term to refer exclusively to experimental forms such as communes, group marriage, cohabiting couples, homosexual unions, and open marriages. Cogswell and Sussman (1972), drawing from their involvement in Forum 14 of the 1970 White House Conference on Children and Youth, use the term "variant" to include all deviations from the traditional nuclear family, "which is characterized by households of husband, wife, and children living apart from both sets of parents with male as the breadwinner and female as homemaker." Our definition of variant thus includes such forms as dual-work, single-parent, and three-generation families which are found across the American class structure, as well as experimental forms which are predominantly middle class in membership. We arrived at this definition of variant in the attempt to avoid negative connotations toward any existing family form and to recognize pluralism which increases options for individuals and families.

Even within the experimental context, "variant" has been used to include a wide variety of family forms which are very different from each other in both structure and dynamics and perhaps to a lesser degree different from each other in goals, values, and aspirations. On the basis of our limited knowledge, it seems reasonable to expect considerable variation within specific family forms such as communes, open marriages, and cohabiting couples. Comparative descriptions among these family forms and analysis of variation within each single form are hampered by insufficient data. On the basis of current information, one can only speculate. However, juxtaposing the traditional nuclear and variant family forms offers analytic advantages for theoretical clarifications of basic concepts in both general and family sociology.

The Myth of the Idealized Nuclear Family

One theme implicit in the papers in this issue is rejection of the myth of the idealized traditional nuclear family;[1] for the authors, as well as the members of experimental family forms they discuss, see the nuclear family as inadequate, restrictive, and counterproductive in meeting individual goals, aspirations, and desired life styles. Birdwhistell's commentaries on this idealized version of family (1966, 1970) suggest its mythical qualities and allude as well to the far-reaching negative consequences it has for American family life. Although his discussion may be characterized as insightful rather than definitive, Birdwhistell's development of this concept provides a background against which variant family forms can be seen more clearly and serves as a provocative analytic tool.

Referring to the image of the American family presented to the public by mass communication and science and used by our legal, social, and

[1] The Rapoports' paper is an exception to this statement in that, in their arguments for equity and free choice among family forms, one is left free to choose the traditional nuclear family forms as well as the variant forms.

clinical experts, Birdwhistell notes that this image is a sentimental model based on two idealized notions. The first ideal is "that one man and one woman should marry one another and contract to satisfy all of the other's emotional and physical needs. Concepts of sexual infidelity were unconsciously extended to include all the personal feelings of the two individuals involving outsiders" (1970). Thus, to be legitimate, all personal attachments must occur within the family; and outside relationships and associations must be depersonalized and formalized. A closed, exclusive, and isolating dyad results.

The second ideal is that parents should be responsible for meeting all their children's needs. This includes holding parents not only legally, morally, religiously, and economically responsible for their children, but also for the personalities they develop. From this perspective, parents are perceived as the cause of any personality deficits or pathologies their children manifest. Although this idealized model is neither attainable nor representative of reality, many Americans believe in the myth and judge the quality of family life by it. Unfortunately, departures from the model are seldom viewed positively; rather, they are seen as failures to be like other families.

Although all cultures and societies hold idealistic models and cultural beliefs that misrepresent daily life, Birdwhistell suggests that, in the case of the sentimental model of the family, the effects of the distortions can only be viewed as deleterious. Serving as the standard for "healthy families," this myth leads professionals such as marriage counselors, social workers, family physicians, clergy, and teachers, who are sanctioned by society to manipulate the lives of individuals, to direct their clients, patients, and students toward unreality or toward passive acceptance of their failures in familial relationships. In the only paper in this issue that deals with professionals, Knapp (1975) documents that a sizeable proportion of marriage counselors in her study group are professionally nonsupportive of sexually open marriage, secret affairs, and swinging. From a more general sociological perspective, this myth also dominates policies and practices of our human service organizations to the detriment of variant family forms (Cogswell and Sussman, 1972).

Birdwhistell points out that the influence of the myth also causes serious complications for the study of families by distorting the perspective of investigators. Marciano's (1975) caveat concerning the values of middle-class investigators who place the negative label of "deviant" on lower-class family variations and the positive label of "variant" on middle-class family variations supports this notion.[2] From a similar perspective, Stein (1975) objects to the fact that investigators, under the influence of the cultural belief that everyone should marry, have ignored the study of singles. With only a few exceptions, family researchers have accepted the sentimental model of the family, with the result that "statistics are made of units derived from this model; anecdotes are collected; and formalistic abstractions are derived from it" (Birdwhistell, 1966). Birdwhistell also points out that the myth brings about a distortion in perspective on the part of families being investigated. They tend to see themselves in terms of the myth and describe themselves in those terms, even when their behavior contradicts this description.

Two consequences for family study ensue from the distortions in perspective brought about by the influence of the sentimental model. For nuclear families, actual family processes and structures are camouflaged by the sentimental model so that it becomes difficult for both investigator and respondent to perceive and describe what is actually occurring; furthermore, professionals and investigators reinforce the sentimental model by assuming that deviations are pathological. It follows that nuclear families who attempt to live in accordance with this idealized model are destined to grow up in and to create new families which could be designated pathological. In addition, experimental variant family forms such as those whose members choose not to marry (Stein, 1975) and those who choose not to have children (Veevers, 1975) also may be labeled pathological, and accordingly, members are pressured by parents, colleagues, and friends to conform to the image of traditional nuclear families—that is, to marry and to have children.

The pervasive influence of the traditional family myth parallels the influence of the myth of male superiority. Male superiority has been so infused into our lives from birth that some individuals often find themselves behaving in terms of this image while simultaneously advocating gender equality. Even champions of gender role equality find that it takes continual self-surveillance at both the cognitive and emotional levels to replace cultural beliefs that have been learned and incorporated into their identity with new ones which they consider more objective, appropriate, and equitable.

[2] Marciano uses the term variant exclusively for experimental family forms of middle-class origin and excludes other deviations from the idealized nuclear family which occur across social classes.

Social Influences Which Encourage and Constrain Development of Variant Family Forms

Since choice of a variant family form or life style implies rejection of the idealized nuclear family, and since the emergence of these forms is a relatively new phenomenon, the following questions arise: What aspects of the traditional nuclear family are being rejected? What recent influences have encouraged the development of these forms? As a starting point for addressing these questions, a further description of the traditional nuclear family and variant families will be useful. In the following discussion there is the implicit assumption that the orientation of traditional nuclear families is based primarily in the value system of the middle-class establishment and that experimental variant family forms are drawing selectively upon the values of the alternative culture to establish new value systems.

According to the myth, the nuclear family provides security for its members—stable heterosexual coupling, economic security for women and children, stable parenting for children, and obligations for mutual support among all members, both in the everyday processes of the family and in times of personal and family crisis. To bring about such security entails a high degree of interdependence among family members for a lifetime, long-range planning, and an emphasis on the future. Concomitant with the provision of security for family members are certain restrictions on personal freedom. For example, sexual exclusivity, with the gradual extension of this norm to include all personal attachments (Birdwhistell, 1970), is the basis for secure but isolated coupling; and marriage for life is implicit in attaining stable parenting. Likewise, the assignment of roles that carry prescriptions for behavior is the means both for specifying rights and obligations of family members toward each other and insuring that they are fulfilled with a minimum of confusion. These overall characteristics, meshed as they are with the economic value system of the middle class, are manifested in families by emphasis on financial success brought about through hard work and delayed gratification, by striving for both intergenerational and individual occupational mobility, and by materialistic consumption as a symbol of success.

According to Conover (1975), it is just this type of family—the affluent, bourgeois, middle-class family with a value orientation based on the Protestant work ethic—that members of the alternative culture are trying to escape. Their aspirations, in contrast to those of the idealized nuclear family, include self-actualization, autonomy, gender equality, intimacy in a variety of interpersonal relations, openness in communication, and sexual variety. There is also an emphasis on the present rather than the future and on immediate rather than delayed gratification. Warm interpersonal relations and concern for personal growth, two characteristics associated with traditional feminine culture, are highly valued. Striving and competition, often associated with traditional male work roles, are devalued. Denigration of the traditional male establishment is symbolized by the long hair, "mod" apparel, and gentleness of interactional style, as expressed by the "flower child." Work is seen as one means for self-actualization, and the psychic income derived assumes greater importance than monetary gain. The alternative culture works toward liberating both men and women from a highly competitive approach to life.

From this array of values drawn from the alternative culture, each experimental variant family form chooses selectively and establishes different priorities. For example, swingers are interested exclusively in sexual variety, although according to Ramey (1975), many have discovered that relationships based solely on sex are unsatisfying and thus have replaced swinging with intimate friendships. Open marriages tend to emphasize mutual self-actualization and gender equality, with some couples agreeing to sexual exclusivity and others to sexual freedom. Alternative-culture cummunes are the variant form most likely to embrace all of the values alluded to above, except that some communes maintain monogamous sexual relationships.

While it is unlikely that all those choosing variant family forms reject all facets of the traditional middle-class nuclear family, they do all appear to find this form inadequate, restrictive, or counterproductive for achieving their individual goals, aspirations, and desired life styles. Since the traditional nuclear family has been the model for many Americans for the last half-century, the question arises as to why it has been only within the last five to ten years that an increasing number of people have begun to publicly choose variant family forms. The answer cannot be traced to a single social cause, but rather to the interaction of many social forces. A very general and obvious explanation is that traditional value systems and their concomitant structural constraints are breaking down as they become less salient to existing social circumstances and events. Influences are prevailing which encourage either accession of new aspirations or the expression of previously inhibited ones or candidness about previously clandestine activities. Authors of papers in this issue do not specifically focus on social factors influencing the emergence of variant family forms. They do allude to this topic, however, by locating the roots in the alternative culture, the women's movement, and the economic conditions prevailing in the United States over the last thirty years. These influences will become more obvious in the ensuing discussion of the breakdown of social constraints which have served in the past to support and perpetuate the traditional nuclear family.

One of the more influential supports for the idealized nuclear family has been the legal system. Weisberg (1975) and Weitzman (1975) indicate how this system encourages the traditional family and discriminates against variant family forms. The traditional form is upheld by four provisions of legal marriage which are part of the unwritten or hidden contract. These provisions are: (1) the husband is head of the household; (2) the husband is responsible for economic support; (3) the wife is responsible for domestic service; and (4) the wife is responsible for child care. At the time these provisions became established in family law, they were based on realistic conditions. Women were economically dependent on men and had no avenues or skills to attain self-support, and men were dependent on wives for domestic services, having few other options. Weisberg (1975) notes that under the early American Puritan legal order, unmarried men were not permitted to dine or lodge alone and were often taxed for their solitary living. Thus, both males and females were essentially obliged to enter and to become locked into the traditional family unit.

Although marriage may provide security for a woman, it means a loss of independent identity and autonomy as she assumes her husband's name, residence, and socioeconomic status. At first glance these conditions may not appear excessively restrictive, but consider, for example, the implications of a wife's legal necessity to assume her husband's residence. "The location of a person's domicile affects a broad range of legal rights and duties, including the place where he or she may vote, run for public office, serve on juries, receive free or lowered tuition at a state school, be liable for taxes, sue for divorce, register a car, and have his or her estate administered" (Weitzman, 1975). A more severe hardship is that in some states, if a woman refuses to accept her husband's choice of domicile, she may be charged with desertion, which is grounds for divorce, and if found guilty may be deprived of property and her right to seek alimony. Since the traditional nuclear family has always tolerated such personal restrictions, why is it only recently that individuals have sought new family forms?

Women in the past may not have perceived these conditions as restrictions because there was seldom a need to maintain a separate residence. If the husband chose to move temporarily or for extended periods to another location, the wife who remained behind with his concurrence was not prosecuted. Now, however, as dual-career families become more prevalent, women have a higher stake in decisions about where to live. Legally, however, the woman must either abide by her husband's choice if he chooses to invoke the legal code or she must suffer the legal consequences.

Weisberg (1975) and Weitzman (1975), call attention to many other restrictions imposed by family law which support the idealized nuclear family and discriminate against variant family forms. Obviously the law has reinforced the evolution of the traditional nuclear family into a primarily closed, restrictive system which functions largely on the basis of stringently applied designation of roles for family members.

Restrictiveness lies at the heart of the objections of those who wish to escape the traditional nuclear family. Two goals espoused by a large number of people entering variant family forms can be seen as a reaction against this restrictiveness. These goals are independence for women and gender role equality. These two goals are primary foci of the women's movement and are important in the emerging value system of the alternative culture. The move toward independence for women has come about largely through the fact that, often from economic necessity, increasing numbers of women have been leaving the home and the exclusive role of the homemaker to enter the work world. Married women have been in the labor force in considerable numbers since World War II; in 1970 40 percent of married women were gainfully employed, presumably making a substantial contribution to their own support and the family budget. It is through the impetus of the women's movement, however, that this reality is coming to have more than economic significance. This movement has contributed to the struggle for women to receive equal pay for equal work and to be hired and promoted to more responsible jobs. Perhaps even more important, it has provided the psychological support for women to acknowledge that it *is* acceptable for them to work outside the home and, moreover, desirable for them to seek and derive fulfillment from extradomestic jobs. With this realization many women have acquired new identities outside of the family and have become career oriented rather than merely working to provide supplementary income for their families. No longer is there a need for women to live through the accomplishments of their husbands and children. Conversely, as the Rapoports (1975) point out, the image of women as inferior is being reduced as they have the opportunity to demonstrate competencies and skills outside the home. The effect of the move toward economic independence for women is to free both men and women from some previous restraints and obligations either to enter or to remain within a traditional marriage.

As part of the general thrust toward gender equality, the women's movement is also attempting to eliminate sex typing of work in the home as well as in the occupational world. The division of labor between the sexes is entrenched in the ideology of American culture and is apparently reflected in all cultures. In this country, however, it is a basic component of the idealized nuclear family, supported both by popular myth and by the legal code: women assume responsibility for the household and the rearing and socialization of the children, and men assume responsibility for economic support and function as the primary representatives of the family to the outside world of business, law, property, and politics.

The Rapoports point out that changes in the division of labor have occurred unevenly in different life sectors. They note that progress has been made toward ideological, political, and economic equality; but while equality of opportunity is much nearer achievement in the occupation sphere, there has been little progress in sex-role equality in the family. Although some working couples share the tasks of household maintenance and parenting, this objective is far from attainment by the majority. The issue is not a question of the male's willingness to help out by performing some of the tasks, but rather the question of who is ultimately responsible for them. If males do not assume more responsibility, then equality is not attained. Redistribution of *responsibility* for household and child-care tasks is a number one priority (Rapoport and Rapoport, 1975). Otherwise women have two full-time jobs—one at work and one at home.

The Rapoports distinguish between role equity and equality, championing variation rather than compulsory adherence to a new stereotype. Equity implies *"fair" distribution both of opportunities and of constraints without regard to gender*. Thus, it may entail inequality—in the sense of "not the same"—if such an arrangement is freely adopted by the individuals concerned. Emphasis on free adoption provides latitude for all types of family forms. Implicit in their paper is permanent couple bonding enhanced with more equitable role responsibilities. Attaining equity in gender roles, however, is a difficult task and will not become operative through cultural prescription alone. Destereotyping of gender roles may occur by adoption of a self-conscious, critical, hypothesis-testing approach that is workable and comfortable to both partners and will enable self-actualization along with a meaningful relationship. The Rapoports indicate succinctly: "this cannot be done if the discussion is confined to the individual family or to abstract notions such as 'most women do so and so or most men are not good at so and so.' Such closed systems of a particular couple relationship and their fantasy reference groups leads to interlocking self-confirming stereotypes which are very difficult to break" (1975).

The Rapoports, in stressing a fair distribution of constraints as well as opportunities, reflect a more realistic, mature, and developed judgment than is evidenced in the other papers. Their discussion led me to realize that, in general, members of experimental variant family forms emphasize *opportunities* and seldom consider *constraints*. Obviously, any close interpersonal relationship that is more than fleeting or temporary imposes some constraints on each partner. Thus, emphasis on opportunity to the neglect of constraints suggests that a relationship would be short-lived. In contrast to experimental variant family forms, the idealized nuclear family emphasizes constraints to the detriment of opportunities. Women and parents assume unfair shares of the obligations which often lead to a negative aura of unappreciated self-sacrifice, especially by wives and mothers, which is neither fair nor healthy. Husbands and fathers, however, are not immune to this reaction, for they too may feel that their striving in the work world is unappreciated by the family.

People entering variant family forms, in their determined attempt to escape the restrictions of the idealized nuclear family, forget that some constraints are necessary if partners as well as they themselves are to achieve "the good life." Thus, one might entertain the working hypothesis that a disregard of constraints is one of the potential deficits of most experimental variant family forms. Without some obligations by members of a family to each other, the relationship would tend to be unstable and individuals could be left without support in times of need.

One variant family that has developed a system to deal with the problem of equitable distribution of constraints is the Twin Oaks Commune (Conover, 1975). Its complex work-credit system is based on psychological desirability of tasks. Each member of the commune must accrue a specified number of work credits each week; however, credit for an hour's work is assigned without regard to gender on the basis of the desirability of the task for the individual performing it. For example, an individual gets more credit per hour for tasks he or she finds undesirable than for those he or she likes to do. Perhaps this type of system, or some modification of it, will help to bring about equitable distribution of responsibilities in a majority of families.

Lorber, in interpreting Lévi-Strauss, suggests that "if we remove the sexual division of labor, we may have destroyed the basic structural mechanism for long-term heterosexual coupling" (1975). Current variant family forms which have attempted to eliminate sex typing of work roles do evidence signs of temporary rather than long-term coupling. One would expect, however, that temporary relationships would not be the norm if these family forms without regard to gender began to deal with constraints as well as opportunities. If variant family forms are to become more established and institutionalized, equitable distributions of constraints will be a problem they will have to face.

Another issue falling under the general rubric of gender role equality is that of sexual freedom for women as well as men. Although there are laws prohibiting fornication, adultery, and cohabitation, these laws are infrequently and randomly enforced (Weisberg, 1975). These prohibitions, as written, apply to both men and women; however, in actual practice, within our culture males have always had more sexual license than females. Sexual exclusivity, prescribed by law and buttressed by the myth of the nuclear family, was originally based on the need to legitimize fatherhood and bloodlines for purposes of inheritance. Now, however, improved medical technology related to birth control has totally separated sexual activity from procreation (Lorber, 1975). Further, use of all of these techniques has recently been legalized. Men and women can now have freedom of choice in sexual partners without fear of pregnancy or childbirth.

Although sex outside of marriage has been counter to traditional family norms, Marciano (1975) points out that new experimental family forms are becoming respectable rebellions and there is questioning in all age groups of the values of monogamous exclusivity. "In this sense, countercultural movements of the past decade have 'stretched' the range of permissive norms by posing life style alternatives so 'radical' as to decrease the sanctions on relatively milder variations, e.g., unmarried cohabitation as a less 'radical' option than the same situation in which children are born to that union." New birth control techniques have also made it possible to fulfill part of the nuclear family stereotype by entering a legal marriage, while modifying the conventional family model by voluntarily choosing to remain childless. Veevers (1975) points out that while childlessness may be a viable option for only a small percentage of couples, it can be fulfilling when there is genuine husband-wife consensus.

In addition to the positive influences of the alternative culture and the women's movement, the economic system appears to have contributed to the emergence of the alternative culture and variant family forms and life styles. In the United States, the relative affluence in the 1940's, 1950's, and 1960's; the increasing proportion of middle class during the past half-century; and the shift in emphasis from production to consumption have been influential. Affluence in North America in the period between 1940 and 1970 far surpassed that of most countries, and the United States and Canada seem to be the locus of most variant forms. However, Marciano (1975) suggests, without illustration or documentation, that the emergence of these forms may be or may become a worldwide phenomenon. According to her analysis, variant family forms may be a consequence of the transition from subsistence to affluence in world economics. Once affluence is established, tangible rewards are taken for granted and cease to motivate or satisfy. As a result, new avenues for pursuit of happiness are sought. If the dissatisfactions spring from the insufficiency of tangible or material goods in providing meaning and happiness, then old life styles are discarded for new ones in all societies regardless of political ideology. In conditions of affluence, deferred gratification of physical wants becomes outmoded and thus sets the stage for experimentation with life styles and invites questioning of all the older assumptions about good, moral, proper, and most meaningful values and behavior. Variant family forms and life styles become one avenue for pursuit of answers to the questions of meaning.

One of the most interesting aspects of the emergence of experimental variant family forms is the fact that membership in these forms is drawn primarily from individuals of middle-class origin. This is substantiated in this issue by Marciani, Stein, Ramey, Kanter et al., and Veevers, and in a previous issue on variant family forms by O'Neill and O'Neill (1972), Berger et al. (1972), and Macklin (1972). Members of most variant forms are children of parents who experienced increasing affluence from the 1940's onward. During this period, there was also a substantial increase in the proportion of middle-class families, which provided a larger pool of children from which variant family membership could be drawn.

Both Marciano (1975) and Conover (1975) raise the question of why children of affluent parents have turned away from the values of their early socialization. As Conover points out, children of white middle-class parents "have most to gain from the establishment culture and institutions that are designed to give them full opportunity for entrance into the professions and higher levels of business and industry" (1975). Why, then, do children of affluence turn away from the focal values of their parents? Conover suggests that generational alienation is the cause. Middle-class youth seem to find the values and life styles of their parents empty, boring, unsatisfying, and detrimental to self-actualization. Viewing the financial success of their parents as inadequate for providing personal happiness and satisfaction, they are not attracted to parental values. They have replaced their parents' values with new ones. "Bluntly put, if having money does *not* lead to happiness, why bother so much about having money?" (Conover, 1975).

Conover suggests that since the current generation of middle-class youth never experienced a severe economic depression, it has been preoccupied with the use of resources instead of their creation for survival. Unlike their parents, who have experienced a depression and are very conscious of and concerned with long-term financial security, the youth would be more inclined to take risks. This is only a partial explanation of an issue which requires imaginative research. Clearer insights mights be attained if investigators dealt with the questions of why some members of the youth generation opt for variant family forms while others select the traditional nuclear family.

Further reasons why members of the middle class or "elites," may be establishing and entering variant family forms is that people of this status are more likely to use knowledge as a resource in examining options than are people at other levels in the societal structure (Marciano, 1975). Elite status enables individuals and groups to buy certain kinds of immunity from repressive sanctioning by their surrounding culture. There are essentially four advantages which elites possess that enable them to establish and maintain variant family forms: (1) they have the ability to take advantage of whatever protective legislation is available; (2) they own private property which, even when held communally, establishes physical barriers against unfriendly surveillance; (3) they possess the ability and means to transfer from a repressive geographical area to one which allows more freedom; and (4) they have the capacity to draw self-definitions from a world view with a higher sense of personal efficacy, which accompanies higher education and income (Marciano, 1975).

STRUCTURAL DIFFERENCES IN IDEALIZED NUCLEAR AND VARIANT FAMILY FORMS

In further speculating about reasons why proponents of variant family forms reject the idealized nuclear family, it would be useful to contrast the two in terms of their structural differences. As mentioned earlier, the term "variant" includes a wide variety of family forms that are structurally different from each other. Systematic comparative descriptions among experimental variant family forms and analysis of variations within each single form are hampered by insufficient data. In very broad and general terms, however, the idealized family structure appears to be tightly constructed, closed, restrictive, and institutionalized while the experimental family structure appears more loosely constructed, open, opportunistic and still evolving. In gross terms the idealized family form emphasizes constraints to the detriment of opportunity, and the experimental variant forms emphasize opportunity to the detriment of constraints. In actuality, for all to have "the good life," individuals in close relationships must achieve a delicate balance between opportunities and constraints. Comparative study of traditional and variant family forms offers investigators a particularly fertile ground for discovering the influence of alternative structures on family behavior and for examining the relative effects of differential emphases on opportunities and constraints.

Another circumstance that makes comparisons of variant forms simultaneously intriguing and difficult for future investigators is that these are newly emerging forms with very short histories. The analytic advantage here is that they provide natural laboratories for investigating the processes by which family forms emerge, evolve, and perhaps become institutionalized. Each form in itself is in process of development. Individuals who initiate or join these new family forms not only live within these forms but have the additional task of developing the forms themselves. As a result of their short histories, there are no ready guidelines for many types of behavior and interrelationships. In this sense, as new or unforeseen events occur, members of different variant forms would be without definitions and thus anomic. They are then faced with the problems of defining the issue, reintegrating it into their perspectives of family life, assigning priorities, and developing means of handling the new event. In an attempt to avoid this kind of dilemma, some couples who either want to modify the traditional nuclear family form or are entering variant family forms are constructing written or oral contracts (Sussman, 1975). These contracts provide some structure to the relationships by establishing expectations for both opportunities and constraints. The development of personal contracts by some members of variant family forms is perhaps our only indication that there are some who have realized that constraints as well as opportunities are necessary for mutually beneficial relationships. In general, however, these contracts tend to deal with anticipated and regularized events, but neglect to consider potential crises with the exception of divorce or separation. On the basis of the Sussman data, variant family forms most likely to draw contracts are open marriages, cohabiting couples, and homosexual couples. As analysis of these data proceeds, further information on the structure of several family forms should emerge.

In this issue only one paper (Kanter et al., 1975) attempts structural analysis of a variant family form. Small group analysis, used to treat both couple and parent/child relationships in communes, is a useful technique for explicating the structural properties of family systems and provides, as well, fruitful leads for other investigators. These authors, firmly basing their study within sociological theory, show very clearly the effects of social structure on small group and dyadic behavior.

Other papers in both this and the preceding issue (Cogswell and Sussman, 1972), however, provide enough information to speculate about general differences between the idealized nuclear family and the emerging myths of variant family forms. They also offer clues permitting one to pose questions and working hypotheses for further research. Following these leads, very general comparisons of traditional with the wide range of variant family forms may be made, using five structural dimensions I have found to be most relevant. These include: (1) social time, (2) social space, (3) number of primary relationships, (4) dyadic relationship, and (5) social organization. An overriding generalization in my discussion is that the idealized nuclear family emphasizes restrictions and experimental variant families reject constraints and emphasize opportunities.

Social Time: Permanent or Temporary

Individuals enter traditional nuclear families with the assumption that membership will continue until death. Although current divorce and separation rates are evidence that marriage is no longer a lifetime relationship, individuals usually enter a legal marriage with the expectation that the relationship is permanent. On the other hand, almost all who enter variant families do so with the expectation that relationships will continue only so long as they serve the mutual benefit of the members. Relationships in variant family forms are based on expectations of trust and openness, which lead to rapid realization of the need to sever relationships that are not mutually beneficial. Beyond this agreement to dissolve unsatisfactory relationships, obligations and responsibilities of one person for another are either absent or are relegated to a low priority in the value system. Emphasis is placed on immediate fulfillment, instead of long-term obligation. In the traditional family, although ties may range from close to distant, members still carry responsibilities and obligations to each other for a lifetime, even if there are periods in the life cycle when some family members do not find the relationships mutually beneficial or when divorce and separation occur. Thus, the traditional family does maintain relationships any member should be able to count on in times of trouble or need.

The fact that obligation is minimized in variant family forms prompts an important sociological question: Are the goals held by those entering variant families adequate or sufficiently inclusive to sustain individuals over a life span? Although there are insufficient data to arrive at an informed opinion, it seems likely that variant family goals are most appropriate in short-term, fair-weather contexts. Perhaps goals such as self-actualization and autonomy drop to lower priority in times of personal crisis when mere survival must take uppermost priority. Generally speaking, it appears that the variant family can handle, perhaps better than the nuclear family, certain types of short-term interpersonal crisis such as identity problems, threat of suicide, divorce, running away, leaving employment, or changing jobs. On the other hand, it is questionable whether individual needs that require substantial effort over sustained periods of time or require substantial financial contributions from long-term savings will be met by variant family forms. In other words, will variant family forms provide the daily care needed for several months by a member who is severely ill or recently disabled? Could or would they contribute large sums of money that might be necessary for bail or lawyers, for forestalling a bankruptcy, or for paying for extensive medical care such as kidney dialysis or open-heart surgery? Within traditional families, there is the expectation that the family will arise to the need if they are physically and financially able. It is yet to be determined whether experimental families would make similar sacrifices and efforts. On the basis of current information, I would be inclined to think that experimental families would default on heavy responsibilities for the care of other members. In making this statement, however, an exception quickly comes to mind.

Although there has been no systematic study of the phenomenon, there is considerable discussion among investigators interested in variant family forms about the banding together of older people to handle some of these sorts of problems. For example, one older person may be confined to a wheelchair but able to see and take care of the accounts, another may have vision loss but be mobile enough to do the shopping, and a third may show some signs of senility but be able to do the heavier work around the house. In times of illness each might assist in the daily care of the others. In essence, these older people have developed a new family form to handle individual deficits and potential crises. This is not to say, however, that all variant family forms could respond as successfully to deficits and crises of its members. The traditional family seems to be more appropriately structured to take on these added burdens, which may occur unexpectedly at any point in an individual's life span.

Social Space: Global or Sectorized Relationships

The traditional family is expected to meet the global emotional needs of its members rather than encourage relationships with outsiders, those who may be more able to meet particular interpersonal and intellectual needs. Reducing the possibility for meaningful lateral contacts, the family experiences the effects of "caging." "If all relationships outside of the cage are formalized and impersonalized or regarded as disloyal or infidelitous, sojourns at the office, at the supermarket, at the PTA meeting, or at church can hardly provide support for growth or development. If all meaningful emotional support must be supplied by this unit, any gained outside borders upon the illicit. Men, women, and children then become cage-dependent" (Birdwhistell, 1966).

Indications that the traditional nuclear family is restrictive are further illustrated through the frequently observed couple front, as described by O'Neill and O'Neill (1972). The couple front precludes self-fulfillment in a number of sectors by eliminating relationships beyond the marital dyad.

The O'Neills point out that couples who maintain a couple front must mesh interests and expectations they hold in common and delete those which are not shared by both partners. Previous and new friendships are based on the same guidelines. Those individuals who are not liked by both members of the couple are avoided. The fact that existing and desired activities and relationships must be abandoned by the individual partners should be sufficient indication that no single person can meet all of another's expectations. Yet, because of the myth of the nuclear family, couples entering a traditional marriage usually go through an abnegation of their previous lives as individuals.

In variant family forms there is a very different structural arrangement. One's life space tends to be divided by life sectors such as home, work, friendship, and leisure, and different meaningful human relationships may be formed in each of these sectors. Bonding is based on the assumption that neither one person nor a single family unit can ever be expected to meet all of an individual's needs and expectations. Put very simply, individuals do not expect to find embodied in a single person one who can fill all multiple roles such as tennis partner, protector, lover, intellectual companion, advisor for business or interpersonal affairs. Therefore, in variant family forms, individuals tend to sectorize their lives and form meaningful relationships in each of the sectors important to their life styles and expectations.

Number of Primary Relationships: Single or Multiple

In contrast to the traditional family where expectation is for a single bonding relationship for life, variant family forms are based on expectations of simultaneous as well as serial multiple relationships. Obviously, husbands and wives have intimate relationships of various types outside of the family system; but because they live under the influence of the myth, there is a tendency to experience guilt, jealousy, or blame when outside relationships are formed. There is also a tendency to hide these relationships from other family members. Members of variant family forms expect multiple relationships and view them as necessary, making no attempt to be clandestine. Even when multiple relationships include sexual intimacy, there is usually openness and communication about them.

Structure of Dyadic Relationship: Role or Person-to-Person

Traditional family members are more likely to relate to each other in terms of roles than are individuals in variant family forms. Although family roles tend to be more diffuse than roles in other social organizations, such as factory, hospital, prison, school, and political party, role still remains a useful concept for family analysis in identifying differences between traditional and variant family forms. For the purposes of this discussion, it is important to point out that role analysis is not the exclusive property of behavioral scientists. Individuals in society at large may not actually use the term "role," but it is obvious that they act and respond within an implicit role frame of reference. For example, even small children make statements in a role context: mothers ought to tuck children in or fix family meals, or go to the grocery store; daddies are supposed to help children with their homework or fix their toys or come to little league games. Adults are even more likely than children to have expectations based on labels such as wife, husband, friend, doctor, and boss. People who use a role framework to guide their expectations of others' behavior tend to rely heavily on stereotypical expectations associated with particular social characteristics. For example, older people are conservative, physicians represent the establishment, school teachers do not wear bikinis, and children of middle-class parents are bourgeois.

In the alternative culture and in variant family forms, role relationships are anathema and person-to-person relationships are honored; role behavior is perceived as negative because it tends to be more formal and restrictive and fixed. Person-to-person relationships, on the other hand, are seen as desirable because they are more spontaneous and informal and can include acceptance of a far broader range of behavior. The alternate culture is opposed to pigeonholing individuals by social characteristics such as age, social class, occupation, education, and ethnic group. Instead, the ethos of the alternative culture proclaims that one person's behavioral expectations about another grow as a consequence of person-to-person contact. Only as people come to know each other are expectations formed, and even then they are imposed far less rigidly than would be the case for those who pattern their behavior within a conceptual framework of role expectations.

Although it is difficult for interaction to proceed without expectations, expectations in the person-to-person relationships valued by the alternative culture include a far broader range of possible or acceptable behavior than those prescribed by roles. Their expectations also shift one's attention to what is of the moment rather than to what occurred in the past or should occur in the future. Further investigation is necessary to determine whether established roles preclude real intimacy, honesty, self-revelation, and open relationships, which are so highly valued by the alternative culture and by most members entering variant family forms and life styles. It appears likely that behavior within a role framework does pose limitations on the variety of alternatives for behavior. In one sense, established roles tend to contain rather than expand potentialities for behavior. Thus, it is likely that both role relationships and the idealized nuclear family are rejected by the alternative culture for the same reason—their *caging* effects.

Social Organizations

One of the most interesting issues for sociological study of traditional and variant family forms would be comparative difference of primary relationships situated in social groups or in social networks. One would expect that structural differences between groups and networks would lead to behavioral differences. Study of variant family forms offers an excellent opportunity to deal with this basic sociological question. The stereotypical nuclear family personifies the small closed group. Among variant family forms, one finds both open and closed networks and open groups. The closed structure of nuclear family groups is probably the main reason that members of the alternative culture opt out of this form. A number of variant family forms are nonpropinquitous networks with intimacy at a distance. Three of these are described in the papers by Veevers (1975), Stein (1975), and Ramey (1975), respectively. On the other hand, communes (Conover, 1975; Kanter et al., 1975), which are propinquitously based groups, appear to promote an open internal dynamic based on person-to-person interaction in lieu of confining role relationships.

If one contrasts the general structures of groups and networks, one would surmise that networks are less restrictive than groups, but groups, at the cost of some freedom and autonomy, may provide more long-term security. Within networks, individuals on their own initiative can more easily expand or contract their encounters with other members of their networks than is possible for individuals living within group contexts. In addition, because variant family networks and groups include larger numbers of people than the traditional family, there are more alternatives for individual relationships, a greater potential for variety, and additional opportunity for sectorized relationships.

The five structural properties of families briefly discussed here in no way exhaust the types of structural comparisons that could be made. These five were used simply because they seem to point up some of the more obvious differences between idealized nuclear and experimental variant family forms. I hope investigators will be challenged to refine, elaborate, and further develop structural comparisons of family forms. Studies along these lines should make contributions to the fields of both general and family sociology.

References

Berger, B. et. al. (1972), The communal family. *Fam. Coord.*, 21:419-427.

Birdwhistell, R. L. (1966), The American family: Some perspectives. *Psychiat.*, 29:203-212.

——— (1970), The idealized model of the American family. *Soc. Casework*, 50:195-198.

Cogswell, B. E. & Sussman, M. B. (1972), Changing family and marriage forms: Complications for human service systems. *Fam. Coord.*, 21:505-516.

Conover, P. W. (1975), An analysis of communes and intentional communities: Sexual and genderal relations. *Fam. Coord.*, 24:453-464.

Kanter, R. M. et al. (1975), Coupling, parenting, and the presence of others: Intimate relationships in communal households. *Fam. Coord.*, 24:433-452.

Knapp, J. J. (1975), Some non-monogamous marriage styles and related attitudes and practices of marriage counselors. *Fam. Coord.*, 24:504-514.

Lorber, J. (1975), Beyond equality of the sexes: The question of the children. *Fam. Coord.*, 24:465-472.

Macklin, E. D. (1972), Heterosexual cohabitation among unmarried college students. *Fam. Coord.*, 21:463-472.

Marciano, T. D. (1975), Variant family forms in a world perspective. *Fam. Coord.*, 24:407-420.

O'Neill, N. & O'Neill, G. (1972), Open marriage: A synergic model. *Fam. Coord.*, 21:403-410.

Ramey, J. W. (1975), Intimate groups and networks: Frequent consequences of sexually open marriages. *Fam. Coord.*, 24:515-530.

Rapoport, R. & Rapoport, R. N. (1975), Men, women, and equity. *Fam. Coord.*, 24:421-432.

Stein, P. J. (1975), Singlehood: An alternative to marriage. *Fam. Coord.*, 24:489-504.

Sussman, M. P. (1975), Marriage contracts: Social and legal consequences. Plenary Address presented to International Workshop on Changing Sex Roles and Consequences for Family and Society. Dubrovnik, Yugoslavia, June 17.

Veevers, J. E. (1975), The moral careers of voluntarily childless wives: Notes on the defense of a variant world view. *Fam. Coord.*, 24:473-488.

Weisberg, D. K. (1975), Alternative family structures and the law. *Fam. Coord.*, 24:549-560.

Weitzman, L. J. (1975), To love, honor, and obey: Traditional legal marriage and alternative family forms. *Fam. Coord.*, 24:531-548.

In the United Kingdom, family psychiatry began at the Ipswich Hospital, in 1949, mainly as a reaction to the then prevailing practice of child psychiatry. Innovative developments followed. The family became the unit, not only for theoretical formulations, but also of clinical psychiatric practice. Family psychopathology is understood in terms of real experience, family diagnosis is arrived at by taking into account the dysfunctioning of the total family, and family therapy, both as family psychotherapy and vector therapy, is applied with the aim of benefiting the family as a whole. As elsewhere in the world, the efforts of a number of British workers have been directed to the problem of schizophrenia and family pathology. The influence of American concepts of family therapy on contemporary practice is explored.

Developments in Family Psychiatry in the United Kingdom

JOHN G. HOWELLS

The differences in the background of psychiatry in the United Kingdom and in the United States are reflected in the history of psychiatric work with families in the two countries. In the United Kingdom, there is a tradition of careful systematic work, emphasis on diagnosis, and the establishment of relatively few centers devoted to dynamic psychiatry. This tradition has been a natural background for the wide systematic approach of family psychiatry. In the United States, dynamic psychiatry is the rule, rather than the exception, with intense concentration on emotional events

---

John G. Howells, M.D., F.R.C. Psych., D.P.M., is Director of the Institute of Family Psychiatry, Ipswich, England.

Reprinted by permission from the *Journal of Marriage and Family Counseling*, vol. 3, January, 1978.

and emphasis on therapy in the psychiatric and parapsychiatric disciplines. In such a milieu, family therapy was a natural development. In both countries there is a background of psychoanalytical work. In England, it is practiced by a small but distinguished school. In the United States, it is a large, rich field indeed.

Family Psychiatry

Family psychiatry began in the United Kingdom as a reaction to neuropsychiatry and to the prevailing practices of child psychiatry in particular. The most dynamic field in psychiatry was that of child psychiatry, but it had a curious bias which must seem extraordinary now to people engaged in family work; it was assumed that the child was sick per se and that his family merely needed guidance in order to handle his illness. It was not conceived that the child's disturbance was a reflection of parental or family disturbance and that the links between the child disorder and the family disorder needed explanation and evaluation. To one working at the Maudsley Hospital, where this approach was prevalent, it was clear that the only way to bring family orientation into psychiatry was to start afresh. Thus, family-oriented work began at the Ipswich Hospital, in 1949, and ultimately an Institute of Family Psychiatry was established there; this Institute is associated with the University of Cambridge. From the beginning it was intended that the family should be the functional unit in clinical psychiatric practice. Starting from this premise, the work was allowed to proceed according to the dictates of the clinical situation. At the same time, from the very beginning, a monitoring system was established to identify and evaluate new developments. New fields of endeavor have been pioneered following this work.

The original definition is found in the first book on family psychiatry (Howells, 1963), based on the work from 1949 to 1959. It reads as follows:

> Family psychiatry is a clinical approach by which a child, an adolescent or an adult, referred from a family because of emotional disorder, is regarded as an indication of family psychopathology. This concept leads to the employment of procedures for investigating the psychodynamics of the whole family in its social and cultural setting and to offering treatment on a family basis. In family psychiatry a family is not regarded merely as a background to be modified to help the presenting patient alone. Family psychiatry accepts *the family itself*

as the patient, the presenting member being viewed as a sign of family psychopathology.

Family psychiatry should, then, embrace family theory, the understanding of family psychopathology, family diagnosis, and family therapy. The end result of endeavor is, of course, to treat the family. Family therapy is important, but is still only a part of a larger field. Indeed, effective treatment can be based only upon the right theoretical constructs, the right notions on family psychopathology, and the right procedures for family diagnosis.

Family Psychopathology

In the small dynamic field in the United Kingdom, psychoanalysis has had an overwhelming impact—to be expected when one remembers that the English school included Melanie Klein, Anna Freud, and Freud himself. The original English school of psychopathology sprang out of the First World War and ultimately led to the formation of the Tavistock Clinic by Crichton Miller and his colleagues. Later, psychoanalysis was to have a considerable influence upon the work of the Tavistock Clinic. The new family approach offered an opportunity to rethink the field of psychopathology. This latter option has been the choice at the Institute of Family Psychiatry, at the same time accepting that in the developing field of psychopathology there is room for differing experiences and differing opinions.

The concepts of psychopathology developed in the Institute are well summarized by the term "experiential." What the individual or family actually experiences is all that counts. There must be no interpretation, i.e., translation of an experience into terms other than those of the individual or the family to whom it belongs. There must be no interpretation in the light of any dogma. The facts are all. Formulations on the structure of the family were developed first. The family has been viewed in fifteen dimensions, five dimensions in the present, five in the past, and five in the future; this model has been slightly modified through the years. The family is regarded as an organism in its own right, with its own structure, characteristics, lines of communication, and, indeed, psyche, the all-important family group psyche.

It became clear that both within and without the structure of the family there was a pattern of forces, which are termed vectors. These vectors could operate for good or ill in the life of the family. The most potent of these vectors arise from attitudes which do not depend upon the functioning of the present family, but are imprinted on the present family by the experiences of the preceding families; the father and mother of the present family being in effect epitomes of their preceding families. Clashing attitudes could thus arise in the present family because of discordance between the two preceding families, mother's family of childhood and father's family of childhood. These clashing attitudes in turn have repercussions upon the children of the present family, who, in their turn, react with every other family member. Thus a pathological situation can be set in motion.

The noxious vectors always come from another emotional source, another person, usually within the family. The recipient of an adverse vector usually reacts by emiting a reciprocally adverse vector. The study of interactions within the family is therefore of great importance. Occasionally, the adverse vectors spring from family experiences outside the family group, e.g., from the extended family, from neighbors, friends, workmates, school mates, and even chance acquaintances. When this was appreciated, the exploration of the pattern of vectors within the family was extended to an exploration of the pattern outside the family.

It was impossible, after time, to shed light upon the way in which vectors affect the family. This depended upon their strength, number, magnitude, and time over which they operate. Our work supported the investigations of other workers in establishing that the greatest damage or greatest good would be done to an individual in his formative years and during his personality development. This factor obviously has great importance for preventive measures. Indeed, it has always been a principle at the Institute that if it is not possible to resolve a situation to bring complete relief to the present family, then efforts should be concentrated on preventing the adverse experiences of this family from having an ill effect, through the children, on subsequent families.

Later work was concerned with the impact of this adverse pattern of vectors on the structure of the family, i.e., what damage could be done and in what form, what coping mechanisms were employed by the family, and what symptomatology the family displayed. It is the symptomatology that usually causes the family, or others, to become aware of its problems. Hence, clinicians usually start with symptomatology as their point of contact with the patients. From this they work back to psychopathology, the elucidation of which allows a realistic, precise family therapy program to be planned.

Family Diagnosis

When there is family disorder with damage to the group psyche of the family, the dysfunctioning within the family manifests itself in symptoms which are ascertained by the family members themselves, or there are signs which are ascertained by a professional worker, a social worker, a family practitioner, a family nurse, etc. The symptomatology is the first point of contact. Quite often the family will manifest signs of somatic dysfunction. It is thus necessary to ascertain that the family dysfunction is not due to an organic disorder. Usually, in the United Kingdom, where every member of the population is on a medical practitioner's list, the screening is undertaken by the family practitioner. The patient is then referred to the Institute of Family Psychiatry.

From the onset, the Institute has not insisted upon the whole family being referred initially. This would have considerable disadvantage. Only those families able to attend as a whole family from the beginning would come, and this would probably exclude the most disturbed families. The Institute therefore accepts initially any member of the family of any age group through intake clinics for adults, adolescents, children, and the aged. It also accepts dyads from the family, the most common dyadic problem being that of the marital couple. Of course it will also accept a whole family. The aim is to take whatever the family offers initially and then to move to the involvement of the entire family at as rapid a pace as a situation will allow. It has been an intriguing side issue of the work to explore why it is that one family member rather than another comes to a psychiatric clinic at one moment in time.

The Institute emphasizes the importance of diagnosis. It insists that the family must be thoroughly understood in its fifteen dimensions before a treatment program is planned. To this end, there is a flexible use of individual, dyadic, or family-group interviews, according to the dictates of the situation. There is no slavish insistence upon a family group meeting alone. Care is taken when adding to the original interview group that the new member is ready for involvement. Equally, when it becomes necessary to see a part of a family on its own, it is important that this should be acceptable to the whole group.

The exploration proceeds by the use of systematic schemata. In Part I there is an exploration of the presenting individual through ten systematic steps. At the end of this procedure it is possible to identify and describe the individual's disorder. In Part II there is a systematic exploration of the family, in ten identical steps, at the end of which it is possible to describe and identify the family's disorder. In Part III, there are informal interviews with the family, so that every part of the fifteen dimensional system of the family can be explored and described. The end result of this endeavor is to be able to identify the pattern imprinted on the present family from its preceding families, the way in which this influences the emotional transactions within the present family and the way in which the present family interacts with extrafamily individuals and groups of individuals.

The method of choice is family group diagnosis; i.e., all family members meeting together with the diagnostician. There is no doubt about the overwhelming importance of family-group diagnosis as a tool for family exploration. Again and again it is emphasized to trainees that the operation of understanding the dysfunctioning of *a* family is distinct and different from the operation of resolving the dysfunction of *the* family. It is accepted that occasionally the two operations may run hand in hand, but they must never be confused.

Family Therapy

Family therapy, treatment of the family, is seen as being divided into two distinct but complementary areas—family psychotherapy and vector therapy.

Family psychotherapy is the effort to effect change in the family-group psyche by using as a tool the psyche of one or more therapists. At the Institute, a number of approaches are employed; individual psychotherapy, dyadic psychotherapy, family group psychotherapy (conjoint family therapy), multiple impact therapy, and multiple family therapy. These interviews are used in a flexible fashion; the one employed is the most appropriate for the task on hand. The standard interview is the family-group interview. Treatment may start with individual therapy, proceed to dyadic therapy, and go on to family-group therapy, or it can start with family-group therapy fragmenting to individual or dyadic therapy, or, indeed, the various approaches may run hand in hand.

The targets for family psychotherapy depend upon that family's psychopathology. This is conceived of in layers of time depending on the antecedental, the actual, and the anticipatory. The most difficult area is that of antecedental therapy; here, the aim is to resolve situations that have their antecedents in the preceding families. In practice, the Institute has learned that within a reasonable period of time, given the limited resources from which we all suffer, it is advisable to concentrate on those areas of experience in the preceding family that are relevant to the present family now; this is termed focal antecedental therapy and is the most valuable in practice. At first, the attempts to resolve the past were undertaken through the husband or wife in the present family; they were expected, in the traditional fashion, to remember family experiences and to work through them. An extremely valuable development has been multigenerational therapy; here, the preceding families are brought into treatment, either the family of the husband or that of the wife or both.

The next level of therapy is actuality therapy, where the treatment is concerned with the resolution of events that occur in the present, usually inside, but sometimes outside, the family. Even with limited resources this therapy can be productive. The third level of working is at the level of subsequent families and is therefore termed anticipatory therapy. The aim here is to anticipate and resolve situations that could happen in the future and which will affect the functioning of subsequent families, i.e., the families of the children. This, of course, links with preventive psychiatry. Testing units for family psychotherapy are multiproblem or hard-core families. The experiences of hard-core problem families are extremely difficult to resolve, certainly at the antecedental level. Some work can be done at the actuality level, but the most fruitful work with these families is at the anticipatory level.

Vector therapy arose from two observations. First, from the observation that neurosis in members of the community fluctuated, sometimes worsening, sometimes improving, and sometimes completely resolving; therefore it was necessary to ask what factors were responsible for the resolution. Second, from the obvious observation that neurosis did not arise from within psychotherapeutic interviews. Thus it follows that extra-interview psychotherapy might be effective.

In clinical work, it also became apparent that from time to time situations would resolve without the intervention of the therapist. We began to examine these situations. Ultimately, it was clear that restitution factors were at work that could act spontaneously to help or worsen a family situation. If they could be observed and identified, then these factors could be made to work under direction. Thus, vector therapy identifies the pattern of the vectors operating within and without the family. Should there be adverse vectors, it reshapes the pattern of the vectors to bring relief to the individual and to the family.

There is no doubt that a program of vector therapy is an essential and valuable aid to the resolution of family dysfunction. It is complementary to, and should go hand in hand with, family psychotherapy.

Supplementing the above therapies are three others: (1) traditional group therapy, (2) multiple-impact therapy—of one day or half-day duration and modified from the work of the Galveston group of workers (Serrano et al., 1962; MacGregor, 1962; MacGregor et al., 1964), (3) multiple-family therapy—as employed by Laqueur et al. (1964), but in our case concentrating on fairly superficial aims. This illustrates how our work has been enriched by American workers.

Research

In 1950, a research unit was instituted. It has had two main functions: (1) *To monitor the clinical work*. From this have arisen theories on family psychopathology, the organization for family referrals, schemata and procedures for family diagnosis, refinement and improvement of family psychotherapy techniques, and procedures for vector therapy. (2) *To conduct formal investigations*. Contributions have been made on evolving tools such as the Family Relations Indicator (Howells and Lickorish, 1967), Index of Severe Psychonosis (I.S.P.) (Howells, in prep. a), Profile of Family Interaction (P.F.I.) (Howells, in prep. b). Other work includes: a 1,000- family survey on family structure and family childrearing practices; a long-term investigation on hard-core or multiproblem families; follow-up studies in schizophrenia; assessments of symptomatology. One of the earliest investigations (Howells and Layng, 1955) concerned the vexing question of separation and deprivation. The belief in the harm done by separation was obstructing the Institute's prevention work. This led to an intervention in recent years, in the form of a plea (Howells, 1974b) to social agencies in particular to use the procedure of separation to rescue battered children.

Prevention

With time, lessons will accrue from clinical work that will be of far greater general application in society. Thus, from the beginning, the Institute was interested in identifying principles, practices, and procedures in society that were antagonistic to the emotional health of the family. Given knowledge, procedures could be created, which, by changing the pattern of adverse vectors in society, would lead to a health promoting or salutiferous society.

Teaching

As the Institute grew, it was necessary, of course, to establish in-service training for psychiatrists, psychologists, social workers, and play therapists. It was felt that effective referral could not take place unless the family practitioner was aware of family psychiatry. Thus, in 1954, the first course, sponsored by the University of Cambridge, was instituted. The aim was to make the family practitioner aware of the significance of family events, of the importance of the family as a patient, and also to enable him, with the assistance of other workers, to handle, through vector therapy, some of the family problems referred back to him from the Institute. Later, courses were instituted for psychiatrists, social workers, and the nursing profession. Nowadays, the audiences tend to be international, and the Institute has outgrown its lecture room, so that the annual courses take place in a beautiful Elizabethan mansion, Hengrave Hall, in the countryside nearby. The medical practitioners' course is in April, the psychiatrists' course in June, the social-worker course in September, and the nursing-profession course in November of each year. Courses and lectures have also been given at many Universities abroad.

Extension of Family Psychiatry

In the United Kingdom dynamic psychiatry is most in evidence in the field of child psychiatry. Thus, the influence of family psychiatry was likely to be felt first in the same field. Trainees in various professions began to pass out of the Institute's training program and establish units in family psychiatry in their new posts; they often found it easiest to do this in the children's field. Attenders at the four annual courses in family psychiatry, from the United Kingdom and from abroad, began to re-examine their practices and adjust to a family model. A Report published in 1972 by the Society of Clinical Psychiatrists (Howells, 1974a), which gave guidance on transforming child psychiatry into family psychiatry, greatly accelerated this movement. Child guidance clinics now became child and family guidance clinics; child psychiatric clinics became child and family psychiatric clinics. Practices varied from partial to complete family psychiatry. In some clinics the child was still regarded as the patient, and family work was employed to bring him health; this of course was individual psychiatry, but a vast improvement on the old approach of regarding the child's sickness in isolation from the family. In some clinics practice moved to family psychiatry proper; the child was regarded as an introduction to a sick family, which thereafter became the patient. Two further books on family psychiatry were published (Howells, 1968, 1975), making a total of only three books on the subject. Sometime after 1961 a committee (later to become a clinic) for Family Psychiatry and Community Mental Health was established at the Tavistock Institute of Medical Psychology (Dicks, 1970).

There were developments in the in-patient field. At first the Cassel Hospital, London, admitted mothers with children (Main, 1958). Later, they admitted fathers as well and found themselves to be the first hospital in the United Kingdom to have in-patient units for families. Later still, a unit for families was opened by Haldane at Cupar, in Fife, Scotland. The economic situation has retarded development in many parts of the National Health Service in the United Kingdom; nevertheless, many psychiatric units have plans for family in-patient units.

Some of the developments in the research field were relevant to family psychiatry, a field so wide that almost any research work in psychology, sociology, or psychiatry could be said to have relevance to it. This was a problem met by Post and Wardle (1962) when attempting to review research work on the family. It is necessary to restrict listing research work to that directly relevant to the central concepts of family psychiatry and exclude such subjects as personality development, deprivation, marriage, etc. Directly relevant to family psychiatry are the studies of British workers such as Howell and Parsloe (1966), Martin and Knight (1962), Brown and Rutter (1966), Davis (1964), Douglas et al. (1968), Carr (1974), Price (1969), Rutter and Brown (1966), Hare and Shaw (1965), and Hare et al. (1966).

Associated Developments

At the Third World Congress of Psychiatry in Montreal, in 1961, family work was discussed for the first time at an international psychiatric congress; three fields of work were represented, family psychiatry from Great Britain, family therapy from the United States, and work on schizophrenia in relation to the family from the United States. The latter two fields, in relation to clinical work in the United Kingdom, will now be overviewed.

The Family and Schizophrenia

In the United Kingdom, the first impact of American work on the family was that which linked family psychopathology and the development of schizophrenia in a family member. The work of Bowen, Lidz, Fleck, Spiegel, Wynne, Grotjahn, and Jackson and his Palo Alto colleagues is well known in the United Kingdom. Laing (1961, 1962a, 1962b; Laing and Cooper, 1964; Laing and Esterson, 1964) has made a far greater contribution in this field than any other British worker. Laing (1965), in his work on the families of schizophrenics, amalgamates the influence of existentialism with psychoanalysis and psychiatry. He regards schizophrenia as a social creation and the outcome of what goes on in the family. The symptoms are "a strategy invented by the person in order to live in what to him has come to be an unlivable situation." In those family systems liable to produce schizophrenics, "mystification" is to be found. "By mystification is meant the *act* of mystifying and the *state* of being mystified." The *act* of mystifying is to befuddle, cloud, and obscure whatever is going on. The *state* of mystification is to maintain the status quo. There is some affinity between Laing's views and those of D. D. Jackson et al. on the "double bind" hypothesis. His concepts have been employed in therapy and good results claimed. The possible social implications of Laing's work has been of great interest to the younger generation. More recently (1976), he has postulated on the significance of birth experiences.

Scott and Ashworth (1965) conceive a "shadow of insanity" which goes to form the attitude by which one member of the family sees and treats another as mad. The behavior of the person seen as mad is one determinant of the attitude. But the shadow is also fed by potent sources beyond the parents' immediate perception of the patient: sources from the past and from the current social field. In so far as those sources, other than immediate perception, determine the shadow attitude, we may say that one person confers a mad identity on another.

Russell Davis (1961) carefully reviews the conflicts of the Oedipus complex which might contribute to the etiology of schizophrenia. He finds that significant elements are a poor relationship between mother and father, or failure of identification with the father, and an abnormal relationship between mother and son. He gives significance to the period when the child is between ten and sixteen years old.

Other British studies include those by Brown et al. (1962), Brown (1966), Wing (1973), and Vaughan and Leff (1976). Leff (1976) has recently reviewed this field.

FAMILY THERAPY

Family therapy was late in coming to the United Kingdom. Almost all its literature derives from the United States. The most significant influences have been those of Ackerman, Bowen, Bell, Satir, and Minuchin. English literature on Family Therapy is as rare as American literature on Family Psychiatry.

In 1971 Chadwick published her review of the British literature in Family Therapy in the ten years 1960-1969. Her main conclusion was as follows, "the outstanding fact was that there was very little British writing on Family Therapy compared with the plethora in other countries, especially Scandinavia and the United States of America." She was disappointed with the use of the term Family Therapy in the United Kingdom— "this author must regrettably conclude by saying that her studies have led her to believe that as yet, in British writing, the term 'family' remains unspecified, while the term 'Therapy' remains undefined." This finding deserves comment. While there may occasionally be loose usage of the term family therapy in the United States it seems to be usually understood to connote the treatment of the family—and often by the group procedure of involving a whole family with the therapist. It is also understood that it is different from family psychiatry; the American psychiatrist Rubinstein (1977) comments ". . . the field of family therapy is to be considered a branch of the broader discipline of family psychiatry."

In a broad search, and often including ambiguous titles, Chadwick could find only 37 articles of family therapy in British journals. Of the 37 articles, seven proved to be written by American authors, one was concerned with physical illness, ten with family psychiatry, leaving nineteen papers associated, often very loosely, with family therapy and mostly arising from social work (Goldberg, 1968; Halliwell, 1969; Hammond, 1963; Howarth, 1962; Irvine, 1961; Laing, 1969; Parsloe, 1966; Robb, 1955; Roberts, 1968; Robinson, 1968a, 1968b, 1969; Skynner, 1969a, 1969b; Spackman, 1962; Spackman and Power, 1962; Webb and Bruen,

1967-1968; Wildman, 1967; Williams, 1967.)

Since 1969 there have been further contributions, and some are more direct contributions, such as from Byng-Hall (1973), Cooklin (1974), Crowe (1973), Dare (1975), and Skynner (1975). Furthermore, two books have been published by a psychiatrist, Skynner (1976), and a social worker, Walrond-Skinner (1976). It is significant that the great preponderance of the literature referred to by both authors is American. A family institute has been founded at Cardiff under the auspices of Barnardos and directed by a social worker trained at the Family Institute of New York. The latter institute has sponsored courses at the Tavistock Clinic, London, and at Cardiff. Training in Family Therapy is available at the Tavistock Clinic, London; at the Family Institute, Cardiff; at the Department of Mental Health, Bristol University; and at the Institute of Group Analysis, London.

References

Brown, G. W. (1966), Measuring the impact of mental illness on the family. *Proc. Roy. Soc. Med.*, 59:18-20.

——— Monek, E. M., Carstairs, G. M., & Wing, J. K. (1962), The influence of family life on the course of schizophrenic illness. *Brit. J. Prev. Soc. Med.*, .16:55-68.

——— & Rutter, M. (1966), The measurement of family activities and relationships. A methodological study. *Hum. Rel.*, 19:241-263.

Byng-Hall, J. (1973), Family myths used as defense in conjoint family therapy. *Brit. J. Med. Psychol.*, 46:239-250.

Carr, J. (1974), The effect of the severely subnormal on their families. In: *Mental Deficiency: The Changing Outlook*, ed. A. M. Clarke & A. D. B. Clarke. New York: Free Press, 1975, pp. 807-839.

Chadwick, A. H. (1971), *A Review of British Literature on Family Therapy Published in British Journals 1960-1969*. M. A. Dissertation, University of Bradford, 1971.

Cooklin, A. (1974), Family preoccupation and role in a conjoint therapy. Paper read to the Royal College of Psychiatrists, June 12, 1974.

Crowe, M. J. (1973), Conjoint marital therapy: Advice or interpretation. *J. Psychosom. Research*, 17:309-315.

Dare, C. (1975), A classification of intervention in child and conjoint family therapy. *Psychother. Psychosom.*, 25:116-125.

Davis, D. R. (1961), The family triangle in schizophrenia. *Brit. J. Med. Psychol.*, 34:53-63.

——— (1964), Family processes in mental illness. *Lancet*, 1:731-734.

Dicks, H. V. (1970), *Fifty Years at the Tavistock Clinic*. London: Routledge & Kegan Paul.

Douglas, J., Lawson, A., Cooper, J., & Cooper, E. (1968), Family interaction and the activities of young children. *J. Child Psychol. Psychiat.*, 91:157-171.

Goldberg, E. M. (1968), Working with the family in the child care field. Concepts, methods and practice. *Soc. Wk.*, 25:9-19.

Halliwell, J. R. (1969), Time limited work with a family at the point of being prosecuted for child neglect. *Case Conference*, 15:343-348.

Hammond, P. (1963), Changing practice in mental hospital social work. *Brit. J. Psychiat. Soc. Wk*, 7:128-135.

Hare, E. H., Laurence, K. M., Payne, H., & Rawnsley, K. (1966), Spina bifida and family stress. *Brit. Med. J.*, 2:757-760.

——— & Shaw, G. K. (1965), A comparison of the health of fathers, mothers and children. *Brit. J. Psychiat.*, 3:467-472.

Howarth, E. (1962), Organisation of family life. In: *The Canford Families. Sociological Review Monograph No. 6*, ed. P. Halmos. Keele: University of Keele, pp. 209-228.

Howell, D. & Parsloe, P. (1966), Working with a family in a child guidance setting. *Brit. J. Psychiat. Soc. Wk*, 8:21-27.

Howells, J. G. (1963), *Family Psychiatry*. Edinburgh: Oliver & Boyd.

——— (1968), *Theory and Practice of Family Psychiatry*. Edinburgh: Oliver & Boyd; New York: Brunner/Mazel.

——— (1974a), Family psychiatry for child psychiatrists, 1972. In: *Contemporary Issues in Psychiatry*, ed. J. G. Howells. London: Butterworths, pp. 39-88.

——— (1974b), *Remember Maria*. London: Butterworths.

——— (1975), *Principles of Family Psychiatry*. New York: Brunner/Mazel; London: Pitman Medical.

——— (in prep.a) *Index of Severe Psychonosis*.

——— (in prep.b), *Profile of Family Interaction*.

——— & Layng, J. (1955), Separation experiences and mental health: A statistical study. *Lancet*, ii:285-288.

——— & Lickorish, J. R. (1967), *Family Relations Indicator*. Edinburgh: Oliver & Boyd; New York: Brunner/Mazel.

Irvine, E. E. (1961), Psychosis in parents. Mental illness as a problem for the family. *Brit. J. Psychiat. Soc. Wk*, 6:21-26.

Laing, R. D. (1961), *The Divided Self*. London: Tavistock Publications; Chicago: Quadrangle Press.

——— (1962a), *The Self and Other*. London: Tavistock Publications; Chicago: Quadrangle Press.

——— (1962b), Series and nexus in the family. *New Left Rev.*, 15:3-14.

——— (1965), Mystification, confusion, and conflict. In: *Intensive Family Therapy*, ed. I. Boszormenyi-Nagy & J.L. Framo. New York: Harper & Row, pp. 343-363.

——— (1969), Intervention in social situations. Paper given to the Association of Family Caseworkers. (Pub. Assoc. Family Caseworkers & Philadephia Assoc. Ltd.)

——— (1976), *The Facts of Life*. London: Allen Lane.

——— & Cooper, R. D. (1964), *Reason and Violence. A Decade of Sartre's Philosophy—1950-1960*. London: Tavistock Publications; New York: Humanities Press.

——— & Esterson, A. (1964), *Sanity, Madness and the Family*, Vol. 1. *Families of Schizophrenics*. London: Tavistock Publications; New York: Basic Books.

Laqueur, H. P., LaBart, H.A., & Morony, E. (1964), Multiple family therapy. *Curr. Psychiat. Ther.*, 4:150-154.

Leff, J. P. (1976), Schizophrenia and sensitivity to the family environment. *Schiz. Bull*, 2:4, 566-574.

MacGregor, R. (1962), Multiple impact psychotherapy with families. *Fam. Proc.*, 1:15-29.

——— Ritchie, A. M., Serrano, A. C., & Schuster, F. P. Jr. (1964), *Multiple Impact Therapy with Families*. New York: McGraw-Hill.

Main, T. F. (1958), Mothers with children in a psychiatric hospital. *Lancet*, ii:845-847.

Martin, F. & Knight, J. (1962), Joint interviews as part of intake procedure in a child psychiatric clinic. *J. Child Psychol. & Psychiat.*, 85:17-26.

Parsloe, P. (1966), The choice of a caseworker method. *Med. Soc. Wk*, 19:7, 233-242.

Post, F. & Wardle, J. (1962), Family neurosis and family psychosis: A review of the problem. *J. Ment. Sci.*, 108:147-158.

Price, J. S. (1969), Personality differences within families. *J. Biosoc. Sci.*, I:177-205.

Robb, J. H. (1955), Experience in an ordinary family. *Brit. J. Med. Psychol.*, 26:215-221.

Roberts, W. L. (1968), Working with the family group. *Brit. J. Psychiat. Soc. Wk*, 9:175-179.

Robinson, M. (1968a), Family based therapy. Some thoughts on the family approach. *Brit. J. Psychiat. Soc. Wk*, 9:188-192.

——— (1968b), The family as the client. *Case Conference*, 14:339-342.

——— (1969), Family reaction to stress. *Med. Soc. Wk*, 22:6, 191-199.

Rubinstein, D. (1977), *The Family Psychiatrist as a Primary Care Physician*. Abstracts, Sixth World Congress of Psychiatry, 339:66.

Rutter, M. & Brown, G. W. (1966), The reliability and validity of measures of family life and relationships in families containing a psychiatric patient. In: *Social Psychiatry*, I, ed. A. Kiev. New York: Science House, pp. 38-53.

Scott, R. D. & Ashworth, P. L. (1965), The "axis value" and the transfer of psychosis. *Brit. J. Med. Psychol.*, 39:97-116.

Serrano, A. C., McDanald, E. C., Goolishian, H. A., MacGregor, R., & Ritchie, A. M. (1962), Adolescent maladjustment and family dynamics. *Amer. J. Psychiat.*, 118:897-901.

Skynner, A. C. R. (1969a), A group analytic approach to conjoint family therapy. *J. Child Psychol. & Psychiat.*, 10:81-106.

——— (1969b), Indications and contra-indications for conjoint family therapy. *Internat. J. Soc. Psychiat.*, 15:4:245-249.

——— (1975), Some consequences of work with natural groups. *Marr. Guidance*, 15:319-324.

——— (1976), *Systems of Family and Marital Psychotherapy*. New York: Brunner/Mazel.

Spackman, I. (1962), Casework as family therapy. In: *The Canford Families. Sociological Review Monograph No. 6*, ed. P. Halmos. Keele: University of Keele, pp. 181-207.

——— & Power, M. (1962), A study in social casework and group work. In: *The Canford Families. Sociological Review Monograph No. 6*, ed. P. Halmos. Keele: University of Keele, pp. 157-179.

Vaughan, C. E. & Leff, J. P. (1976), The influence of family and social factors in the course of psychiatric illness. *Brit. J. Psychiat.*, 129:125-137.

Walrond-Skinner, S. (1976), *Family Therapy: The Treatment of Natural Systems*. London: Routledge & Kegan Paul.

Webb, R. A. & Bruen, W. J. (1967-1968), Multiple child parent therapy in a family therapeutic community. *Internat. J. Soc. Psychiat.*, 14:50-55.

Wildman, M. (1967), Communication in family therapy. *Brit. J. Psychiat. Soc. Wk.*, 9:75-79.

Williams, H. (1967), Problems of family casework in a statutory setting. *Soc. Wk.*, 24:4, 18-15.

Wing, J. K. (1973), Social and familial factors in the causation and treatment of schizophrenia. In: *Biochemistry and Mental Illness*, ed. L. L. Iverson & S. P. R. Rose. London: The Biochemical Society, pp. 156-163.

Family Psychopathology

Psychopathology—the systematic understanding of family dysfunction—opens the road to the development of exact schemata for family diagnosis and to the fashioning of precise methods for family therapy. More enthusiasm is engendered by therapy, in any form, than by systematic research into psychopathology. Here, however, are valuable contributions on five aspects relevant to family psychopathology: the size of the family, the conflict behavior in marital couples, the parent-adolescent relationship, and the depressivelike behavior in monkey families.

Taking general system theory as his base, the author attempts to bring order to family psychopathology. It is suggested that from this approach can come new understanding that will assist clinical judgments and a typology of the family process.

A General Systems Approach to Severe Family Pathology

STEPHEN FLECK

Tolstoy's *Anna Karenina* begins with the statement that all happy families are similar and that all unhappy families are unhappy in their own fashion. A general systems approach to family study and assessment may help, not to disprove Tolstoy (because family clinicians must agree with him), but to bring some measure of order into the chaotic world of family pathology. The clinical participant-observer needs a superordinate framework and referential system to categorize and order his observations of family behavior. Like other systems, the family can be examined and evaluated according to five criteria: (1) its central functions and goals, (2) its leadership, (3) the regulation of the boundaries among system components and between the group and the outside, (4) managerial links and affective bondages, and (5) the effectiveness and relevancy of communication inside the system and between it and the outside world (Astrachan and Redlich, 1969; von Bertalanffy, 1968; Rice, 1971).

These five system constituents and forces are distinguishable in any functioning complex but are also interdependent, and malfunction of one sector affects all others. For instance, leadership declines if there is communication disturbance, and boundary diffusion and affective imbalances

---

Stephen Fleck, M.D., is Professor of Psychiatry and Public Health, Department of Psychiatry, Yale University School of Medicine.

Reprinted by permission of the American Psychiatric Association from the *American Journal of Psychiatry*, vol. 133, pp. 669-673, June, 1976. Copyright 1976.

can interfere with task pursuit. It is the circularity of these attributes and forces that must be appreciated, as well as the cumulative effects of dysfunction or deficiencies. One defect passed on along an assembly line may render the end product unworkable, and developmental failure at a particular stage in the human organism can interfere with the emergence of an internally and socially integrated adult (Parsons, 1964).

Biosocial and cultural givens require that the family humanize the young by teaching them not only about themselves and how to live within the family but also about the mores and cultural values of the society. In addition to these evolutionary goals of the family as the keystone of society, and the aforementioned system functions, this group must also accomplish tangible and specific tasks related to self-sustenance.

The evolutionary tasks are as follows: effecting a marital coalition capable of forming a triad of parents and infant, nurturing and weaning the infant to enable it to exist as a body apart from the mother, and imparting language and intrafamilial behavior modes epitomized by the resolution of the oedipal phase. Furthermore, the family must introduce the child into society through school and through peer relationships, which provide familiarization with society's tools and values. Tools include formal learning, communication mastery, and competence in abstract and symbolic thinking and expression. After puberty the child turns again more toward relationship issues, establishing not only his/her sexual identity but also undertaking more lasting and intimate relationships with peers. The family system is involved in all these stages: malfunction may burden and handicap offspring severely, particularly in the process of emancipation from the family to become a full-fledged adult member of society (Parsons, 1964; Fleck, 1972; Minuchin, 1970).

As a system, however, the family is more than an evolutionary production line. Parents must not only function as gender-typical adults in their society, but also tend to the other system parameters. Boundaries must be managed so that within the group each member is afforded a sense of "I" as well as "we." Boundary is a difficult concept, but is essential for a sense of integrity for the individual and the family. Boundary has two dimensions, time and space, each with tangible and intangible aspects. For instance, boundary management between the family and its community must be appropriate to subcultural norms (e.g., when a child enters school). Later, the child must cross the boundary comfortably for other purposes and for longer periods without losing the sense of family belonging, which must persist through life lest a person lose contact with his past. Another crucial boundary within the family is generational, distinguishing the parents as leaders and teachers and the children as followers and learners.

Affect flow in the family is another basic function, also determined by the parents' behavior and leadership. In brief, the maintenance over time of a positive balance of good feelings and mutual fondness is essential. The initial physical closeness between parents and child must be reduced so that a more abstract de-eroticized sense of closeness evolves, with sexual intimacy limited to the parents. The resolution of conflicts and the modulation of feeling intensity through example are the leaders' tasks in maintaining a harmonious and functioning group (Fleck, 1972).

Communication distinguishes human behavior from all other. Animals exchange signals and can even recognize feeling states in another being (Darwin, 1872), but only humans can make feelings explicit, learn the history of their species, and mentally project future actions through language-derived symbols and abstract ideation before implementing it. Linguistic competence in the family consonant with communication styles of the society is therefore as crucial to the evolvement of individual integrity as it is to effective social participation (Lidz, 1973; Piaget, 1954; Scheflen, 1972). Observing familial communication, therefore, is also a major examination tool of family functioning, just as dyadic interviews and participant observation constitute the psychotherapist's matrix for evaluating intrapersonal processes.

Clinical Illustrations

The following is an opening vignette from a meeting of a family and two hospital staff members:

Mother: It's nice to have such lovely weather. (It is pouring outside the window.)
Daughter: I am Nikita Khrushchev.
Father: (Shakes head mildly and lights a cigarette.)
Therapist: Daughter seems to be responding to mother's nonfactual statement.
Mother: It is raining, but how are you, Doctor? You look well.
Father: We had a good visit.
Daughter: Can I have a cigarette?

Therapist: A good visit?
Father: Yes, of course we didn't go out but I had some good talks with daughter.
Therapist: Yes?
Daughter: (Leaves room.)

One need hardly be a skilled observer or student of family process to conclude that this is indeed a very disturbed group of people, leaving one guessing as to who might be the patient. It is also not difficult to draw inferences about the individual malfunctionings exhibited, through the use of the referential systems of psychoanalysis and psychodynamics. General systems principles also seem useful to categorize the behavior and dynamics of this unhappy group.

One can say that in one sense no communication was taking place—these people did not even greet each other, and no one validated anyone else's statement or behavior. The comment about the weather is a classic opening gambit for strangers seeking to begin an agreeable discourse. In this instance it was also an idiosyncratic distancing gambit; it sought no agreement because it contradicted the obvious. However, it was not lost as a stimulus, eliciting a crazy response from the daughter and a kind of nonverbal "let's ignore it" from the father. The father's first statement was equally inconsistent with his own attitudes and wishes. Another conventional gambit, "We had a good visit," is nice to say if one wants to elicit agreement, but it was nonfactual; indeed, the good visit he had wanted, even demanded, was that his daughter should be allowed to be with the family away from the hospital. His wish had not been granted, and everyone in the room knew this.

Communication in this group was thus earmarked by misstatements about observable or known facts and mutual nonvalidation, arousing a high level of anxiety and anger in the participants. After the daughter's departure, communication between the parents continued in a challenging and disagreeable manner, and neither seemed attentive to the other's intent or discomfort (Scheflen, 1972; Wynne and Singer, 1963). Communication could also be categorized as fragmenting with regard not only to meaning but to the individuals involved. This gave the family therapists an opportunity to try to reduce fragmentation, which in this instance did not succeed. But we can agree with Wynne and Singer (1963) that this type and style of communicating is indeed damaging to and pathognomonic of at least one schizophrenic member in the family.

Family behavior can also be assessed in the framework of task performance—by immediate tasks in a therapy session and by examining longitudinally the general and basic evolutionary family task performance. In this instance the family had been informed in previous sessions that the task was to converse with each other, to improve contact with each other, and to understand their difficulties better. Task performance in the vignette was nil if not negativistic, arousing the observer's suspicion that the broader spectrum of evolutionary task achievements may have been equally deficient if not destructive. Indeed, the family history revealed that there was not one phase during which this triad functioned adequately or in a manner appropriate to the daughter's age and developmental needs.

The mother suffered recurrent illnesses requiring lengthy hospitalizations almost from the time of her daughter's birth; an effective mother-daughter relationship never developed because, even when physically present, the mother was rarely emotionally available to her daughter. There was no consistent mother substitute, this role having been filled by a succession of maids, two older sisters, and the father to a considerable extent. Yet it was not a typical single-parent family. The maternal behavior on the part of the father interfered with the emergence of any real oedipal situation, let alone any resolution, and this particular father's maternal attention to the daughter extended through puberty. During this period there was no real family unit, in part because of the wide age spread among the children but also because of the mother's recurrent but unacknowledged difficulties.

At about puberty the daughter began to show psychotic symptoms and behavior and became the identified patient for the next six or seven years. On the other hand, the family had not identified the mother as a psychiatric patient and still referred to her illnesses as infections, in spite of her having been on antipsychotic medications for years. In terms of evolutionary family tasks, the psychotic daughter never approached any emancipation phase and faltered in early adolescence, thus requiring psychiatric hospitalization. She is claimed to function on an age level of four.

One can discern the extreme degree of failure in every phase of system goals, representing almost in caricature our formulation, advanced some twelve years ago, of schizophrenia as a deficiency disease of family functioning and task performance (Fleck, 1972; Lidz, 1973; Lidz et al, 1965).

In this chaotic family, boundary management was equally pathological. In the session, the family members exhibited rigidly drawn noncontiguous boundaries, each withdrawn from the others in idiosyncratic stance. However, we also observed extreme intrusiveness, a violation of ego and intergenerational boundaries in the form of inappropriate physical contact between father and daughter. She had also perceived her mother as being sexually interested in her.

Children are usually expected to negotiate family boundaries without undue discomfort when entering school, which presupposes some degree of separation mastery within the family. The children in this family were tutored at home because of the father's fear of his children suffering contamination and infections in school. Boundaries were overcontrolled and rigid instead of being permeable and transgressible in line with children's age-appropriate needs. The isolation of the identified patient almost from birth illustrates further boundary mismanagement, punctured by inconsistent intrusions almost literally into her body space.

The parental role reversal was blatant, and obvious role-model defects in both parents constituted leadership failure, evident even in this brief vignette. Considering this family from the standpoint of system integrity, we see a system that mismanages boundaries, is not led properly, and in which affective bondages and interactions (communication in particular) interfere with self-definition and task performance. Such a system can neither function nor achieve goals, whether these are givens or explicitly defined as in the family meeting.

A brief description of contact (or noncontact) with the family of another hospitalized patient may illustrate further boundary mismanagement and other system defects. According to the social worker's record,

> This family met on common ground in their wish not to be involved with the hospital or in treatment. Family meetings were difficult for all of them, particularly for the mother and the son (the identified patient). They collaborated in trying to keep discussions as irrelevant as possible and had a variety of maneuvers to avoid engaging themselves. The father used a style of legal interrogation with his son and was apt to get into lengthy debates about the details of an event. He also claimed total ignorance of anything having to do with emotions, interpersonal relations, or treatment. He became quite irritated with his wife when she occasionally revealed that he had been angry with his son, with the social worker, or with the way a family meeting had gone, but usually denied having said any such thing.

The mother's tactics included attempts to discuss the social worker's personal life, other patients, current events, and psychological theories. When the session became more personal, she tried to force her son to confess that he had a happy childhood; she was quite angry at the hospital staff for stimulating him to think about his life and his feelings. As she became more disturbed and vulnerable, her intense conflict between her feelings of hostility and rejection toward the patient and her enormous guilt about these feelings were increasingly apparent.

The identified patient was the second child and only son in a family of four and was clearly not wanted by the mother. Her then three-year-old daughter already was in a day nursery when the second pregnancy occurred. She had at this point turned her interest and energy toward various community activities and was also very much involved with another man. Shortly after being sent to nursery school at age three, the son developed poliomyelitis, from which he eventually recovered completely. Because his prolonged illness had produced regression and developmental stagnation, he was not even ready for nursery school by the time he was four; his mother, however, ignored such messages from teachers and insisted on continuing with the out-of-home program so that she could pursue and nurture her community interests and ties, which interfered with the family's needs at the time and with family life. In this instance, boundary management failed because it was not congruent with this child's emotional needs or with engendering a sense of family unity and bondage.

Movements of the young across the family boundaries are predicted on separation mastery and on the child's inner certainty that a person out of sight is not lost (object constancy), neither of which can occur in the context of pretense or sham, which characterized the parents' affective and communicative behavior with each other and with their children. The son's psychosocial immaturity, evidenced by separation difficulties, was ignored.

This boundary mismanagement is different from that of the first example. In both families, contact is avoided so that there is little affect flow, and everyone remains encapsulated. In the first family, distance alternates with intrusive excursion into each other's affective space, and encapsulation, even autism, is achieved through symbolic distortion and idiosyncratic, nonvalidating communication (Minuchin, 1970; Wynne and Singer, 1963). In the second family, communication sounds and seems rational but is not truthful or expressive. Feelings are avoided and denied but not distorted, projected, and/or fantasized. The second family spawned a psychopath, the identified patient, who became a master in the family's instrumental, manipulative, and nonexpressive communication style. "Manipulative communication" means that the speaker focuses on whatever reaction he wants to elicit in the listener, whether the intent is pleasing, duping, or angering the other.

In this family, with a very disturbed, intermittently depressed, but mostly sociopathic patient, more than one essential systems paradigm was violated. Boundaries were mismanaged intrafamilially by imposing emotional distance and extrafamilially through pushing the younger members beyond the family sphere before adequate individuation and separation mastery had been achieved. The generation boundary, although too wide, was not violated; however, nurturant tasks were accomplished marginally at best. Goal pursuit in general was inadequate and deceitful, both in the therapy setting and in the life of the family; for instance, no attention was paid to the patient's misconduct and deceitfulness unless evidence was furnished from outside by schools or police.

Finally, emancipation was never joined as an issue at the usual age because of the antecedent evolutionary task failures in mastering separation, although the patient was physically out of the home in various boarding schools from early adolescence. Yet his misbehavior, leading to repeated expulsions, was never acknowledged as such, let alone as a veiled message of his unpreparedness to live without parental care.

There was a good deal of verbal emphasis on love, but both the record and the session behavior were replete with indications of mutual rejection and hostility between the spouses and between mother and son. Communication in sessions was often disputatious, especially when unacceptable affects had to be denied. Whereas interparental communication was superficial, rational, and seemingly logical, it was neither affective nor truly responsive, and the patient often talked in fragmentary fashion, like a child unready to think in sentences. Communication was substantively deficient in that it lacked expressiveness, and affective exchange was not taught or practiced; instead, communication was manipulative. Leadership was perfunctory and stereotypic but not grossly aberrant. It was deceitful because of the emphasis on appearances; i.e., whatever looks all right is all right. Thus we find communication and leadership marginally acceptable, but affective forces, boundary regulation, and some family tasks grossly deficient.

Discussion

I have attempted to demonstrate briefly one method of how to order initially confusing, disturbed, and disturbing family behaviors. These two examples derive from very aberrant families, each with at least one member in need of psychiatric hospitalization.

The information obtained both from direct participant observation and from historical exploration can be ordered by examining the basic characteristics of any general system—task and goal pursuits, leadership, boundary regulation, affective bondages, and effective communication. Since the central mission of the modern nuclear family is the nurturance, enculturation, and guidance of the younger generation into adulthood, the history must be relied on for the most part to provide relevant data (Fleck, 1963, 1972; Lidz, 1973; Lidz et al., 1965). However, leadership, communication, boundary management, and the affective bonds are also observable and available for inferences from behavior in family meetings (Minuchin, 1970; Scheflen, 1972; Bowen, 1971). These procedures have only been indicated here and should be described in greater detail in the future.

It can be pointed out that this approach may serve not only to conceptualize family functioning and malfunctioning along two axes, historical and cross-sectional, but also to establish a family typology, specifying normal and abnormal system functioning and performance according to the aforementioned principal-system paradigms.

Families as severely disturbed as those I have described demonstrate multiple (and in one instance global) system deficiences; many more families have system deficiencies that are more discrete and do not affect all parameters of system integrity and all evolutionary stages of family task performances (Minuchin, 1970; Wynne and Singer, 1963; Alanen, 1966).

As far as schizophrenia is concerned, this illustration and like considerations confirm our earlier thesis of pervasive family system deficiencies in the background of young schizophrenic patients (Lidz et al., 1965). In the first example, the parents were severely disturbed, rendering the formation of an effective parental coalition and leadership impossible. The parent-patient triad seems deficient in all evolutionary phases, and there are boundary violations of personal space and defects in family-community relationships. Emotional bonds are inconsistent, probably incestuous in quality, and anxiety laden. Communication was ineffective in both families—bizarre, fragmented, and fragmenting to the speakers in the first and amorphous and dissimulating in the second (Wynne and Singer, 1963; Lidz et al., 1965; Alanen, 1966).

The second family as a system was different from the first. Although both parents could be considered neurotic (the mother suffered various psychosomatic symptoms, the father showed obsessive-compulsive traits), neither was grossly disturbed, and they effected a workable albeit superficial marital coalition. However, the coalition did not extend to the parental tasks, and leadership and affective assertions in the family were a sham. Crises and family failures were denied instead of coped with, and boundaries were kept noncontiguous within the group and were almost nonexistent between the family and the outside. Communication was earmarked by its exclusively instrumental usage (an emphasis on its sounding right whether or not it was true and meaningful). The sham behavior extended to the family's task performances—there was nurturance without warmth, enculturation without substance (the principle that as long as behavior looks all right, it is all right). There was no family togetherness in leisure or crisis, and emancipation was also a sham in that the patient's signals of his inability to cope with separations were ignored.

Conclusions

The general systems approach of defining a family typology seems useful in ordering family behavior data and may also correlate with certain of the major clinical entities, a prospect reinforced by other family records so analyzed. This correlation may be more quantitative or cumulative than qualitative. The data so far suggest that the number and severity of systems defects may distinguish pathological outcomes rather than any particular intrinsic defect.

In summary, scrutinizing families as an open system allows us to arrive at sequential judgments and categorizations that differ from such simple polarities as normal versus abnormal or healthy versus pathogenic. General systems theory permits cross-sectional and longitudinal examination of the group not only in terms of the special group that is the family but also as it pertains to any collective of interacting forces. Judgments about the system's behavior and past performance in terms of the family's role as the keystone of society can then be made independent of presenting disturbances, symptoms, or traditional clinical classifications.

References

Alanen, Y. O. (1966), The family in the pathogenesis of schizophrenia and neurotic disorders. *Acta. Psychiat. Neurol. Scand.* (Suppl. 189), 42:1-654.

Astrachan, B. & Redlich, F. C. (1969), Leadership ambiguity and its effect on residents' study groups. *Internat. J. Group Psychother.*, 19:487-494.

Bowen, M. (1971), Principles and techniques of multiple family therapy. In: *Systems Therapy*, ed. J. Bradt & C. Moynihan. Washington, D.C.: Bradt & May, pp. 187-206.

Darwin, C. (1872), *The Expression of the Emotions in Man and Animals*. New York: Philosophical Library, 1955.

Fleck, S. (1963), Psychiatric hospitalization as a family experience. *Acta Psychiat. Neurol. Scand.* (Suppl. 169), 39:1-24.

——— (1972), Some basic aspects of family pathology. In: *The Manual on Child Psychopathology*, ed. B. B. Wolman. New York: McGraw-Hill, pp. 189-204.

Lidz, T. (1973), *The Origin and Treatment of Schizophrenic Disorders*. New York: Basic Books.

——— Fleck, S., & Cornelison, A. (1965), *Schizophrenia and the Family*. New York: International Universities Press.

Minuchin, S. (1970), The use of an ecological framework in the treatment of a child. In: *The Child in His Family*, ed. E. J. Anthony & C. Koupernick. New York: John Wiley, pp. 41-57.

Parsons, T. (1964), *Social Structure and Personality*. New York: Free Press.

Piaget, J. (1954), *The Construction of Reality in the Child*, trans. M. Cook. New York: Basic Books.

Rice, A. K. (1971), *Learning for Leadership: Interpersonal and Intergroup Relations*. New York: Barnes & Noble.

Scheflen, A. (1972), *Body Language and Social Order: Communication as Behavior Control*. Englewood Cliffs, N.J.: Prentice-Hall.

von Bertalanffy, L. (1968), *Organismic Psychology and Systems Theory*. Worcester, Mass.: Clark University Press.

Wynne, L. C. & Singer, M. T. (1963), Thought disorder and family relations of schizophrenics. II. A classification of forms of thinking. *Arch. Gen. Psychiat.*, 9:199-206.

The significance of the number of family members in a family in determining the number and size of relationships is explored; this obvious factor is often ignored, and the author's emphasis on the importance of numbers is a timely reminder. Attention is given to total and subtotal patterns of relationships. In the matrix of relationships, however, not all have equal weight in a given context.

Balance Theory: Possible Consequences of Number of Family Members

J. S. B. LINDSAY

There are many useful clinical concepts developing in family psychiatry that, though valid and reliable in clinical work, have no theoretical frame or model. The relationship betwen actual behavior and the inferred structure remains unclear, difficult to demonstrate or measure. Taylor (1970), in confronting these issues, has presented a model based on the Cartwright and Harary (1956) signed graph and balance theory that offers considerable heuristic possibilities in this area. He argues from the basic propositions:

1. that dyadic relationships can be categorized in two classes, positive and negative;
2. that a group (or family) will tend toward balance so that the product of the signs of all dyads is positive;
3. that each member will have a proportion (from none to all) of his dyads positive.

One of the basic corollaries of balance theory is that the balanced group or family can be divided into two, and only two, subsets or coa-

J.S.B. Lindsay, M.D., M. Phil., F.R.C. Psychiat., is from Townsville General Hospital, Townsville, Queensland, Australia.

Reprinted from *Family Process*, vol. 15, pp. 245-249, 1976.

litions, even though one subset may be a single member. As a result of this, the model "predicts" that relatively few out of all the possible combinations are actually used and that the single deviant (scapegoat) maximizes the mean proportion of positive dyads for the group (family) members. This mean proportion is Taylor's "average emotional income" (1970).

These concepts are all based on the continued presence of all members of the group or family. In an interview or therapy session or through the other time intervals, the propositions argue for the continued interaction of all members. However, each group (or family), according to size, is made up of so many possible dyads, so many possible triads, and so forth. These can be arranged as in Pascal's triangle (see Table 1).

TABLE 1

	Size of group (family)					
	1	2	3	4	5	6
Number of dyads		1	3	6	10	15
Number of triads			1	4	10	20
Number of tetrads				1	5	15
Number of pentads					1	6

If we turn our attention away from the whole group interacting, there are other additional subtotal patterns of relationship that can occur. It is surely relevant to include these in any consideration of the family. Four important patterns need to be considered (Caplow, 1957).

Patterns of Relationship

A. *The total number of potential relationships in a group size n,* between individuals and/or subgroups, is given by $(3^n - 2^{n+} + 1)/2$. This series includes any group(s) and/or individual relationships in which the total is less than n. In a group of five, it will include all the 2 + 1, 3 + 1, 2 + 2 combinations as well as the 3 + 2 and 4 + 1 combinations. It increases rapidly from one dyadic relationship (n) to 6, 25, 90, 301, 966 as n increases.

B. *If all possible relationships for any one specified member of a group of size n* are examined, a similar but smaller series is found: 1, 5, 19, 65, 211, 665, $(3^{n-1} - 2^{n-1})$. The ratio of one specified member's possible relatedness (B) to the total relatedness (A) converges on 0.66 as n increases.

C. In a group such as the family, all members have to relate in one or another way. A family of four will spend more time as two pairs or a three and a single than other nonfamily groups of four. The *total combinations of relationship in which the sum of the members relating equals n* is given by $(2^{n-1} - 1)$.

D. This formula $(2^{n-1} - 1)$ also gives the number of *all potential relationships for any individual member*. The variations obtaining for a family of four can be seen in Figure 1.

Subtotal Relationships

Within these subtotal relationships are several patterns that are of concern. For instance, there are, in the given example, only seven inclusive relationships (C) compared with the overall total of 25 (A); C/A = 0.28. It is therefore proposed to look at:(1) the ratio of inclusive relationships to all overall relationships (C/A as above). This emphasizes the importance of the nontotal, noninclusive relationships for such concepts as "encapsulation," "family splitting," etc.; (2) the ratio for one member's subtotal relatedness (i.e., [B] minus [C] to the total pool of subtotal, noninclusive relatedness (i.e., [A] minus [C]). This raises the issue of noninvolvement in this internal subtotal relatedness and appears to be prototypically triadic; (3) the ratio of one member's relatedness as an individual (D) and his relatedness as a subgroup member ([B] minus [D]). This, in effect, relates to his power or dominance as an individual and his possible skills and prowess as a group member.

1. Overall Subtotal Relationship Patterns

The ratios between the number of situations in which all members related (C) and the number of all possible relationships (A) are 1.0, 0.5, 0.28, 0.166 . . . for 2, 3, 4, 5 . . . members. This series may give some indication of the potential diffuseness or noninclusiveness of relationship as a family increases in size. It also emphasizes that the Taylor model does not take note of the many less-than-total relationship patterns.

FIGURE 1

1. Father - mother
2. Father - son
3. Father - daughter
4. Father - children
5. Father - women
6. Father - mother & son
7. Father - all others
8. All others - son
9. All others - daughter
10. All others - mother
11. Parents - children
12. Father & daughter - mother & son
13. Men - women
14. Men - mother
15. Men - daughter
16. Parents - son
17. Parents - daughter
18. Father & daughter - mother
19. Father & daughter - son
20. Mother - son
21. Mother - daughter
22. Mother - children
23. Son - daughter
24. Son - women
25. Daughter - mother & son.

D (items 1–7) ← $(2^{n-1} - 1) = 7.$

C (items 7–13) ← $(2^{n-1} - 1) = 7.$

B (items 1–19) ← $(3^{n-1} - 2^{n-1}) = 19$

A (items 1–25) $\frac{(3^n - 2^{n+1} + 1)}{2} = 25$ →

Variations in Patterns of Relationship for a Family of Four

These ratios can be seen as indices of the relative dependence of each family member for relatedness to the other(s) for various sizes of whole family. In the dyad, there is no way for any one to relate except to the other member. In a triad, there are three ways in which a dyad subgroup and a single can relate, but also three ways in which dyads can form leaving the odd single out. So half the possible ways of relating do not include all the members of a family of three. As the family gets larger, the difference between whole family (i.e., all members) relatedness and internal subtotal relationship patterns increases.

A conflict that disrupts a dyad leads to the end of that dyadic relationship. A conflict in a triad may be located or confined in one subtotal dyad while the triad remains intact, or it may lead to the disruption of the triad so that it does not exist anymore. Only a dyad and a separate single remain. This encapsulation of a conflict in a subgroup or disruption of the whole group are equally likely in the triad ($p = 0.5$). With larger families the chances of encapsulation of conflict in a subgroup increase, and chances of disruption decrease.

Conflicts and stresses do not necessarily involve all the family members. The relative availability of relatedness not involving all the members within the family group is suggested as a way in which conflict and stress can be internalized within the family without threats to the boundaries of the family.

2. Individual Subtotal Relationship Patterns

This pool of subtotal family relatedness is given by (A) minus (C). If we next turn to one specified member (e.g., father), he is involved in all the relationships (B), which, however, also include the inclusive relationships (C). So *his* pool of noninclusive relationships is (B) minus (C). Hence the possible relatedness for any given number within the subgroup relationships in the family is the ratio of [(B) − (C)] / [(A) − (C)] which reduces to two-thirds for all values of n (≥ 3). For any given family member, no matter the family size, there is: (a) an involvement in any and all the problems that involve the whole family; (b) a fixed two-thirds chance of being included in any internal (i.e., nontotal) family relatedness, stressful or not; and (c) a one-third chance of not being involved in such internal relatedness.

This argument is clear in the smallest relevant group size of three. Any pair can form an internal subgroup, and any given member belongs to two of the three possible pairs. This is the smallest family group that may have some self-perpetuating qualities (e.g., father, mother, and child) by being two generations and both sexes. It is interesting, however, to note that the same ratio exists for groups of larger size. This is not without consequence in thinking of intrafamily dynamics. However, the choice of relatedness of this order (⅔ : ⅓) is classically that of a triad—the simplest example.

3. One Member's Subtotal Relatedness Patterns

The third issue concerns the individual relating as an individual (D) and his overall relating as a member of a subgroup and an individual (B). The ratio of individual relating (D) to relating as a subgroup member is D/(B − D) (1.5, 0.58, 0.30, 0.17 . . . for 3, 4, 5, 6 . . . members). These figures imply a diluting effect of size on the possible dominance or power of any one member in terms of subtotal noninclusive relating patterns.

There is here a particular change in the ratios, from the 1.5 for the triad to lower values (<1.0) for larger-size groups. In the triad there are five relationships for any one member (B) and one where that member is excluded (e.g., see Figure 2).

FIGURE 2

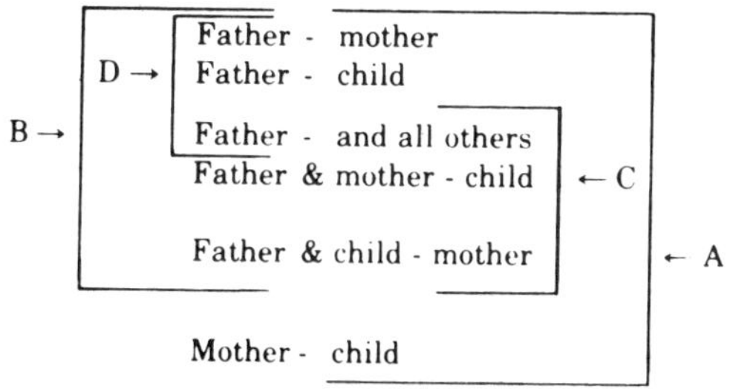

Possible Combinations of Relationships in a Triad

In three (D) of the five, ego is a monad and only outnumbered in one relationship. As a member of two dyadic coalitions in a triad, he has to share power with this dyadic co-partner but is not outnumbered. The patterns inherent in the triad, including the primary triad of father-mother-child, have been described in detail by Caplow (1968). His observations also serve to underline the unique place that the triad has in the pattern of family interrelationships.

With the tetrad, these triadic potentialities change. The triad may now become one of the subgroups that can exist and form an encapsulated subgroup relating to the other member. The single member now has nearly as many relationships in which he is a member of a dyad or triad as a separate monadic entity.

In the dyad there is no alternative to the one-to-one relationship. With the triad the possibility of diluting one member's effect is present but minimal. The tetrad presents the first situation in which this effect becomes a significant factor.

Comment

Attention has been focused hitherto entirely on the numerical aspects of the interactions between family members. This approach does imply that the different members of the family group are all given equal weight. Each member has to stand up and be counted as in taking a census. Individual members of families are not all equal, however, and the relationships possible between, for example, four sibs, though numerically large, will not have the weight of the parental dyad.

Each member of the family constructs his social interpersonal reality out of the matrix of relatedness in the family. There are critical differences between the parental dyad, sibling relationships, and parent-child relationships that are highly significant in this process. Furthermore, we may categorize the relationships as one- or two-generational, and as hetero- or homosexual. It is customary to use these terms as if they referred to the dyad, and yet it is typical of the family that it has both generations and both sexes all in together. The nature of this togetherness is important in family psychiatry, for it alters the perspective from a dyadic one-to-one point of view to include the ramifications of triadic, tetradic, and larger situations. In this paper some of the implications of the numerical factor have been examined. It is certainly not the intention to imply that this numerical factor of itself is of sole significance, but rather it is, in the words of Simmel (1902), ". . . how the form and inner-life of a societary group are determined by the numerical relationships of the same."

References

Caplow, T. (1957), Organisational size. *Admin. Sci. Quart.*, 1:484-504.

——— (1968), *Two Against One*. Englewood Cliffs, N.J.: Prentice-Hall.

Cartwright, D. & Harary, F. (1956), Structural balance—A generalisation of Heider's theory. *Psychol. Rev.*, 63:277-293.

Simmel, G. (1902), The number of members as determining the sociological form of the group. Trans. A. W. Small, *Amer. J. Sociol.*, 8:1-46; 158-196.

Taylor, W. R. (1970), Research on family interaction, I: Static and dynamic models. *Fam. Proc.*, 9:221-232.

The purpose of the study presented here was to examine, using mixed-motive games, the reciprocal perception of husband and wife while engaged in a conflict situation. The management of the conflict itself is observed by the same method.

Conflict Behavior in Clinical Couples: Interpersonal Perceptions and Stable Outcomes

NATHAN B. EPSTEIN and JACK SANTA-BARBARA

The role of interpersonal perceptions in the management of marital conflicts has not received much empirical study. Considerable evidence (Allport, 1958; Bronfenbrenner, 1961; Deutsch, 1969) indicates that protagonists in a conflict perceive each other differently from the way they perceive themselves, but how these perceptions relate to the manner in which protagonists interact, and how their interpersonal perceptions change as a function of their interactions have not been studied extensively.

The mixed-motive-game paradigm lends itself to the study of interpersonal perceptions in conflict situations by providing a framework in which to gather data concerning a number of variables. The particular

This project was supported by the Medical Research Council of Canada.

Nathan Epstein, M.D., is with the Department of Psychiatry, McMaster University Faculty of Health Sciences, Hamilton, Ontario.

Jack Santa-Barbara, Ph.D., is with the Department of Research, Hamilton Psychiatric Hospital, Department of Psychiatry, McMaster University, Hamilton, Ontario.

Reprinted from *Family Process*, vol. 14, no. 1, March, 1975.

mixed-motive games used in the present study are presented in Figure 1. The Prisoner's Dilemma (PD) and Chicken (CK) games shown are two of the most frequently used versions of two-person, two-choice games. Both Row and Column players each have two choices, C and D; the C choice is considered a cooperative one, the D choice a defecting one.

FIGURE 1

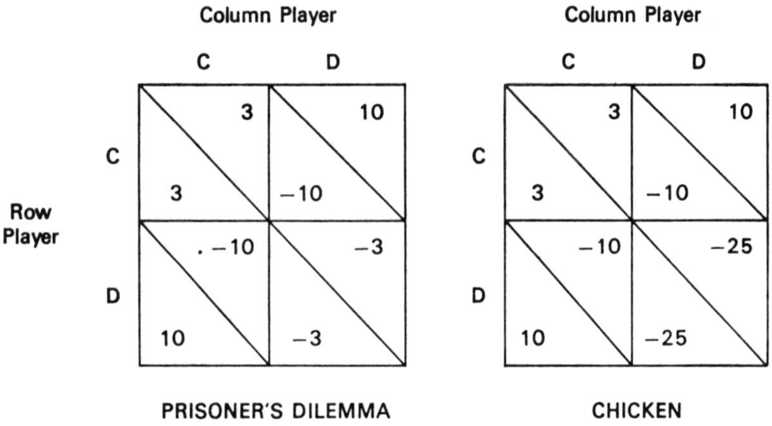

The Prisoner's Dilemma and Chicken Games

Mutual gain (3 points each), or cooperation, is possible only if both players make a C choice. However, greater unilateral gains (10 points) may be made if one player defects while the other cooperates. The player who cooperates unilaterally not only loses the satisfaction of a cooperative outcome but also suffers the loss of 10 points (−10), while the partner gains 10. In order to avoid this situation and still make a cooperative choice, one must trust the other player to also cooperate. But if one feels certain that the other will cooperate, one may then be tempted to take advantage of the other's cooperativeness and make a D choice, thereby gaining the highest possible payoff. The structural aspects of these games, which induce each player to both cooperate and compete, identify these games as mixed-motive games. If both players simultaneously attempt to gain their highest unilateral payoff (i.e., each makes a D choice), then both lose. The amount of loss associated with a mutual defection (A DD state) is the dimension that differentiates the PD and CK games shown in Figure 1. A DD state results in a payoff of −3 for each player in the PD game, and −25 in the CK game. Players are sensitive to both structural changes and payoff changes within a particular game (Rapoport and Chammah, 1965; Vinacke, 1969).

Because the potential losses associated with a mutual defection are greater in the CK than in the PD game, a rational player is inhibited from seeking the highest unilateral gain in the CK game. Only if the partner is seen as more inhibited or submissive will the other player risk the potential loss of a mutual defection and attempt to gain the largest payoff.[1] The CK game, then, involves not only a trust dimension, as does the PD game, but also a "brinksmanship" component.

Typically, mixed-motive games are played for many trials, without benefit of explicit communication, and without tapping the dimensions of interpersonal perception. By requiring each player to predict his partner's choice on each trial, in addition to making his own choice, data are made available concerning (a) how cooperative each player perceives the other to be; (b) how accurate each player is at predicting the other's moves; and (c) what each player does (i.e., which choice he makes) when he predicts that his partner is about to cooperate, for example, rather than defect. This last class of variables permits an investigation of the subjects' intentions, clarifying the reasons for a particular choice. For instance, although a D choice is commonly regarded as an exploitative one, this is true only if the player perceives the other as likely to cooperate on that trial. However, if a player believes it likely that the partner will defect on a particular trial, a D choice may then be interpreted as a defensive move, rather than an exploitative one.

Several studies have used this predict-play technique for examining some of these variables. When dyads composed of strangers play each other, the level of accuracy in predicting the opponent's response is very low, usually at the chance level (Tedeschi, 1968). Subjects in these situations tend to overpredict the other's level of cooperativeness (Halpin and Pilisuk, 1967; Santa-Barbara, 1972; Tedeschi et al., 1968; Worchel, 1969). (It must be recalled that the other must be seen as cooperating if one is to realize a gain in these situations.) It has also been demonstrated (Halpin and Pilisuk, 1967) that subjects' predictions change as a function of whether they believe they are playing against a machine or another

[1] A fuller description of the psychology of these mixed-motive games is presented elsewhere (Rapoport and Chammah, 1965, 1966).

real subject, even though the response sequence is in fact identical. This finding indicates that the players take into account what they perceive as the "other's" motivations.

Terhune (1970) has demonstrated that the predict-play combinations of subjects vary as a function of certain personality variables. For instance, subjects high on Need Achievement, as measured by the TAT, produce the highest level of cooperative intentions (predict C and play C), and high Power-Oriented subjects produced the lowest level of cooperative intentions, but the highest level of exploitative ones (predict C and play D).

When these predict-play combinations are related to stable outcomes, it is found that dyads who reach a stable state of high cooperation are characterized by other cooperative and exploitative intentions prior to stabilizing their interactions (Santa-Barbara, 1972). On the other hand, dyads who reach a state of high conflict express more exploitative than cooperative intentions prior to asymptote.

To date, there is only one study reported in the literature relating interpersonal perceptions to conflict behavior in a mixed-motive game in which the protagonists are married couples (Bean and Kerchoff, 1971). In this case, interpersonal perceptions were measured by asking the graduate-student couples who served as subjects to respond to various personality inventories as they thought their spouses would respond. The couples' responses to these questionnaires were then correlated with their behavior in a PD game in which each spouse thought he was playing against his spouse but actually played against a preset program. This study by Bean and Kerckhoff (1971) reports several complex interactions between conflict behavior, sex of spouse, and duration of conflict. However, the study did not address itself to the issue of how one spouse's perception of the other actually affected that spouse's behavior in the conflict situation itself. Since one partner may perceive his spouse differently in a conflict situation from the way he does in general, this question is also of some interest to the study of marital conflict behavior. In addition, the Bean and Kerckhoff study does not provide any information concerning the spouses' actual interactions in a conflict situation or their interpersonal perceptions while resolving a conflict.

Previous data using mixed-motive games with clinical couples have indicated that different couples resolve these conflicts in very different ways (Santa-Barbara and Epstein, 1974). A small proportion of couples reach a stable, cooperative solution, and they are labeled Doves. Other couples reach a stable outcome of high mutual conflict, and they are referred to as Hawks. A Dominant-Submissive pattern also emerges, in which one spouse gains at the other's expense. And finally, there are couples who do not reach any type of stable outcome—they are referred to as Mugwumps. It has also been demonstrated that couples categorized in this way differ on a number of demographic and treatment characteristics (Santa-Barbara and Epstein, 1974). The data to be reported in the present study are concerned with the interpersonal perceptions of these various types of couples and the role these perceptions play in the process of their attempts at conflict management.

The purposes of the present study were to determine (a) how husbands and wives perceive each other in a conflict situation (i.e., as cooperative or exploitative); (b) how accurate their perceptions of each other actually are; and (c) how these interpersonal perceptions relate to their actual interactions in the conflict situation, as expressed by their predict-play combinations. Specifically, it was expected that the Dove couples would perceive each other as being more cooperative, prior to attaining a stable cooperative outcome, than each of the other groups. The Doves were also expected to be more accurate than each of the other groups prior to attaining a stable outcome and to express more cooperative intentions than each of the other groups. This would be demonstrated by the highest proportion of predict-C and play-C combinations of all the couples studied. By contrast, the Hawk couples were expected to demonstrate the highest level of exploitative intentions prior to a stable outcome, as expressed by their level of predict-C and play-D combinations. The Hawks were also expected to express the highest proportion of defensive responses (i.e., predict-D and play-D). This expectation is in line with the findings that unmarried dyads who become Hawks are characterized by a high level of defensive intentions in a variety of conflict situations (Santa-Barbara, 1972).

The Dominant-Submissive couples were expected to be characterized by a submissive member who makes more appeasement intentions than his/her spouse prior to a stable outcome, as indicated by their proportion of predict-D and play-C combinations.

One of the reasons for including both a PD and CK game in the present study was to determine the couples' sensitivity to the structural aspects of the conflict expressed in these games. The PD and CK games are identical except for the amount of loss associated with a mutual defection. If the couples were sensitive to this dimension of the conflict, those in the CK game were likely to express more appeasement (predict-D and play-C) and cooperative (predict-C and play-C) intentions and fewer defensive (predict-D and play-D) and exploitative (predict-C and play-D) intentions than those couples in the PD game. However, this effect was expected only for the Dove and Dom-Sub couples, for the Hawks and Mugwumps have been found to be insensitive to the structural aspects of these situations (Santa-Barbara and Epstein, 1974).

METHOD

The husbands and wives who participated in this study were drawn from the patient population of the Chedoke Child and Family Centre in Hamilton, Ontario. The population consists primarily of intact, middle-class, Ontario-born families who are free of severe psychopathology. The reasons for the couples' contact with the clinic consisted of educational and/or behavioral disorders in their children. A more detailed description of the demographic and other characteristics of the subjects who participated is available in an earlier report (Santa-Barbara, 1974), as well as a full description of the experimental design and procedures.

Essentially, each couple played either the PD or CK game described in Figure 1 for 300 trials. Each spouse had full information concerning his own and the other's payoff, but couples were not allowed to communicate. Couples were classified as Doves, Mugwumps, Dominant-Submissive, or Hawks according to predetermined criteria, defined in terms of the couples' stable behavior in the conflict situations (Santa-Barbara and Epstein, 1974). In order to attain a certain criterion, a couple had to make a certain proportion of a particular response state for at least 75 criterion (CR) trials. The criterion for a couple becoming a Dove consisted of 20/25 mutually cooperative (CC) response states for the CR trials. Because of the instability of the mutually defecting (DD) response state, the criterion for the Hawks was set lower at 12/25 DDs for the CR trials. The criterion for the Dominant-Submissive couple was that one spouse receive at least 12/25 CDs (unilateral losses) for the CR block. Couples who did not attain any of these criteria are referred to as Mugwumps.

The couples' data prior to the CR trials are referred to as preasymptotic trials, and the data subsequent to the CR trials are called Post-CR trials. This method of data organization permits an examination of true interaction measures (e.g., the asymptotic criterion states) and their relationship to a variety of other game and nongame variables. By clearly delineating preasymptotic behavior from the stable CR behavior, it is possible to examine the true interaction processes that distinguish the criterion groups before they stabilize. Because these preasymptotic interactions are independent of the stable outcomes, they provide a description of how couples interact with each other in order to resolve their conflict in a particular way. This technique has proven useful in identifying consistent patterns of interaction that are not predictable on an a priori basis. For instance, it was found that one of the distinguishing characteristics of dyads who became Doves was that, prior to stabilizing at a cooperative state, they retaliated against their partners' defections at a rate equal to, and in some cases greater than, that of the Hawk dyads (Santa-Barbara, 1972; Santa-Barbara and Epstein, 1974). This aspect of the Doves' preasymptotic interactions was conceptualized in terms of a firmness component and was considered essential for the development of a stable cooperative state in these games.

The purpose of the present study was to examine these preasymptotic interactions of the various outcome groups in terms of their interpersonal perceptions and intentions and to examine how they changed during the course of the conflict.

The preasymptotic trials were Vincentized[2] into fifths in order to examine trends over trials. Major analyses were performed using a four-factor (Game × Outcome Group × Sex × Trials) analysis of variance, with repeated measures on the Trials factor. Arcsine transformations were performed on all probability data prior to analysis of variance as recommended by Weiner (1962). Individual comparisons, when appropriate, were made, using the Newman-Keuls procedure. Data from the first ten couples to reach each of the criterion states in each game are reported here. Eighty couples, 40 in each game, and ten in each outcome group, were involved.

[2] Vincentizing is required in order to deal with the different number of trials required by different couples to reach criterion. If a couple took 100 trials to reach criterion, each Vincent fifth contains 20 trials for that couple (Woodworth and Schlosberg, 1961). The average number of preasymptotic trials for each group ranged from 91 to 129. The first 100 trials of the Mugwumps' data are considered their preasymptotic trials.

Results and Discussion

Perception of Spouse's Level of Cooperation

What is the relation between cooperative couples' perception of each other and how cooperative they actually are? If each partner perceives the other as being cooperative, is this likely to induce each partner to himself cooperate? Table 1 presents the proportion of cooperative responses predicted over preasymptotic trials[3] and over CR and Post-CR trials, collapsed over game and sex. The first point to note in Table 1 is that all groups predict more cooperation than defection. Other studies using this procedure also report an overprediction of cooperative responses (Halpin and Pilisuk, 1967; Santa-Barbara, 1972; Tedeschi et al., 1968; Worchel, 1969). The Doves predicted more cooperation than the Hawks, as hypothesized, but they did not predict more cooperation than either the Dominant-Submissive couples or Mugwumps over preasymptotic trials. The relation between the couples' interpersonal perceptions

TABLE 1

PROPORTION OF COOPERATIVE RESPONSES PREDICTED BY EACH OUTCOME GROUP OVER PREASYMPTOTIC, CR, AND POST-CR TRIALS

Outcome[1]	Trial Blocks[2]		Post-CR
	Preasymptotic	CR	
Doves	.718	.789	.806
Dom-Sub	.623	.697	.621
Mugwumps	.650	.647	.640
Hawks	.597	.652	.601

[1] ANOVA effect for Outcome Group ($F = 2.96$; $df = 3, 144$; $p < .05$). Newman-Keuls indicate Doves > Hawks ($p < .01$).

ANOVA effect for Trials by Outcome Group by Sex interaction ($F = 2.01$; $df = 18{,}864$; $p < .01$) Newman Keuls indicate that wives > husbands in Dove group over CR and Post-CR trials ($p < .05$).

[2] ANOVA effect for Trials ($F = 3.30$; $df = 6{,}864$; $p < .01$) and Trials by Outcome Group interaction ($F = 1.64$; $df = 18{,}864$; $p < .05$). Newman-Keuls indicate Doves > Hawks over preasymptotic trials (blocks 1, 2 & 4; $p < .05$); Doves > Mugwumps and Hawks over CR trials ($p < .05$) and Doves > Dom-Sub, Mugwumps and Hawks over Post-CR trials ($p < .05$).

[3] All analyses of variance were performed on five preasymptotic trial blocks, plus the CR and Post-CR blocks. However, the preasymptotic data is essentially flat in all cases, and the data are therefore collapsed over preasymptotic trials in this and all subsequent tables.

and interactions was complex. Perceiving one another as cooperative was associated with actual cooperative behavior only for the Doves. For each of the other groups, each spouse expected more cooperation than defection from his partner, but they did not reciprocate this expected cooperation. Even over CR and Post-CR trials, when the couples' behavior had stabilized on a noncooperative outcome, these couples continued predicting that their spouses would cooperate. These results differ from those of Kelley and Stahelski (1970) who found that competitively oriented subjects tend to perceive their partners as competitive. Whether the different results are attributable to the different procedures used in the two studies or to differences in the kind of subjects employed (college students or married couples) is not yet known.

All groups except the Doves were, of course, highly inaccurate in their predictions. Table 2 contains the proportion of correct predictions made by each group over trials, and collapsed over game and sex. The Doves made more correct predictions than each of the other groups over each trial block. However, the Doves' relatively higher proportion of correct predictions was little better than chance accuracy over the preasymptotic trials. It is somewhat surprising that the development of a stable, cooperative outcome was not preceded by a higher level of accurate perceptions on the part of the Doves. The accurate perception of particular actions seems less important than the general attribution of spousal cooperativeness for these Dove couples. For the other couples a very different process appeared to be operating. These couples pre-

TABLE 2
PROPORTION OF CORRECT PREDICTIONS BY EACH OUTCOME GROUP OVER PREASYMPTOTIC, CR, AND POST-CR TRIALS

Outcome[1]	Trial Blocks		Post-CR
	Preasymptotic	CR	
Doves	.565	.761	.736
Dom-Sub	.428	.413	.386
Mugwumps	.422	.440	.424
Hawks	.429	.364	.404

[1] ANOVA effects for Outcome Group ($F = 33.22$; df $= 3{,}144$; $p < .001$) and Trials by Outcome Group interactions ($F = 6.49$; df $= 18{,}864$; $p < .01$). Individual comparisons indicate the Doves are more accurate than each of the other groups over preasymptotic trials (blocks 2–5; $p < .05$), as well as over CR and Post-CR trials ($p < .01$).

dicted a high level of cooperation, but were largely inaccurate in doing so. Their perceptions of each other seemed to reflect wishful thinking (they must expect their spouses to cooperate if they are to gain) rather than an attribution of spousal cooperativeness.

The fact that the Doves' level of predicted cooperation was lower than their actual levels of cooperation over the CR and Post-CR trials (P[C] > .90 [see Santa-Barbara and Epstein, 1974]) supports the notion that their predictions did not represent wishful thinking as they did in other groups. This lower level of perceived cooperativeness is accounted for in terms of the husbands in the Dove couples predicting defections by their wives (P[D] = .31) over the CR and Post-CR Trials. The Dove husbands expected their wives to defect even though they had reached a high, stable level of mutual cooperation. Wives, on the other hand, expected defections from their husbands very infrequently (P[D] = .08) over these trial blocks. Rather than wishful thinking, the husbands' predictions indicated a certain degree of suspicion that their wives would not continue cooperating. The husbands continued cooperating over the course of the game in spite of this suspicion. However, the effect of this suspicion on the long-term stability of the cooperative outcome for this group is an interesting but unexplored issue.

Intentions and Conflict Resolution

By examining the predict-play combinations, a more refined analysis of the couples' conflict-resolution processes is possible. Examining the actual moves the couples made (Santa-Barbara and Epstein, 1974) summarizes their interactions. Adding their predictions to their actual moves indicates their intentions in playing the game the way they did. Table 3 presents the proportion of cooperative intentions for each group, over trials, and collapsed over game and sex. As predicted, the Doves expressed more cooperative intentions than each of the other groups over each trial block. When the Dove couples expected a cooperative move from their spouse, they were most likely to cooperate themselves. The Hawks were least likely to combine a cooperative response with an expectation of cooperation from their spouse. The Hawks were more likely to be exploitative when they expected their spouse to cooperate.

Table 4 presents the proportion of exploitative intentions for each group, over trials, and collapsed over game and sex. The Hawks made more exploitative intentions than the Doves. However, this difference

TABLE 3
PROPORTION OF COOPERATIVE INTENTIONS (PREDICT C AND PLAY C) FOR EACH OUTCOME GROUP, OVER PREASYMPTOTIC, CR, AND POST-CR TRIALS

Outcome[2]	Trial Blocks[3]		Post-CR
	Preasymptotic	CR	
Doves	.553	.753	.747
Dom-Sub	.451	.334	.289
Mugwumps	.304	.311	.306
Hawks	.287	.165	.184

[1] ANOVA Game by Outcome Group effect ($F = 2.08$; $df = 3,144$, $p < .05$; CK > PD for Dove and Dom-Sub couples.

ANOVA Sex effect ($F = 4.12$; $df = 1,144$; $p < .05$). Wives > Husbands.

[2] ANOVA effect for Outcome Group ($F = 53.67$; $df = 3,144$, $p < .001$). Individual comparisons indicate that Doves make more cooperative intentions than each of the other groups ($p < .01$), and the Mugwumps make more than the Hawks ($p < .05$).

[3] ANOVA Trials by Outcome Group interaction ($F = 10.16$; $df = 6,864$; $p < .001$). Individual comparisons indicate that Doves make more cooperative intentions than all other groups over each trial block ($p < .01$), and Mugwumps differ from Hawks on CR and Post-CR blocks ($p < .01$). Dom-Sub couples also differ from Hawks on CR and Post-CR blocks ($p < .01$).

TABLE 4
PROPORTION OF EXPLOITATIVE INTENTIONS (PREDICT C AND PLAY D) FOR EACH OUTCOME GROUP, OVER PREASYMPTOTIC, CR, AND POST-CR TRIALS

Outcome[2]	Trial Blocks[3]		Post-CR
	Preasymptotic	CR	
Doves	.190	.035	.059
Dom-Sub	.291	.364	.332
Mugwumps	.316	.337	.334
Hawks	.347	.487	.417

[1] ANOVA effect for Game ($F = 5.57$; $df = 1,144$; $p < .02$). PD > CK.

[2] ANOVA effect for Outcome Group ($F = 17.02$; $df = 3,144$; $p < .01$). Doves < all other groups ($p < .01$).

[3] ANOVA effect for Trials by Outcome Group interaction ($F = 10.3$; $df = 18,864$; $p < .001$). Individual differences indicate that Hawks > Doves on 3–5th preasymptotic blocks ($p < .01$). On CR & Post-CR blocks Hawks > ($p < .05$) and Doves < ($p < .01$) each of the other groups.

did not emerge until the third block of preasymptotic trials. Early in the game, the Dove couples expressed as many exploitative intentions as the other groups. These couples were able to express individualistic intentions, but abandoned them in favor of a mutually beneficial outcome when the situation warranted it. This result is similar to that found by Raush and his colleagues in their study of marital-conflict behavior (1974). The Hawks, on the other hand, not only expressed exploitative intentions early in the game but continued to express predominantly exploitative intentions even after stabilizing on a mutually destructive outcome. This behavior implies a rigidity that also fits Raush et al.'s (1974) description of a destructive conflict process.

The Hawks' process of conflict resolution was further impeded by a higher degree of defensiveness than existed for the other groups. Table 5 presents the proportion of defensive intentions for each group, over trials, and collapsed over game and sex. The Hawks showed a tendency to be more defensive than the Doves from the very start of their interactions. The Hawks, then, not only perceived their partners as more likely to defect than did spouses in the other groups, but they also responded to this suspected defection by defecting themselves. This early suspicious-defensive posture assumed the characteristics of a self-fulfilling prophesy, for the Hawks locked in on a prolonged and mutually destructive interchange.

A final intention that may be examined in the present data is that of

TABLE 5
PROPORTION OF DEFENSIVE INTENTIONS (PREDICT D AND PLAY D) FOR EACH OUTCOME GROUP, OVER PREASYMPTOTIC, CR, AND POST-CR TRIALS

Outcome[1]	Trial Blocks[2]		
	Preasymptotic	CR	Post-CR
Doves	.121	.014	.014
Dom-Sub	.192	.179	.224
Mugwumps	.176	.182	.186
Hawks	.232	.257	.276

[1] ANOVA effect for Outcome Group ($F = 5.75$; df $= 3, 144$; $p < .001$). Hawks > Doves.
[2] ANOVA effect for Trials by Outcome Group interaction ($F = 2.61$; df $= 18,864$; $p < .001$). Doves < all other groups on CR and Post-CR trials ($p < .01$). Hawks > Doves on first preasymptotic block ($p < .06$).

appeasement, that is, making a cooperative response even though the partner is expected to defect. The Doves made significantly more appeasement responses than the Hawks,[4] but this was due primarily to the Dove husbands' high level of appeasement over CR and Post-CR trials. In addition, the submissive members of the Dominant-Submissive couples also made more appeasement responses than their dominant spouses.[5] Of interest is that their level of appeasement intentions (about .20) was much lower than their actual level of submissiveness (at least .60) (Santa-Barbara and Epstein, 1974). They seemed to admit their subordination, but tended to grossly underrate its magnitude.

Effects of Game Structure on Marital Conflict Behavior

Both game structure and variations in payoffs within a particular game tend to exert a powerful influence on the subjects' behavior (Rapoport and Chammah, 1965, 1966; Vinacke, 1969). By including both PD and CK games in the present study, it is possible to examine the differential sensitivity of the various outcome groups to this structural aspect of the conflict situation.

Both the Dove and Dominant-Submissive couples were sensitive to the structural difference between a PD and CK game in the way they interacted in these situations (Santa-Barbara and Epstein, 1974). This was also true of their intentions, but to a lesser degree. More cooperative intentions were expressed by the Doves and Dominant-Submissive couples in the CK game than by those in the PD game. These couples appreciated the high losses possible if one played competitively in the CK game and avoided this outcome by assuming a stronger cooperative orientation. The Mugwumps and Hawks, on the other hand, were either insensitive to, or disregarded, this structural difference and altered neither their behavior nor their intentions.

All groups made more exploitative intentions in the PD game than their counterparts in the CK game. There were no effects of game structure on either the defensive or appeasement intentions. Although the

[4] Analysis of variance indicates a significant Outcome Group effect ($F = 4.06$; $df = 3,144$; $p < .01$).

[5] Analysis of variance indicates a significant Trials by Role effect ($F = 2.92$; $df = 6,216$; $p < .01$). Individual comparisons indicate that the submissive members made more appeasement intentions than their dominant spouses on the last preasymptotic block as well as over CR and Post-CR trials ($p < .01$).

Doves and Dominant-Submissive couples in the PD game played very differently from those in the CK game, this sensitivity to the structural aspects of the conflict was not reflected as extensively in their intentions.

Sex Differences in Marital-Conflict Behavior

In their study of marital-conflict behavior, Raush and his colleagues (1974) indicate that few sex differences were found. The results of the present study are similar. The wives in the present study predicted higher levels of cooperation and expressed more cooperative intentions than their husbands. These were the only sex differences found. These findings that husbands and wives did not have more distinctive sex-role characteristics with regard to conflict processes is surprising, given the extent of sex differences reported for attitudes, values, and personality characteristics (Barry, 1970). Such intrapsychic differences may have little influence on the various interaction measures used in the present study and by Raush et al. (1974). Although a variety of personality dimensions affect behavior in mixed-motive games, very little is yet known concerning the ways various personality dimensions interact in the development of different stable resolutions to conflict situations (Santa-Barbara, 1972; Terhune, 1970).

Conclusions

Mixed-motive games can be useful devices for studying a number of dimensions of marital-conflict behavior. These games can provide true interaction measures that offer a coherent view of the perceptual and behavioral processes involved in the development of various types of stable resolutions to a conflict situation. These game-derived measures are also related to a variety of demographic and treatment variables (Santa-Barbara and Epstein, 1974).

In addition to the different behavioral interactions that precede the development of the various stable outcomes (Santa-Barbara and Epstein, 1974), different perceptual and intentional processes also characterize the various outcome groups. Couples who become Doves perceive each other as being more cooperative and express more cooperative intentions than other couples. Although the Doves express the same proportion of exploitative intentions as other groups early in the game, they soon shift to expressing cooperative and appeasing intentions. The Hawks, on the other hand, begin with a suspicious-defensive posture that increases in intensity through their interactions. The Hawks, as well as the Mugwumps and Dominant-Submissive couples, express intentions that are clearly discordant with their behavior. The Hawks, for example, continue to express a high proportion of exploitative intentions even after stabilizing on a mutually destructive outcome. Rather than attributing a generalized cooperativeness to their spouses as the Doves do, the Hawk couples engage in wishful thinking that their spouse will give in to their demands.

The difference between the Doves and other groups is perhaps best summarized by Raush et al.'s (1974) categorization in terms of flexible or rigid relationships. The Doves' flexibility is indicated by their shift from an initially exploitative to a cooperative posture. In addition, the Doves, as well as the Dominant-Submissive couples, are responsive to the structural aspects of the conflict situation. The Hawks and Mugwumps, on the other hand, rigidly adhere to the same type of behavior throughout the game and are insensitive to the structural aspects of the games.

Few sex differences in conflict behavior were found, in spite of the well-documented differences in attitudes, values, and personality dimensions (Barry, 1970) between the sexes.

References

Allport, G. W. (1958), *The Nature of Prejudice*. New York: Doubleday.

Barry, W. A. (1970), Marriage research and conflict: An integrative review. *Psychol. Bull.*, 73:41-54.

Bean, F. D. & Kerckhoff, A. C. (1971), Personality and person perception in husband-wife conflict. *J. Marr. & Fam.*, 33:351-360.

Bronfenbrenner, U. (1961), The mirror image in society—American relations. *J. Soc. Issues*, 17:45-56.

Deutsch, M. (1969), Conflicts: Productive and destructive. *J. Soc. Issues*, 25: 7-42.

Halpin, S. M. & Pilisuk, M. (1967), Probability matching in the prisoner's dilemma. *Psychonomic Sci.*, 1:269-270.

Kelley, H. H. & Stahelski, A. J. (1970), Social interaction basis of cooperators' and competitors' beliefs about others. *J. Personal. Soc. Psychol.*, 16:66-91.

Rapoport, A. & Chammah, A. (1965), *Prisoner's Dilemma*. Ann Arbor: University of Michigan Press.

——— ——— (1966), The game of chicken. *Amer. Behav. Scientist*, 10:10-14, 23-28.

Raush, H. L., Barry, W. A., Hertel, R. K., & Swain, M. A. (1974), *Communication, Conflict and Marriage*. San Francisco: Jossey-Bass.

Santa-Barbara, J. (1972), Modes of conflict resolution and stable outcomes. Unpublished.

——— & Epstein, N. B. (1974), Conflict behavior in clinical families: Preasymptotic interactions and stable outcomes. *Behav. Sci.*, 19:100-110.

Tedeschi, J. T. (1968), A theory of influence within dyads. *Proceedings of the XVI International Congress of Applied Psychology*. Amsterdam, August, 1968.

——— Steele, M. W., Gahagan, J. P., & Aranoff, D. (1968), Intentions, predictions, and patterns of strategy choices in a PD game. *J. Soc. Psychol.*, 75:199-207.

Terhune, K. W. (1970), Effects of personality in cooperation and conflict. In: *The Structure of Conflict*, ed. P. G. Swingle. New York: Academic Press, pp. 193-235.

Vinacke, W. E. (1969), Variables in experimental games: Toward a field theory. *Psychol. Bull.*, 71:293-317.

Weiner, B. J. (1962), *Statistical Principles in Experimental Design*. New York: McGraw-Hill.

Woodworth, R. A. & Schlosberg, H. (1961), *Experimental Psychology*. New York: Holt, Rinehart & Winston.

Worchel, P. (1969), Temptation and threat in non-zero-sun games. *J. Conflict Resolution*, 13:103-109.

Using the families of narcissistically disturbed adolescents, the authors study the regulation of self-esteem by the parents and the implication, for the adolescents, of failure in this regulation. For the resolution of such situations, they recommend a combination of long-term conjoint family therapy with psychoanalytically oriented individual therapy for the adolescent.

Concurrent Family Treatment of Narcissistic Disorders in Adolescence

DAVID A. BERKOWITZ, ROGERT L. SHAPIRO, JOHN ZINNER, and EDWARD R. SHAPIRO

The concept of narcissism has, from its inception, been related to family dynamics. In his initial formulations on narcissism, Freud (1914) stated that parents attempt to recapture the lost narcissism of their own childhood by looking to their offspring to fulfill their own unrealized aspirations. For some youngsters, parental expectation has provided the fuel for ego-syntonic accomplishment and success. For others, achievement is obtained, but at a price, and is accompanied by neurotic suffering. For still others, alienation from the family, regressive retreat, and profound

David A. Berkowitz, M.D., is Assistant Professor of Psychiatry, Tufts University School of Medicine, Boston, Massachusetts.

Roger L. Shapiro, M.D., is Professor, Department of Psychiatry and Behavioral Sciences, George Washington University, Washington, D.C.

John Zinner, M.D., is Associate Professor, Department of Psychiatry and Behavioral Sciences, George Washington University, Washington, D.C.

Edward R. Shapiro, M.A., M.D., is Instructor, Department of Psychiatry, Harvard University School of Medicine, and Assistant Psychiatrist, McLean Hospital, Belmont, Massachusetts.

Reprinted from *The International Journal of Psychoanalytic Psychotherapy*, vol. 3, no. 4, November, 1974.

disturbances in self-esteem result, with an associated sense of failure. It is the treatment of this last group of adolescents and their families that we shall address in this paper.

Benedek (1959) has proposed that in each "critical period" the child revives in the parents their related developmental conflicts. This revival can lead either to pathologic manifestations or to a new level of integration in the parent. For example, it has frequently been noted (Benedek, 1959; Rangell, 1955; Searles, 1959) that the resurgent oedipal situation in the adolescent may lead to a rekindling of unresolved conflicts around sexuality in the parents. Zinner and Shapiro (1974) have presented evidence from family observations that this revived oedipal conflict in parents results in their dissociation of drive and control during this period.

We have observed in the families of narcissistic adolescents that, parallel to a reawakening of sexual conflicts, there is a reawakening in parents of conflicts concerning self-esteem during the period of their children's adolescence. We have been impressed with the great pressures in these families brought to bear by the parents on the adolescent to achieve, perform, and succeed in order to stabilize parental self-esteem.

In a previous report (Berkowitz et al., 1974) we concluded from clinical observations that severe narcissistic disturbance in the adolescent is related to the inordinate amount of defensive externalization of conflict by his parents. Parents with serious conflicts in self-esteem experience the adolescent as if he were an extension of their own psychic organization and use him, in specifiable ways, to support their self-esteem. They are overinvolved in the adolescent's life and demonstrate an excessive need to control him. In order to maintain their own precarious narcissistic equilibrium, these parents project into the adolescent unacceptable aspects of their own negative evaluations of themselves. Such family interaction represents one form of pathological self-esteem regulation in the parents, namely, the externalization of conflict between contradictory view of the self through the use of the child as a narcissistic object.

In cases where the child is used to maintain parental self-esteem, we have found it useful to employ conjoint family therapy concurrently with individual therapy for the adolescent. Analytically oriented family therapy allows observation of and therapeutic intervention into the massive pathological externalization of conflict characteristic of these families. In this paper we intend to explore the use of this technique in assisting family members to acknowledge as part of the self what has been projected, a process that may be referred to as reinternalization. We shall focus specifically on the utility of family therapy in promoting the reinternalization of conflicts around self-esteem. Not only does reinternalization help the narcissistic adolescent, it also facilitates growth in all members of the family.

EXTERNALIZATION OF CONFLICT

Externalization of individual dynamic conflict has frequently been noted as a basis of intrafamilial psychopathology (Framo, 1965, 1970; Wynne, 1965; Brodey, 1965; Dicks, 1967; Zinner and Shapiro, 1972). Intrapsychic conflict is transformed into interpersonal conflict through the unconscious defensive mechanism of projective identification (Zinner and Shapiro, 1972). Members of the family split off disavowed or cherished aspects of themselves and project them into others within the family group. These projections govern family members' perception of and behavior toward one another when family group behavior is dominated by unconscious fantasies, which determine meanings of family members to one another. Family members relate toward others onto whom they project aspects of themselves in the same manner as they would were these projections internalized. Internalized conflict *within* individuals is externalized, assuming the form of interpersonal conflict *between* family members.

A clinical example will illustrate the externalization of narcissistic conflict resulting in pathological maintenance of self-esteem. The father of a patient with a severe narcissistic disturbance showed this adolescent son a report card from his own childhood on which the father had received all A's. The father led the son to believe that this was a "typical" and "usual" report card for the father when, in fact, it was the *only* one of its kind. The father hid all other information to the contrary in order to "set a good example" for the son. The father's rationale for this behavior was, "If people don't think I'm better than I am, they will think I'm worse than I am." In his statement the father reveals an underlying discrepancy reflecting two contradictory perceptions of himself. He appears to attempt a resolution of this conflict by projecting onto others his own poor view of himself. It is as if he were saying, "I must inflate myself in order to overcome my poor view of myself that is reflected in others' opinions of me." Moreover, when the son brought home his own report card with a C, the father would not permit the boy to show it to his siblings for fear that they would "tear [him] apart." In this statement the father sees his inadequacy in his son, and he projects his intolerance of that inadequacy onto the siblings, creating a re-enactment of his internal struggle within the sibship.

By locating his own problems with achievement in the son, the father mitigates any inner distress at not living up to his own expectations. By projecting his own poor self-esteem onto his adolescent son, the father encourages the son to feel that he is inadequate and can never live up to the father's expectations in the same fashion as the father himself feels that he cannot live up to the expectations of his own ego ideal. The father has thus externalized internal conflicts in self-esteem. He has temporarily defended against the depression that would ensue from an acknowledgment of his own sense of failure. In this manner, the depression and loss of self-esteem which the parent experiences when failing to live up to his ego ideal is transformed into anger at the adolescent who has come to embody the poorly performing self. The discrepancy within an individual between the actual self and an ideal, aggrandized version of the self has thus been transmuted into interpersonal conflict between family members.

In the process of viewing family interaction, the therapist may obtain valuable clues about the origins of narcissistic vulnerability in the parents. Frequently, the relationships between parents and split-off aspects of themselves projected onto their offspring serve to recapture lost nuclear family relations that bore on the self-esteem of the parent when he was a child. Parental dependence on the adolescent, we have found, derives significantly from the parents' own relationships (now internalized) with primary objects, which led to early narcissistic fixations. In these families, a basic function of the child is to maintain parental self-esteem by colluding in re-enacting with the parent these unresolved relationships from the parents' families of origin which significantly affected the development of their self-esteem.

For example, we have previously (Berkowitz et al., 1974) reported extensively on a case where the mildest display of rebelliousness from the younger of two adolescent daughters remobilized for their mother an earlier source of narcissistic fixation, her relationship to a rival sibling with whom she had competed desperately and in vain for her *own* mother's approval. The current raging battles over household chores between our present mother and, in her words, her "rejecting" daughter now served to replicate in almost exact detail this earlier relationship with the mother's triumphant and hated sister from her own childhood.

Self-Esteem Regulation in the Family

In normal development, given an environment of "optimal frustration" (Kohut, 1971), the early dependency on parental figures is gradually relinquished as the individual develops increasing autonomy from these objects. The growing individual gradually internalizes regulatory functions performed by the parent, which, in depersonified form, become part of enduring internal psychic structure. For example, the mother soothes the infant and, by regulating tension for him, keeps traumatic anxiety from occurring. As he develops more autonomy he takes this tension-regulatory function over for himself. Gradually, in similar fashion, the individual acquires the necessary structure to monitor internally his self-esteem so that states of impending narcissistic disequilibrium are apprehended through signals of anxiety (see Tolpin, 1971), depression, or shame. The healthy ego, utilizing these signals, can then restore homeostasis by acting to effect change in the self or in the environment.

In successful development, derivatives of primitive overestimations and underestimations of the self are gradually blended together into an integrated, cohesive self wherein modulated regulation of self-esteem has become an internalized function. The developing child feels neither wholly omnipotent and grandiose nor totally helpless and inferior. Rather, the self-representation contains modulated, more realistic evaluations of assets and liabilities. In normal development, omnipotence and grandiosity are gradually transformed into healthy pride in realistic achievement. Similarly, feelings of helplessness are tempered into the capacity to experience realistic disappointment in the self without feeling overwhelmed and utterly devalued. However, failure in this development of psychic structure for self-esteem regulation leads to wide mood swings and excessive dependence on the confirming approval of external objects to maintain narcissistic equilibrium.

We find that parents of narcissistic adolescents have themselves failed to develop adequate psychic structure for relatively independent self-esteem regulation. Under careful scrutiny, they can be found to demonstrate the two classic hallmarks of narcissistic vulnerability (Reich, 1960; Kohut, 1968, 1971; Kernberg, 1970). First, they evidence extreme vacillations in self-regard with, on the one hand, haughty, grandiose, and controlling behavior, preoccupation with attempts to feel great and important, and an omnipotent, inflated self-concept. On the other hand, they experience themselves as weak, powerless, worthless, inadequate, and inferior. Second, and intimately related to these alternating states of self-regard, they demonstrate an inordinate overdependence on and intense hunger for the confirming approval of others, coupled with an extreme sensitivity to overt criticism or mere absence of praise. They thus rely to an excessive degree on the behavior of objects to determine their own subjective experience of self-esteem.

We find that parents with defective psychic structure of this kind have not achieved a true autonomy from early objects. Instead, they tend to depend on their present offspring as representatives of these objects for narcissistic supports in order to maintain their precarious self-esteem. The situation becomes a very difficult one when their children reach adolescence, as the phase-specific task of separation becomes particularly threatening to them. A new scrutiny of his parents by the adolescent is an integral part of the adolescent process of separation from the family. Normatively, he challenges his previous idealizations of them through questioning their values and life style in an attempt to formulate his own. This questioning, we have observed, can be experienced by a narcissistically vulnerable parent as a devastating challenge to his omnipotence. Just as the parent must allow himself early in the child's life to be idealized (Kohut, 1971), so, too, must parental self-esteem be sturdy enough to withstand the onslaughts of the adolescent in his attempt to disengage from them and develop his own identity.

We have found, in the families we have studied, that the parents experience this aspect of separation and individuation of children at levels of unconscious fantasy as a threat to parental self-esteem. The parents experience behaviors that herald separation and autonomy, not as a desirable goal for the adolescent, but rather as a narcissistic injury. In their resulting anger and anxiety, these parents often reactively devalue the adolescent and attempt to restore their own narcissistic equilibrium by projecting onto him their disowned negative valuations of themselves (Berkowitz et al., 1974).

What in the developing child motivates his active participation in the parents' self-esteem system? Certainly the mechanism of projective identification cannot function without a willing recipient for the projections. We have suggested previously that the child unconsciously attempts to modify his subjective self-experience and self-evaluation in accord with parental projections. He will do so to the extent that he cannot tolerate parental anxiety or his own anxiety over the consequence of the parents' narcissistic rage and withdrawal when he does not comply.

Equally important, however, is the narcissistic gratification that accrues from the child's participation in this type of relationship. To be a narcissistic object for the parents is a role that holds a powerful and seductive appeal. Indeed, to feel so vital to one's parents' existence and to figure so prominently in the vacillations of their self-esteem provide fuel for the child's omnipotent grandiosity. The child's realization of his power to determine his parents' self-experience contributes to a heightened regressive pull to maintain this situation and his vital role in it. The adolescent finds himself in a dilemma. If he moves out of this role, the consequence is painful because the parent becomes furious and might, he fears, abandon him. Yet, to remain in the role, gratifying as it may be on one level, comes into conflict with the adolescent's developmental need to separate. The adolescent thus perceives only two alternatives in the relationship to the parents. Either he continues to be a narcissistic object for the parents or he risks alienation from the family and loss of the relationship. Not infrequently in our work, we observe that when in therapy the nature of the parents' relationship to the adolescent begins to change and they allow him more independence and separateness, the adolescent will experience this as a loss and attempt to reinvolve the parents by some new acting out.

Concurrent Family Treatment

Despite recent advances in the psychoanalytic understanding of narcissistic character pathology (Kohut, 1968, 1971, 1972; Kernberg, 1970), it is commonly agreed that this type of patient presents special problems in treatment. Because of a failure in the development of autonomy of self-esteem, they depend upon others for regulatory functions that would normally be part of internal psychic structure. It is therefore characteristic of the transferences formed by narcissistic personalities that they deprive the therapist of a recognition of his own separate existence (Kohut, 1968; Kernberg, 1970). The therapist is often treated, in a variation of "mirror transference," as an extension of the patient's self or merely as an impersonal function (Kohut, 1968). At other times the therapist may be idealized, in which case anything that deprives the patient of the therapist creates an unbearable lowering of self-esteem (Kohut, 1968). The patient therefore responds to the slightest separation, rebuff, or most minute disruption of the transference with hostile devaluation of the therapist (Kernberg, 1970) and withdrawal into a cold, narcissistic rage (Kohut, 1968).

These special problems of treatment are compounded by adolescence itself. Prior to adolescence, the parental ego is the child's legitimate ego extension, a condition that is an "integral aspect of childhood dependency in the service of anxiety control and self-esteem regulation" (Blos, 1967). In adolescence, however, psychological separation—the loosening of infantile object ties—is a central developmental task.

Separation is greatly complicated in families of narcissistic adolescents because the parents require the adolescent to perform a self-esteem regulating function, as we have described. In these families, parental need for narcissistic control results in drastic responses to the child's attempts to separate. The adolescent's either/or alternatives are made more extreme by the narcissistic rage arising in the parents in response to the erosion of control over him. Adolescents struggling to achieve the normative developmental task of separating from the parents in such families are thus likely to experience intense feelings of isolation and alienation.

From our perspective, the disordered self-esteem of the narcissistic adolescent is an internal problem deriving from early family relationships. However, it is significantly exacerbated by the nature of the current family interaction. These current interactions, as they reflect implicit parental perceptions of the adolescent as a narcissistic object, form a major basis for his developing identity (Shapiro, 1967; Berkowitz et al., 1974). To the extent that these current relationships are based on externalizations of parental conflict, we believe there is a specific indication for concurrent individual psychoanalytic therapy for the narcissistic adolescent *and* conjoint treatment for the family.

The establishment of a reliable working alliance with both the parents and the adolescent is the task of the initial phase of concurrent individual and family treatment (Shapiro et al., 1977). The formation of this alliance is facilitated by the increasing utilization by family members of the therapist's capacity to observe. Such a utilization allows members to observe their regressive behavior in the family group in comparison with their transference behavior in marital and individual therapy. Once perceived as helpful in this task, the therapist is in a position to aid family members both to acknowledge as part of themselves what has been projected and to begin to internalize the previously projected conflict. Intrapsychic conflict is perpetuated when it is externalized; in contrast, resolution is possible when the struggle is experienced as residing within the individual.

The process of reinternalization enables each family member to achieve a greater degree of separateness from the others. As the narcissistic interactions—the ways in which one member of the family uses another to regulate his own self-esteem—are clarified and interpreted, the separate existence of each family member is defined. The possibility then becomes available for new and more mature relationships among the members of the family, which allow increased autonomy of self-esteem for each.

For the adolescent, family treatment provides a path out of his either/or dilemma. It facilitates his normative developmental task of separation-individuation without the threat of total alienation. It helps to free him from parental pressure and from his own complicity with parental projection. Thus, he can no longer define himself as forced into a particular position by his parents, but must bear the responsibility for his own actions and choices.

For the parents as well, family therapy facilitates their own increasing separateness. It helps to increase their autonomy, freeing them from their dependence on the adolescent as the measure of their worth. The reinternalization of conflict in the parents makes possible its gradual resolution, facilitating psychic growth as the relevant genetic material is recalled and worked through. The family session is not the only arena for this work. In our work with these families we provide a second therapist for marital therapy for the parents. This therapist is co-therapist in the family sessions with the adolescent's individual therapist.

When reinternalized, parental conflict in the realm of self-esteem which has been revived during the adolescence of their offspring can lead, in Benedek's (1959) phrase, to a "new level of integration" in the parents. We find, in fact, that in families which derive benefit from treatment, improvement in the adolescent is usually paralleled by a related progressive development in the parent. For example, one mother constantly sought to raise her own self-esteem through the accomplishments of her husband and children. She continually berated her adolescent daughter for poor grades in school and felt that all the problems resided with the daughter. In family treatment, however, the mother came to realize that she was herself feeling impoverished. Once having acknowledged this, through the marital therapy the mother was able to discover within herself dormant interests and talents. She struggled to overcome her anxiety in entering a complicated and creative professional endeavor which provided her much satisfaction in the long run. Gradually, she became able to support her self-esteem, mitigating to an extent the previous reliance upon her husband and daughter for narcissistic sustenance.

Clinical Observations

We shall now present family and individual excerpts to illustrate the use of long-term concurrent conjoint family therapy for the reinternalization of conflict in the area of self-esteem. Our case example is drawn from over 50 adolescent inpatients and their families treated by our group on a residential unit at the National Institute of Mental Health. Treatment modalities included intensive psychoanalytically oriented individual psychotherapy for the adolescent, weekly conjoint family therapy, and conjoint marital therapy for the parents.

Many of our adolescent patients have, in Kernberg's (1967) terminology, a borderline personality organization, with others evidencing a higher order of character structure. However, in all of our adolescent patients, we find profound psychological disturbances in the narcissistic realm, manifested by severe vacillations in self-esteem and by an overdependence on others for the maintenance of narcissistic equilibrium.

An adolescent patient with serious narcissistic disturbance is Hal, who was admitted to our unit at age eighteen with a history of school and work failures, truancy, delinquency, and drug use. Of above-average intelligence, Hal had dropped out of high school. He became outraged at each of his successive short-lived jobs when he was not accorded special privileges, pay raises, or rapid promotions. He felt entitled to go "right to the top," complaining that most jobs were "beneath [his] dignity" and "for peasants." He raced cars and motorcycles in order to feel powerful, and described how dealing drugs made him feel important because he carried "that much worth" in his pockets. His frequent drug use enabled him to entertain grandiose fantasies, such as his having an entire city named after him with endless roads upon which to race his cars or his being a great artist waiting to be discovered.

Hal's father is a serious, quick-tempered, suspicious man, prone to vacillations in his self-esteem. He has been extremely critical of his children, especially of Hal. At the same time he has been intensely overinvolved in their lives. When Hal delivered newspapers early in his adolescence, the father frequently arrived on the scene to inspect his work and severely criticize whatever imperfections he could find.

Hal's father was abandoned by his own father at a very early age and raised by a depressed and withdrawn mother who subsequently was hospitalized on several occasions. Constantly searching for approval as a youngster, Hal's father felt overshadowed and worthless in all endeavors in comparison with his favored older brother. He frequently complained that Hal was "ripping [him] off" just as he had felt "ripped off" by his brother.

The following excerpts from two audio-taped conjoint family sessions at different stages in the treatment will illustrate the use of family therapy in the reinternalization of narcissistic conflict.

Early Stage

This session occurred early in the treatment and reflects a typical family interaction. The father, in an angry tone of voice, opens the session by berating the son for his appearance. In his statement, the father protects his own self-esteem by maintaining a view of himself as more successful while he sees his son as the one who is more self-depreciating. He further portrays his son, in contrast to himself, as capitulating to these self-depreciating feelings: Hal cares so little about himself that he will surrender to a life of drugs.

The son is thus a narcissistic object for the father, used to preserve the father's self-esteem. By perceiving Hal as the one who gives in to his feelings of low self-esteem, the father projects onto the son his own derogatory picture of himself, thereby ridding himself of those feelings. The father's anger at first appears to be a response to the tendency he perceives in Hal to capitulate to these depressed feelings and turn to drugs. However, this anger also represents the narcissistic rage that is aroused by the son's associating with his peers, seeking relationships outside the family, and separating himself from the father's control.

Father [with increasing anger]: The thing that bothers me is I don't think you give a damn enough about yourself or what you're doing. When I saw you last Thursday you looked extremely disheveled and hangdog. And you look pretty much that way this afternoon, although not quite so much. And I—I feel—and your, your manner, you care nothing about your appearance. You know it bugs us. It bugs your mother and, in particular, probably me more than anybody, but this—I feel the way you, the way you dress—your appearance reflects how you feel about things. You don't *give* a damn. That's how you, that's how I think you feel. And with an attitude like that I feel you're just gonna go—the chances are, with you walking around with some of the friends that you've been associated with in the drug business. . . .

The son explains that he is not feeling bad about himself and in fact has been neat and appropriately dressed when he is out on a pass. However, the father continues angrily to portray Hal as the one who needs to do some thinking about himself. The therapist recognizes a repetitive theme of the father speaking about himself through his son and intervenes:

Therapist: It seems to me—your father feels you are—so lacking in concern about yourself, he feels it's something about your not valuing yourself, your seeming depressed and looking disheveled. I thought you [to father] were talking about yourself again when you were talking about Hal, and about your own feeling belittled, when you're feeling very depressed or very unimportant.

Father: Oh, when somebody puts me down I get angry! But I usually don't show it. And it comes back and bites me during the night and in my own thoughts, and nothing gets resolved by that. But that's what—I do get angry. And you're right, most of the time I think that I feel I don't do things well. There's something about—very tense here, and I don't remember what you were saying in the first place. What you were asking me, I don't remember that . . . .

In the preceding excerpts, the father begins by belittling the son and accusing him of not caring about himself. The therapist interprets this as largely a projection of the father's own feeling of being belittled. The father replies first that he feels belittled by others. ("Oh, when somebody puts me down I get angry") and then acknowledges that he *does* experience much self-doubt ("You're right, most of the time I think that I feel I don't do things well"). He then becomes anxious and represses this thought.

It is evident that after some interpretive work is done on the projection onto the son and its relation to the father's own self-esteem, the father begins to acknowledge the source of the projection as emanating from within himself. However, at this early stage in the treatment, the father is not able to tolerate for more than a moment the reinternalization of his projection. The interpretation has resulted in increased anxiety rather than in the father's further self-reflection.

Hal's older sister has found the therapist's interpretation pertinent, however, and attempts to further the therapeutic work of the session:

Sister [Turning to father]: I think what Dr. X says is true, that you very much underestimate yourself. I mean, how often did Mom and I, when you were writing these little things, suggest a writer's course, or say, "Why don't you write a book or something?" And you'd say, "Oh, I couldn't do that."

At this point, the mother effectively derails further exploration of this issue, saying, "Well, back to this discussion of the weekend passes . . . ." By shifting the focus from an exploration of the defensive functions of the father's perception of the son, the mother protects the father from further examining his own unconscious motivations. An appropriate therapeutic intervention at this juncture would be to notice the collusive interaction developing and to work on understanding the shared anxiety that has generated this shift.

Later Stage

Several months later in the treatment, members of the family have begun to identify with the therapeutic task. The therapeutic alliance has been more firmly established, so that family members are able to perform ego-observing functions which initially had been performed exclusively by the therapists. In the session from which the following excerpt has been taken, the father has been bitterly expressing his anger and disappointment in both Hal and his younger brother, Jeff, who he feels are failures because they have each dropped out of athletic competition.

Therapist: What was so disappointing to you when he quit the team?

Father: Well, I guess ah—well, I guess I put myself in his shoes, I would have felt great finding out that I could swim so well and ah . . . .

Mother: It just hit me—that I think it's the reverse of that—when you say that you put yourself in his shoes and you would have felt great if you found out that you were that good a swimmer. I remember back at college, when you didn't follow through on the shot-putting, and you were, you felt so badly that—I forget who the coach was—disappointed at you dropping out . . . .

Father: Yeah, I—

Mother: I think there's a connection there. You didn't following through on something and that's why—it may have brought back memories of . . . .

Father: Yeah, maybe this is a sort of—substitute for my own not following through—that if he would have stayed then he would have—uh—

Mother: [Laughing] Compensated, in a way.

Father: Yeah, yeah, I hadn't thought of it that—

Hal: I was thinking of me throwing the shot—and ah—how, how to not—

Father: Well, the kiss of death seemed to be when I worked with you, with it for a while and—then you dropped it.

Therapist: I wonder how it makes you feel to have the feeling that your father is so dependent on your successes?

Jeff: Like a burden, you know. Kind of like a burden, in a way, because then—if you don't succeed, then you feel bad about it.

Father: Well, when he said "burden" there, that rang a bell with—that's everything it really is, the burden to see Hal quit and the burden to see Jeff quit. And I guess—I'm sure it would [half-laugh] be easy to say that ah—I'm looking for them to up my [laughs] opinion of myself.

In this particular excerpt, it is the mother who initially makes the observation that the intensity of the father's disappointment and belittling rage arises from his own dropping out ("I remember back at college, when you didn't follow through on the shot-putting . . . you felt so badly . . ."). However, all members of the family are at this point in the treatment engaged in the therapeutic process. The sons are now at greater liberty to express their experience of the father's pressure to achieve (". . . kind of like a burden . . .") and to introspect on their reactions to this pressure (". . . if you don't succeed—then you feel bad about it"). The father is able to recognize the internal source of his distress ("Yeah, maybe this is a sort of substitute for my own not following through") and, with a sense of humor,[1] to acknowledge and reinternalize the projection of his own poor self-esteem ("I'm sure it would be easy to say that—ah—I'm looking for them to up my opinion of myself"). Very little intervention is necessary on the part of the therapist.

In this second family session, the discrepancy between the father's actual and ideal self becomes more readily apparent. He feels that *he* has been the failure and disappointment. Earlier, this discrepancy had been transmuted, through externalization, into interpersonal conflict between himself and his son. During the session, with the mother's help, the

[1] See Kohut (1966) in this respect.

father is able to recognize that his excessive dependence upon the achievements of his offspring is really in the service of increasing his own precarious self-esteem.

The Impact of Reinternalization in Family Therapy on Individual Therapy

A shift in the family dynamics between the first and second family sessions has allowed Hal to become more observant of himself. In the earlier session the father was preoccupied only with criticizing his son, while the son was preoccupied with defending himself against this criticism. Reflection was impossible for either of them. In the later family session the father was able to reflect on his narcissistic use of the son so that he no longer needed to rely on him for the maintenance of his own self-esteem. He no longer needed to perceive the son as the embodiment of unacceptable aspects of himself. It is this shift in the family that makes possible the kinds of self-observation that Hal demonstrates in the following excerpt. If this shift had not occurred, Hal would have continued to be thrown back on a perpetual, unmodified narcissistic relationship in his family.

In individual therapy a few weeks after the second family session, Hal demonstrates a new comprehension of his own narcissistic sensitivity. The individual therapist is soon to go on a vacation, and Hal has observed within himself a coincident recent increase in the intensity of his dependency in his relationship with a girl. In the session, he begins to compare this relationship to previous ones.

> *Hal:* Monday it seemed like what I was trying to fight was somehow finding a comforter, you know, or another mother or another therapist in her or something. . . . But I think if I feel good about myself inside—there isn't a feeling of if she isn't there that I can't exist. The way I'd go about it before was just latch on, make the other person my life—that's my father. He takes me and my sister and brother, and pretty soon he loses his sense of value from himself or something and makes the kids his life; if they fuck up, he fucks up . . . . the scary part is when I notice myself turning someone like a girl into my own mind or something—if I get dropped or jilted, it destroys me. I just feel I'm trying to build something up for myself where you have a certain foundation and the rest of it's built up. And if all that falls down, you still have your foundation.

> But I think—the usual pattern of before is where it's destroyed all the way down to the foundation and then there's nothing.

Hal's insight into his own narcissistic vulnerability, while precipitated by the forthcoming separation from his individual therapist, draws heavily on his observations of an experience in the concurrent family treatment. He recognizes in himself the tendency he has, like that of his father, to depend excessively for the maintenance of his self-esteem on external objects. Moreover, Hal demonstrates in his statement an awareness that this dependency on a "comforter" (therapist, girlfriend) has been vital to his very existence and that it is related to his *internal* estimation of himself. In this example, a separation from the therapist which might ordinarily have precipitated an acute withdrawal from therapy was instead utilized by the adolescent to further his understanding of his own conflicts in self-esteem.

Summary

We have described the dynamics and treatment of a form of pathological self-esteem regulation characteristic of the families of narcissistically disturbed adolescents. The parents themselves demonstrate a failure in the development of adequate psychic structure for self-esteem regulation which leads to an overdependence on external objects for the maintenance of self-esteem. This externalization of intrapsychic conflicts around self-esteem in these families results in the use of offspring as narcissistic objects: shortcomings perceived in the child are experienced as reflecting the parents' own inadequacies and are responded to by narcissistic rage and devaluation. The child is then required to maintain parental self-esteem by functioning as a recipient for the parents' unacceptable depreciated estimations of themselves which they project onto him.

Because the child is used as a narcissistic object, the parents are compelled to control him. The period of adolescence is particularly threatening to the parents because of the adolescent's phase-specific disengagement from the family and search for new objects. The narcissistic rage resulting from the perceived threat to the parents leads to an intensification of their devaluing projections into the adolescent.

The adolescent complies with the parents' narcissistic use of him because of both his anxiety about abandonment and the gratification of his own grandiosity which participation in this intense relationship affords him. Consequently, he has greater than normal difficulty in separating, and his own self-esteem is further impaired through identification with these parental projections.

Psychoanalytically oriented conjoint family treatment, concurrently with individual therapy for the adolescent, provides an intervention into the externalization of intrapsychic conflicts by family members. It can produce dynamic shifts within the family which allow the individual adolescent to develop increased insight into his own narcissistic sensitivity and to move beyond it.

It should be emphasized that the sequence illustrated in this paper represents a concentrated summary of a longer and more complex therapeutic process which requires extensive working through. The sequence does, however, illustrate the management of a central dynamic in this therapeutic process. Reinternalization of narcissistic conflict—acknowledging as part of the self what has been projected—makes possible its gradual resolution. The separate existence of the developing adolescent and of his parents is established, providing the possibility of an increasing autonomy of self-esteem for each.

References

Benedek, T. (1959), Parenthood as a developmental phase. *J. Amer. Psychoanal. Assn.*, 7:389-417.

Berkowitz, D., Shapiro, R., Zinner, J., & Shapiro, E. (1974), Family contributions to narcissistic disturbances in adolescents. *Internat. Rev. Psychoanal.*, 1:353-362.

Blos, P. (1967), The second individuation of adolescence. In: *The Adolescent Passage*. New York: International Universities Press, 1979, pp. 141-170.

Brodey, W. (1965), On the dynamics of narcissism: I. Externalization and early ego development. *The Psychoanalytic Study of the Child*, 20:165-193. New York: International Universities Press.

Dicks, H. (1967), *Marital Tensions. Clinical Studies Toward a Psychological Theory of Interaction*. New York: Basic Books.

Framo, J. (1965), Rationale and techniques of intensive family therapy. In: *Intensive Family Therapy: Theoretical and Practical Aspects*, ed. I. Boszormenyi-Nagy & J. Framo. New York: Harper Medical Books, pp. 143-212.

——— (1970), Symptoms from a family transactional viewpoint. In: *Family Therapy in Transition*, ed. N. Ackerman. *Internat. Psychiat. Clinics*, 7:125-171.

Freud, S. (1914), On narcissism: An introduction. *Standard Edition*, 14:67-102. London: Hogarth Press, 1957.

Kernberg, O. (1967), Borderline personality organisation. *J. Amer. Psychoanal. Assn.*, 15:641-685.

——— (1970), Factors in the psychoanalytic treatment of narcissistic personalities. *J. Amer. Psychoanal. Assn.*, 18:51-85.

Kohut, H. (1966), Forms and transformations of narcissism. In: *The Search for the Self*, ed. P. Ornstein. New York: International Universities Press, 1978, pp. 427-460.

——— (1968), The psychoanalytic treatment of narcissistic personality disorders. In: *The Search for the Self*, New York: International Universities Press, 1978, pp. 477-509.

——— (1971), *The Analysis of the Self*. New York: International Universities Press.

——— (1972), Thoughts on narcissism and narcissistic rage. In: *The Search for the Self*, ed. P. Ornstein. New York: International Universities Press, 1978, pp. 615-658.

Rangell, L. (1955), The return of the repressed "Oedipus." *Bull. Menninger Clinic*, 19:9-15.

Reich, A. (1960), Pathological forms of self-esteem regulation. In: *Psychoanalytic Contributions*. New York: International Universities Press, 1973, pp. 288-311.

Searles, H. (1959), Oedipal love in the countertransference. In: *Collected Papers on Schizophrenia and Related Subjects*. New York: International Universities Press, 1965, pp. 284-303.

Shapiro, E., Shapiro, R., Zinner, J., & Berkowitz, D. (1977), The borderline ego and the working alliance: Indications for family and individual treatment in adolescence. *Internat. J. Psycho-Anal.*, 58:77-87.

Shapiro, R (1967), The origin of adolescent disturbances in the family: Some considerations in theory and implications for therapy. In: *Family Therapy and Disturbed Families*, ed. G. Zuk & I. Boszormenyi-Nagy. Palo Alto: Science and Behavior Books, pp. 221-238.

Tolpin, M. (1971), On the beginnings of a cohesive self. *Psychoanalytic Study of the Child*, 26:316-352. New York: International Universities Press.

Wynne, L. (1965), Some indications and contraindications for explanatory family therapy. In: *Intensive Family Therapy: Theoretical and Practical Aspects*, ed. I. Boszormenyi-Nagy & J. Framo. New York: Harper Medical Books, pp. 289-322.

Zinner, J. & Shapiro, R. (1972), Projective identification as a mode of perception and behavior in families of adolescents. *Internat. J. Psycho-Anal.*, 53:523-529.

——— ——— (1974), The family group as a single psychic entity: Implications for acting out in adolescence. *Internat. Rev. Psycho-Anal.*, 1:179-186.

In another significant contribution from the University of Wisconsin Primate Laboratory, investigation shifts from infant to young adult rhesus monkeys reared in nuclear families. Young adult monkeys were separated from their families and placed with (1) friends, (2) friends and strangers, (3) in isolation. The third group of monkeys developed depressive-like behavior. The significance of the finding is cautiously discussed. It seems that the separation led to deprivation, and it is this, rather than the separation per se, which is the damaging agent.

Depressive Behavior in Adult Monkeys Following Separation from Family Environment

STEPHEN J. SUOMI, CAROL D. EISELE, SHARON A. GRADY, and HARRY F. HARLOW

Considerable research in the past decade has disclosed a striking similarity between the reaction of infant rhesus monkeys to separation from mothers and/or peers and the human infant syndrome of anaclitic depression (for a review of the pertinent literature, see Harlow and Suomi, 1974). Efforts to generate depressive psychopathology in older monkeys, however, have been far less successful to date. It has repeatedly been found that social separations produce temporary protest but no depression in adolescent monkeys (e.g., Bowden and McKinney, 1972). The failure to produce depressive activity in adolescent and adult monkeys tends to undermine any arguments that the monkey-separation data represent a viable model for adult human depression. Questions have frequently been raised (Rie, 1966) whether human anaclitic depression should be included in the same

---

From the University of Wisconsin.
Reprinted from *Journal of Abnormal Psychology*, vol. 84, no. 5, 1975.

category or classification as more common adult depressions. Thus, if the monkey-infant-separation data do not even generalize to monkey adolescents and adults, how can one in good faith argue that they generalize to human adolescents and adults?

To date, it has only been shown that monkey adolescents do not exhibit depressive reactions to peer separations. The possibility still remains that older primates are capable of exhibiting depressive reactions to social separations, if the circumstances and attachment relationships are appropriate. For example, findings from the infant-monkey data indicate that if the attachment bond severed by separation is not particularly strong, depression is unlikely to result. Because there is little evidence that the juvenile peer bonds broken in the previous studies involved strong specific attachments prior to separation, it is conceivable that these adolescent monkeys were inappropriate subjects for production of depressive behavior following social separation.

In order to investigate this possibility, we studied the response to social separation of young adult monkeys whose behavior patterns indicated that strong social bonds existed just prior to separation. These were monkeys born and housed all their lives in nuclear family apparatuses, with total and continual access to both parents and siblings and limited access to other adult pairs and their offspring. The development and maintenance of social attachments among these monkeys have been previously described in detail (Ruppenthal et al., 1974). It was hypothesized that monkeys reared through sexual maturity in this social environment would be vulnerable to social separation, provided that the separation environment was appropriate. The following study was thus performed.

Method

Subjects and Procedure

The subjects were six male and four female five-year-old sexually mature rhesus monkeys *(Macaca mulatta)*, each of whom was a first-born offspring of nuclear family parents. All subjects had been raised from birth in nuclear family apparatuses, according to the procedure described by Ruppenthal et al. (1974).

In the present study, each subject was physically removed from its family unit and placed in one of three environments for a period of eighteen weeks. Two males and two females who had all been reared in the same four-family unit and who thus had continuous exposure to each other from birth were housed together in a 175 × 175 × 125-cm group cage (familiar subjects). Two male-female pairs, each reared in different units, were housed together in a second 175 × 175 × 125-cm group cage (mixed subjects). The remaining two subjects, both males, were housed individually in 75 × 70 × 75-cm cages, where they could see and hear but not physically contact other monkeys (individual subjects). After eighteen weeks of separation, all subjects were returned to their original nuclear family environments.

Data Collection and Analysis

Throughout the 126-day separation, each subject was observed for a five-minute period, both morning and afternoon, five days per week. Three observers who were previously trained in a rigorous laboratory criterion of reliability (overall Pearson $r > .95$) recorded subject behaviors, employing a fifteen-second modified frequency scoring system with behavioral categories previously established and defined (Suomi, 1974). Subjects were always scored between 9:30 and 11:30 A.M. and between 1:00 and 3:00 P.M. Prior to separation and following reunion, subjects were scored on a daily basis according to the procedure described by Ruppenthal et al. (1974).

Data collected during separation were summed over two-week periods from each subject. The sums for each behavior were then compared across groups by Mann-Whitney U tests. Statistical significance was set at $p < .05$ for a one-tailed test.

Results

The results of this study revealed major differences in the nature of reaction to separation among the young adult monkeys, even though the subjects did not differ significantly across groups prior to separation (confirming data may be found in Ruppenthal et al., 1974). The familiar and mixed group subjects showed little, if any, adverse reaction to family removal. They did not differ significantly from each other in levels of any behavior during any time period, with three exceptions: familiar subjects showed more social grooming in the seventh two-week block of separation but lower levels of proximic behavior (being within 1 m of another monkey) during the fourth and sixth time blocks than did mixed subjects.

Also, familiar monkeys showed higher levels of environmental exploration throughout the separation than all other subjects.

In contrast, the two individual subjects reacted to separation in a manner far more similar to that previously reported for anaclitically depressed infant monkeys. As can be seen in Figure 1, they exhibited significantly higher overall levels of stereotypy (movements maintained in a rhythmic and repetitive fashion for at least three cycles) than all other monkeys. They groomed themselves significantly less during the latter part of the separation; not surprisingly, their physical appearance deteriorated. More importantly, later in the separation they exhibited significant levels of self-clasping (prolonged holding of some body part with hands or feet other than for support of body part and/or bending top portion of body downward while tucking head into chest, giving the appearance of curling up into a ball), behaviors never exhibited by the group-housed monkeys. Self-clasping is the primary definitive behavior of the despair phase of anaclitic depression in infant monkeys (for a review of the data, see Harlow and Suomi, 1974, or Kaufman and Rosenblum, 1967).

FIGURE 1

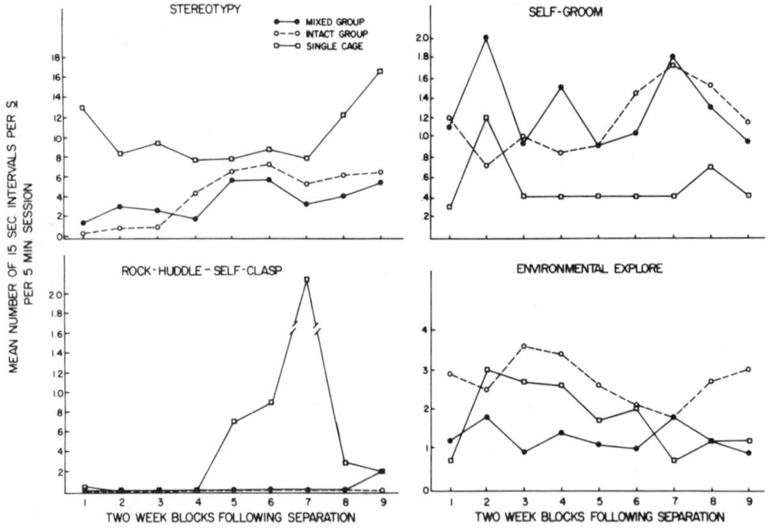

Median Levels of Behavior during Family Separation

Immediately following reunion, activity levels declined in all groups and interfamily hostility was high. However, within several weeks all monkeys, except one individually housed male, had returned to preseparation levels of most behaviors. The male who displayed long-term behavioral changes had been one of the most active and playful of the subjects prior to this solitary confinement, showing extremely high levels of social interaction with adult as well as younger animals in his group. Following reunion, he remained passive and nonresponsive to social stimuli long after the other subjects had returned to preseparation behavior patterns. Both individually separated males exhibited subsequent sexual deficiencies, even though both had been more than adequate prior to separation.

Discussion

The results of the present study clearly indicated that semi-adult monkeys are capable of exhibiting depressive reactions to social separations, although they also demonstrated again that not all social separations invariably result in psychopathology. In the present case all subjects who were group-housed exhibited little, if any, adverse reaction to the removal from their family units. The only monkeys seriously affected by the loss of family and friends were those housed individually, and their reactions were depressive in nature, similar in sequence and in form to those seen in infants and labeled anaclitic depression.

The fact that the present subject population was exceedingly small, with only two monkeys exhibiting the critical response patterns, precludes further definitive generalization. Rather, we view these data as merely suggestive. The present findings indicated that it is possible to elicit depressivelike activity in older monkeys using procedures that resemble those found effective in study of younger subjects. But, in addition, the fact that these findings are generally consistent with a wide range of parametric data collected on separation reactions among infant monkeys is suggestive of fruitful approaches to the study of depressive behavior in adolescent and adult subjects in future research efforts.

References

Bowden, D. M. & McKinney, W. T. (1972), Behavioral effects of peer separation, isolation, and reunion on adolescent male rhesus monkeys. *Devel. Psycho-*

biol., 5:353-362.
Harlow, H. F. & Suomi, S. J. (1974), Induced depression in monkeys. *Behav. Biol.*, 12:273-296.
Kaufman, I. C. & Rosenblum, L. A. (1967), The reaction to separation in infant monkeys: Anaclitic depression and conservation-withdrawal. *Psychosom. Med.*, 29:648-675.
Rie, H. E. (1966), Depression in childhood. *J. Amer. Acad. Child Psychiat.*, 5:653-685.
Ruppenthal, G. C., Harlow, M. K., Eisele, C. D., Harlow, H. F., & Suomi, S. J. (1974), Development of peer interactions of monkeys reared in a nuclear-family environment. *Child Devel.*, 45:670-682.
Suomi, S. J. (1974), Social interactions of monkeys reared in a nuclear family environment versus monkeys reared with mothers and peers. *Primates*, 15:311-320.

Family Diagnosis

Family diagnosis involves a systematic investigation of family dysfunction in all its aspects to establish the existence, description, and nature of the pathology in a given family; on this rests the planning of the therapeutic program.

Here are five contributions; one is concerned with a family-history method and four with special techniques—the Family Concept Test, the Family Puppet Interview, the Family Drawing Test, and a family art session.

Judgments about family members are often obtained from another family member. This paper throws light on the reliability of this procedure. The area of research is affective disorder. The unit of study is the diagnostic label given to a family member. The diagnoses made on a relative by (a) the recollection of the proband alone and (b) the recollection of other family members are compared with the diagnoses made on relatives by direct psychiatric interview. The findings establish the value of direct interviewing and give guidance on using the recollections of probands both in clinical work and family research.

Accuracy of the Family-History Method in Affective Illness: Comparison with Direct Interviews in Family Studies

JULIEN MENDLEWICZ, JOSEPH L. FLEISS, MIMA CATALDO, and JOHN D. RAINER

An increasing amount of research is being reported on the role of familial factors in the cause of the affective disorders. The methods of investigation include twin stuides (Zerbin-Rüdin, 1969), studies that estimate the likelihood of illness (the morbidity risk) in specified relatives (Slater, 1938;

From the Department of Medical Genetics, New York State Psychiatric Institute (Julien Mendlewicz, M.D., and John D. Rainer, M.D.); Columbia University College of Physicians and Surgeons (Drs. Mendlewicz, Rainer, and Joseph L. Fleiss, Ph.D.); the Biometrics Research Unit, New York State Department of Mental Hygiene (Dr. Fleiss); and Rockland State Hospital, New York (Mima Cataldo, M.A.).

This investigation was supported in part by the Belgian American Educational Foun-

Luxenburger, 1942; Sjögren, 1948; Stenstedt, 1952; Kallmann, 1954; Leonhard, 1959; Angst and Perris, 1968; Winokur et al., 1969), and genetic linkage studies (Reich et al., 1969; Winokur and Tanna, 1969; Mendlewicz et al., 1972, 1975). A number of these studies have relied either solely on the proband or on one other family member as well for information about illness in other relatives (Slater, 1938; Luxenburger, 1942; Sjögren, 1948; Stenstedt, 1952; Leonhard, 1959). In many instances, such reliance is unavoidable. Some relatives may refuse to undergo a psychiatric evaluation, others may have moved out of the researchers' geographic area, and others may have died.

In other instances, however, a number of relatives of each proband might be available for evaluation, but the researcher chooses not to interview them directly for reasons of convenience or economy. Instead, he applies the family-history method and makes diagnoses on these relatives based on the recollections of the proband or of the proband plus only one interviewed relative.

The purpose of the present study is to assess the accuracy of the family-history method in affective disorders. We compared the diagnoses made on relatives by direct psychiatric interviews with the relatives' diagnoses based on the proband's recollection alone and with the relatives' diagnoses based on the recollections of the other interviewed family members. We also examined the reliability of information obtained by the investigators who independently interviewed relatives of affectively ill probands.

METHODS

SUBJECTS

This report is part of a systematic morbidity risk study of relatives and spouses of patients with affective illness who were admitted to the Lithium Research and Treatment Clinic of the New York Psychiatric

dation, by General Research Support grant E 303-165F, and by National Institute of Mental Health grant MH 21586-03.

Ronald R. Fieve, M.D., collaborated on this investigation and allowed us to study his patients. Jean Endicott, Ph.D., and Robert L. Spitzer, M.D., assisted in the analysis of the CAPPS data.

Julien Mendlewicz is currently at the Free University of Brussels, Erasme Hospital, Department of Psychiatry.

Reprinted from the *Archives of General Psychiatry*, vol. 32, March, 1975.

Institute between 1968 and 1972 (Mendlewicz and Rainer, 1974). The patient sample consisted of 134 bipolar (manic-depressive) probands (41.8% male) and 65 unipolar (depressive only) probands (20% male).

Most of the patients were referred by private physicians, outpatient clinics, and both public and private mental hospitals. The existence of secondary cases (i.e., of affectively ill relatives) in the patients' families was not a criterion for either referring or accepting a patient to the Lithium Clinic.

In studying psychiatric disturbances among the spouses and first-degree relatives (parents, siblings, and children) of the probands, we have relied on personal interviews with these relatives whenever possible, in preference to the family-history method. When interviewing a proband's relative, the investigator was kept blind to whether the proband's diagnosis was unipolar or bipolar. All available relatives were interviewed using the Current and Past Psychopathology Scale (CAPPS), a clinical semistructured interview for measuring current mental state and past history (Endicott and Spitzer, 1972).

Seven hundred sixty spouses and first-degree relatives of the bipolar probands were still living; 83% of them were personally examined. The interview rate was the same in the families of the unipolar probands: 84% of their 365 living spouses and first-degree relatives were interviewed. Eight percent of all living relatives refused to be interviewed, even after repeated requests. The remaining living relatives lived too far from New York for them to be personally examined.

Diagnostic Criteria

The proband's diagnosis was made independently by two clinicians blind to the family-study data. The criteria used in diagnosing both the probands and their relatives were similar to those of Leonhard (1959), Angst and Perris (1968), and Winokur et al. (1969). Bipolar illness was diagnosed in probands and relatives who had a history of clear-cut manic behavior and of depressive episodes severe enough to require treatment or hospitalization, or to cause a disruption in everyday activities for at least three weeks. The depressive episodes had to be characterized by depressed mood along with such symptoms of a physiological shift as a decrease in appetite, sleep, and energy level. The episodes could be accompanied by guilt, decreased concentration, and suicidal thoughts. Manic episodes had to include such symptoms as euphoria, hyperactivity, decreased need for sleep, pressure of speech, flight of ideas, and irritability. Periodicity of illness (two or more episodes of manic or depressive symptoms) with symptom-free intervals was one of the criteria used for the diagnosis of bipolar illness.

A diagnosis of unipolar depression was made for those subjects who had never experienced mania or hypomania, but had experienced one or more depressive episodes severe enough to require treatment or hospitalization. For both bipolar and unipolar illness, there had to be no personality disintegration before or following psychotic episodes, nor could there be another pre-existing psychiatric or medical disease that might be associated with an affective symptomatology, according to the concept of "primary affective disorder" (Robins and Guze, 1972).

Sample Procedure

One hundred forty of the total 199 families were completed, in that all available living relatives had been personally examined at the time of this study. In the remaining 59 families, available relatives were either still being interviewed or had refused to be interviewed. We are not including data on these families because no way exists of checking on the accuracy of information provided about such relatives from interviewed family members.

One relative, designated the "study relative," was selected at random from each of the 140 completed families. Diagnoses were available on each study relative from the following sources.

1. Based on the information he or she elicited during the administration of the CAPPS, the interviewer made a diagnosis designated the "interviewer diagnosis." The interviewer diagnoses, as well as those from the other sources, were combined into five categories: bipolar illness; unipolar illness; alcoholism; all other disorders (including schizophrenia); and no psychiatric illness. Schizophrenia was originally kept separate from all other disorders, but only three study relatives were given this diagnosis by any source.

2. A computer program, DIAGNO II, (Spitzer and Endicott, 1969) was available for accepting as input the ratings made on the items of the CAPPS and providing as output standard American Psychiatric Association diagnoses (American Psychiatric Association, 1968). A new program was written to provide in addition the two nonstandard diagnoses that were of special importance in this study, bipolar affective illness and

unipolar affective illness. (The rules used by the computer for these diagnoses are available on request.) The diagnosis generated on each study relative by these two programs was designated the "computer diagnosis."

3. Each proband was asked to report on the psychiatric history of each of his first-degree relatives, including age of onset when appropriate. The age of onset was taken as the age at first episode, a more sensitive criterion than the age at first hospitalization (Mendlewicz et al., 1972). On the basis of this report, the interviewer formulated a "diagnosis from the proband."

4. After each first-degree relative was interviewed with the CAPPS, he was asked to report on the psychiatric histories of all other relatives in the family. The diagnoses made on the study relative from the reports of all other family members (including the proband) bearing a specified relationship to him were combined into a single "most serious diagnosis" as follows: If at least one of the diagnoses from the other family members was bipolar illness, this was taken as the most serious diagnosis. If none of these diagnoses was bipolar illness, but at least one was unipolar illness, then unipolar illness was taken as the most serious diagnosis. Proceeding similarly, the remaining diagnoses in decreasing order of seriousness were alcoholism; other disorders, including schizophrenia; and no psychiatric illness. The most serious diagnosis based on the reports of all other family members, irrespective of relationship to the study relative, was also determined.

Statistical Methods

The statistic-weighted kappa was used for measuring the degree of agreement on individual study relatives between diagnoses from different sources (Spitzer et al., 1967). This statistic, which gives differential weights to the various possible diagnostic disagreements and which corrects the obtained proportion of weighted agreement for the amount expected by chance, ranges from negative values for poorer than chance agreement through 0 for just chance agreement to +1 for perfect agreement. Weighted kappa is interpretable as an intraclass correlation coefficient, i.e., the quantity 1 minus weighted kappa is the proportion of variance associated with disagreement (Fleiss and Cohen, 1973).

Table 1 presents the agreement weights used in this study. They vary from 1 for exact agreement to 0 for what we considered the most serious

TABLE 1
DIAGNOSTIC AGREEMENT WEIGHTS FOR USE IN WEIGHTED KAPPA

	Diagnosis From Second Source				
Diagnosis From One Source	Bi-polar	Uni-polar	Alco-holism	Other	Not Ill
Bipolar	1.0	0.8	0.4	0.2	0.0
Unipolar	0.8	1.0	0.6	0.3	0.1
Alcoholism	0.4	0.6	1.0	0.4	0.2
Other	0.2	0.3	0.4	1.0	0.2
Not ill	0.0	0.1	0.2	0.2	1.0

disagreement (a diagnosis of bipolar illness based on one source, but one of not ill based on another source). All other disagreements are given weights between the extremes based on clinical judgments of their relative seriousness.

McNemar's test for matched proportions was used to determine whether or not the proportion of study relatives diagnosed affectively ill (either unipolar or bipolar) by one source differed significantly from the proportion so diagnosed by a different source (Fleiss, 1973).

A small-scale reliability study was conducted to provide information about agreement between the two investigators who interviewed the relatives. Ten relatives who had initially been interviewed by one of the investigators were reinterviewed independently from nine to twelve months later by the other investigator who was unaware of the results of the first interview. Their agreement was measured on diagnosis and on the ratings made on the CAPPS. Information about agreement was also provided by comparing the proportions of study relatives variously diagnosed by the two interviewers. Each interviewer independently evaluated his or her own sample of study relatives, with two diagnoses emerging from the evaluation: the clinical diagnosis and that provided by the computer given the CAPPS ratings. If the two interviewers' distributions for either of these diagnoses differed, this would constitute evidence for their employing different criteria.

Results

Table 2 gives various characteristics of the 140 randomly selected study relatives. Within each category of relative, bipolar illness was diagnosed more frequently for male relatives than for females, whereas unipolar illness tended to be diagnosed more frequently for female relatives than for males. Because sample sizes would become too small if the study relatives were stratified by sex, and because it is diagnostic agreement that we are interested in rather than rates, male and female relatives are hereafter combined.

TABLE 2
CHARACTERISTICS OF STUDY RELATIVES (SR)

Proband's Relationship to SR	Sex of SR	N	Age of SR, yr: Mean	S.D.	SR's Diagnosis by Interview*: BP	UP	Alc	Oth	Not Ill
Child	Male	10	68.1	5.4	.30	.10	.10	0	.50
	Female	24	63.0	9.9	.13	.54	.04	.08	.21
Sibling	Male	23	45.8	12.1	.26	.09	.17	.22	.26
	Female	39	49.1	11.9	.23	.38	.05	.08	.26
Parent	Male	15	28.1	8.0	.33	.13	0	.07	.47
	Female	20	27.8	7.6	.15	.35	0	.20	.30
Spouse	Male	7	56.9	13.1	0	.14	0	.14	.72
	Female	2	57.0	5.7	0	0	.50	0	.50

* Bipolar indicated by BP; unipolar, UP; alcoholism, Alc; and other, Oth.

Interrater Agreement

The diagnoses given by the two interviewers to the ten relatives they independently examined (four of unipolar illness, one of chronic alcoholism, two of personality disorder, and three of no mental illness) were in perfect agreement. Their mean intraclass correlation coefficient on the eight factors of current psychopathology of the CAPPS was 0.86; the mean reliability coefficient on the 18 factors of past psychopathological disorder was 0.80. The reliabilities of the scales describing depression and mania were all in excess of 0.87.

One of the two relative interviewers (J.M.) examined 78 (56%) of the 140 study relatives; the other (M.C.) examined the remaining 62 study relatives. The clinical diagnoses they made on the subjects they interviewed, and the computer diagnoses based on their CAPPS ratings are tabulated in Table 3. The two interviewers' distributions on both sources of diagnosis were similar, confirming the comparability of their diagnostic and rating criteria.

TABLE 3
DIAGNOSES ON STUDY RELATIVES BY TWO INTERVIEWERS

Diagnosis	Interviewer Diagnosis, % J.M. (N = 78)	Interviewer Diagnosis, % M.C. (N = 62)	Computer Diagnosis, % J.M. (N = 77*)	Computer Diagnosis, % M.C. (N = 62)
Bipolar	19	23	19	18
Unipolar	27	32	21	23
Alcoholism	9	3	1	2
Other	13	10	18	14
Not ill	32	32	40	43
Total	**100**	**100**	**99**	**100**
χ^2	2.60		0.50	
df	4		4	
P level	NS		NS	

*** Current and Past Psychopathology Scale incomplete on one study relative.**

Internal Consistency

To determine whether or not the interviewer diagnoses made on the study relatives were consistent with their CAPPS ratings, we measured the degree of agreement between the study relatives' interviewer diagnoses and computer diagnoses, which were derived from the CAPPS ratings according to fixed rules. Table 4 cross-classifies these two sources of diagnosis for the 139 study relatives on whom a CAPPS was completed. The resulting value of weighted kappa, 0.48, is low, mainly because of the stringent rules built into the computer program for diagnosing a psychiatric illness and, therefore, a high likelihood that the computer diagnosis would be not ill. Another reason for the relatively low degree of overall chance-corrected agreement is that the computer gave the diagnosis of either obsessive-compulsive or depressive neurosis to ten study relatives, none of whom was so diagnosed by the interviewer.

Chance-corrected agreement was substantially better for the two diagnoses of special importance in this study, bipolar illness and unipolar illness. The respective values of unweighted kappa, the appropriate statistic for measuring agreement on a single category (Spitzer et al., 1967), were 0.84 and 0.64. These values are sufficiently high to confirm consistency between the interviewers' ratings of psychopathological disorder and their diagnoses of bipolar or unipolar illness based on those ratings.

The evidence for interrater agreement and for internal diagnostic consistency was strong enough to warrent the use of the interviewer diagnosis on the study relatives, as a standard against which to compare the diagnoses on the study relatives from the reports of the probands and the reports of the other family members.

TABLE 4
INTERVIEWER AND COMPUTER DIAGNOSES AGREEMENT ON STUDY RELATIVES

Interviewer Diagnosis	Computer Diagnosis: Bi-polar	Uni-polar	Alco-holism	Other	Not Ill	Total
Bipolar	24	1	0	2	2	**29**
Unipolar	0	26	0	6	9	**41**
Alcoholism	0	0	2	0	6	**8**
Other	2	1	0	4	9	**16**
Not ill	0	2	0	11	32	**45**
Total	**26**	**30**	**2**	**23**	**58**	**139**

Diagnosis from the Proband

In one family only, the proband refused to provide information about the selected study relative, in this case the proband's spouse. They had been separated six months after their marriage, but the spouse nevertheless came in for interview. Data on the degree of agreement between the interviewer diagnosis and the diagnosis from the proband for the remaining 139 study relatives are given in Table 5.

TABLE 5
STUDY RELATIVE'S (SR) INTERVIEW AND PROBAND REPORT DIAGNOSES AGREEMENT

Characteristic of Proband	No. of SRs	Weighted Kappa	% Diagnosed Affective by Interviewer	% Diagnosed Affective From Proband	P*
All probands	139	.50	50	42	.05
Unipolar probands	41	.52	44	39	.75
Bipolar probands	98	.49	53	43	.05
Child of SR	34	.59	59	56	1.00
Sibling of SR	62	.45	52	39	.06
Parent of SR	35	.44	49	34	.23
Spouse of SR	8	.83	12	25	1.00

* Binomial probability for McNemar's test.

The values of weighted kappa indicate that, for the most part, agreement on individual study relatives between the interviewer's diagnosis and that based on the proband's report was only modest. Unipolar probands reporting about their relatives agreed with the interviewer diagnosis to the same degree as did bipolar probands. Irrespective of their diagnosis, probands who were siblings of the study relatives agreed with the interviewer diagnosis to the same degree as did probands who were parents of the study relative. Agreement was somewhat improved when the proband was the child of the study relative, i.e., when the proband was reporting about his parent, but such agreement was still not high. When the proband was reporting about his spouse, however, the diagnosis based on his report agreed well with that obtained by the investigator who interviewed the spouse.

With the exception of probands reporting about their parents or spouses, there tended to be systematic and sometimes significant underreporting by the probands of affective illness in their relatives. Half of all study relatives were diagnosed affectively ill by the investigators who interviewed them, whereas 42% were so diagnosed on the basis of the probands' reports.

Seventy study relatives were given an interviewer diagnosis of affective illness. Their mean age of onset, as determined by the interviewer, was 29.2 years with a standard deviation of 11.3 years. The diagnosis from the proband for 20 of these 70 study relatives was not ill, and, for an additional seven of them for whom the proband reported a psychiatric disorder, he was unable to estimate his relative's age of onset. For the remaining 43 study relatives, the proband overestimated the age of onset by a mean of 4.9 years (paired t ratio $= 5.82$, df $= 42$, $p < .01$). Overestimation did not seem to vary with the proband's relationship to the study relative.

Most Severe Diagnosis

Agreement with the study relative's interviewer diagnosis, as measured by weighted kappa, tended to improve when the most serious diagnosis based on the reports of all the other family members (see Table 6) was taken instead of that based on the proband's report alone. Agreement continued to be best when the diagnosis was based on the report of the study relative's spouse, poorest when the most serious diagnosis was based on the reports of the study relative's siblings or parents, and

TABLE 6
AGREEMENT OF STUDY RELATIVE'S (SR) INTERVIEW
AND MOST SERIOUS DIAGNOSIS FROM OTHER FAMILY MEMBERS

Characteristic of Other Family Members	No. of SRs	Weighted Kappa	% Diagnosed Affective: Interviewer	Most Serious Diagnosis	P*
All other members	140	.64	50	49	.84
Children of SR	33	.64	57	57	1.00
Siblings of SR	76	.50	57	43	.02
Parents of SR	64	.52	48	36	.08
Spouse of SR	25	.73	48	52	1.00

* Binomial probability for McNemar's test.

intermediate when it was based on the reports of the study relative's children.

The somewhat improved agreement just noted was not at the expense of an overestimation of affective illness. Even taking the most serious of the diagnoses they reported, parents and siblings still underestimated affective illness to one degree or another in the study relative. The proportions based on the most serious diagnosis reported by the study relative's children, his spouse, and all other family members, however, are virtually identical to those made by the interviewer.

Comment

Several methodological problems exist in studying familial factors in psychiatric disorders. Ascertainment bias is possible whenever one studies samples of hospitalized patients or outpatients attending clinics within certain geographical areas, because factors found to be associated with an illness might actually be associated with seeking treatment (Fleiss, 1973). In family studies, relatives who refuse to be interviewed directly or who have died may have different characteristics from those relatives who make themselves available for an interview. Information about non-interviewed relatives must be derived from the reports by interviewed members of the family, but the magnitude and direction of bias cannot be determined. These sources of bias are present in our studies as well as in all other family psychiatric studies with which we are familiar.

Even when all family members are interviewed, bias is possible if the interviewers are not kept blind to the proband's diagnosis. In our family studies, we have made every effort to keep the interviewers of the relatives ignorant of whether the proband's diagnosis was bipolar or unipolar illness, although the known excess of bipolar over unipolar probands in our sample may have influenced the relatives' interviewers. Evidence presented elsewhere suggests that the influence, if present, was insignificant (Mendlewicz and Rainer, 1974). An additional control in our studies was to rely on one team of clinicians to diagnose the probands and on another team of interviewers to examine the family members.

Our most important result is that, as a group, probands underreport psychiatric (and especially affective) illness in their relatives. This result is similar to that of Winokur et al. (1969) who studied relatives of only bipolar probands. They found a false-negative rate (the proportion of relatives, out of those judged ill by direct examination, who were diagnosed not ill on the basis of the proband's report) of 58% and a false-positive rate (the proportion of relatives, out of those judged well by direct examination, who were diagnosed ill on the basis of the proband's report) of 3%.

Rimmer and Chambers (1969) studied relatives of alcoholic probands and found a false-negative rate of 63% and a false-positive rate of only 3%. Our error rates are in the same direction as those of Winokur et al. (1969) and Rimmer and Chambers (1969), but not as strong. In our series, 68% of all study relatives were diagnosed psychiatrically ill by the interviewer; the false-negative rate among these was 33%. Our false-positive rate was 7%. There were three false-positives, all diagnosed unipolar on the basis of the proband's report.

The underestimation of illness based on the proband's report varied as a function of his relationship to the study relative. Probands provided more accurate reports about their parents than about their other first-degree relatives. The most likely explanation for this finding is that probands are especially likely to witness directly abnormal behavior in ill parents whose highest period of risk for affective illness (middle to late adulthood) (Slater and Cowie, 1971) overlaps the period within which the probands would be expected to be members of their parents' households. In contrast, the siblings and children of probands tend to enter the period of risk when they no longer live with the proband, thus reducing the chances of the proband's directly observing any illness in them.

Although the number of probands who were spouses of the study relatives was small, the results of Table 5 suggest that probands were also accurate reporters about their spouses. (The apparently large difference between the proportions of spouses diagnosed affectively ill by the interviewer and from the probands' report results from a disagreement on only a single individual.) Although probands appeared to be fairly accurate reporters about illness in their parents and spouses, the observed overestimation of age of onset of ill relatives based on the probands' recollection held as well when the proband was reporting about an ill parent or an ill spouse.

When other family members in addition to the proband report about a given relative, a number of methods exist for combining all of their reports into a single diagnosis. Perhaps the simplest method is to take as the diagnosis the one given most frequently by the informants. This method was tested in this study, and a serious underestimation of illness resulted. The reason was that, in most families, the diagnosis reported most frequently for the study relative was not ill.

The method used in this study, in which the study relative's diagnosis was taken as the most serious of those reported by all other family members, resulted in virtual identity between the rates of affective illness as determined by the interviewer of the study relative and by the most serious diagnosis from other family members. Siblings and parents of study relatives continued to be less accurate reporters than children and spouses.

Conclusions

We have no means of checking on the accuracy of reports about dead relatives or about relatives who either refuse to be interviewed or live too far away. Whereas it may be safe to assume that our result about the differential accuracy of different kinds of family members can be generalized to dead relatives, it would be unwarranted to make this assumption about other unavailable relatives. For example, reports about relatives who have moved far away are likely to be even less accurate than those about relatives who remain in the same area. Caution suggests that living but unavailable relatives not be included in any family studies of affective illness, no matter what diagnoses have been reported on them by the proband and other interviewed family members.

Before drawing more specific conclusions from the results reported here, we must distinguish among three kinds of family studies: studies of assortative mating, studies of morbidity risk, and pedigree analyses.

In studies of assortative mating, interest is in the proportion of ill individuals who marry other ill individuals. Our results indicate that probands are accurate reporters about their spouses and that, more generally, one member of a married couple is an accurate reporter about the other. If one member of a couple has been interviewed, and has provided information about the other, it therefore may not be necessary to interview the partner if interest is only in the presence or absence of illness, but a direct interview is necessary if one wants to estimate, in addition, personality characteristics and marital dynamics.

In studies of morbidity risk, the concern is with the likelihood of illness in relatives of the proband other than the spouse. If the proband's parents are dead, or are available for interview, but the investigator chooses not to have them interviewed for reasons of economy, it may be sufficient to rely on the reports of the proband alone, or of the proband and his siblings, in order to establish the presence or absence of illness in their parents. Ages of onset are likely to be overestimated, however.

For estimating morbidity risk in relatives other than parents, the proband is an inaccurate reporter not only on age of onset but on the fact of illness itself. For determining the presence or absence of illness in a nonliving child or sibling of the proband, the investigator should base the diagnosis on the report of that relative's surviving spouse, if the spouse is available. Failing this, the investigator should take as the diagnosis the most serious of those based on the reports of the dead relative's children. Failing either of these kinds of interview, the investigator should take as the diagnosis the most serious of those based on the reports of all interviewed family members.

Finally, in pedigree studies, concern is with the presence or absence of illness in specific family members. Only the diagnosis based on the report of a spouse has a moderately high value of weighted kappa, the statistic that measures agreement on individual subjects. If, in a given family, one or more relatives of the proband are dead but their surviving spouses can be interviewed, then the diagnosis based on the spouses' reports may be used with some confidence. If, however, such relatives' spouses have not been interviewed, then these relatives should not be included in any genetic analyses.

Taken in their entirety, our results imply that no source of information about psychiatric illness in relatives of affectively ill probands is as good as direct examination of these relatives, both in terms of agreement on individual relatives (measured by weighted kappa) and agreement in the proportions diagnosed ill. Therefore, the investigator engaged in familial research in the affective disorders should make every attempt to have each living relative interviewed directly.

References

American Psychiatric Association (1968), *Diagnostic and Statistic Manual of Mental Disorders, II*.Washington, D.C.

Angst, J. & Perris, C. (1968), Zur Nosologie endogener Depressionen. *Arch. Psychiat. Nervenkr.*, 210:373-386.

Endicott, J. & Spitzer, R. L. (1972), Current and past psychopathology scales: Rationale, reliability, and validity. *Arch. Gen. Psychiat.*, 27:678-687.

Fleiss, J. L. (1973), *Statistical Methods for Rates and Proportions*. New York: John Wiley.

——& Cohen, J. (1973), The equivalence of weighted kappa and the intraclass correlation coefficient as measures of reliability. *Educ. Psychol. Measure*, 33:613-619.

Kallmann, F. J. (1954), Genetic principles in manic-depressive psychosis. In: *Depression*, ed. P. Hoch & J. Zubin. New York: Grune & Stratton, pp. 1-24.

Leonhard, K. (1959), *Aufteilung der endogenen Psychosen*. Berlin: Akademie-Verlag.

Luxenburger, H. (1942), Zirkuläres (manisch-depressives) Irresein: Erbbiologischer Teil. In: *Handbuch der Erbkrankheiten*, Vol. 4, ed. A. von Gütt. Leipzig: Thieme, pp. 83-129.

Mendlewicz, J., Fleiss, J. L., & Fieve, R. R. (1972), Evidence for X-linkage in the transmission of manic-depressive illness. *JAMA*, 222:1624-1627.

—— —— ——(1975), Linkage studies in affective disorders: I. The Xg blood group and manic-depressive illness. In: *Genetic Research in Psychiatry*, ed. R. R. Fieve, D. Rosenthal, & H. Brill. Baltimore: Johns Hopkins University Press, pp. 219-232.

——Fieve, R. R., & Rainer, J. D., et al. (1972), Manic-depressive illness: A comparative study of patients with and without a family history. *Brit. J. Psychiat.*, 120:523-530.

——& Rainer, J. D. (1974), Morbidity risk and genetic transmission of manic-depressive illness. *Amer. J. Hum. Genet.*, 26:692-701.

Reich, T., Clayton, P. J., & Winokur, G. (1969), Family history studies: V. The genetics of mania. *Amer. J. Psychiat.*, 125:1358-1369.

Rimmer, J. & Chambers, D. F. (1969), Alcoholism: Methodological considerations in the study of family illness. *Amer. J. Orthopsychiat.*, 39:760-768.

Robins, E. & Guze, S. B. (1972), Classification of affective disorders: The primary-secondary, the endogenous-reactive, and the neurotic-psychotic concepts. In: *Recent Advances in Psychobiology of the Depressive Illness*, ed. T. A. Williams, M. M. Katz, & J. A. Shield. Washington, D.C.: Department of Health, Education and Welfare, publication No. (HSM) 70-9053.

Sjögren, T. (1948), Genetic-statistical and psychiatric investigations of a West Swedish population. *Acta Psychiat. Neurol. Scand.*, suppl. 52, pp. 1-102.

Slater, E. (1938), Zur Periodik des manisch-depressiven Irreseins. *Z. Gesamte Neurol. Psychiat.*, 162:794-801.

——& Cowie, V. (1971), *The Genetics of Mental Disorders*. London: Oxford University Press.

Spitzer, R. L., Cohen, J., Fleiss, J. L., et al. (1967), Quantification of agreement in psychiatric diagnosis. *Arch. Gen. Psychiat.*, 17:83-87.

——& Endicott, J. (1969), DIAGNO II: Further developments in a computer program for psychiatric diagnosis. *Amer. J. Psychiat.*, suppl. 125, Jan:12-21.

Stenstedt, A. (1952), A study in manic-depressive psychosis. *Acta Psychiat. Neurol. Scand.*, suppl. 79, pp. 1-111.

Winokur, G., Clayton, P. J., & Reich, T. (1969), *Manic-Depressive Illness*. St. Louis: C. V. Mosby.

——&Tanna, V.L. (1969), Possible role of X-linked dominant factor in manic-depressive disease. *Dis. Nerv. Sys.*, 30:89-93.

Zerbin-Rüdin, E. (1969), Zur Genetik der depressiven Erkrankungen. In: *Das depressive Syndrome*, ed. H. Hippius & H. Selbach. Munich: Urban & Schwarzenberg, pp. 35-36.

The Family Concept Test has been developed in order to obtain a quantifiable description of an individual's family concept, i.e., it explores the child's and parents' expectations regarding their family unit. Here the test is employed to achieve two research objectives. Its further use in clinical and research work is advocated.

Dimensions of the Family Concept and Their Relation to Gender, Generation, and Disturbance

FERDINAND VAN DER VEEN

The family concepts of parents and children have been the focus of a program of research on the family of the disturbed child and family intervention. They are considered to play a critical mediating role in the development and alleviation of childhood disturbance (cf. van der Veen et al., 1964; van der Veen and Novak, 1974). The family concept is a heuristic construct for conceptualizing and investigating the individual in relation to the family system. Analogous to the self-concept, it is a cognitive-emotional "schema" that is composed of interrelated perceptions, attitudes, feelings, and expectations regarding one's family unit. Some fundamental assumptions regarding the family concept are: that it

---

From the Institute for Juvenile Research, Chicago, Illinois.

Supported in part by USPHS Grants MH 13633, and 15503 "Family Concept Child Adjustment and Psychotherapy," F. van der Veen, Principal Investigator. Data collection was carried out with the cooperation of the Dane County Mental Health Center, Madison, Wisconsin; the Family Service and Guidance Center, Topeka, Kansas; and the Tucson Child Guidance Clinic, Tucson, Arizona. Appreciation is extended to Dr. Kenneth Howard for statistical consultation, Dr. Michael O'Mahoney for statistical analysis, and Anita Waszak for assistance with data analysis. A portion of the study was presented under the same title at the Annual Meeting of the American Psychological Association, 1971 (van der Veen and O'Mahoney, 1971).

develops principally from interaction within the family over an extended period of time; that it exerts a potent and lasting influence on behavior; and that it is subject to change and revision under a variety of conditions, including formal intervention such as family therapy.

The *Family Concept Test* has been developed in order to obtain a quantifiable description of an individual's family concept. The test is described in detail in the Method section below. Studies employing the test have investigated the relationship of the family concepts of fathers, mothers, and children to child adjustment (Novak and van der Veen, 1970; van der Veen, 1965; van der Veen et al., 1964; van der Veen and Novak, 1974), marital adjustment (Kimmel, 1970; van der Veen et al., 1964), school achievement (Strauss, 1970), child type (i.e., aggressive vs. withdrawn) (Janzen, 1972; Kimmel, 1970), parental attitudes (van der Veen and Novak, 1971), and family intervention methods (Hardcastle, 1973; Raskin and van der Veen, 1970; Reiter and Kilmann, 1975; Wattie, 1973). These studies have primarily focused on global types of variables, such as agreement between the concepts of different members ("family congruence"), the degree of correspondence between an individual's real and ideal family concepts ("family satisfaction"), and the correspondence between a person's family concept and an expert concept of the ideal family ("family effectiveness" or, formerly, "family adjustment"). Little research has been done, however, concerning the specific content of the test items.

The present study carried out an analysis of the test items in order to achieve two objectives: to develop adequate measures of family concept content dimensions for use in family research and clinical assessment, and to investigate the effects of gender, generation, and child disturbance on these content dimensions in order to understand their relationship to family role and the emotional health of the members.

METHOD

FAMILY CONCEPT TEST

The Family Concept Test consists of 80 one-sentence descriptions of social and emotional aspects of family life (see Table 1 for examples of the items). All items were constructed to apply to the entire family unit. This method of item construction avoided the overwhelming complexity of assessing the quality of each possible relationship structure within the family (e.g., mother-child, father-mother, child-child). It is assumed that the qualities most salient for an individual, regardless of the particular person grouping in which they occur, will receive most emphasis in her or his description of the family as a whole. The items were formulated at a family-oriented child guidance clinic and therefore reflect the experience and interests of social workers, psychologists, and psychiatrists in a treatment setting (cf., M. van der Veen and Ostrander, 1961). Out of an original list of over 200 items, 80 were retained on the basis of item relevance, comprehensiveness, and clarity, as judged by fourteen staff members.

TABLE 1
FIRST-ORDER FAMILY CONCEPT FACTORS AND ITEM LOADINGS

Factor 1. *Consideration vs. Conflict*		*Item Loading*
50.	We are considerate of each other.	.60
26.	We are usually calm and relaxed when we are together.	.53
75.	We rarely hurt each other's feelings.	.49
73.	We forgive each other easily.	.43
63.	We have respect for each other's feelings and opinions. . .	.42
5.	Each of us tries to be the kind of person the others will like.	.39
28.	We respect each other's privacy.	.38
	Negative:	
25.	There are many conflicts in our family.	−.67
10.	Each of us wants to tell the others what to do.	−.65
56.	We often become angry at each other.	−.63
59.	We are critical of each other.	−.60
45.	We make demands on each other.	−.50
31.	We often upset each other without intending it.	−.47
Factor 2. *Family Actualization vs. Inadequacy*		
1.	We like to do new and different things.	.54
78.	We can adjust well to new situations.	.52
80.	We are full of life and good spirits.	.47
60.	We are satisfied with the way in which we now live.	.44
70.	We are a strong, competent family.	.40
39.	We encourage each other to develop in his or her own individual way.	.39
	Negative;	
8.	We want help with our problems.	−.49
30.	We tend to worry about many things.	−.46

→

TABLE 1 (Continued)

37.	We do not understand what is causing our difficulties.	–.36
29.	Accomlishing what we want to do seems to be difficult for us.	–.35
Factor 3. *Open Communication*		
12.	We feel free to express any thought or feeling to each other.	.56
	Negative:	
20.	We do not talk about sex.	–.58
42.	There are some topics which we avoid talking about.	–.52
71.	We just cannot tell each other our real feelings.	–.51
74.	We are usually somewhat reserved with each other.	–.40
Factor 4. *Community Sociability*		
65.	We are sociable and really enjoy being with people.	.62
18.	We get along very well in the community.	.58
3.	We have a number of close friends.	.53
79.	We are liked by most people who know us.	.49
	Negative:	
24.	We do not like each other's friends.	–.46
Factor 5. *Family Ambition*		*Item Loading*
38.	Success and prestige are very important to us.	.60
67.	It is important to us to know how we appear to others.	.51
72.	We are not satisfied with anything short of perfection.	.48
Factor C. *Internal vs. External Locus of control*		
2.	We usually can depend on each other.	.47
(46.)	We take care of each other.[a]	.38
51.	We can stand up for our rights if necessary.	.32
	Negative:	
22.	If we had more money most of our present problems would be gone.	–.47
15.	It is not our fault that we are having difficulties.	–.44
68.	Our decisions are not our own, but are forced upon us. . .	–.39
57.	We live largely by other people's standards and values.	–.38
62.	We resent each other's outside activities.	–.35
Factor 7. *Togetherness vs. Separateness*		
9.	We do many things together.	.60
13.	Our home is the center of our activities.	.49
47.	Our activities together are usually planned and organized.	.41
(55.)	We depend on each other too much.[b]	.40

TABLE 1 (Continued)

	Negative:	
61.	Usually each of us goes his own separate way.	−.55
36.	We do not spend enough time together.	−.42
Factor 8. *Family Loyalty*		
48.	The family has always been very important to us.	.66
35.	We need each other.	.60
46.	We take care of each other.	.53
(14.)	We are an affectionate family.[c]	.52
23.	We are proud of our family.	.51
	Negative:	
69.	We are not really fond of one another.	−.44
Factor 9. (General item set). *Closeness vs. Estrangement*		
7.	We feel secure when we are with each other.	
41.	We have warm, close relationships with each other.	
14.	We are an affectionate family.	
44.	We really do trust and confide in each other.	
	Negative:	
11.	There are serious differences in our standards and values.	
17.	We do not understand each other.	
21.	We get along much better with persons outside the family. . .	
58.	We are not as happy together as we might be.	

[a]Item scored only on Factor 8, not on Factor 6, to avoid factor overlap.
[b]Item not scored because it was deleted in a later, multiple choice, version of the test.
[c]Item scored only on Factor 9, to avoid factor overlap.

Q-sort administration of the test consists of the presentation of items on separate cards, with instructions to place them in nine piles ranging from "least like" (0) to "most like" (8), for "your family as it is now" (the *real family concept*) and for "your family as you would ideally like it to be" (the *ideal family concept*). A fixed number of cards are placed in each pile: 3, 6, 9, 13, 18, 13, 9, 6, 3, respectively.

The reliability (stability) of item and global scores has generally been found to be high. In a study comparing different response formats for the test items (van der Veen et al., 1970) it was found that the 80-item test-retest correlations for the real family concepts averaged .69 (n = 75) and .80 (n = 77) for the Q-sort and multiple-choice forms respectively, over a four-week time span. Test-retest correlations for global scores ranged from .87 to .95. Only data from the Q-sort form of the test for the real family concept are used in the present study.[1]

SUBJECTS

Q sorts for family concepts of the real family were available for fathers, mothers, sons, and daughters from both disturbed and nondisturbed families. Almost all subjects were Caucasian, and most resided in medium to large cities. They represent a broad range of parental educational levels and occupations, excluding only the extreme high and low ends of these distributions. The total sample consisted of the following groups: *Disturbed sons and daughters:* the identified patients in clinic admissions of age twelve and over; *nondisturbed siblings:* adolescents with no marked problems who were siblings of identified patients; *clinic fathers and mothers*: the parents of identified patients; *fathers and mothers of low- and high-adjustment children*: parents of children who were of low or high social and emotional adjustment at school, based on ratings of school records; *university community sons, daughters, fathers, and mothers*: members of families obtained through the ninth-grade enrollment list of a school located in a small university town (about half of these fathers had college degrees); and *male and female college students*: students enrolled in undergraduate college psychology courses. Sample sizes for these groups are listed in Table 3 in the Results section.

ANALYSIS

The item intercorrelations were factor analyzed by means of the method of principal components to obtain the major content dimensions of the test. Both first- and second-order analyses were carried out. The first-order analysis consisted of the principal components of the intercorrelations of the 80 items for the real family Q sorts of 406 subjects. Successive Varimax rotations were performed in order to be able to identify the most stable, meaningful, and independent dimensions (Howard and Gordon, 1963). For the second-order analysis a similar procedure was followed for the intercorrelations of first-order factor scores for 503 subjects.[2]

[1] A manual, research abstracts, factor scoring procedures, and other information regarding the Family Concept Test are available upon request.

[2] Sample size increased as more data became available for members of disturbed families in successive phases of the study.

To assess the effects of sex, generation, and disturbance the sample was divided into sixteen subgroups according to family position and disturbance and other characteristics of the constituent groups. One-way analysis of variance over all of the subject groupings, as well as Duncan Multiple Range Tests and other analyses of variance and *t*-tests, were undertaken for this phase of the study.

Results

Statistical aspects of the analyses will be presented first, followed by factor descriptions that include the effects of group characteristics on each factor.

First-Order Factor Analysis

Fifteen first-order factors with eigenvalues greater than one were extracted from the intercorrelations of the 80 item scores. These were rotated successively from 15 to 4 factors, with the 7-factor rotation selected as best representing a stable and meaningful item-loading pattern. Because one of the factors at this rotation divided into two distinct components at a later rotation, it was separated into two factors (3 and 8). This resulted in the identification of 8 individual factors, which accounted for about 30% of the item variance. Table 1 presents items, item loadings, and descriptive labels for each factor. An item was included in a factor if it had a substantial loading on that factor and was also not loaded highly on any other factor. This procedure was followed to maximize factor coherence and separation. Factors were scored by obtaining the mean of the raw scores for the items listed in Table 1, with negatively loaded items reversed.

Correlation of item with factor scores revealed a set of eight items that had substantial correlations ($> .30$) with four factors (1, 3, 7, and 8), but which had not been included because of their factor overlap. In order to include these powerful items in the factor domain they were combined into a separate item set, for convenience termed Factor 9 (see Table 1).

Second-Order Factor Analysis

The results of the analysis of group differences on the first-order factor scores showed two major patterns of group effects (see below), an indication that a second-order factor analysis would be appropriate. For the second-order analysis, the first-order factor scores were intercorrelated and factored, excluding Factor 9. Two principal components emerged with eigenvalues greater than one, and these were rotated and retained for interpretation. They accounted for 46% of the variance of the eight-by-eight correlation matrix. The loadings of the first-order factors on the second-order ones are presented in Table 2. Two distinct loading patterns for the first-order factors were evident. Only one factor (5. Family Ambition) failed to load clearly on either of the second-order factors. The correlation between factor scores for the two second-order factors was .35 (n = 503), or about 11% mutual variance, indicating good factor separation.

TABLE 2
FACTOR LOADINGS FOR THE SECOND-ORDER FACTOR ANALYSIS (VARIMAX ROTATION)

First-Order Factor	Second-Order Factor A	Second-Order Factor B
1. Consideration vs. Conflict	.61	.33
2. Family Actualization vs. Inadequacy	.30	.64
3. Open Communication	.60	.19
4. Community Sociability	−.15	.78
5. Family Ambition	−.22	−.13
6. Internal vs. External Locus of Control	.33	.56
7. Togetherness vs. Separateness	.75	−.02
8. Family Loyalty	.77	.03

Note: Underlined loadings indicate those first-order factors selected for inclusion in the second-order factor. Although not listed in the table, Factor 9 (the general item set) was added to the components of Factor A because of its high correlation with that factor.

Analysis of Effects of Gender, Generation, and Disturbance

For this phase the factor scores of 924 subjects were analyzed. Second-order factor scores consisted of the means of the component first-order factor scores. Factor 9 is included as a component of Factor A because of its high correlation with the other components of that factor. Group means on both the first- and second-order factors, and the F ratios for one-way analyses of variance across groups are presented in Table 3. All

TABLE 3
GROUP MEANS AND *F* RATIOS FOR THE FAMILY CONCEPT FACTORS

		First-Order Factors									Second-Order Factors	
Group	n	1	2	3	4	5	6	7	8	9	A	B
Sons												
Disturbed	51	3.8	4.0	4.0	4.8	4.0	4.4	3.7	4.8	4.1	4.1	4.4
Siblings	12	3.7	4.3	4.4	5.1	3.6	4.8	3.7	4.8	4.0	4.1	4.7
Univ. Com.	13	4.0	4.4	4.1	5.8	4.1	4.9	4.0	4.7	4.4	4.3	5.1
College	31	4.2	4.6	4.1	5.0	3.8	5.2	3.2	5.2	4.3	4.2	4.9
Daughters												
Disturbed	43	3.9	3.9	3.8	4.6	4.0	4.7	3.6	5.0	3.8	4.0	4.4
Siblings	10	4.2	4.7	4.3	5.0	3.9	5.0	3.4	6.4	4.6	4.6	4.9
Univ. Com.	23	4.4	4.9	4.3	5.4	3.5	5.3	4.7	5.9	5.0	4.8	5.2
College	36	4.2	5.0	4.1	5.2	3.4	5.4	3.5	5.3	4.4	4.3	5.2
Fathers												
Clinic	253	4.4	4.1	4.7	4.8	3.4	5.2	4.5	5.9	4.8	4.8	4.7
Univ. Com.	25	4.8	4.8	4.6	5.0	3.4	5.6	4.6	5.9	5.3	5.0	5.1
Low Adj.	17	4.8	5.1	4.9	4.6	3.5	5.7	5.2	6.0	5.6	5.3	5.1
High Adj.	20	4.8	5.1	4.8	5.3	3.7	5.2	4.8	6.1	5.5	5.2	5.2
Mothers												
Clinic	328	4.3	3.9	4.7	4.8	3.1	5.1	4.4	5.9	4.8	4.8	4.6
Univ. Com.	25	4.6	4.8	4.7	5.2	3.3	5.5	4.5	6.2	5.4	5.1	5.2
Low Adj.	17	5.0	4.9	5.1	4.8	3.7	5.5	5.1	6.4	5.7	5.5	5.1
High Adj.	20	5.0	5.0	5.1	5.2	3.0	5.4	5.0	6.6	5.7	5.5	5.2
F Ratio[a]		5.0	14.9	5.5	3.1	3.7	7.0	9.5	8.7	8.6	12.3	10.3

Note: All entries are item mean equivalents on a scale from 0 (low) to 8 (high).
[a]For $p = .01$, $F = 1.9$ (df. 15/908).

of the *F* ratios are significant beyond the .01 level. Significant findings for the multiple comparison and other variance analyses are summarized in the factor descriptions that follow. Estimates of factor means for various subject groupings are included in parentheses. A comprehensive overview of major group differences will be given in the Discussion section.

First-Order Factors

Factor 1: Consideration vs. Conflict. Consideration and harmony characterize the positive end of this factor, while conflict and anger are typical of its negative pole (see items in Table 1). Children perceive less consideration in the family than parents (4.0 vs. 4.7). Members of nonclinic families are higher than members of clinic families (4.7 vs. 4.0). There is a slight trend for females to be higher than males, within their respective groupings (see Table 3).

Factor 2: Family Actualization vs. Inadequacy. The positive pole consists of liking to do what is new, adjusting well, and zestfulness, while the negative pole represents worry and wanting help with problems. It is surprising that the desire for help is found on this factor rather than Factor 1, on which conflict is so strongly represented. From the point of view of the family members, seeking help may be more a result of lack of growth and enjoyment in the family than of conflict, with which it is more commonly associated. All members of disturbed families are lower on actualization than corresponding members in nondisturbed families (4.2 vs. 4.9). In fact, the five lowest groups on this factor are all members of disturbed families.

Factor 3: Open Communication. This factor emphasizes unfettered communication—the open expression of feelings and thoughts, including sexual concerns. All children are lower on open communication than all parents (4.1 vs. 4.8). Disturbed children tend to be slightly lower than other children (3.9 vs. 4.2).

Factor 4: Community Sociability. Sociability, friendships, being liked, and getting along well in the community characterize this dimension of the family concept. Disturbed children are lower than all other child groups on sociability (4.6 vs. 5.2), and the university-community children are the highest of all groups (5.6). Low-adjustment fathers and mothers (nonclinic parents with children low in school adjustment) are among the lowest groups (4.7) on this factor, though they are among the highest on most other factors (see Table 3). It is possible that the low-adjustment child's poor school adjustment reflects a lack of integration into the community by the family as a whole.

Factor 5: Family Ambition. Success, prestige, and concern with the opinions of others are hallmarks of this factor. Children tend to be higher than parents on family ambition (3.8 vs. 3.4), especially in disturbed families. Excluding the low-adjustment group, there is a weak trend for fathers to be higher than mothers (3.5 vs. 3.2).

Factor 6: Internal vs. External Locus of Control. The positive pole indicates that family members can depend on each other and stand up for their rights, while at the negative end the family reacts to forces beyond its control (lack of money, externally caused difficulties and decisions, others' standards and values). Disturbed children see the family as less in control of its fate than nondisturbed children (4.5 vs. 5.0), and members of disturbed families are in general lower than members of other families (4.9 vs. 5.4). Low-adjustment fathers are the highest group and higher than other fathers on this factor (5.7 vs. 5.2). The probably exaggerated emphasis on family autonomy by these fathers may be a result of their avoidance of community participation in combination with their high family involvement (see factors 4 and 7).

Factor 7: Togetherness vs. Separateness. At the high end of this factor the family is the center of many activities together, while at the low end the members go their own separate ways. Members of disturbed families are lower on togetherness than members of nondisturbed families (3.8 vs. 4.7). Also, all children are lower than their parents (3.7 vs. 4.8). Appropriately, college students perceive the least togetherness of all of the child groups (3.4). Low-school-adjustment parents are highest of all groups (5.1) on this factor, probably the other side of the coin of their low community sociability.

Factor 8: Family Loyalty. This factor concerns family devotion and pride. The positive items are that the family is very important, that the members need and care for one another, and that they are affectionate and proud. The negative item maintains that there is a lack of fondness for one another. This factor resembles the concept of "familism," which denotes strong belief in the importance of the family (cf. Burgess and Locke, 1953). Family loyalty differentiates along both generation and sex, with sons, daughters, fathers, and mothers showing successively higher means (4.8, 5.8, 6.0, 6.3). Nondisturbed girls are much higher on loyalty than other child groups (6.2 vs. 4.8), while both nondisturbed and disturbed boys are the lowest of all groups (4.9) on this factor. Clinic parents tend to perceive less loyalty than other parents (5.9 vs. 6.2), though this is more true of mothers (5.9 vs. 6.4) than fathers (5.9 vs. 6.0).

Factor 9: Closeness vs. Estrangement. The positive end of this item set is characterized by close, warm, and trusting relationships, while the negative end represents lack of understanding, serious differences in values, a preference for other relationships, and unhappiness. Members of nondisturbed families are clearly higher on closeness than members of disturbed families (5.3 vs. 4.3). There is also a large difference due to generation, with parents perceiving more closeness in the family than children (5.4 vs. 4.3).

SECOND-ORDER FACTORS

Factor A: Family Integration. This factor is composed of the following first-order factors: Family Loyalty, Togetherness vs. Separateness, Consideration vs. Conflict, Open Communication, and the item set Closeness vs. Estrangement. A family concept high on Family Integration therefore describes a family that is loyal, home-centered, considerate, communicative, and close. These dimensions have in common a focus on the quality and structure of interpersonal relations within the family unit. There is an emphasis on positive family relationships, on the cohesiveness of the family, and on devotion to it.

Family Integration shows few differences with respect to gender, though there is a trend for nonclinic males to be slightly lower than females (4.7 vs. 5.0). The effect of generation, however, is very pronounced: All parent groups perceive higher family integration than all child groups (5.2 vs. 4.4), with the exception of university-community girls (see Table 3). Family Integration also differentiates along disturbance within generational categories, i.e., disturbed children are lower than nondisturbed children (4.0 vs. 4.4), and parents of disturbed children are lower than other parents (4.8 vs. 5.3).

Factor B: Adaptive Coping. First-order factors with high loadings on this dimension are: Community Sociability, Family Actualization vs. Inadequacy, and Internal vs. External Locus of Control. As its label indicates, the components of Adaptive Coping concern the way in which the family adapts to the world around it: Can it build effective community relations? Is it able to venture outward and to enjoy life, or is there an atmosphere of helplessness? Does it have a sense of control over its own destiny? These traits have in common an action orientation, an ability to deal with the world, which contrasts markedly with the focus on internal family relations found for Family Integration. There were no effects of gender on Adaptive Coping, with a minor exception that college females were higher than college males. For generation, the only significant effect was that disturbed children are somewhat lower on Adaptive Coping than their parents (4.4 vs. 4.7). However, striking differences were found in relation to disturbance. Disturbed children are significantly lower on Adaptive Coping than all other groups (4.4 vs. 5.0). And all members of disturbed families are lower than all members of nondisturbed families (4.6 vs. 5.1) on this factor.

Discussion

For ease of reference, an overview of the major group effects for all of the factors is summarized in Table 4. For the effects of gender, it can be seen that there is little consistent relationship between any of the family concept factors and the sex role of the family member. The one clear exception is Family Loyalty, a factor that is higher for daughters than sons and for mothers than fathers. The emphasis in our culture on greater family commitment and devotion from women than men is probably responsible for this factor difference.

With respect to generation, it is evident that Family Integration and all of its component factors (Considerateness, Open Communication, Togetherness, Loyalty, and Closeness) are higher for parents than for children (see Table 4). On Family Loyalty, daughters are as high as parents, so that only sons are lower than parents on this factor. The remaining factors do not differentiate the parents from the children of normal families. In disturbed families, however, Adaptive Coping is higher for the parents than for their disturbed child, and the disturbed child perceives greater Family Ambition than the parents.

It may be concluded for the effect of generation that the family-integration dimensions of the family concept are consistently more positive for parents than for children, while dimensions concerning adaptation within the larger society show little difference across generations. Put somewhat differently, adaptability and community relations in the normal family are equally satisfactory (or unsatisfactory) for parents and children, but internal family relationships are distinctly less satisfying for children than for parents. Thus the "normal" family appears to contain a strong potential for conflict between parents and children. This "generational stress" in interpersonal satisfaction is presumably related to the greater power and control enjoyed by the parents over the family.

The generational difference in Adaptive Coping for clinic families is probably due to the child's disturbance, since this factor is very sensitive to disturbance. This explanation does not, however, account for the disturbed child's perception of greater Family Ambition, a factor not related to disturbance. It is possible that the disturbed child overperceives and/or his parents underperceive pressures for success and conformity in these families.

The most pervasive factor differences occur in relation to disturbance:

TABLE 4
SUMMARY OF MAJOR GROUP DIFFERENCES FOR FIRST- AND SECOND-ORDER FAMILY CONCEPT FACTORS

Family Concept Factor	Significant Differences in:		
	Gender	Generation	Disturbance
A. Family Integration		Parents > (higher than) children	Nondisturbed Families > Disturbed Families
1. Consideration vs. Conflict		Parents > children	Nondisturbed > Disturbed
3. Open Communication		Parents > children	
7. Togetherness vs. Separateness		Parents > Children	Nondisturbed > Disturbed
8. Family Loyalty	Daughter > Sons Mothers > Fathers	Parents > Sons	Nondisturbed > Disturbed
9. Closeness vs. Estrangement		Parents > Children	Nondisturbed Mothers > Disturbed Mothers
B. Adaptive Coping	College females > College males	Parents > Disturbed Children	Nondisturbed > Disturbed
2. Actualization vs. Inadequacy			Nondisturbed > Disturbed
4. Community Sociability			Nondisturbed Children > Disturbed Children
6. Internal vs. External Locus of Control			Nondisturbed Children > Disturbed Children
5. Family Ambition[a]		Disturbed Children > Parents	

[a]Factor 5 is not included in either of the second-order factors.

Disturbed family members are lower than members of nondisturbed families on seven of the nine first-order factors (see Table 4). On Family Considerateness, Togetherness, Closeness, and Actualization, this difference was found for both parents and children. On Community Sociability and Locus of Control, it was found for children, and on Family Loyalty it occurred for mothers. Though there is a trend for disturbed children to perceive less open communication than nondisturbed ones, this variable is not consistently related to disturbance. This is somewhat surprising in light of the attention given to difficulties in communication in family pathology and treatment. What may be at issue here is not the amount of communication but its quality. The items in the Open Communication factor do not directly concern the consequences of communication in terms of understanding, closeness, or the resolution of problems. The outcome of communication is more a part of other factors, such as Considerateness, Loyalty, and, especially Closeness, all of which are strongly related to disturbance.

As would be expected from the first-order factor results, both Family Integration and Adaptive Coping are associated with disturbance. Adaptive Coping differentiates especially clearly between disturbed and nondisturbed families. All members of families with disturbed children perceive their families as coping less adequately than do the members of families without a disturbed child. This pervasive difference implies that adaptive coping may be an essential family characteristic for the child's adjustment, and perhaps that family integration makes its main contribution through enhancing the family's adaptive ability.

The large number of factors found to be sensitive to disturbance reinforces the value of the Family Concept Test as an overall measure of family health. They strengthen an assumption inherent in the family concept approach, namely, that effects of family conditions depend upon and are mediated by the family concepts of the members (van der Veen et al., 1964; van der Veen and Novak, 1974). Following Holland's (1970) far-reaching conceptual framework, it is plausible that the family concept factors represent dimensions necessary for adequate "familization" of the child. Familization is the process whereby the family develops a shared evaluative-cognitive meaning-structure, a "universe of meaning," regarding the family and its members. Such a shared meaning-structure develops through consensual validation in family interaction and provides the necessary "anchoring points" for appropriate action by the members (cf. Holland, 1970, pp. 418-422). The family concept is a component of the universe of meaning, and it would follow that family concept factors represent aspects of the consensual validation process within the family or of those family conditions closely related to it.

The relationship between family interaction and family concepts has been investigated for normal three-member family groups, with the parents and their ninth-grade child participating in a "revealed differences" exercise (cf. van der Veen, 1974). The findings of the study with respect to the family concept factors may be summarized as follows: Frequency of aggressions between family members was mainly related to the adaptive coping factors. Significant associations were found with mother's factor

4, father's factors 3, 6 and B, and child's factors 5, 6 and B. Amount of the assertiveness between the members, i.e., simultaneous speech and interruptions, was associated with most of the factors, especially for the mother's and child's concepts of the family (mother's factors 1, 2, 3, 4, 8, 9 and A; child's factors 1, 2, 4, 6, 8, 9, A and B; father's factors 7, 8, 9 and A). Father and mother dominance (speaking time, speaking order, and influence on final decisions) were pervasively related to the child's factors (1, 2, 6, 8, 9, A and B), but negligibly to those of the father (only factor 8) or mother (none). Inequality of participation was associated with a few of the factors (mother's factor 7, father's factor 3, and child's factors 6 and B). Caution is necessary with respect to the direction of these relationships. The factors were positively related to behavior of the father, but negatively to mother's behavior. Associations with the child's behavior depended on the parent toward whom the behavior was directed, again positive in relation to father and negative to mother. Overall, there was some support for the conclusion that the family concept factors are related to observable aspects of family behavior.

In addition to obtaining scores on separate dimensions, the factors may also be used to construct a profile. Plotting the factor scores of a person or group on a grid that automatically converts raw scores to standard scores, such as that used for the MMPI, provides an immediate graphic basis for comparison between individuals and groups. While detailed consideration of such a grid is beyond the scope of this paper, an example of a profile comparison may serve to demonstrate its usefulness. When the group means in Table 3 are ranked on each factor and the ranks of, for example, the Disturbed Sons and Nondisturbed Brothers are plotted over all factors, profiles result like those presented in Figure 1. From the profiles of the two samples it is apparent that they are generally similar, with the important exception of three factors: Open Communication, Community Sociability, and Family Ambition. Nondisturbed brothers view the family as more communicative, more sociable, and less ambitious than the disturbed sons. Such a comparison suggests, as a hypothesis for consideration, that poor communication, lack of extrafamilial ties, and pressures for success may be especially pathogenic family conditions from the point of view of the adolescent boy.

While no claim can be made for the comprehensiveness of the original item domain, the second-order factors are surprisingly similar to major dimensions of small-group-interaction research, such as internal stability (Family Integration) and task effectiveness (Adaptive Coping). Parsons

FIGURE 1
FAMILY CONCEPT FACTOR PROFILES FOR DISTURBED SONS
AND NONDISTURBED MALE SIBLINGS

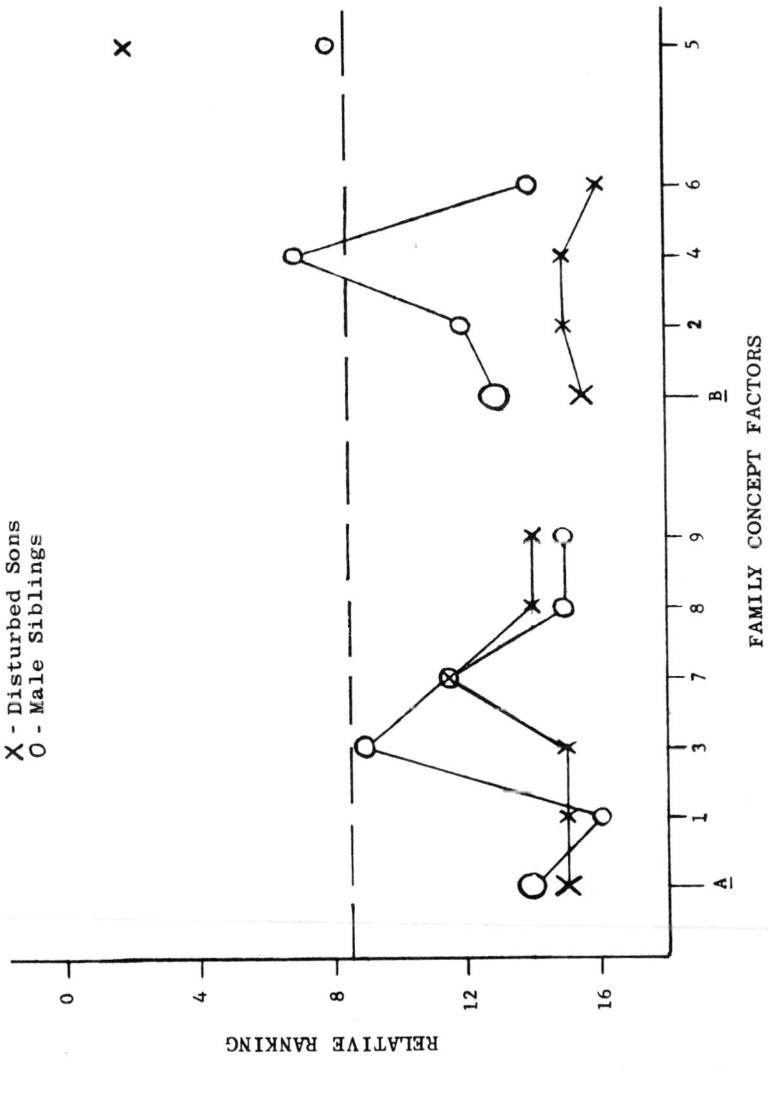

and Bales (1955) speak of the instrumental-expressive distinction "as essentially the differentiation of function, and hence of relative influence, in terms of 'external' vs. 'internal' functions of the system (p. 47)." They describe the instrumental function as adaptive and external-goal oriented, and the expressive function as maintaining integrative relations between members. Straus (1964) reviewed a number of factor-analytic studies in a theoretical paper on family structure. He marshalled an impressive array of findings upholding his contention that the two dimensions of power and support are of universal importance in the socialization of the child. Power and support are functionally similar to the Adaptive Coping and Family Integration factors, respectively. The correspondenc of the higher-order factors to these widely obtained dimensions of group interaction and family structure strengthens the generality and validity of the factor structure of the test.

Summary and Conclusion

In summary, factor analysis of the Family Concept Test revealed 8 first-order factors plus a coherent set of items which correlated highly with 4 of the original factors. The factors represent a wide array of social-emotional aspects of family life. A second-order analysis revealed two higher-order factors encompassing 7 of the 8 original factors. The higher-order factors are similar to the major instrumental and expressive dimensions obtained in small-group research and to the power and support dimensions found in family research. Variance analyses for sixteen subgroups show that Family Integration and its component factors (Family Consideration, Open Communication, Togetherness, Loyalty, and Closeness) are strongly related to generation, with parents higher than children on these dimensions. Except for Open Communication, these factors are also higher for members of nondisturbed as opposed to disturbed families. Adaptive Coping and its component factors (Family Actualization, Community Sociability, and Internal Locus of Control) are strongly related to disturbance, with lower family adaptation in the concepts of all members of disturbed families than in those of nondisturbed families. Family Loyalty is the only dimension clearly related to gender, with females perceiving greater family loyalty than males. It is concluded that the factors of the Family Concept Test appear to be meaningful and important attributes of the family concepts of parents and children and that they warrant further use in family evaluation and research.

References

Burgess, E. W. & Locke, H. J. (1953), *The Family*, 2nd ed. New York: American Book Co.

Hardcastle, D. R. (1973), Effects of a family counseling program on parents' family satisfaction, perceived integration, and congruence, and on specific behavior patterns in the family. Unpublished.

Holland, D. (1970), Familization, socialization, and the universe of meaning: An extension of the interactional approach. *J. Marr. & Fam.*, 32:415-427.

Howard, K. I. & Gordon, R. A. (1963), Empirical note on the "number of factors" problem in factor analysis. *Psychol. Rep.*, 12:247-250.

Janzen, C. (1972), A study of the relationships between parental family concepts and child personality in disturbed children. Unpublished.

Kimmel, D. C. (1970), Interacting family components: An analysis of the interrelationship between child behavior, marital adjustment, and family perceptions. Unpublished.

Novak, A. L. & van der Veen, F. (1970), Family concepts and emotional disturbance in the families of disturbed adolescents with normal siblings. *Fam. Proc.*, 9:157-171.

Parsons, T. & Bales, R. F. (1955), *Family, Socialization and Interaction Process*. New York: Free Press.

Raskin, N. & van der Veen, F. (1970), Client-centered family therapy: Some clinical and research perspectives. In: *New Directions in Client-Centered Therapy*, ed. J. T. Hart & T. M. Tomlinson. New York: Houghton Mifflin, pp. 387-406.

Reiter, G. F. & Kilmann, P. R. (1975), Mothers as family change agents. *J. Counsel. Psychol.*, 22:61-65.

Straus, M. A. (1964), Power and support structure of the family in relation to socialization. *J. Marr. & Fam.*, 26:318-326.

Strauss, G. H. (1970), The relationship of family concept to variables of school adjustment, grades 4, 5, and 6. Unpublished.

van der Veen, F. (1965), The parent's concept of the family unit and child adjustment. *J. Counsel. Psychol.*, 12:196-200.

——— (1969), Family psychotherapy and a person's concept of his family: Some clinical and research formulations. Mimeographed manuscript. Chicago: Institute for Juvenile Research.

——— (1974), Family interaction and congruence of family concepts among adolescents and their parents. Presented at the Annual Conference of the National Council on Family Relations, St. Louis.

——— Howard, K. I., & Austria, A. M. (1970), Stability and equivalence of scores based on three different response formats. *Proceedings, 78th Annual Meeting*. Washington, D.C.: American Psychological Association, pp. 99-100.

——— Huebner, B., Jorgens, B., & Neja, P., Jr. (1964), Relationships between the parent's concept of the family and family adjustment. *Amer. J. Orthopsychiat.*, 34:45-55.

——— & Novak, A.L. (1971), Perceived parental attitudes and family concepts of disturbed adolescents, normal siblings and normal controls. *Fam. Proc.*, 10:327-343.

——— ——— (1974), The family concept of the disturbed child: A replication study. *Amer. J. Orthopsychiat.*, 44:763-772.

———& O'Mahoney, M. T. (1971), Dimensions of the family concept in relation to emotional disorder and family position. *Proceedings, 79th Annual Meeting*. Washington, D.C.: American Psychological Association, pp. 451-452.

van der Veen, M. & Ostrander, K. (1961), Developmental and initial use of a family concept Q sort with clinicians and clients of the Dane County Guidance Center. Unpublished.

Wattie, B. (1973), Evaluating short-term casework in a family agency. *Soc. Casework,* 54:609-616.

A review of family assessment techniques leads to describing the Family Puppet Interview, a procedure that involves the whole family simultaneously.

Family Puppet Interview

ELEANOR C. IRWIN and ELAINE S. MALLOY

Family Assessment Techniques: A Review

In recent years, family therapists have explored numerous innovative techniques for facilitating meaningful communication and interaction among family members in therapy. Particularly during the initial assessment meeting, therapists have searched for ways to elicit diagnostic information without relying upon the usual verbal history-taking interview.

Toward this end, Minuchin et al. (1967) have devised a number of task situations. Family members are asked, for example, to work out a menu with their favorite foods or to come to some agreement on how to spend ten dollars. Watzlawick (1966), convinced that human behavior is patterned, also creates situations to stimulate typical family interactions, believing with many that the process of the communication is more important than the content. Some of his suggestions are to ask the family to plan something they could all do together or to ask parents to discuss the meaning of a proverb that they later teach to their children.

Family sculpture (Papp et al., 1973; Simon, 1972) is an activity in which each member of a family takes turns arranging the others to create

Eleanor C. Irwin, Ph.D., is Expressive Arts Therapist, Pittsburgh Child Guidance Center; Clinical Assistant Professor of Child Psychiatry (Speech and Drama), Department of Psychiatry, University of Pittsburgh.

Elaine S. Malloy, M.S.W., is Family Therapist, Family Therapy Clinic, Western Psychiatric Institute and Clinic, University of Pittsburgh, Department of Psychiatry.

Reprinted from *Family Process*, vol. 14, no. 2, 1975.

a living, spatial, relational tableau of the family. This nonverbal technique can reveal family relationships in terms of space, attitude, alliances, and underlying feelings. A wealth of verbal material often emerges following this symbolic representation.

In an attempt to limit unrewarding, conflict-producing patterns of interaction, conjoint play therapy (Safer, 1965) includes both parent and child in play activities. In the playroom setting, typical interactive behavior reactions readily appear in the experience of the therapy hour and can be dealt with in the "here and now."

Some facilitative techniques of family assessment include the use of projective materials. The Family Rorschach method (Loveland et al., 1963), for example, is designed to study family interaction directly. The therapist explains the task and then observes the family's interaction as they proceed to interpret the inkblots to each other and attempt to reach consensus in their responses. Levy and Epstein (1964) discuss the administration of the Rorschach test to individual members and then to the family as a whole in an effort to elaborate understanding of family functioning. Comparisons are made in the individual's psychological functioning between working independently and in the family context.

Many art therapy techniques have been used with families. Kwiatkowska (1967) suggests that the informality and indirectness of this approach facilitates the lessening of defenses and controls in communication and that symbolic representation of a family's drawing can lead to gradual clarification of areas of conflict. Techniques described by Kwiatkowska (1967) include the "joint family scribble" in which each member does a quick scribble and the whole family joins efforts to make a picture, providing a vehicle for associations. Rubin and Magnussen (1974) supplied a range of media to enable members to produce a two- or three-dimensional family portrait as well as a joint mural and occasional free drawings or products. In the Conjoint Family Drawing, Bing (1970) asked members to draw a picture together as they see themselves as a family. The drawing can be analyzed in terms of the finished picture as well as the process experienced by the family.

All of these activities share a common purpose: namely, to stimulate verbal and nonverbal communication, revealing how a family mobilizes itself toward a goal or task. This kind of family interaction has been viewed by many as the "pivotal point for awareness and intervention in work with families" (Kempler, 1968).

The Puppet Interview

In clinical work with children, the use of puppets has been valuable both diagnostically and therapeutically because of the richness of the symbolic material elicited in the child's spontaneous play (Irwin and Shapiro, 1975). In the individual interview, the child is asked to select a number of hand puppets from a representative variety[1] and then is asked to use these puppets to make up a "pretend" television story. Following the child's story, the clinician gathers associations to the material by "interviewing" the puppets and/or the puppeteer, much as one interviews a performer after a show. In this post-play puppet interview, the child is encouraged to associate to portions of his story as the therapist seeks to validate clinical hunches or clarify portions of the material. In the final part of the assessment, the therapist talks with the child about the story itself and its possible relationships to his real-life situation.

Because of its value as a facilitative technique, even among constricted patients, the authors explored the use of spontaneous puppet play in assessing family groups, particularly those with children between the ages of five and twelve.

Family Puppet Interview

Families were seen at two outpatient clinics: The Pittsburgh Child Guidance Center where a variety of child and family treatment modalities are offered, and the Family Therapy Clinic of Western Psychiatric Institute and Clinic which focuses primarily on the family as a unit.

Frequently, sessions have been conducted by the authors working individually, but the authors have also co-led sessions with the referring therapists when appropriate. Requests for a Family Puppet Interview are often made during the diagnostic phase, although, as in the case of the

[1] It is important that the readymade, hand puppet selection include a variety of types and styles of puppet characters. The authors have found it useful to use approximately twenty puppets, including both realistic as well as fantasy ones. Fantasy types, such as the devil, witch, pirate, skeleton, king, queen, prince, and princess, as well as realistic "people" puppets of all ages, offer a wide range in selection. The doctor and the policeman are favorites; those that have more of a "fantasy" quality are more readily chosen than the highly realistic ones. Many times, animals are chosen to represent some aspect of the self or others. Therefore, "domestic" animals (cat, dog) as well as "wild" animals (alligator, dragon, crow with oral aggressive features) should be included.

Collins family (reported later) interviews have also taken place during ongoing treatment when a specific issue or difficulty has arisen.

The Family Puppet Interview, generally one-and-a-half hours in duration, can be taped and used later with the family in ongoing therapy. If a one-way mirror and adjacent observation room is available, it can permit the therapists to view the interaction during the session when the family is left alone to plan together. The authors (and colleagues who have utilized this procedure) have found this kind of family interview particularly useful in viewing decision-making within the family, observing family patterns, and studying symbolic communication between family members.

Generally, the session takes place in a room with chairs arranged in a circle, the therapist and the entire family having come together to begin the session. A basket with a few dozen assorted puppets and a large puppet stage are in the room.

The Procedure

Initially, each family member is asked what he has been told to expect in the day's meeting and his notion of why the family needs to come to the clinic. Each member is asked to define the problem(s) as he sees it; most often, the family consensus identifies one member as "the problem." An important outcome sought in this initial joint family task is to help members begin to view their family as an interactional system, in which each is involved with all the others.

To present the rationale and task of the puppet story, the therapist might say, "The purpose of our meeting is to get to know you as a family. One way to become better acquainted is to ask you to do something together. Sometimes it is difficult at first, especially for kids, to feel comfortable in talking directly about problems and feelings. At the clinic, we have found that this is made easier when parents and children join together in an activity. So now I am going to ask you as a family to play together for awhile. Here is a basket of puppets. Take a few minutes to look through them and choose a few that interest you."

Up-ending a large basket of puppets on the floor, the therapist encourages the family members to leave the formality of their chairs, giving tacit permission for them to "regress" together in a play situation. As the family members select their puppets, the therapist observes their individual behaviors and their interaction, noting which puppets are selected, rejected, avoided, etc. Sometimes one member intrusively selects puppets for another, while others seem to wait for subliminal feedback about their choices. The puppet(s) may represent some aspect of the self (i.e., the way the individual sees himself or the way he wishes or fears himself to be) or significant others. The idiosyncratic meaning the puppet has for the puppeteer, however, may become clear through the poststory discussion when members are asked to think about which puppets they chose and why.

Once the family has made its selection, the remainder of the puppets are put away. In order to "warm up" the family to the task, each member is asked to introduce his puppets by giving them a name and making a statement or two about each one.

The task of planning a story is presented to the family as follows: "Now I would like you to work together to make up a story using these puppets. I will go in the next room and watch through the window while you plan. Just try to decide how the story might begin. It is important that this be a made-up story, not one you have seen or read."

Observing from another room, it is often possible to determine family roles, i.e., which member functions as organizer, dominator, disciplinarian, scapegoat, victim, pacifier, etc. Family alliances and subgroups often become visible, as do characteristic patterns of interaction.

The therapist returns to the room when the family seems to have the beginning of a story planned. Most families, but not all, work best when "hidden" behind a puppet stage, which provides psychic as well as aesthetic distance.[2]

Sitting in front as the "audience," the therapist then asks the family to begin by having each puppet character introduce himself. If the family seems reluctant or unsure, the therapist might move the family into action by "cuing" them with, "Now we have the Jones Family Special." If further help is needed, the therapist can get them started by saying, "Could the first puppet character introduce himself?" or suggest, "Let's see what happens in the opening scene of the story. Where does it take place, and what is the first thing that happens?" To discourage the family (or one of the members) from narrating the story, the therapist can say: "Don't tell me; *show* me how it happens." The therapist's spontaneity

[2] The puppet stage need not be elaborate and can even be made from heavy cardboard. However, it must be large enough to accommodate the family members.

and flexibility often serve as a model for the family, giving tacit permission for them to "let go" and experience a sense of pleasure in play.

Most often, stories come to a natural ending. Sometimes, however, as conflict emerges in the story, a family gets stuck and (as in real life) the family demonstrates its inability to resolve the difficulty. In such a situation, the therapist can intervene and either help the family find a satisfactory ending or explore the alternative endings each member might prefer.

When the story is either completed or stopped (for one reason or another), the therapist can continue the interaction by talking directly to the puppets or suggest that certain puppets talk to each other about problem areas in the story. It often happens that family members become quite invested with their puppets and consequently insist the story end a certain way. Therefore, the therapist can pursue conflicts between puppets and explore significant themes as they appeared in the story, effecting closure if it is needed.

Postplay Discussion

When the puppets are put away, the members return to the discussion circle where they are encouraged to associate to the story they have just played. Each member might be asked to think of a title for the story; a theme, moral, or lesson that one might learn from the story; the character each would most want to be; the character each would least like to be, etc. To get some idea of the observing ego of the family, members are asked to comment on ways in which the story (or the planning) is representative of their family. The therapist then tries to help the family connect the story with issues that seem relevant to the conflict areas for them.

At the end of the session, the family is thanked for its participation and encouraged to continue to share with each other any additional feelings or notions related to the experience, particularly those which seem to fit with their unique family patterns. In this way, the family participates in the experience, the interpretation, and further planning.

Clinical Data

To illustrate the procedure and process, four cases were chosen to highlight different aspects of the interviews: Case I—the behavioral information that is available in the process of initial puppet selection by family members; Case II—the way a therapist's intervention and support can help a family get organized; Case III—the use of the postplay discussion to relate the planning and story itself to typical family interactions and conflicts; and Case IV—the puppet interview in ongoing therapy to focus on previously unspeakable issues.

Case I: Puppet Selection

The initial selection of puppets is often filled with intriguing vignettes of interaction. The George family was referred for the puppet diagnostic interview because of the parents' tendencies to intellectualize and deny feelings, especially aggressive ones. The family listened wordlessly as the directions for the task were given. When the puppets were spilled out on the floor, however, Mr. George asked for clarification, "Are there certain kinds of puppets we should choose?" Told he could pick any he liked, he anxiously pursued the therapist with questions: "Is this to be all nonverbal, or what? How many should we take?. . ." etc.

In contrast to his father's anxiety, Tommy, aged twelve, inspected the puppets and quickly chose the devil and the skeleton, "I know what the story's gonna be. . .'The Haunted Castle'. . . and the devil and skeleton are gonna be in charge." His father laughed, "Oh, yeah?" Stephen, age ten, picked up the pirate with the patched eye and scarred face. Holding it over his face, he said to nobody in particular, "Hi, folks . . . gimme all your money." He laughed softly to himself. Mother chose two furry puppets, a lion and a dog, and absent-mindedly rubbed their soft fur against her face as she waited for the others to finish. The lion, she said, was "reformed—he's not fierce anymore," and the dog. . ."well, he was like Joe, the family dog, who had been 'put to sleep.' " Tears filled her eyes as she talked. Louise, the fourteen-year-old, fingered the puppets in a bored, desultory way, then chose the witch and the queen. Later she related the story of the wicked witch trying to kill Snow White because she was jealous of her beauty (a theme of jealousy and rivalry that was later evident in interaction with her mother). Father was the last to finish. He chose two females, emphasized emphatically that they were "kind, not mean, ladies . . . they have caring eyes"; they play tricks, but "nice tricks, not mean tricks."

Comment: In spite of the parents' tremendous efforts to control the plot line and eliminate any trace of conflict, the children succeeded in playing a story filled with rage, competitiveness, and self-destruction. The parents' fear of aggression, their attempts to control the process as well as the plot of the story were evident in their initial approach to the task. The puppet choices, therefore, give not only symbolic clues concerning identification, interest, and motivation, but provide information about typical family interactional patterns.

Case II: Therapist's Intervention

On occasion, the members become so engrossed in the story that they leave the symbolic area of expression of feelings and begin to act them out. The F. family consisted of mother, father, and son, Kevin, aged seven. They were referred because the child's speech difficulties were thought to have a psychogenic basis.

Both parents were heavyset, neatly dressed. Both father and son had high-pitched voices, nervous laughs. The parents followed Kevin anxiously into the room, pursuing him with their eyes and words as he paced about. In addition to his infantile speech, the problem, as they saw it, was Kevin's lack of independence.

When invited to play with the puppets, the parents began to cajole, coax, plead with their son—"Come and play with the puppets . . . look at the pretty puppets. . . ." Kevin would have none of it, but did stop long enough to inspect the King puppet, which he dropped nervously. He began to pace the floor, whining, "I don't wanna play." The parents looked helpless.

At that point, the therapist intervened, picked up the King puppet and said, "Good morning," to Kevin, as though acknowledging a formal introduction. Intrigued, Kevin giggled. "Do you know my name?" the therapist asked. Kevin responded, "King Friday." Inviting his cooperation, "King Friday" continued, "Hmmm. . .I see you know me. Can you help me? I can't seem to find out what's going on here."

Responding to the conscious, as well as the unconscious, invitation, Kevin took the King puppet. Mother immediately followed suit and chose a Princess puppet. Turning to her son with her puppet, Mother asked, "Can I be your wife?" Kevin laughed nervously, "No." Without pausing or seeming to hear, mother continued, "Am I pretty enough?" With this, father joined them in play. The drama began to be enacted on the floor without the benefit of a stage. Choosing another female puppet, father suggested that *this* puppet be the King's Bride. Kevin shook his head,

"No." (Mother, meanwhile, had assumed that Kevin had said, "Yes," to her earlier question, and was already pretending to be the King's wife, "fixing up" the castle, etc.) Father was quiet for a few minutes, watching his wife and son interact. Suddenly, he chose a raggedy-looking puppet and said, "Oh, look Kevin. The robber had kidnapped the King's bride. Better save her." Putting the Bride on a table, he cried, "Help, help," in a falsetto voice. At first, Kevin ignored the cries; then, dropping the King, he picked up a policeman and went after the robber, pretending to shoot him. Father immediately took the crocodile puppet, saying in a teasing voice, "The crocodile is going to get you." Manipulating the crocodile's mouth, father nipped at Kevin's policeman. Excited and frightened, Kevin dropped the policeman puppet, began to giggle louder and more hysterically. He picked up the King puppet and began to weakly defend himself against his father's crocodile.

Mother joined the foray. Using the Princess puppet as an extension of herself, she hit her husband sharply on the arm. "Don't do that, you bad man. Stop that." Father ignored mother and followed Kevin, who by now was crouched behind the table, giggling hysterically. Father's puppet nipped Kevin on the backside, then he returned to the circle, still laughing. In a few seconds, Kevin also returned, and the story continued. The Princess and the King were pretending to go to bed because it was night. Father took the skeleton puppet and began to make spooky noises as though to haunt them. Annoyed, Kevin took the Judge, (an old man) and pronounced sentence on father's skeleton: "You're dead, and you have to go to jail." Father again picked up the crocodile puppet and began to nip at Kevin's Judge. In a frenzy, Kevin picked up the policeman and "shot" everybody, including himself. . . .

Comment: The puppet interview revealed not only the family dynamics and the struggle to control their thinly diguised, primitive impulses, but also indicated the direction of future therapy. The family needed the firm support of a therapist to help define their boundaries in order to begin to work on separation and individuation.

Case III: Postplay Discussion

A confusing series of subplots emerged in the story by the Davis family. There was little mutuality among the four children and minimal participation by the mother. When asked to relate the story to their life situation, however, the members were able to describe many areas of conflict for them as expressed through the story.

The Davis family was referred from an agency where each of the sons, James, twelve, and Donald, ten, had been identified as patients: one for acting-out and the other for his withdrawal tendencies. Despite high IQ's, they were not achieving in school and had no friends. The sons, two daughters (Daphne, eleven, and Cathy, six), mother, and her fiancé, Mr. Carter, who lived with them, were asked to participate in a family session together. When the five members of the Davis family arrived, mother's fiancé was not with them. Mother, an attractive woman with a responsible position as a nurse, was mostly silent and withdrawn. Of her fiancé, she sighed, "He finked out as usual." None of the children knew the purpose of the visit to the clinic. Donald, the acting-out son with an IQ of 136, offered himself meekly, "I'm retarded."

While the children chose puppets and enthusiastically began to plan a story, Mrs. Davis watched, looking sad and depressed. Daphne, who talked incessantly, was the most dominant contributor to the complicated story that had numerous subplots. It was as though each family member used the structure of the story to enact his own fantasy, oblivious of the others. Except for Daphne's efforts to control and integrate the story, the participants seemed to work separately, each minimally involved with the others. In general, the plot revolved around a series of nighttime, scary events. In a haunted village, the farmer's daughter was kidnapped by spooks (skeletons and devils, played by the boys). Daphne played the role of the kidnapped girl ("the best one"), as well as Professor Goofus, who offered sage advice to an unheeding group, "We should work together in teams."

Throughout the drama, Mother remained silent and uninvolved, except for two brief moments: One, as an old lady living on the outskirts of the haunted village (not unlike her position in the family), she called out repeatedly, "Help me, help me. . .I need help. Don't leave me. I can't stay here by myself." Second, as a "pet dragon" (berated by the others as useless), she protested, "I'm a good dragon. . .I chase rainbows and live with the old lady. I try to help her, but she's never satisfied. She's old and dotty." In a momentary overt alliance with "the old lady," Donald relinquished his skeleton and devil puppets and picked up a boy. "I'm the son of the old lady who lives with the dragon. . .I hate the dragon. . .he bit me on the nose."

When asked how the story might remind them of their own lives, all the children agreed there was some similarity to Mr. Carter who, like the pet dragon, never helps "the old lady." According to the children, Mr. Carter stays home while Mrs. Davis works from three to eleven P.M., which was the "scary time." Only Daphne ("the best one") was able to speak up to him; the others were all afraid. "He smacks all the time," Daphne complained.

Mrs. Davis, continuing to react as though helpless to influence any changes, shrugged off Daphne's comments but concurred with the negativity, "When he's there, he's horizontal, either asleep or in front of the TV."

Comment: The session with the Davis family provided an opportunity for them to represent in the symbolic form of their story a microcosm of their family interactions: the conspicuously absent person in the form of the mean dragon who did not help, the old lady repeatedly calling out for help, and the boys as spooks and skeletons acting out devilishly. Both in the story and in the fragmented planning experience, the mother was for the most part uninvolved, which seemed to underscore her abdication of the parental role to lead, protect, and stabilize the family. In the postplay discussion, the Davis family related many significant issues from the hour's experience to their life together in general.

Case IV: Ongoing Treatment

The previous examples have illustrated the use of the Family Puppet Interview in the initial assessment phase of treatment. However, this interview technique can be used in ongoing therapy, particularly if the family seems to have reached a stalemate and is unable to deal directly with a particular issue. Such is the case with the Collins family.

The mother and two sons had been involved in family therapy intermittently for a period of months since the parents' divorce. Despite an underlying torrent of sadness relative to the father's absence from the home, the sons were unable to express their sense of loss. One was hostile and withdrawn, while the other was hyperactive. The mother's depression was immobilizing. The recent death of a much loved family dog was characteristically not talked about or grieved. A third loss seemed imminent. One of the children was allergic to the family cat, which might also have to be "put away." It was around the issue of what to do with the cat that the mother and therapist agreed to use the puppets to play out what appeared to be a symbolic theme for the family's recent losses. Within the story the children selected a wizard and doctor in attempts to "cure" the cat to enable it to remain with the family.

In the poststory discussion, when the family was asked how the story reminded them of real life, the older son covered his face. The previously unspeakable subject of their dog's death emerged, and the son who had negatively resisted participation in any form of therapy began to sob. Through tears and a choked voice, he talked about how he had nursed the dog night and day in its illness, but was not able to prevent its death. At a deeper level, he was also mourning the dissolution of his parents' marriage, which he likewise had been unable to prevent. He was joined in his tears by his younger brother and mother. Eventually, the discussion centered on the subject of their father. The boys talked of times both good and bad, and the family cried together for what was lost.

Comment: The facilitative aspects of the puppet interview seemed to break through to previously unspeakable sadness in the Collins family. During this session, they began, for the first time, to confront their grief directly rather than through mother's depression, older son's hostility, and younger son's hyperactivity.

Discussion

The Family Puppet Interview provides many opportunities to observe the visible as well as the covert ways that family members communicate with each other. The puppet choices, the conflicts expressed in the fantasy, the postplay discussion when members are invited to associate to the story, the inquiry about the relationship of the story to the family's functioning, all give important clues about the family and the available ego strength for confronting problems.

As a family fantasy gets played out through the dramatization of a story, conflict emerges within the characters' interactions. The form and content of these family fantasies usually center around one or more themes that often seem to be an additional, symbolic response to the therapist's initial question to the family: Why did you come to the clinic?

While this interview has been used with families of diverse backgrounds, there are some for whom it seems to be more appropriate. Families, for example, who find it difficult initially to communicate in the usual verbal ways often respond with enthusiasm and pleasure to the invitation to play with appealing materials. The experience may even afford relief from the usual demand to "put things into words." As is true with children, many families are more eloquent in their symbolic play than they are in verbal interviews.

The second family population for whom this interview seems to be especially valuable is the obsessive-compulsive, highly organized, intellectualized family. When the defense against feeling is strong, members tend to inspect and ruminate over each verbal offering, a tendency that can be minimized in play and action. Insistence on "playing it out" helps cut through the intellectualization, as does the therapist's consistent refusal to listen to narratives. This emphasis upon the spontaneity of the responses in the play often "gets through" the defensive maneuvering of such families.

In summary, therefore, the puppet play with its universal character types appears to be a useful procedure for families in lessening ego controls and the usual defenses. In emphasizing the make-believe aspect of play, families can often be helped to play, fantasize, and look at family functioning in a nonthreatening way.

References

Bing, E. (1970), The conjoint family drawing. *Fam. Proc.*, 9:173-194.

Irwin, E. & Shapiro, M. (1975), Puppetry as a diagnostic and therapeutic technique. In: *Psychiatry and Art*, vol. 4, ed. I. Jakab. Basel: S. Karger, pp. 86-94.

Kempler, W. (1968), Experiential psychotherapy with families. *Fam. Proc.*, 7:88-99.

Kwiatkowska, H. (1967), Family art therapy. *Fam. Proc.*, 6:37-55.

Levy, J. & Epstein, N. (1964), An application of the Rorschach Test in family investigation. *Fam. Proc.*, 3:344-376.

Loveland, N., Wynne, L., & Singer, M. (1963), The family Rorschach: A method for studying family interaction. *Fam. Proc.*, 2:187-215.

Minuchin, S., Montalvo, B., Guerney, B., Rosman, B., & Schumer, F. (1967), *Families of the Slums*. New York: Basic Books.

Papp, P., Siverstein, O., & Center, E. (1973), Family sculpting in preventive work with well families. *Fam. Proc.*, 12:197-212.

Rubin, J. & Magnussen, M.G. (1974), A family art evaluation. *Fam. Proc.*, 13:185-200.

Safer, D. (1965), Conjoint play therapy for the young child and his parent. *Arch. Gen. Psychiat.*, 13:320-326.

Simon, R. (1972), Sculpting the family. *Fam. Proc.*, 11:49-59.

Watzlawick, P. (1966), A structural family interview. *Fam. Proc.*, 5:256-271.

Based upon Abegg's book on the Family Test, the author discusses this family assessment technique by the use of drawing. He stresses its importance as an introduction to child and family therapy.

On the Use of the Family Drawing Test

D. ARN. VAN KREVELEN

Last year the Swiss pediatrician W. Abegg (1973) published the first book on the Family Test (with the subtitle: Children Draw Their Family), a procedure of European origin first described by Porot (1952) in France and six years later the subject of a thesis by Bakalou (1958). We ourselves have used it often, not so much for diagnostic purposes, but rather as an introduction to psychotherapy. The test belongs to the category that does not require expensive test material: a sheet of paper, one or more pencils, and the examiner's sound brain are sufficient.

The underlying principle of this drawing test is that a child may bring to expression in his design the family relationships as seen by him through his eyes. The point is to invite a child to draw his family and to leave him to it. The instruction may be circumstantial, such as the one used by Abegg ("Draw for me—before your next visit—on a not-too-large sheet of paper, with a pencil and colored pencils, or any other drawing material, just as you wish, your family; that is to say, all persons whom you consider belonging to it, including yourself.") or, according to us, preferably briefly and to the point: "Who lives in your family?" and, immediately after the child's answer, "Now I would like you to draw everybody." By giving the child a sheet of paper and a pencil of his own choice, the examiner makes the task easier for the child and gets exactly what he wishes.

Reprinted from *Acta Paedopsychiatrica*, vol. 41, no. 3, 1975.

From Abegg's formulation it may be seen that he does not object to having the child make his drawing at his own home, which might be dictated by lack of time during the consulting hours. Abegg has every confidence in the cooperation of the parents, or to use a better word, in their readiness and ability to let the child alone to do his job. We, on the contrary, anticipate that the parents will assist their child. For that reason, we never allow the mother (father, parents) to be present in the playroom where the child carries out his task. The examiner who allows the subject to make his performance away from his consulting (play) room, deprives himself of the opportunity to observe the child during his activity.

This may be considered a further disadvantage of this procedure, for it is essential to watch the child and to listen to his verbal expressions, just as it is necessary to note in what way the drawing is being made. The drawback of all tests in which a subject must do something is that they may seduce the examiner to become absent-minded, to concentrate upon something else which is irrelevant to the situation. The fact must be stressed that any test which loses its communicative aspect is only a rudiment of what it should be. Tests may be a great help to consolidate contact with a child, even if no word is spoken at all. But the examiner should be "present." Being together with a child creates an atmosphere of understanding and good will. This is one of the mysteries of play therapy.

As is the case with many tests, the family test must be closed by an inquiry. The examiner cannot do it without the child's explanation of his drawing. It needs no comment that it is easier for a child to elucidate his performance if he is in a position to do this immediately afterward. The interaction between examiner and child does not appear to full advantage if the drawing was made at the subject's house. Then the inquiry would lose its significance.

We confine the alternative of colored pencils to the test of Wartegg. Abegg is accustomed to present, apart from an ordinary pencil, six colored ones: blue, red, yellow, green, brown, and black. Of special interest is his observation that a clue to the child's feelings may be seen in the colors he chooses. If a child applies the same color to different persons, the latter would represent similar emotional values. Hence, a child who colors one of his parents with the same pencil he used for himself would betray his emotional ties.

The evaluation of the performance and its result include a subjective facet, which is the weak spot of the test. Nonetheless, a few directives may be of use. Attention must be paid to the way in which the drawing has been executed, carefully or shoddily. This is of special importance if some parts (persons) of the drawing differ in this respect from others. Importance should also be attached to eventual corrections and completions. The sequence in which the members of the family are drawn is also deserving of attention. Usually, the first person to be drawn is the father, followed by the mother. According to Abegg, she is the largest in size, in conformity with her role as the most important relational object. The children are drawn in their birth order. Departures from this rule are considered to be meaningful.

The same applies to *Fehlleistungen* to the effect of suppressions. There is a great chance that children who "forget" themselves feel repudiated, slighted, or wronged. If other persons of the family are missing, it may mean that they are psychically eliminated too; at all events, the relationship between the young drawer and the missing member(s) is probably not of the warmest.

Another characteristic of the drawing which is revealing is the distance between the members of the family. People who are closely bound together—in the drawer's opinion—stand closely side by side. It may be presumed that the material distance (upon the sheet of paper) is a symbol of the emotional distance—as judged by the drawer. Abegg made the observation that only-children draw themselves between the two parents, this would point to a need of protection.

The size of the persons drawn is significant too. We already pointed to Abegg's observation that it is the mother who has the largest size. But this would only be true if she has a large place, too, in the heart of the drawer. It often happens that the child, out of need to force himself to the front (which may be, of course, an overcompensation), draws himself as the largest person. Rivalry conflicts with older siblings may thereby come to the surface. In general, it may be concluded that the size of the persons stands for their emotional significance and importance.

As has already been said, the inquiry at the end is conclusive. The meaning of the figures must be explained by the subject himself. The optimal way to do this is by drawing the child into a pleasant free and easy chat, tempting him to digress on the weal and woe of and in his family, which gives the examiner sufficient starting-points for psychotherapeutic talks with the child.

And with the family, too. Abegg gives many examples of therapeutic dialogues with the parents that were beneficial to the family as a whole.

The simple family test has far-reaching possibilities, insofar as—precisely because it is so unsophisticated—it is most impressive to the persons who recognize their personal weaknesses in their portraits.

The family test may be supplemented by other drawing tests. Abegg makes use of a self-portrait, the drawing of a house, the drawing of a tree, of the school, and a free drawing. We have been accustomed to add the two-houses test, which has the advantage that it is focused on the same object: the assessment of existing or failing relationships within the family (Figure 1). The method is as follows: the examiner himself draws two similar houses as widely apart as the sheet of paper allows. It is made clear to the child that the houses are alike with regard to size, beauty, quality, and price. He is told that the members of the family must separate for a while, and he is asked to carry out the separation. If the child has accomplished this, he is told that one of the people in one of the houses is allowed to take a holiday in the other house. The child may then decide which person will do so. After the person has returned, a family member from the other house may take up his residence with the members he had abandoned in the beginning. This test, too, offers opportunities to reveal and to discuss family relationships.

It appears that Abregg has had a wide experience with the family test. His book is based upon 400 drawings of children between the ages of three years, four months and fifteen years, nine months. His book contains no less than 37 illustrations, most of which are extremely striking.

In a treatise on drawing tests, illustrations should be included. For that reason we conclude this article by presenting three telling examples of our own collection.

A. A nine-year-old boy, the younger of two sons of a family characterized by what we once described as "emotional neglect of a business-milieu," pictures his feelings of being excluded and abandoned by award-

FIGURE 1

ing himself a place to the side of the family. Whereas his brother (carrying himself like a challenging fighter, but without hands) is standing between the parents, he himself stretches both his arms in the direction of his parents. His explanation of the gesture is different: he is about to catch a ball thrown by his older brother, still invisible behind his father's back. Remarkable is the lack of attention of his parents. The mother "watches passing cars," the father "waves his hand to somebody he knows, but most people he knows are unknown to me." The boy's feeling of loneliness is confirmed by the choices he made in the Pigem-van Krevelen-Kritzberg test (van Krevelen, 1953). His first choice is a tree "because one belongs also to Nature," whereas a negative choice is "a hippo, then you would live so far away from your own country." The general impression this drawing makes is that of firmness: the persons appear one by one obtrusive and powerful, although the drawer himself seems to require help (Figure 2).

FIGURE 2

Subject's interpretation	**She is looking (At what?) At the cars that run outside**	**He is playing with the ball**	**He is waving (To whom?) To somebody he knows. Most people he knows, I don't know**	**I am catching the ball. The ball is just behind Daddy.**

B. Quite different is the family drawing of a seven-year-old boy, the only boy between two girls in a physician's family. Here the family members are driven down to the lower edge of the sheet. The drawing lacks the expressiveness of the former one. The boy's poor achievement after his school entrance makes him an object of criticism in the family. Our examination revealed that he was dyslectic. The mother is the parent whose ambivalence is most striking; she is disappointed in her son. She is represented as a sort of fury with unkempt hair and piercing fierce eyes. At first the boy "forgot" to represent himself. After his attention had been drawn to this omission, he found some space remaining at the left side of the sheet. There he drew himself high upon a ladder, as if to catch others' eyes. His question: "Don't you find that I look a bit small?" also evidences his feelings of insufficiency (Figure 3).

FIGURE 3

C. Finally, we give an example of the effect of the size of the used sheet. In the drawing of an eight-year-old hyperthymic girl, the father has not been omitted for unconscious motives; as the result of the child's miscalculation, she failed to put him in line with the other members of the family. Oedipal wishes compelled the child to procure the father such a large space that there was only room left for him "moving upon the faces" of the other family members. It becomes obvious that the format of the piece of paper should not be too small lest the examiner be seduced into drawing wrong conclusions (Figure 4).

It is not superfluous to repeat that the interpretation of children's drawings remains a precarious task. For that reason, the family test may only be evaluated in combination with other data available: the child's history, the interview with the child, the results of other tests, and, last

FIGURE 4

Subject's interpretation — **is Daddy** / **is me** — **is Peter** — **is Nancy** — **is Mamma**

(Who is the gaiest of all?) Daddy. He often plays with us. Peter may sometimes sit upon Daddy's back. Me too, but I must be very cautions, because Daddy just had crick in his back.

but not least, the examiner's general impression based upon his experience. A great advantage is that the test is extremely suitable for an introduction to therapeutic interviews with the child and his parents.

References

Abegg, W. (1973), *Der Familientest. Kinder zeichnen ihre Familie*. Zurich/Stuttgart: Werner Classen Verlag.

Bakalou, K. (1958), *Kinder zeichnen ihre Familie*. Diplomarbeit. Zurich: Schule F. soz. Arbeit.

Porot, M. (1952), Le dessin de la famille. *Pédiatrie*, 7:1-17.

van Krevelen, D. Arn. (1953), *De tekening als hulpmiddel by de psychologische beoordeling van kind en volwassene*. Tekentests. Leiden: Stenfert Kroese.

The authors describe a two-hour family art session as a family assessment technique in a clinical program.

A Family Art Evaluation

JUDITH A. RUBIN and MAX G. MAGNUSSEN

In January of 1969, the Pittsburgh Child Guidance Center employed an art therapist on a part-time basis with some hope and enthusiasm and a number of reservations. While the use of art as a diagnostic and treatment tool is far from new (Bender, 1958; Hammer, 1958), the separate profession of art therapy is a fairly recent conception (Kramer, 1958, 1971; Naumburg, 1947, 1966; Ulman, 1961, 1971), and the newness of such work in a traditional child guidance center has made for an exciting and dynamic experience in program development. Because there was no history of an art program at the clinic, it was necessary to find ways in which the specific skills fo this new worker might be usefully integrated into the ongoing work of the institution. From the tentative beginnings through the present full-time program, there has been much sharing and exploring between the art therapist and other staff members in order to initiate, implement, and evaluate each new way of using art at the Center. Our current conception of the role of art in prevention, diagnosis, and therapy is a broad one, emphasizing flexibility in the use of expressive media in order to serve different needs.

This paper was first delivered as part of an illustrated slide-lecture at the Annual Meeting of the American Association of Psychiatric Services for Children, November, 1971. The authors wish to acknowledge their indebtedness to Marvin I. Shapiro, M.D., for his major role in establishing and facilitating the use of the expressive arts at the Pittsburgh Child Guidance Center.

Judith A. Rubin, M. Ed., A.T.R., is Art Therapist at the Pittsburgh Child Guidance Center, Pittsburgh, Pennsylvania.

Max G. Magnussen, Ph.D., is Chief of Clinical Child Psychology, Pittsburgh Child Guidance Center, Pittsburgh, Pennsylvania.

Reprinted from *Family Process*, vol. 13, no. 2, June, 1974

The focus of this paper is on a particular diagnostic technique, the family art evaluation, developed by the art therapist and a clinical child psychologist with the support and consultation of a child psychiatrist. Through a survey of the literature, personal contact, and correspondence with clinicians using family art interviews, staff role-playing within the Center, and planning sessions to identify meaningful variables appropriate to the clinic population, a format was developed for use within the Child Guidance Center. Important sources for the development of our methodology were the work in "family creative analysis" in diagnosis and treatment at Hillside Hospital (Zierer et al., 1966), the art therapy sessions with families as part of "multiple impact therapy" at the Texas Institute of Child Psychiatry (Kraft and Austin, 1968), the study of "family art diagnosis and evaluation" currently under way in the outpatient clinic of McLean Hospital (Snider, 1970), and the extensive work with "family art evaluation" and "family art therapy" at the National Institutes of Mental Health (Kwiatkowska, 1962, 1967a, 1967b, 1971).

Setting

All members of the family living at home and age four or above are seen in a large room containing a round table, two smaller rectangular tables, two double easels, and a supply table (see Figure 1). They may be referred at any point in the diagnostic evaluation or during treatment, and the referring clinicians may co-lead the session with one of the authors or may lead it themselves with our consultation. Although shorter time periods have been tried, two hours have been found to be a comfortable span of time for most families. We find it most useful, like Kwiatkowska (1967a), to have minimal information about the family prior to the evaluation, in order to observe as freely and objectively as possible. Another reason for this preference is that, at our present stage of development with this approach, we are interested in comparing findings from family art evaluations with results from other diagnostic approaches also being used with the families.

Format

Through experimentation with possible modifications, we have arrived at the following tasks:

1. *Individual picture from a scribble*. Seated around the circular table,

FIGURE 1

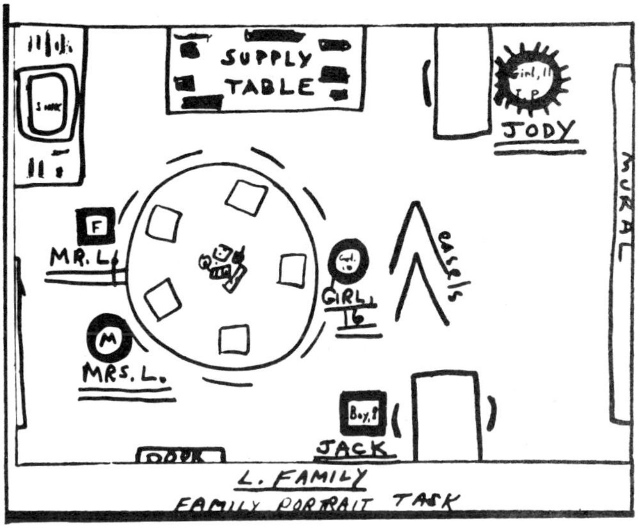

L. Family Map. As can be seen in the above "map" of family members' locations in the room during the second task, Mr. and Mrs. L. and their sixteen-year-old daughter stayed together, verbally interacting, at the round table at which they had developed their scribbles, while the adopted youngsters, Jack and Jody (the eleven-year-old I.P.) each isolated themselves at separate tables away from the trio and worked silently at the task. Jody was the identified patient.

each member chooses from the drawing tools in the center (pencils, crayons, chalk, markers, pens) and, on the small (9" × 12") white drawing paper in front of him, draws a continuous line scribble with his eyes open or closed, whichever he prefers. When finished, each is encouraged to examine his scribble from all possible points of view, in order to "see" pictures in it. Each is then encouraged to select one or more images, elaborating them into a picture to which he then gives a title. When all are done, they take turns placing their developed "scribble drawings" on the easel, the creator of the picture first describing his work, the others then responding to it (see Figures 2, 3, 4).

2. *Family portraits*. Each individual is asked to create a portrait of the family in two or three dimensions, abstractly or realistically. They are shown the range of media available on the supply tables and sink (drawing materials as in Task 1, water colors, tempera paints, finger

FIGURE 2

Mrs. T.'s Scribble Drawing. At first, unable to "see" anything in her line, Mrs. T. finally said it reminded her of a "barbed wire fence, like in a concentration camp." She thus let us know how she felt about being "cooped up" with five active children to care for alone and perhaps about the art evaluation itself.

paints, clay, wood scraps, glue, assorted sizes and colors of construction paper). The possible work spaces in the room are pointed out (easels, tables, floor), and each person is encouraged to work wherever he wishes. When all have completed a representation of the family, the works are taped on the wall or placed on the table so that all portraits are simultaneously visible. Each person describes his work, the others commenting and questioning as they wish (see Figures 1, 5, 6, 7).

3. *Joint mural.* The family is asked to create a picture together on the large (3' × 6') paper taped on the wall, using thick poster chalks. It is suggested that they first decide on a topic and then work on the picture. When the mural is finished, all regard it and are encouraged to discuss the group experience (see Figures 8 and 9).

4. *Free products.* If an individual completes either of the first two tasks before all members are done, he is encouraged to create art products using any medium and topic he desires (see Figures 10 and 11).

Despite previous preparation by the referring clinician, most family

FIGURE 3

Mr. L.'s Scribble Drawing. At first Mr. L. said his scribble drawing "might as well be a Bum as a Clown," but finally entitled it "Clown," emphasizing the lighthearted elements. He thus suggested some ambivalence in his self-image and reinforced our impression that he used humor as a defense against strong feelings, especially of depression.

members, especially adolescents and adults, are apt to be self conscious about their lack of ability in art. As they first enter and are seated around the table, an attempt is made, therefore, to explain the purpose and nature of the interview and to elicit any questions or concerns they may have before beginning. It is emphasized that artistic skill is not expected and is irrelevant, that individuals are encouraged *themselves* to explain and explore the meanings of what they produce and that the evaluation is conceived of as a learning experience for both family and clinicians.

Prior to the termination of the interview, a "debriefing" occurs in which the family is encouraged to explore any concerns, questions, or issues about themselves individually or as a unit, that may have arisen

FIGURE 4

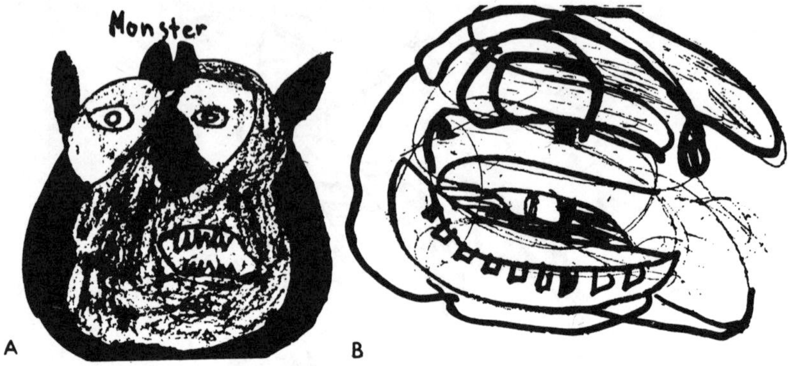

Children's Scribble Drawings. Carl and Carla T., eight-year-old twins, each saw monsters in their scribbles. Carl, the initial referral, said his monster (left) was a boy of six who was "stupid, eating everything, eating people. People call him names like 'bighead' or 'stupid.' " Carla described hers (right) as a girl monster who "likes to go and eat people's guts and eat people when they bother her sometimes." The disorganization of her drawing, and her equally oral-aggressive criticism of others' pictures, led to her being seen as a patient in addition to her brother.

in the course of the session. The referring clinician (who usually observes through a one-way mirror, if not a participant) will offer further assistance in this area in the future. Some families have productively used the session itself as a means of self-analysis, both individually and collectively.

Although colleagues sometimes express concern about the threatening possibilities of a family art evaluation, our experience has been that after initial familiarization with the process, most families have become quite comfortable. No one has become serverely anxious or shown serious difficulties about revealing themselves to others. The atmosphere typically becomes increasingly informal and relaxed. Our impression is that this is due, in part, to the opportunity for selection of an ego-syntonic medium, style, and location during the second task. In addition, the presence of younger children in many of our families is an asset to their more self-conscious parents and older siblings, for they tend to enjoy the procedure, often requesting more of such sessions, and they clearly help the others by their natural, spontaneous behavior.

FIGURE 5

Mr. L.'s Family Portrait. Mr. L. said he was "trying to get a feeling of closeness." Actually, he drew himself, his wife, and his two natural children in a tight group, then effectively isolated his two adopted children (Jack and Jody). They are slightly apart from the others and were drawn last, although he had stated that he drew the family "in the order of the ages of the children."

FIGURE 6

Jack L.'s Family Portrait. Jack, Mr. L.'s eight-year-old adopted son, chose for his family picture to represent only his baby brother in their shared bedroom, describing himself as "outside trying to get in." Further evidence of sibling rivalry was evident in his response to his mother's family drawing (Figure 7). He said with irritation that her picture of the baby was "too big!"

FIGURE 7

Mrs. L.'s Family Portrait (Parallel Data). Mrs. L. said she drew the family "holding hands—a happy, close family." This picture helped to confirm our feeling that Jody and Jack were being subtly excluded from the family circle (or at least put on the periphery). A similar impression was gained from father's family drawing (Figure 5), Jack's family portrait (Figure 6), and the way in which the members positioned themselves during the second task (Figure 1). The persistent verbal denial by both parents of any conflicts within the family suggested that the task of emotionally including the two adopted children had not been fully accomplished.

FIGURE 8

Mural by L. Family. The L. family considered several options and was able, with little friction, to come to a joint decision to draw a dinosaur. Although eight-year-old Jack did not participate initially, annoyed that his idea had not been chosen, he finally joined the others, who were working together smoothly, efficiently, and with evident pleasure in the joint endeavor. The bright, playful fantasy and overall organization of the mural reflect the imaginative strengths and cohesive potential of the family group that created it.

FIGURE 9

Mural by T. Family. The T. Family, unable to engage in any group discussion prior to drawing, impulsively began to work independently and somewhat competitively, as reflected in the scribbled attacks in several portions. Nevertheless, a general sense of shared family identity is reflected in the nonverbal communication of a theme (houses) among members, while the disorganization and confusion apparent throughtout the hectic two-hour session are also evident in the disjointed, isolated, patchwork quality of the final result.

FIGURE 10

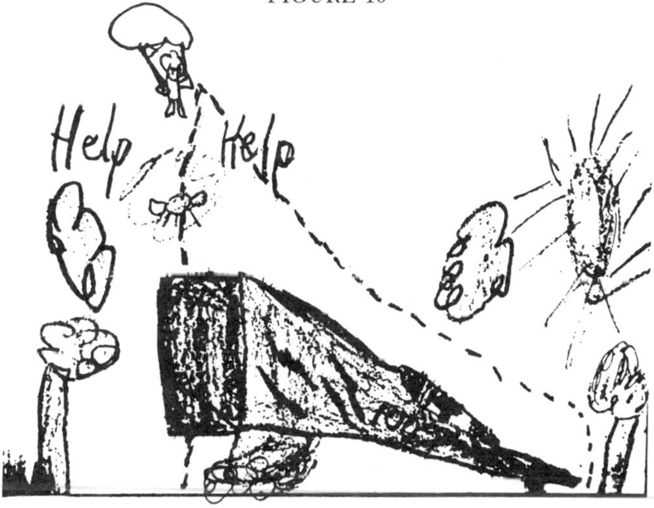

Glen's Free Drawing. This crayon drawing by Glen was a graphic appeal for "help," the word shouted by the boy in the parachute, who is being shot at from below by an older boy in the dragster. Glen, age six, attempted to both emulate and challenge his older brother throughout the session, while his mother effectively withdrew from any kind of interaction with either boy. He seemed to feel unprotected and vulnerable, and the story about his drawing was that the two therapists would rescue the boy (clearly a projection of himself).

FIGURE 11

Mrs. B.'s Free Drawing. Mrs. B. was tense, constricted, and withdrawn throughout the art session; her pictures were tight, compulsive, and unelaborated, her verbalization sparse. Her drawing of a teepee, made while waiting for the others to finish family portraits, is somewhat looser than her other products. Her association was that the Indian inside was sending smoke signals, asking for help for an unspecified problem, much as she herself, hiding behind an anxious silence, was mutely asking for assistance at the clinic.

Rationale

The sequence of tasks is carefully designed to provide maximal information about individual and family characteristics with minimal stress. Thus, the making of a *scribble* as the first task puts the nonartist at ease. Seated together around a table provides a setting conducive to informal communication among family members, and since paper is provided at each seat, the only choice required is the drawing medium. The technique itself is drawn from others' work in education (Cane, 1951), therapy (Naumburg, 1966), and diagnosis with both individuals (Ulman, 1971) and families (Kwiatkowska, 1967a). The request to develop a picture from an image or images perceived in a scribble presents each family member with the task of structuring his self-created, ambiguous stimulus (see Figures 2, 3, 4). Like the Rorschach, the projective content and associations are idiosyncratically valid, as are the formal aspects of how the person performs the task. Further projective data on each individual are available as he responds to other members' drawings during the discussion. Who sits next to whom, who interacts with whom, and what the interaction is provide further useful data.

The second task requires not only the production of a *family portrait*, a not uncommon procedure (Appel, 1931; Burns and Kaufman, 1970, 1972; Cummings, 1952; Hammer, 1958; Hulse, 1951, 1952; Koppitz, 1968; Kwiatkowska, 1967a; Reznikoff and Reznikoff, 1956; Wolff, 1942), but also provides a free choice of materials and working location. The "abstract family portrait" (Kwiatkowska, 1967a) is suggested as a possibility, though it is rarely done, and no specific instructions are given beyond the initial request to create the family using any medium. Thus, the products range from static to active, from heads to full and realistic drawings, paintings, reliefs, or sculptures in both clay and wood scraps. It is not uncommon for diagnostically significant omissions, condensations, and elaborations to occur, nor is it infrequent that an individual will create a second representation of the family in another medium, often revealing even more than the first. Although no one has refused to attempt this task, it is interesting to note that all family members in two disorganized homes with absent fathers had great difficulty in completing the assignment, one mother commenting sadly that "we are really not a family."

In addition to the projective significance of such factors as sequence of figures drawn, relative size, position, etc., we have additional data concerning family relationships from the way in which the members position themselves in the room and interact spontaneously in the course of this second task (see Figure 1). As with the "scribble drawings," much is learned from responses to others' productions as well as from each individual's projected image of the family.

The range of possible media available enables us to observe closely individual styles and models of operation, ranging from the careful precision of a fine-line drawing to the controlled freedom of a brush painting or the possible disorganization of some finger paintings. Flexibility or rigidity of response to such possible variables as the running together of water color paints may also be observed. Not only may the individual's selection and handling of the medium be significant, but equally revealing are the responses of other family members (see Figure 6).

The last procedure requires the family to make (and sometimes to abdicate) a joint decision and to implement it in regard to a commonly assigned task. In format it is not unlike other group mural techniques, and as a group task it is related to the joint projects used by others in family art interviews (Kwiatkowska, 1967a; Snider, 1970; Zierer et al., 1966). Thick poster chalks are our preferred medium, for early experimentation with free choice of media made it clear that others (e.g., tempera paint) were too time-consuming. In the open-ended, free-choice decision-making around content, with not even a beginning like a scribble to focus upon, individually significant themes quickly emerge, as does the family's internal, decision-making structure. The degree and kind of organization in the final product reflect the family's ability to function in a unified fashion. The manner in which members participate in both the decision-making and execution phases of this task gives further evidence of family characteristics and interaction patterns. In the open-ended discussion following the group task, further information is gathered, such as how typical or atypical the interaction seemed to family members (see Figure 8 and 9).

Relation to Other Diagnostic Approaches

In common with any assessment approach involving the whole family, an opportunity for direct observation of interaction is available. Like any activity approach to family diagnosis (Drechsler and Shapiro, 1961), the family art evaluation provides an event in the present that can be observed as it occurs (here and now), and can be the focus for discussion in the group. Because more than one person is active at one time, multiple observational opportunities are available.

And, as with any diagnostic approach using art and nonverbal communication, defenses are frequently bypassed. As in group art therapy, communication through shared focus on products is often easier for family members in regard to each other, as well as to the clinicians. Those who have systematically compared family art evaluations with family diagnostic interviews have consistently noted the additional significant understandings obtained with the former (Kwiatkowska, 1967a; Snider, 1970).

There seems to be no question that "the family art evaluation session gives an unusually rich amount of information with a minimal expenditure of the family's and the therapist's time" (Kwiatkowska, 1967a). Since this interview has been adjunctive to more traditional diagnostic procedures at our clinic, it has been possible to informally compare and contrast the findings from it with those of other assessment approaches. On a small sample of cases, we have tried to arrive at diagnostic formulations independent of other approaches to the family within the Center. In general, it has been possible to demonstrate that remarkably similar findings occur; on one occasion, however, the family art evaluation resulted in a change in the identified patient (see Figure 4). If a two-hour art evaluation can arrive at the same conclusions and treatment recommendations as more time-consuming, traditional approaches, one or the other might be superfluous for certain kinds of evaluation problems and purposes. While we are hardly prepared to advocate the abandonment of traditional assessment procedures, we are impressed with the efficacy and efficiency of the family art evaluation. The family art approach to evaluation is routinely used at NIMH (Kwiatkowska, 1971). The need for further and more definitive research in the area of comparisons of different diagnostic approaches is evident.

The most obvious strength of the family art evaluation lies in the rich and varied sources of diagnostic data, providing a built-in system of checks and balances for assessment. In the course of the three tasks and discussions, we observe a great deal of behavior—verbal and nonverbal, independent and interactional—on the part of each individual family member. We collect a great deal of symbolic data from the products produced—from their form, content, process, and style of execution—and from the associations to them from each individual in terms of his own works and those of others. By systematically varying the specificity and degree of choice (in topic, medium, location, etc.) inherent in each task, as well as the degree of closeness or interaction necessary for its completion, we are able to gather extensive data on both individual and family dynamics. Because of the richness and simultaneity of observational possibilities, we find that two clinicians are, indeed, an asset in the sessions. The opportunity to review videotape or audiotape records of some interviews has provided further information.

The advantages that seem to accrue from the combination of multiple sources of data reside in the possiblity of finding what differently derived impressions have in common (see Figure 7). For example, if symbolic art content tends to correlate highly with observed behavior, the diagnostic impression is reinforced. To further verify or refute such an impression, the examiners might point out to the family the similarity or inconsistency of findings, thus eliciting further reactions from them. In this way, the family is involved directly and openly in determining the significance of its productions, interactions, and verbalizations. The family assists in analyzing data, interpreting it, and rejecting or accepting the impressions. To illustrate the procedure of putting together the various sources of data, it may help to look at Family L., some of whose products are reproduced and described here (Figures 1, 3, 5, 6, 7, 8).

Both parents thought they had successfully handled their own feelings regarding their two adopted children and had integrated the children well into the family unit. However, there was ample evidence of the two children's subtle exclusion: their vocal concern that their art work would not be acceptable to their parents; their sitting apart from the others during the second task (Figure 1); Jack's drawing the "family" as consisting of the baby only, who was displacing him from his bedroom (Figure 6); father's unconscious sequencing and placement of figures in his family drawing (Figure 5); and mother's placement of the two on the edges of her family portrait (Figure 7). Although the referral had been made because of Jody's underachievement in school and possible "learning disability," it was clear that her position in the family could well be one source of her problem and that intervention efforts would best be directed to the system as a whole, especially the parents.

Use in the Clinic

In the development and implementation of our family art evaluation, it was necessary initially for the authors to provide a good deal of information to colleagues—presentations and demonstrations of the approach, rationale for the procedures, built-in safeguards for any potential threat to clients' well-being, etc. It understandably takes time for clinicians to become familiar with and to utilize a novel approach. Patients tend to accept the procedures of the family art evaluation, as noted earlier, quite readily and without noticeable adverse effects. With an increasing emphasis on family approaches to diagnosis and therapy on the part of many staff members, the popularity of art-centered family tasks has continued to grow in the four years since they were first introduced.

A good example of clinicians' positive expectancy effects is that of co-therapists (child psychiatrist and social worker) of a parents' group. After one month of weekly group meetings, the members were told that each entire family was to come in for a session that would be videotaped and later reviewed in the group. All five families were seen for a family art evaluation within the next few weeks, no one dropping out of the group or in any way indicating that the procedure had disrupted their treatment. In fact, they proceeded to review their tapes within the couples' group, taking two weeks for each family. They discussed them in detail, attempting in the process to learn more about themselves and to promote constructive change (Henderson and Lowe, 1972).

As part of the introduction of family art evaluation into the Center, a "family art interest group" was formed following an initial presentation of the procedure to the staff. Various members of that study group and others have introduced occasional art activities into conjoint family interviews, as have many members of a group doing multiple impact therapy (Kraft and Austin, 1968). These findings confirmed for us Kwiatkowska's observations that such procedures are eminently teachable, requiring minimal background in art (Kwiatkowska, 1967a, 1971). In addition, the possiblity of modifications for different purposes has been well exemplified in these experiences.

We have also conducted conjoint family art therapy (Kwiatkowska, 1967a, 1967b, 1968) during the past two years with two families, based in large part upon their response to the family art evaluation. Of course, the techniques utilized for this vary considerably because of the nature of treatment, as opposed to diagnostic, goals. In attempting to understand individuals as well as the family system within which they operate, we find the family art evaluation an impressively efficient tool, though one which is still in the process of being refined and sharpened. What is impressive is that variations in procedures have occurred to meet individualized clinical needs of families, clinicians have increased their techniques in dealing with their patients, and a substantial amount of significant and meaningful data is reported to have emerged in most cases

References

Appel, K. E. (1931), Drawings by children as aids to personality studies. *Amer. J. Orthopsychiat.*, 1:129-144.

Bender, L. (1958), *Child Psychiatric Techniques*. Springfield, Ill.: Charles C Thomas.

Burns, R. C. & Kaufman, S. H. (1970), *Kinetic Family Drawings*. New York: Brunner/Mazel.

——— ——— (1972), *Actions, Styles and Symbols in Kinetic Family Drawings*. New York: Brunner/Mazel.

Cane, F. (1951), *The Artist in Each of Us*. New York: Pantheon Books.

Cummings, J. D. (1952), Family pictures: A projection test for children. *Brit. J. Psychol.*, 43:53-61.
Drechsler, R. & Shapiro, M. I. (1961), A procedure for direct observation of family interaction in a child guidance clinic. *Psychiat.*, 24 (2):163-170.
Hammer, E. F. (1958), *The Clinical Application of Projective Drawings*. Springfield, Ill.: Charles C Thomas.
Henderson, P. & Lowe, K. (1972), Reducing focus on the patient via family videotape playback. Unpublished.
Hulse, W. C. (1951), The emotionally disturbed child draws his family. *Quart. J. Child Behav.*, 3:152-174.
——— (1952), Childhood conflict expressed through family drawings. *J. Proj. Tech.*, 16:66-79.
Koppitz, E. M. (1968), *Psychological Evaluation of Children's Human Figure Drawings*. New York: Grune & Stratton.
Kraft, I. A. & Austin, V. (1968), Art therapy in the educational use of multiple impact therapy. In: *Psychiatry and Art*, Vol. 1, ed. I. Jakab. New York: S. Karger, pp. 106-115.
Kramer, E. (1958), *Art Therapy in a Children's Community*. Springfield, Ill.: Charles C Thomas.
——— (1971), *Art as Therapy with Children*. New York: Schocken Books.
Kwiatkowska, H.Y. (1962), Family art therapy: Experiments with a new technique. *Bull. Art Ther.*, 1:3-15.
——— (1967a), The use of families' art productions for psychiatric evaluation. *Bull. Art Ther.*, 6:52-69.
——— (1967b), Family art therapy. *Fam. Proc.*, 6:37-55.
——— (1971), Family art therapy and family art evaluation. In: *Psychiatry and Art*, Vol. 3, ed. I. Jakab. New York: S. Karger, pp. 138-151.
Naumburg, M. (1947), *Studies of the "Free" Art Expression of Behavior Problem Children and Adolescents as a Means of Diagnosis and Therapy*. Nervous and Mental Disease Monograph, No. 7, 1947. (Distributed by Grune & Stratton, N.Y.)
——— (1966), *Dynamically Oriented Art Therapy: Its Principles and Practice*. New York: Grune & Stratton.
Reznikoff, M. & Reznikoff, H. R. (1956), The family drawing test: A comparative study of children's drawings. *J. Clin. Psychol.*, 12:167-169.
Snider, M. (1970), Personal communication.
Ulman, E. (1961), Art therapy: Problems of definition. *Bull. Art Ther.*, 1:10-17.
——— (1971), The professional development of art therapy. *Amer. J. Art Ther.*, 10:186, 216-221.
Wolff, W. (1942), Projective methods for personality analysis of expressive behavior in pre-school children. *Char. & Pers.*, 10:309-330.
Zierer, E., Sternberg, D., & Finn, R. (1966), The role of family creative analysis in family treatment. *Bull. Art Ther.*, 5:47-63, 87-104.

Family Symptomatology

Family psychopathology reveals itself by symptoms of dysfunction which may occur either in the soma or in the psyche. When a family or a family member becomes aware of dysfunction and is fearful enough about his health, he seeks help from a clinical service. The range of family symptomatology is wide, as reflected in these papers—from physical manifestation (psychosomatic disorder) to emotional and behavioral disorder to the controversial field of schizophrenia in family members.

Psychosomatic disorders are a common manifestation of family psychopathology. In this critical review an attempt is made to isolate the evidence for the links between the family's emotional system and the precipitation of physical symptoms.

Family Process and Psychosomatic Disease

W. W. MEISSNER

The influence of psychological factors in the precipitation and etiology of certain diseases has been carefully investigated and established in recent years. Psychological factors seem to play a considerable role, for example, in the production of gastric ulcers (Lidz and Rubenstein, 1959). Even though the operation of stress factors has been well established in this regard, our ideas about the ways in which stress factors affect the local physiology and functioning of the gastric mucosa are far from precise or specific. It is more or less generally accepted that certain types of personality organization are more susceptible to such psychosomatic influences and tend to react to stress or conflict by somatic dysfunction. But here again, our ideas lack specificity, particularly with regard to the types of personality organization that demonstrate such susceptibility and the aspects of personality functioning that are critical in the occurrence of physical dysfunction.

W.W. Meissner, S.J., M.D., is Associate Clinical Professor of Psychiatry, Harvard Medical School; Staff Psychiatrist, Cambridge Hospital, Cambridge, and Massachusetts Mental Health Center, Boston; Faculty Member, Boston Psychoanalytic Institute.

Reprinted from the *International Journal of Psychiatry in Medicine*, vol. 5, no. 4, 1974.

Psychosomatic Hypothesis

The hypothesis underlying the intensive study of the relations between patterns of physical illness and varieties of emotional traumata has postulated that the connecting link is stress, specifically that the emotional disruption from traumatic events causes a disorganization of autonomic and hormonal regulatory systems, possibly mediated by the limbic system (MacLean, 1955). Attempts have been made to specify the personality constellations which relate to the incidence of certain kinds of illness. Attention in this area has been drawn to the frequency of maladaptive patterns of personality functioning, but success in establishing an association between specific personality types and patterns of dysfunction with patterns of illness has been limited. The more deeply such patterns were studied, the more obvious it became that they were more complicated. Specificity begins to break down in that patients may show a variety of patterns of functioning, e.g., a patient with peptic ulcer may demonstrate either overt dependency or reactive counterdependency. Moreover, the assumption of a linear correlation between the level of physiological integration and the level of personality integration is moot and open to criticism (Grolnick, 1972).

In recent years significant evidence has been gathered pointing to the influence of dynamic factors within the family process in the psychogenesis of maladaptive emotional behavior (Meissner, 1964; Lidz and Fleck, 1965; Wahl and Golden, 1966). The study of such psychodynamics within family structures has left the impression that dynamic patterns of family interaction have a marked impact not only on the psychological adjustments of its members, but also on the patterns of physical health and illness. There has been a shift and a refocusing of attention from the level of intrapsychic dynamics as such to the level of the organization of the family and its functiong, specifically as a unit within itself and as embedded within a larger context of the social community and its culture (Mutter and Schleifer, 1966; von Bertalanffy, 1966; Scheflen, 1967a, 1967b).

In psychosomatic processes, psychological influences operate in conjunction with a configuration of other factors, and the emotional component may be quite variable. In the case of duodenal ulcer, for example, the psychosomatic process is quite different from that of tuberculosis, and this in turn differs significantly from that involved in obesity. We presume that emotional and dynamic factors are in fact operative, and merely suggest a link between emotional dysfunction related to psychosomatic illness and the discernible patterns of family dynamics and interaction.

Dynamic Factors

The association of emotional maladaptation and physical illness has been well established in a number of instances. Certain forms of pathology reflect a primary involvement of emotional factors in combination with genetic dispositions. In duodenal ulcer, for example, patients generally manifest a pattern of hyperreactivity (Mirsky, 1960) and a tendency to hypersecretion. Psychologically they show intense oral dependency (Lidz and Rubenstein, 1959; Mirsky, 1960; Ruesch et al., 1948; Pilot et al., 1957; Lieberman et al., 1959; Marshall, 1960) which often takes the form of reactive striving for self-sufficiency (Lidz and Rubenstein, 1959; Weiner et al., 1957; Wilner, 1959). The onset of ulcer symptoms is usually precipitated by emotional disturbances and stress related to situational factors, including separation from or loss of emotionally important persons (Ruesch et al., 1948; Pilot et al., 1957). This has been described in terms of a regressive submission to an internalized, punitive mother figure (Garma, 1957, 1958; Garma et al., 1960). In this connection, Wolff and his associates (1968) indicate that interpersonal distress is one of many life stresses impinging on individuals with certain pathological reactivities of autonomic and endocrine systems.

The patient with ulcerative colitis is generally passive, conforming, and dependent (Lidz and Rubenstein, 1959; Jameson, 1959; Finch and Hess, 1962; Wijsenbeek et al., 1968; McMahon et al., 1973), a pattern which has been interpreted as a regressive seeking of the dependent position (Lidz, 1959; Sperling, 1959). The role of oral-aggressive impulses (Garma et al., 1960; Fontana, 1958) and self-destructive rage has also been stressed (Sperling, 1957). Dysmenorrhea is often associated with an infantile personality organization (Benedek, 1959), which is marked by attitudes of hopelessness, self-abnegation, and self-sacrifice (Selbmann, 1957).

Other conditions of organic dysfunction may have no identifiable etiological agent, but seem to involve strong emotional components. Often, hypertensives seem to develop attitudes which provoke stressful interactions with other people (Wahl, 1960; Kalis et al., 1961). They often manifest dependency conflicts with an inability to handle aggressive and hostile impulses (Moses et al., 1956; Glock and Lennard, 1957; Reiser and Bokst, 1959) as well as frequent counterdependency striving (Glock and Lennard, 1957). Such dependency conflicts and psychosexual insecurity are also frequently found in hyperthyroid patients (Philippopoulos, 1959; Bennett and Cambor, 1961). Difficulties in handling hostility, overcompensating self-sufficiency, ambition, and striving for independence are common characteristics (Bennett and Cambor, 1961; Lidz, 1949; Ham et al., 1950; Boswell et al. 1967). In the case of anemic patients, a frequent characteristic is a hostile feminine identification (Lidz and Rubenstein, 1959), usually linked to depressive symptomatology.

Still other disease processes have been found to be produced in one way or another by pathological agents, but emotional factors seem to be involved in the susceptibility to the action of the agent and the onset of symptoms. In rheumatic fever as well as streptococcal infection, attention has been drawn to the mother-child interaction. In such cases the mother is characteristically overprotective, apparently as a reaction to negative feelings. Guilt feelings are apparently intensified by the child's illness (Brazelton et al., 1953). Similarly, tonsillitis has been described as "the regular primordial symptom of a neurotic structure in which pregenital and oral-retentive inhibitions are factors of central importance" (Schellack, 1957a, 1957b). Tuberculosis patients have been described as sensitive, anxious, and emotionally labile (Holmes et al., 1957). They often manifest strong dependency needs and affectional needs which are highly conflictual (Neumann, 1959; Wittkower and White, 1959). Even arthritic patients have been shown to lead relatively quiet lives and to manifest traits of shyness and social inadequacy (King, 1955). They frequently manifest inferiority feelings along with tendencies to self-sacrifice, and experience considerable difficulty in handling aggression, often dealing with strong hostility feelings by reaction formation (King, 1955; Cleveland and Fisher, 1960). Such arthritic women have been described as overtly aggressive personalities with marked masculine protest (Johnson et al., 1947).

Diabetes is another condition of pathological dysfunction, in which the basic defect is in the regulation of insulin metabolism and pancreatic islet activity, but in which emotional factors and interpersonal influences play a significant role (Hinkle and Wolff, 1952; Stein and Charles, 1971). Diabetics have been described as markedly passive and needing affection (Rome and Robinson, 1959). Their basic conflict seems to relate to infantile wishes to be taken care of (Mirsky, 1948) and a regressive seeking of maternal attention by assuming a dependent and demanding position (Rosen and Lidz, 1949; Raychaudhuri, 1958).

Even in more primarily organic conditions such as cancer and leukemia (Greene, 1958, 1959; Green and Miller, 1958) emotional factors seem to play a potential role. The influence of psychological factors on the occurrence and course of cancer is obviously secondary to the primary distortion of cellular metabolism, but even so, certain interesting consistencies have been noted. Cancer patients tend to show a fairly consistent set of personality characteristics: they are relatively selfless and undemanding (Renneker, 1957), easy to please and unaggressive (Perrin and Pierce, 1959), they manifest a pattern of self-sacrifice, patience, and self-effacement (Perrin and Pierce, 1959), and they often have preneoplastic feelings of hopelessness, helplessness, and despair (Goldfarb et al., 1967). Such patients also often manifest an unresolved emotional attachment to the mother (Perrin and Pierce, 1959).

The impact of studies of this kind has not been very profound, nor have the results proven very illuminating. The dynamic patterns have not been sufficiently specific to enhance the therapeutic management of psychosomatic disorders. Moreover, the overlap in psychological patterns among many types of disease processes has tended to confuse rather than to clarify issues. Consequently, the patterns of personality functioning as specifically related to the pathophysiology or pathogenesis of psychosomatic illnesses have been gradually slipping into disrepute. Beyond these varying patterns which emerge from the study of the pathogenesis of disease processes, there remains a consistent residue of common personality dysfunction—almost a least common denominator of psychosomatic involvement—to which we can usefully turn our attention.

Our intention here is not to criticize the individual approach, but to suggest that another meaningful set of data and relationships can be achieved by focusing on the family as a unit of interaction and analysis. More accurately, we may be able to deepen our understanding of psychosomatic processes by an understanding of the involvement of the patient as a member of the family system.

Family Interaction

Maternal Dependence

The importance of the emotional interaction in the family has been investigated in a number of disease entities, as, for example, in leukemia

(Greene, 1958, 1959; Greene and Miller, 1958). The oral-retentive inhibitions in cases of tonsillitis seem to be related to maternal dependence (Schellack, 1957a, 1957b). Similar conflicts seem to be involved in the handling of aggression among arthritics, who are extremely dependent on the maternal figure, who is seen as strong, demanding, and domineering, in contrast to the father, who is regarded as relatively passive and inconsistent (Cleveland and Fisher, 1960; Alexander, 1954). Arthritic women have a tendency to dominate and control their children and as young girls manifested a tendency toward rebellion expressed in the form of tomboyishness (Alexander, 1954). Similar denials of dependency needs in hyperthyroid patients are thought to be related to ambivalent feelings toward the mother (Boswell et al., 1967; Conrad, 1934; Alexander et al., 1961). Parallel problems in the response to maternal narcissism and domination have also been investigated in asthmatic patients (Bastiaans and Groen, 1955; Knapp, 1969).

Unresolved emotional attachments to the mother have also been identified in cancer patients (Perrin and Pierce, 1959). Ulcerative colitis is of particular interest in this regard, since the family constellation often involves an aggressive dominating mother and a passive intellectual father (Finch and Hess, 1962). The relationship with the mother in these cases is nearly symbiotic in character (Sperling, 1959; Titchener et al., 1960; Josselyn et al., 1966), with an intense degree of ambivalence (Lidz and Rubenstein, 1959). The colitis attack may in fact be precipitated by a threat of loss in the patient's critical dependency relationships (Lieberman et al., 1959; Jameson, 1959; Lindemann, 1950a; Krakowski, 1967; Karush et al., 1968).

Impact on Infant and Child

Another important area of study has been the examination of the psychosomatic impact on infants and small children of interactions with the mother (Fries, 1944; Spitz, 1946; Joseph, 1948; Kanner, 1972; Rank et al., 1948; Gerard, 1953; Garner and Wenar, 1959). Benedek (1949), for example, describes the communication and somatic expression of neurotic conflict from mother to child within the mother-child unit. Such forms of somatic compliance have been examined in detail in cases of obesity (Bruch and Touraine, 1940; Bruch, 1962, 1964, 1965), the occurrence of dermatological lesions (Forrer, 1960), and other illnesses (Grinker and Robbins, 1954). These studies emphasize the detailed patterning of psychosomatic disorders in relation to parental conflicts. The focus is generally not on specific correlations between unconscious conflicts or traumata and particular psychosomatic manifestations (Garner and Wenar, 1959), but stresses the general material quality as well as the detailed aspects of caretaking activity in the mother.

The role of the father in these interactions is given little attention (Wold, 1973). The husband seems to play a critical role in the early postpartum period when the mother's own desires to be mothered are more prominent (Benedek, 1949). In other cases, however, the appearance of symptoms in the child can serve to interfere with the relationship between the parents, as in Coolidge's (1956) study of asthma. Other distortions may be rooted in maternal projections onto the child, as, for example, a mother's tendency to feed the child as a means of allaying her own anxieties as a contributing factor to obesity (Bruch, 1962, 1965). The child may also serve as an "organ of parental hypochondriasis" as exemplified by Kanner's (1972) case of the mother whose symptoms of hypochondriacal constipation disappeared after the birth of her daughter, but were replaced by her continued complaints about the child's constipation until the child was finally brought to clinical attention. When the child's capacity to eliminate was restored, the mother's constipation returned. Generally the evidence suggests that the mother is the more influential parent with regard to attitudes about health and bodily functioning (Buck and Laughton, 1959; Mechanic, 1965).

Emotional Disruption

Noteworthy in disease process is the frequency with which the occurrence of emotionally disrupting events, particularly the loss of significant objects, is related to the onset or exacerbation of symptoms (Rahe et al., 1967; Hamilton, 1970). This has been observed frequently in the precipitation of tuberculosis (Holmes et al., 1957; Wittkower and White, 1959; Flarsheim, 1958; Kissen, 1958; Mezei and Levendel, 1959), asthma (Long et al., 1958; Jacobs et al., 1966; Liebman et al., 1974), anemia (Lewin, 1959), arthritis (Alexander, 1954; Shochet et al., 1969), hypertension (Wahl, 1960), duodenal ulcer (Ruesch et al., 1948; Pilot et al. 1957), peptic ulcer (Coddington, 1968), and colitis (Lieberman et al., 1959; Jameson, 1959). The onset of symptoms in leukemia in both children and adults seems to have been triggered by the loss of an emotionally significant person (Greene, 1958, 1959; Greene and Miller, 1958). Even in cancer, it has been found that the onset of neoplastic manifestations is often preceded by the loss of a significant relationship by a period of from several months to nearly two years (Neumann, 1959; Perrin and Pierce, 1959; LeShan, 1959, 1961).

These findings strongly suggest that the level of physical functioning is related to the emotional level of adjustment, which is strongly influenced by the pattern of interaction in the family system. The conjunction of symptom onset or exacerbation with such emotional patterns of disruption is a more convincing argument than the mere conjunction of illness with general personality patterns. Careful study of the factors influencing the occurrence of beta-hemolytic streptococcal infections identified acute or chronic family stress as an important factor, along with age, season, and closeness of contact with the source of infection (Meyer and Haggerty, 1962). Similarly, Schmale's (1958) study of 42 hospitalized patients produced evidence of actual or threatened or symbolic object loss and feelings of helplessness and hopelessness prior to the onset of symptoms in 41 of these patients.

Similar patterns of parental involvement and family interaction have been identified in both psychosomatic processes and strictly psychological disturbances. Thus, the patterns of symbolic infantilization so frequently seen in a relationship between a disturbed child and its mother have also been identified in psychosomatic contexts (Finch and Hess, 1962; Long et al., 1958; Mohr et al., 1958). The disturbance of the mother-child relation in psychosomatic cases may often be more severe than in schizophrenia (Lidz et al., 1957). In ulcerative colitis, for example, the conflict between the mother's needs to keep the child dependent and her own unconscious destructive impulses may be central to the pathology. The child may thus develop a "surrogate ego" which becomes functionally and more or less permanently dependent on the mother (Finch and Hess, 1962).

Parallel Symptoms

A striking finding in disturbed families is the parallelism between physical and psychological disturbance. Both the onset of illness and the recovery of the patient can precipitate changes in other members of the family (Haley, 1962). Similar patterns of precipitation may be involved in psychosomatic reactions as well, particularly in connection with emotional disruptions within the family system. The evidence, however, does not support the "clustering" of psychic and somatic symptoms (Kreitman et al., 1966), in the sense that patients with the greatest somatic morbidity might show a higher incidence of psychiatric difficulties. There is some evidence, however, to support clustering among family members, rather than within one member.

Marital Factors

Similar patterns of interaction have been studied in married couples. Study of the spouses of psychiatric clinic patients indicates that they present physical symptoms more frequently than controls. Early in the course of the marriage, patients and their spouses showed no significant correlations on measurements of introversion, neuroticism, and physical health, while the control couples did show a significant correlation. After a number of years of marriage, however, the correlation between patients and spouses on neuroticism and mental health increased, while it diminished in control couples. Wives seemed more likely to reflect the illness of the husband than vice versa (Kreitman, 1964). Similarly, Kellner (1963) found that the wife's illness followed upon the husband's twice as often as the reverse. He observed in some of these cases that one spouse seemed to labor to remain healthy so that the other might remain ill.

Other studies of recurrent psychosomatic illness indicate that exacerbations tended to coincide with periods of increased marital tension (Honker, 1964). Patients whose hypochondriacal symptoms masked an underlying depressive illness (Marder and Hoogerbeets, 1967) showed a much greater degree of marital disharmony and sexual maladjustment and a higher incidence of psychosomatic disorders than a group of non-hypochondriacal depressives. The somatic symptoms seem to serve as a neurotic control mechanism, which may have a stabilizing function in a relatively brittle and conflictual marital relationship (Kreitman et al., 1965; Lesse, 1967).

As Haley (1963) has suggested, the function of symptoms in such a delicately balanced emotional system, whether psychosomatic or psychological, can often be to protect the spouse by denying a marital problem and avoiding its resolution. Double messages and double binds are a frequent occurrence in such situations. Haley cites the example of impotence in a husband in response to his wife's demand for his assertiveness in sexual matters while she was unable to tolerate the required surrender to him. In the same fashion, spouses will undermine a partner's attempt to get rid of the apparently distressing symptoms lest this clear the way for exposing their own pathology. The husband whose wife ceases to be frigid may suddenly become impotent, or the woman whose husband's headaches no longer prevent them from going out of the house may begin to experience her own agoraphobia (Blinder and Kirschenbaum, 1967). A similar interlocking pattern has been described in couples in which the wife had rheumatoid arthritis and the husband peptic ulcer. Their equilibrium was maintained by the wife's controlling and dominating behavior interlocking with the husband's need to be controlled and dominated (Cobb et al., 1969). Evidence to suggest that the incidence of physical illness may be correlated with the degree of neuroticism in the family system is supported by Kellner's (1963) finding that relatives of neurotic patients are seen more frequently in general practice than patients from other families.

Patterns of Disruption

An impressive aspect of this family interaction is the relationship between the pattern of illness and disruptive events within the family (O'Connor et al., 1966). The "transmission of illness" within the family system has been amply documented (Hopkins, 1959). The family patterning may affect a wide diversity of childhood conditions, including enuresis or familial tics (Apley and MacKeith, 1962). Children with recurrent nonorganic pains frequently show emotional disturbances along with a tendency to similar pain and nervous disorders in their respective families (Apley, 1958).

The effect of psychiatric disturbances in a parent on a child's health is described in Kellner's (1963) extensive study of family health patterns in general practice and in other similar studies (Buck and Laughton, 1959; Mechanic, 1965; Apley, 1958). Mothers tend to hold a more central role in these constellations: the more neurotic or disturbed the mothers, the more psychosomatic and behavioral disorders could be observed in the children. Kellner's study suggests a higher incidence of physical illness in families with functional complaints. The commonest sequence was onset of physical illness in one family member followed by an exacerbation of neurotic symptoms in another. Mother-child interactions seemed to outnumber father-child interactions. Careful evaluation of a three-year study of general-practice experience with 25 families revealed that 21 of them demonstrated repetitive attendance patterns described as constant illness, regular periodicity, clustering, and simultaneity. In all four patterns, dynamic interactional factors played a significant role, including substitution of one member for another when the usual pattern seemed disrupted, and transfer of symptoms between parents and children (Peachey, 1963).

In a previous discussion of this subject (Meissner, 1966), we presented a case in which the removal of a favorite son from the family setting was followed by an outbreak of symptoms in both parents. The symptoms were consequently relieved upon the son's return. The disruption in this particular family, caused by the removal of the son, apparently set off a chain reaction. The mother's emotional stability depended to a great degree on her involvement with the son, and the father's stability in turn depended on his involvement with the stronger figure of his wife as well as with the son. Examples of waves of mental and physical disturbance following the death of a singularly favored daughter or son or similar waves affecting even grandchildren after the death of grandparents have been described.

It is evidence of this sort that gives rise to the suggestion that patterns of occurrence and the course of psychosomatic illnesses can be related to patterns of interaction within the family system, just as the occurrence and course of certain forms of psychopathology have been found to bear significant relationships to the pattern of family dynamics (Meissner, 1964). Certain studies have suggested a positive correlation between psychosomatic symptoms and the degree of family cohesiveness. Students from broken homes were found to have fewer psychosomatic symptoms than students from unhappy and unbroken homes (Nye, 1957). Similarly, Stewart's (1962) long-term prospective study related subsequent psychosomatic disease to social and emotional adjustment in adolescents. The psychosomatic group, strikingly enough, showed better family and social adjustment than the behaviorally maladjusted group. Likewise, the comparison of the families of males with duodenal ulcer with families of delinquent males revealed a significantly lower degree of discord and conflict in the families of the ulcer group (Goldberg, 1958).

Emotional Involvement

A consistent element in these family situations is that the patient is caught up in an emotionally loaded, often tense and conflictual interaction within the family. The close emotional involvement of the family members with each other is characteristic and has been observed in disturbed families where the pathology is more specifically psychological (Meissner, 1964; Bowen, 1960). Similar patterns of emotional involvement may be found in families in which somatic decompensation plays a part in the etiology of the physical illness. Within this family affective system, patterns of emotional contagion have been described (Dunbar, 1954; Ackerman, 1958).

The close connection between depressive tendencies and psychosomatic and hypochondriacal symptoms is frequently seen clinically (Marder and Hoogerbeets, 1967; Kreitman et al., 1965; Lesse, 1967; Stewart, 1962; Engel, 1955; Vogel and Bell, 1960; Engel and Schmale, 1967). Thus, where depressive moods or defenses against depressive affects dominate the family interaction, a high incidence of psychosomatic disturbance might be expected. Various mechanisms may be brought into play which contribute to family cohesion but mitigate against the expression of feelings, particularly negative or dysphoric feelings (Goldberg, 1958), suggesting Wynne's concept of "pseudomutuality" (1958). There seems to be an affective level of interaction which underlies a shared family myth to the effect that the family's psychological survival requires repression of all aggressive impulses (Gehrke and Kirschenbaum, 1967). The family members in cases of psychophysiological disturbances have particular difficulty in expressing relatively intense separation anxiety. Looff (1970) found that, in families in which children had somatic conversion reactions, all of the family members experienced difficulty in verbalizing affects connected with sexual maturation and functioning. Blocked verbal communication was common in these families as compared with the families experiencing other forms of psychopathology.

In many of these cases, the patient seems to be functioning at a less than mature level and reveals a relatively infantile personality organization (Ruesch, 1948). This immaturity is often reflected in various forms of passivity and dependency, but may also be reflected in more compensatory and hyperadequate modes of adaptation. Immaturity may express itself either as a form of inadequacy or as a form of hyperadequacy (Bowen, 1960). Moreover, there may be some grounds for suspecting a relationship between these patterns of immaturity and susceptibility to specific illnesses, e.g., hyperthyroid and intestinal ulcer patients tend toward a pattern of hyperadequacy. The evidence in support of this conjecture, however, is slight.

These patterns of immature functioning may be played out in the family interaction in quite regular fashion. The relationship between husband and wife frequently falls into a pattern of reciprocal functioning in which one partner assumes a position of dominance and/or strength and/or control over the family, while the other assumes a reciprocal position of submission and/or dependency and/or passivity (Johnson et al., 1947; Goldberg, 1958). Similar patterns can be identified in the relationships of the respective partners' families of origin. These reciprocal patterns are the most common form of expression of immaturity in the family system, but there may be other cases in which dependent and inadequate positions may be assumed by both spouses. These patterns can also be observed quite strikingly in psychologically disturbed families (Meissner, 1964; Lidz and Fleck, 1965) as shown in Witkin's (Greene and Miller, 1958; Grinker and Robbins, 1954; Haley, 1963) studies of field dependence/independence and psychological differentiation. Psychosomatic disorders, tendencies to somatize, and deep-seated dependency problems tend to cluster at the low level of differentiation (Karp et al., 1969).

Multigenerational Influence

Entering the marriage relationship does not isolate the respective spouses from continuing emotional entanglements with their own families of origin. When we discuss the patterns of family interaction, we must consequently extend the interactional influence to span a chain of emotional involvements which extend over several generations. Ultimately, the patterns of emotional involvement influencing psychosomatic processes are multigenerational in character. Sometimes the eruption of illness in a grandchild, for example, may be seen subsequent to the death or serious illness of a grandparent.

Bowen (1960, 1965, 1966; Bowen et al., 1959) has described what he calls the "family projective system," which is an expression of these patterns of affective interaction. In such a system, the soma of one family member is conceived of as reciprocating with the psyche of another. The projection may occur on the level of actual physical illness as well as on the level of hypochondriacal symptoms. In Bowen's terms, the psychosomatic dysfunction becomes one of the mechanisms which less mature personalities resort to in order to control the emotional intensity of excessive (symbiotic) closeness.

SELECTION OF THE PATIENT

The involvement of the patient in the emotional interaction within the family is reflected in his emotional closeness and attachment—or it may just as easily be reflected in the converse pattern of aggressive rebelliousness and hostility. What is involved here frequently seems to be a dependency conflict. Moreover, the involvement tends to be selective—that is, within the nuclear family, the emotional investment from and involvement with the parents tends to affect one child rather than another. The reasons why the selected patient becomes involved are complex and must include the parental dynamics as well as the prevailing family context. This takes the form of the displacement of an intense and long-standing emotional problem between the parents onto one of the children. Physical factors such as congenital deformities or early disease may play a role (Apley and MacKeith, 1962; Vogel and Bell, 1960; Schonfeld, 1966). But we must resist the temptation to view the patient as the passive victim of forces within the family system. He is an active participant and influences the system as much or more than he is influenced by it (Meissner, 1966; Anthony, 1970).

Within the resulting triad, the feelings of helplessness and the acting out of these feelings in illness take place (Dysinger, 1961). When the selected patient improves, this tends to unsettle the fragile stability within the triad and leads to attempts on the part of the other members to mitigate against improvement. The understanding of the variety of factors which play into and influence such patterns of selective involvement in the family system is an extremely interesting and as yet poorly understood area in the investigation of family dynamics.

In many cases, the onset of disease symptoms is related to and consequent on a period of emotional disruption within the family, particularly consequent on the loss of a significant other person (Pinderhughes, 1971). Loss of such significant relationships, followed by a period of inadequate and morbid grief which is then replaced by the disease state, has been traced in ulcerative colitis (Engel, 1955; Lindemann, 1950b), rheumatoid arthritis (Ludwig, 1952), leukemia (Greene and Miller, 1958), and even anniversary psychosomatic reactions (Hilgard, 1952; Fischer and Dlin, 1972), as well as a variety of other forms of organic decompensation (Schmale, 1958; Vincent, 1955; Chen and Cobb, 1960; Rosenbaum, 1963; Parkes, 1964). The more general finding, however, in the family context, is not specifically the loss of a significant object, but a variety of disruptions which upset the emotional balance in the family system. The onset of symptoms can be related to periods of emotional disruption which can be manifested in a variety of ways. Typical events include death, serious illnesses, divorces, psychotic breakdowns (Wyler et al., 1971; Myers et al., 1971). Some events, like marriages and births, are not characteristically disruptive, but they entail shifts in the family configuration which may have a disorganizing effect emotionally. Again, such patterns of emotional disorganization can run through significant segments of the family and can span several generations.

A serious question has been raised, however, about such findings, namely the problem of self-selection. Grolnick (1972) has suggested that the data may reflect a tendency for depressed and somatically susceptible subjects to report separation concerns more readily. The problem of case self-selection is in general a persistent source of error in much psychosomatic research (Rawnsley, 1968).

The selective involvement in the affective system within the family is a particularly important aspect of the family functioning, since the concurrence of physical symptoms and emotional crises tends to affect those members of the family whose involvement in the emotional structure is particularly intense. The emotional disorganization within the family does not affect all members of the family equally, but rather according to this principle of selectivity, in proportion to the degree of involvement. In this view, then, the presence or absence of such involvement or its intensity becomes crucial in understanding the emotional factors which may play a part in the precipitation of disease symptoms, and which thereby contribute to the total ecology of the disease process (Meissner, 1966).

Differential Responsiveness

The parallelism of these familiar patterns of psychopathology and physical pathology suggests that similar factors may be operating within the family system in both cases. This raises a question about differential responsiveness: that is, why the response to emotional disruption within the family should express itself as psychological symptoms in some involved members but as physical symptoms in others. The discriminating factors remain unclear, but the identification of a pattern of minor somatic dysfunction in relation to lesser emotional crises may make it possible to predict those members of the family who might develop more severe symptomatology in recognizable situations of emotional disruption.

From another point of view, however, the phenomenon of alternation of symptoms makes the understanding of these processes more complex. Grinker and Robbins (1954) have described a patient in whom the psychogenic pain cleared when he was able to express his aggressive impulses, but when the pain had disappeared the patient developed a paranoid condition. Our increased sensitivity to these kinds of interaction raises questions for which the evidence is incomplete.

Kellner (1963) suggests that family illnesses tend to occur in clusters, with psychosomatic illness promoting further instability in the family system, precipitating secondary somatic disruptions. We still do not know, however, how general this phenomenon may be, whether it occurs only in certain kinds of illness or certain types of family system, or whether it affects only certain members of these systems. While the alternation of symptoms between psychosomatic disorder and psychosis has been questioned as a common individual mechanism (O'Connor and Stern, 1967), it seems to be relatively discernible among members of the family system. Both parallel pathology and reciprocal pathology—that is to say, improvement of the patient associated with deterioration of another member of the family system—have been described as characteristic of psychosomatic processes (Meissner, 1964), but more detailed information is required about specific patterns of family interaction.

Family Affective System

The evidence discussed here seems to point in a relatively consistent direction. An earlier study on family dynamics and their influence in psychosomatic illnesses (Meissner, 1966) led to the formulation that the family affective system is the construct linking these different strands of evidence. The approach can be summed up in the following points:

(1) The patient is a relatively less than mature person whose immaturity is directly proportional to the degree of emotional involvement in the family affective interaction.

(2) Through this emotional involvement the patient is caught up in the affective system of the family, which is constituted by the emotional involvements of the members of the immediate family.

(3) The functioning of the involved individual depends on the balance of emotional forces within the family system. His own basic insecurity

and instability is compensated and more or less stabilized through emotional interactions with other members of the family system.

(4) Certain emotionally significant events can disturb the balance of emotional interrelationships within the family system and create disorganization within the affective system; this affects the patient on a deeply emotional level since the stabilization of the patient's own emotional lability is achieved through and dependent on the balance within the system.

(5) Disorganization or emotional disruption in the family system can precipitate an emotional crisis in such deeply involved members. With the emotional supports withdrawn, the individual lacks sufficient inherent ego resources to maintain adequate functioning on all levels. Consequently, the individual responds with a form of decompensation. In psychosomatic illnesses, the decompensation is specifically somatic, i.e., expressed in terms of somatic dysfunction (Engel and Schmale, 1967).

This formulation serves to raise more problems than it solves, but it may also focus on some important questions about psychosomatic processes. Psychosomatic processes are extremely complex phenomena which reflect the operation of multiple influences. The family context enters the picture as only one factor, functioning in combination with a complex and multiple etiological series. Consequently, the degree of its involvement in the precipitation of illness may be quite variable.

Our formulation focuses on the impingement upon the involved and affected member of the family system, but it also directs our attention to the patterns of involvement and interaction within the family itself. This shift of orientation emphasizes that the unit of analysis, and the unit to which the psychosomatic process can be meaningfully related, is the family system itself. The family system is not coextensive with the family group, either as nuclear family or as extended family, but it is a structured emotional system within which the balance of emotional vectors is intimately related to the functioning of the involved members.

Within this system homeostatic mechanisms operate to bring about adjustments, in which psychopathology and physiopathology function to bring about error-activated adjustment (Jackson, 1964). Jackson (1961, 1965, 1966; Watzlawick et al., 1967) observed redundancies of behavior in the family group with inferred rules or "relationship agreements" which operated on an unconscious level within the family system. Psychosomatic reactions are one form of response within a family system that operates according to overly rigid rules. Haley (1964), studying sequences of who talks after whom, showed that families with a deviant member—whether psychiatrically (e.g., schizophrenic) or pathophysiologically (e.g., ulcerative colitis)—demonstrate relatively fixed and rigid homeostatic patterns. Similarly, in families of children with ulcerative colitis, Jackson and Yalom (1966) found restrictive patterns of expression, particularly when they involved disagreement or negative messages. While such patterns of disordered homeostatic adjustment and communication have a descriptive validity, the formulation here and previously (Meissner, 1966) proposes that such mechanisms operate in the context of an underlying affective family system, which becomes relatively closed and thus forces the system to adapt and maintain internal equilibrium by these pathological means.

We are suggesting, then, that the family affective system be regarded as the structure within which the psychosomatic process is elaborated. The patient externalizes by his symptoms the pathology that is inherent in the family system. It is fair to say that there is a stage in this process at which all the involved members of the family system are potentially and indifferently patients. When the system is thrown into disequilibrium or is disrupted by an emotionally disturbing event or sequence of events, the disequilibrium disturbs the emotional adjustment and the functional adaptation of the involved members. This disruption issues in a variety of symptomatologies—in some, the realignment of emotional vectors precipitates emotional instability, depression, anxiety, or other psychopathology; in others, the realignment precipitates psychosomatic disorders.

References

Ackerman, N. (1958), *The Psychodynamics of Family Life*. New York: Basic Books.

Alexander, F. (1954), The psychosomatic approach in medical therapy. In: *The Scope of Psychoanalysis*. New York: Basic Books, 1961, pp. 345-358.

——— Flagg, G. W., Foster, S., et al. (1961), Experimental studies of emotional stress: I. Hyperthyroidism. In: *The Scope of Psychoanalysis*. New York: Basic Books, 1961, pp. 364-377.

Anthony, E. J. (1970), The impact of mental and physical illness on family life. *Amer. J. Psychiat.*, 127:138-146.

Apley, J. (1958), Common denominators in the recurrent pains of childhood. *Proc. Roy. Soc. Med.*, 51:1023-1024.

——— MacKeith, R. (1962), *The Child and His Symptoms—A Psychosomatic Approach*. Philadelphia: Davis.

Bastiaans, J. & Groen, J. (1955), Psychogenesis and psychotherapy of bronchial asthma. In: *Modern Trends in Psychosomatic Medicine*, ed. D. O'Neill. New York: Hoeber, pp. 242-268.

Benedek, T. (1949), The psychosomatic implications of the primary unit—mother-child. *Amer. J. Orthopsychiat.*, 19:642-654.

——— (1959), Sexual functions in women and their disturbance. In: *American Handbook of Psychiatry*, I, ed. S. Arieti. New York: Basic Books, pp. 727-748.

Bennett, A. W. & Cambor, C. G. (1961), Clinical study of hyperthyroidism: Comparison of male and female characteristics. *Arch. Gen. Psychiat.*, 4:160-165.

Blinder, M. & Kirschenbaum, M. (1967), The technique of married couple group therapy. *Arch. Gen. Psychiat.*, 17:44-52.

Boswell, J. I., Jr., Lewis, C. P., Freeman, D. F., & Clark,, K. M. (1967), Hyperthyroid children: Individual and family dynamics: A study of twelve cases. *J. Amer. Acad. Child Psychiat.*, 6:64-85.

Bowen, M. (1960), A family concept of schizophrenia. In: *The Etiology of Schizophrenia*, ed. D. Jackson. New York: Basic Books, pp. 346-372.

——— (1965), Family psychotherapy with schizophrenia in the hospital and in private practice. In: *Intensive Family Therapy*, ed. I. Boszormenyi-Nagy & J. Framo. New York: Hoeber, pp. 213-243.

——— (1966), The use of family theory in clinical practice. *Comprehen. Psychiat.*, 7:345-374.

——— Dysinger, R., & Basamania, B. (1959), The role of the father in families with a schizophrenic patient. *Amer. J. Psychiat.*, 115:1017-1020.

Brazelton, T. B., Holder, R., & Talbot, B. (1953), Emotional aspects of rheumatic fever in children. *J. Pediat.*, 43:339-358.

Bruch, H. (1962), Falsification of bodily needs and body concepts in schizophrenia. *Arch. Gen. Psychiat.*, 6:18-24.

——— (1964, Psychologic aspects of overeating and obesity. *Psychosomat.*, *5:269-274*.

——— (1965), Anorexia nervosa and its differential diagnosis. *J. Nerv. Ment. Dis.*, 141:555-566.

——— & Touraine, G. (1940), Obesity in childhood: V. The family frame of obese children. *Psychosom. Med.*, 2:141-206.

Buck, C. M. & Laughton, K. B. (1959), Family pattern of illness—the effect of psychoneurosis in the child. *Acta Psychol. Neurol. Scand.*, 34:165-175.

Chen, E. & Cobb, S. (1960), Family structure in relation to health and disease: A review of the literature. *J. Chron. Dis.*, 12:544-567.

Cleveland, S. E. & Fisher, S. (1960), A comparison of psychological characteristics and physiological reactivity in ulcer and rheumatoid arthritis groups: I. Psychological measures. *Psychosom. Med.*, 22:283-289.

Cobb, S., Schull, W. J., Harburg, E., et al. (1969), The intrafamilial transmission of rheumatoid arthritis. *J. Chron. Dis.*, 22:193-296.

Coddington, R. D. (1968), Peptic ulcers in children. *Psychosomat*, 9:38-43.

Conrad, A. (1934), Psychiatric study of hyperthyroid patients. *J. Nerv. Ment. Dis.*, 79:505-656.

Coolidge, J. C. (1956), Asthma in mother and child as a special type of communication. *Amer. J. Orthopsychiat.*, 26:165-176.

Dunbar, H. F. (1954). *Emotions and Bodily Changes*. New York: Columbia University Press.

Dysinger, R. (1961), The family as the unit of study and treatment: II. Family perspective on the diagnosis of individual members. *Amer. J. Orthopsychiat.*, 31:61-68.

Engel, G. (1955), Studies of ulcerative colitis: III. The nature of psychologic processes. *Amer. J. Med.*, 19:231-255.

——— & Schmale, A. H. (1967), Psychoanalytic theory of somatic disorder: Conversion, specificity, and the disease onset situation. *J. Amer. Psychoanal. Assn.*, 15:344-365.

Finch, S. M. & Hess, J. H. (1962), Ulcerative colitis in children. *Amer. J. Psychiat.*, 118:819-826.

Fischer, H. K. & Dlin, B. (1972), Psychogenic determination of time of illness or death by anniversary reactions and emotional deadlines. *Psychosomat.*, 13:170-173.

Flarsheim, A. (1958), Ego mechanisms in three pulmonary tuberculosis patients: A contribution to the study of the psychosomatic process. *Psychosom. Med.*, 20:475-483.

Fontana, A. E. (1958), Colitis ulcerosa: Presentación de un caso. *Rev. Psicoanal. (Buenos Aires)*, 15:261-277.

Forrer, G. (1960), Psychosomatic compliance in an infant. *J. Mich. Med. Soc.*, 59:1399-1402.

Fries, M. (1944), Psychosomatic relationships between mother and infant. *Psychosom. Med.*, 6:159-162.

Garma, A. (1957), Oral-digestive superego aggressions and actual conflicts in peptic ulcer patients. *Internat J. Psycho-Anal.*, 38:73-81.

——— (1958), Peptic ulcer and pseudo-peptic ulcer. *Interent J. Psycho-anal.*, 39:104-107.

——— Sperling, M., Orgel, S. Z., et. al. (1960), Symposium on disturbances of the digestive tract. *Internat J. Psycho-Anal.*, 41:444-466.

Garner, A. & Wenar, C. (1959), *The Mother-Child Interaction in Psychosomatic Disorders*. Urbana, Ill.: University of Illinois Press.

Gehrke, S. & Kirschenbaum, M. (1967), Survival patterns in family conjoint therapy. *Fam. Proc.*, 6:67-80.

Gerard, M. W. (1953), Genesis of psychosomatic symptoms in infancy. In: *The Psychosomatic Concept in Psychoanalysis*, ed. F. Deutsch. New York: International Universities Press, pp. 82-95.

Glock, C. Y. & Lennard, H. L. (1957), Studies in hypertension: V. Psychological factors in hypertension: An interpretative review. *J. Chron. Dis.*, 5:174-185.

Goldberg, E. M. (1958), *Family Influences and Psychosomatic Illness*. London: Tavistock Publications.

Goldfarb, C., Driesen, J., & Cole, D. (1967), Psychophysiologic aspects of malignancy. *Amer. J. Psychiat.*, 123:1545-1552.

Greene, W. A., Jr. (1958), Role of a vicarious object in the adaptation to object loss: I. Use of a vicarious object as a means of adjustment to separation from a significant person. *Psychosom. Med.*, 20:344-350.

——— (1959), Role of a vicarious object in the adaptation to object loss: II. Vicissitudes in the role of the vicarious object. *Psychosom. Med.*, 21:438-447.

——— & Miller, G. (1958), Psychological factors and reticuloendothelial disease: IV. Observations on a group of children and adolescents with leukemia: An interpretation of disease development in terms of the mother-child unit. *Psychosom. Med.*, 20:124-144.

Grinker, R. & Robbins, F. (1954), *Psychosomatic Case Book*. New York: Blakiston.

Grolnick, L. (1972), A family perspective of psychosomatic factors in illness: A review of the literature. *Fam. Proc.*, 11:457-486.

Haley, J. (1962), Whither family therapy? *Fam. Proc.*, 1:69-100.

——— (1963), Marriage therapy. *Arch. Gen. Psychiat.*, 8:213-234.

——— (1964), Research on family patterns: An instrument measurement. *Fam. Proc.*, 3:41-65.

Ham, G. C., Alexander, F., & Carmichael, H. T. (1950), Dynamic aspects of the personality features and reactions characteristic of patients with Grave's disease. In: *Life Stress and Bodily Disease*, ed. H. G. Wolff, S. G. Wolf, & C. C. Hare. Baltimore: Williams & Wilkins, pp. 451-457.

Hamilton, J. W. (1970), Masked depression: Progressive somatization as a response to object loss. *Psychiat. Quart.*, 44:583-588.

Hilgard, E. (1952), Experimental approaches to psychoanalysis. In: *Psychoanalysis as Science*, ed. E. Pumpian-Mindlin. Palo Alto: Stanford University Press, pp. 3-45.

Hinkle, L. E., Jr., & Wolf, S. (1952), Summary of experimental evidence relating life stress and diabetes mellitis. *J. Mt. Sinai Hosp.*, 19:537-570.

Holmes, T. H., Hawkins, N. G., Bowerman, C. E., et al. (1957), Psychosocial and psychophysiologic studies of tuberculosis. *Psychosom. Med.*, 19:134-143.

Honker, F. (1964), Physical illness in disturbed marriages. *Med. Times*, 92:206-208.

Hopkins, P. (1959), Health and happiness and the family. *Brit. J. Clin. Prac.*, 13:311-313.

Jackson, D. (1961), The monad, the dyad, and family therapy. In: *Psychotherapy of the Psychoses*, ed. A. Burton. New York: Basic Books, pp. 318-328.

——— (1964), Family illness and the principle of homeostasis. Unpublished.

——— (1965), The study of family. *Fam. Proc.*, 4:1-20.

——— (1966), Family practice: A comprehensive medical approach. *Comprehen. Psychiat.*, 7:338-344.

——— & Yalom, I. (1966), Family research on the problem of ulcerative colitis. *Arch. Gen. Psychiat.*, 15:410-418.

Jacobs, M. A., Friedman, S., Franklin, M. J., et al. (1966), Incidence of psychosomatic predisposing factors in allergic disorders. *Psychosom. Med.*, 28:679-695.

Jameson, G. K. (1959), Steroid therapy adjuvant to psychotherapy of childhood ulcerative colitis. *Dis. Nerv. Syst.*, 20:130-134.

Johnson, A., Shapiro, L., & Alexander, R. (1947), Preliminary report on a psy-

chosomatic study of rheumatoid arthritis. *Psychosom. Med.*, 9:295-300.
Joseph, B. (1948), A technical problem in the treatment of the infant patient. *Internat. J. Psycho-Anal.*, 29:58-59.
Josselyn, I. M., Littner, N., & Spurlock, J. (1966), Psychologic aspects of ulcerative colitis in children. *J. Amer. Med. Women Assn.*, 21:303-306.
Kalis, G. L., Harris, R. E., Bennett, L. F., & Sokolow, M. (1961), Personality and life history factors in persons who are potentially hypertensive. *J. Nerv. Ment. Dis.*, ,132:457-468.
Kanner, L. (1972), *Hypochondriasis in Child Psychiatry*. Springfield, Ill.: Charles C Thomas, pp. 598-607.
Karp, S. A., Winters, S., & Pollack, I. W. (1969), Field dependence among diabetics. *Arch. Gen. Psychiat.*, 21:72-76.
Karush, A., Daniels, G. E., O'Connor, J. F., & Stern, L. O. (1968), The response to psychotherapy in chronic ulcerative colitis: I. Pretreatment factors. *Psychosom. Med.*, 30:255-276.
Kellner, R. (1963), *Family Ill Health: An Investigation in General Practice*. Springfield, Ill.: Charles C Thomas.
King, S. H. (1955), Psychosocial factors associated with rheumatoid arthritis: evaluation of literature. *J. Chron. Dis.*, 2:287-302.
Kissen, D. M. (1958), Some psychological aspects of pulmonary tuberculosis. *Internat. J. Soc. Psychiat.*, 3:252-259.
Knapp, P. H. (1969), The asthmatic and his environment. *J. Nerv. Ment. Dis.*, 149:133-151.
Krakowski, A. J. (1967), Psychophysiologic gastrointestinal disorders in children. *Psychosomat.*, 8:326-330.
Kreitman, N. (1964), The patient's spouse. *Brit. J. Psychiat.*, 110:159-173.
——— Pearce, K. I. & Ryle, A. (1966), The relationship of psychiatric, psychosomatic and organic illness in a general practice. *Brit. J. Psychiat.*, 112:569-579.
——— Sainsbury, P., Pearce, K., et al. (1965), Hypochondriasis and depression in out-patients at a general hospital. *Brit. J. Psychiat.*, 111:607-615.
LeShan, L. (1959), Psychological states as factors in the development of malignant disease: A critical review. *J. Nat. Cancer Inst.*, 22:1-18.
——— (1961), A basic psychological orientation apparently associated with malignant disease. *Psychiat. Quart.*, 35:314-330.
Lesse, S. (1967), Hypochondriasis and psychosomatic disorders masking depression. *Amer. J. Psychother.*, 21:607-620.
Lewin, K. K. (1959), Role of depression in the production of illness in pernicious anemia. *Psychosom. Med.*, 21:23-27.
Lidz, T. (1949), Emotional factors in the etiology of hyperthyroidism: Report of preliminary survey. *Psychosom. Med.*, 11:2-8.
——— (1959), General concepts of psychosomatic medicine. In: *American Handbook of Psychiatry*, I, ed. S. Arieti. New York: Basic Books, pp. 647-658.
——— Cornelison, A. R., Terry, D., & Fleck, S. (1957), The intrafamilial environment of the schizophrenic patient: I. The father. *Psychiat.*, 20:329-342.

——— & Fleck, S. (1965), *Schizophrenia and the Family*. New York: International Universities Press.

——— & Rubenstein, R. (1959), Psychology of gastrointestinal disorders. In: *American Handbook of Psychiatry*, I, ed. S. Arieti. New York: Basic Books, pp. 678-689.

Lieberman, M.A., Stock, D., & Whitman, R. M. (1959), Self-perceptual patterns among ulcer patients. *Arch. Gen. Psychiat.*, 1:167-176.

Liebman, R., Minuchin, S., & Baker, L. (1974), The use of structural family therapy in the treatment of intractable asthma. *Amer. J. Psychiat.*, 131:535-540.

Lindemann, E. (1950a), Modifications in the course of ulcerative colitis in relationship to changes in life situations and reaction patterns, life stress, and bodily disease. *Res. Nerv. Ment. Dis. Proc.*, 29:706-723.

——— (1950b), Modification in the course of ulcerative colitis in relationship and reaction patterns. In: *Life Stress and Bodily Disease*, ed. H. G. Wolff et al. Baltimore: Williams & Wilkins, pp. 706-723.

Long, R. T., Lamont, J. H., Whipple, B., et al. (1958), A psychosomatic study of allergic and emotional factors in children with asthma. *Amer. J. Psychiat.*, 114:890-899.

Looff, D. (1970), Psychophysiologic and conversion reactions in children—selective incidence in verbal and nonverbal families. *J. Amer. Acad. Child Psychiat.*, 9:318-331.

Ludwig, A. O. (1952), Psychogenic factors in rheumatoid arthritis. *Bull. Rheum. Dis.*, 2:33-34.

MacLean, P. D. (1955), The limbic system ("visceral brain") and emotional behavior. *Arch. Neurol. Psychiat.*, 73:130-134.

McMahon, A. W., Schmitt, P., Patterson, J. F., & Rothman, E. (1973), Personality differences between inflammatory bowel disease patients and their healthy siblings. *Psychosom. Med.*, 35:91-103.

Marder, L. & Hoogerbeets, J. D. (1967), Psychosomatic disease as a masked depression. *Psychosomat.*, 8:263-271.

Marshall, S. (1960), Personality correlates of peptic ulcer patients. *J. Consult. Psychol.*, 24:218-223.

Mechanic, D. (1965), Perception of parental responses to illness: A research note. *J. Hlth. Hum. Behav.*, 6:253-257.

Meissner, W. W. (1964), Thinking about the family—psychiatric aspects. *Fam. Proc.*, 3:1-40.

——— (1966), Family dynamics and psychosomatic processes. *Fam. Proc.*, 5:142-161.

Meyer, R. J. & Haggerty, R. J. (1962), Streptococcal infections in families: Factors altering individual susceptibility. *Pediat.*, 29:539-549.

Mezei, A. & Levendel, L. (1959), Étude objective des facteurs nuisibles au developpement de la personnalité chez les malades tuberculeux. *Hyg. Ment.*, 48:316-322.

Mirsky, I. A. (1948), Emotional factors in patients with diabetes mellitus. *Bull. Menn. Clin.*, 12:187-194.

——— (1960), Physiologic, psychologic and social determinants of psychosomatic disorders. *Dis. Nerv. Sys.*, 21:950-956.

Mohr, G. J., Josselyn, I. M., Spurlock, J., & Barron, S. H. (1958), Studies in ulcerative colitis. *Amer. J. Psychiat.*, 114:1067-1076.

Moses, L., Daniels, G. E., & Nickerson, J. L. (1956), Psychogenic factors in essential hypertension. *Psychosom. Med.*, 18:471-485.

Mutter, A. Z. & Schleifer, M. J. (1966), The role of psychological and social factors in the onset of somatic illness in children. *Psychosom. Med.*, 28:333-343.

Myers, I. K., Lindenthal, J. J., & Pepper, M. P. (1971), Life events and psychiatric improvement. *J. Nerv. Ment. Dis.*, 152:149-157.

Neumann, C. (1959), Psychische Besonderheiten bei Krebspatientinnen. *Zeitachr. f. Psychosom. Med.*, 5:91-101.

Nye, F. I. (1957), Some family attitudes and psychosomatic illness in adolescents. *The Coordinator*, 6:26-30.

O'Connor, J. F., Daniels, G., Karush, A., et al. (1966), Prognostic implications of psychiatric diagnosis in ulcerative colitis. *Psychosom. Med.*, 18:375-381.

——— & Stern, L. (1967), System alternation—An evaluation of the theory. *Arch. Gen. Psychiat.*, 16:432-436.

Parkes, C. M. (1964), Effects of bereavement on physical and mental health: A study of the medical records of widows. *Brit. Med. J.*, 2:274-279.

Peachey, R. (1963), Family patterns of illness. *Gen. Pract.*, 27-82-89.

Perrin, G. M. & Pierce, I. R. (1959), Psychosomatic aspects of cancer: A review. *Psychosom. Med.*, 21:397;421.

Philippopoulos, G. S. (1959), Thyrotoxicosis and its psychosomatic approach. *J. Nerv. Ment. Dis.*, 128:415-424.

Pilot, M. L., Lenkoski, L. D., Spiro, H. M., & Schafer, R. (1957), Duodenal ulcer in one of identical twins. *Psychosom. Med.*, 19;221-227.

Pinderhughes, C. A. (1971), Somatic, psychic, and social sequelae of loss. *J. Amer. Psychoanal. Assn.*, 19:670-696.

Rahe, R. H., McKean, J., Jr., & Arthur, R. J. (1967), A longitudinal study of life-change and illness patterns. *J. Psychosom. Res.*, 10:355-366.

Rank, B., Putnam, M., & Rochlin, G. (1948), The significance of the "emotional climate" in early feeding difficulties. *Psychosom. Med.*, 10:279-283.

Rawnsley, K. (1968), Case self-selection and psychosomatic research. *Proc. Roy. Soc. Med.*, 61:1126-1128.

Raychaudhuri, A. K. (1958), A case of diabetes mellitus: A study in psychosomatic medicine. *Psychosom. Med.*, 20:33-41.

Reiser, M. F. & Bokst, H. (1959), Psychology of cardiovascular disorders. In: *American Handbook of Psychiatry*, I, ed. S. Arieti. New York: Basic Books, pp. 659-677.

Renneker, R. E. (1957), Countertransference reactions to cancer. *Psychosom. Med.*, 19;409-418.

Rome, H. P. & Robinson, D. B. (1959), Psychiatric conditions associated with metabolic, endocrine, and nutritional disorders. In: *American Handbook of Psychiatry*, II, ed. S. Arieti. New York: Basic Books, pp. 1260-1288.

Rosen, H. & Lidz, T. (1949), Emotional factors in the precipitation of recurrent diabetic acidosis. *Psychosom. Med.*, 11:211-215.

Rosenbaum, M. (1963), Treatment of psychosomatic disorders. In: *The Psychological Basis of Medical Practice*, ed. H.L. Lief. New York: Harper & Row, pp. 501-509.

Ruesch, J. (1948), The infantile personality: The core problem of psychosomatic medicine. *Psychosom. Med.*, 10:134-144.

——— Christiansen, C., Harris, R. E., et al. (1948), *Duodenal Ulcer*. Berkeley: University of California Press.

Scheflen, A. (1967a), Explaining communicative behavior: Three points of view. In: *Expanding Theory and Practice in Family Therapy*, ed. F. Beatman & S. Sherman. New York: Family Service Association of America, pp. 93-98.

——— (1967b), On the structuring of human communication. *Amer. Behav. Scient.*, 10:8-12.

Schellack, D. (1957a), Neurosenpsychologische Faktoren in der Aetiologie und Pathogenese der Tonsillitis: I. *Zeitschr f. Psychosom. Med.*, 3:265-276.

——— (1957b), Neurosenpsychologische Faktoren in der Aetiologie und Pathogenese der Tonsillitis: II. *Zeitschr f. Psychosom. Med.*, 4:15-21.

Schmale, A. H., Jr. (1958), Relationship of separation and depression to disease: A report on a hospitalized medical population. *Psychosom. Med.*, 20:259-277.

Schonfeld, W. (1966), Body-image disturbances in adolescents: IV. Influences of family attitudes and psychopathology. *Arch. Gen. Psychiat.*, 15:16-21.

Selbmann, M. (1957), Depressives Erleben and Mentruationbeschwerden. *Zeitschr f. Psychosom. Med.*, 3:180-190.

Shochet, B. R., Lisansky, E. T., Schubart, A. F., et al. (1969), A medical-psychiatric study of patients with rheumatoid arthritis. *Psychosomat.*, 10:271-279.

Sperling, M. (1957), The psycho-analytic treatment of ulcerative colitis. *Internat. J. Psycho-Anal.*, 38:341-349.

——— (1959), Psychiatrische Aspekte der ulcerative Colitis. *Zeitschr. f. Psychosom. Med.*, 5:171-178.

Spitz, R. (1946), Anaclitic depression. *The Psychoanalytic Study of the Child.*, 2:313-342. New York: International Universities Press.

Stein, S. P. & Charles, E. (1971), Emotional factors in juvenile diabetes mellitus: A study of early life experience of adolescent diabetics. *Amer. J. Psychiat.*, 128:700-704.

Stewart, L. (1962), Social and emotional adjustment during adolescence as related to development of psychosomatic illness in adulthood. *Psychol. Monogr.*, 65:175-215.

Titchener, J. L., Riskin, J., & Emerson, R. (1960), The family in psychomatic process. *Psychosom. Med.*, 22:127-142.

Vincent, C. E. (1955), The loss of parents and psychosomatic illness. *Soc. Sci. Res.*, 39:404-408.

Vogel, E. F. & Bell., N. W. (1960), The emotionally disturbed child as a family scapegoat. *Psychoanal. Rev.*, 47(2):21-42.

von Bertalanffy, L. (1966), General system theory and psychiatry. In: *American*

Handbook of Psychiatry, III, ed. S. Arieti. New York: Basic Books, pp. 705-721.

Wahl, C. W. (1960), The psychodynamics of hypertension. *Calif. Med.,* 92:336-337.

——— & Golden, J. S. (1966), The psychodynamics of the polysurgical patient: report of sixteen patients. *Psychosom.,* 7:65-72.

Watzlawick, P., Beavin, J., & Jackson, D. (1967), *The Pragmatics of Human Communication.* New York: Norton.

Weiner, H., Thaler, M., Reiser, M. F., & Mirsky, I. A. (1957), Etiology of duodenal ulcer: I. Relation of specific psychological characteristics to rate of gastric secretion (serum pepsinogen). *Psychosom. Med.,* 19:1-10.

Wijsenbeek, H., Maoz, B., Nitzan, I., & Gill, R. (1968), Ulcerative colitis. *Psychiat. Neurol. Neurochir.,* 71:409-420.

Wilner, M. (1959), Dependency and ulcer: Dependency and familial attitudes in peptic ulcer and control groups. *Dissert. Abst.,* 19:2661-2662.

Wittkower, E. D. & White, K. L. (1959), Psychophysiologic aspects of respiratory disorders. In: *American Handbook of Psychiatry,* I, ed. S. Arieti. New York: Basic Books, pp. 690-707.

Wold, P. (1973), Family structure in three cases of anorexia nervosa: The role of the father. *Amer. J. Psychiat.,* 130:1394-1397.

Wolff, H. & Wolf, S. (1968), *Stress and Disease.* Springfield, Ill.: Charles C Thomas.

Wyler, A. R., Masuda, M. & Holmes, T. H. (1971), Magnitude of life events and seriousness of illness. *Psychosom. Med.,* 33:115-122.

Wynne, L. C., Ryckoff, I. M., Day, J., & Hirsch, S. L. (1958), Pseudomutuality in the family relations of schizophrenics. *Psychiat.,* 21:205-220.

This chapter comprehensively reviews and summarizes the relevant literature on the family background of compulsive drug abusers and lists factors of value in further research on the families of drug abusers.

The Families of Drug Abusers: A Literature Review

HENRY T. HARBIN and HOWARD M. MAZIAR

Compulsive drug users are being observed, tested, and researched with increasing intensity and thoroughness. Compulsive drug users are defined as individuals who are irresistibly driven to inject or ingest physiologically addicting drugs and who are unable to willfully and voluntarily terminate their drug use. With the exception of methadone maintenance programs, the treatment alternatives have not significantly expanded the hope of handling effectively the problem of compulsive drug users (Dole et al., 1968; DuPont, 1973). Many of the research efforts continue to search for a chemical answer to a supposed chemical problem (Hammond, 1971). A few investigators look at a broader spectrum: the sociological and epidemiological factors that may generate and maintain the problem of drug abuse (Clinard, 1957; Lindesmith, 1968). Although some researchers and clinicians have studied the individual psychodynamics of compulsive drug users, fewer have searched for answers to the etiology of compulsive drug use from a family perspective (Rado, 1933). There seems to be even less experimental work done in studying treatment considerations through the family approach. A need exists for some coordination and management

Henry T. Harbin, M.D., and Howard M. Maziar, M.D., are from the Institute of Psychiatry and Human Behavior, University of Maryland, Baltimore, Maryland.

The authors wish to acknowledge the assistance of Drs. Leon Wurmser and Helm Stierlin in the preparation of this paper.

Reprinted from *Family Process*, vol. 14, no. 3, September, 1975.

of the amount and type of research being done with drug abusers so that the funds presently used will not be wasted on repetitive or obscure work that does not help to generate more efficient treatment models.

The importance of the family in the formation of psychiatric disorders has been recognized since Freud. However, inclusion of the family as a way of treating mental problems has evolved chiefly during the last two decades, and it is becoming increasingly a potent therapeutic alternative, especially with children and adolescents (Freedman and Kaplan, 1967). In drug abuse, as has happened historically with other psychiatric problems, family treatment has been slow to develop, but family research has been even slower. We hope this review of the available literature that explores the family background of compulsive drug users will enable future experimenters and financial backers of research to determine more effectively what studies should be done on families of drug abusers.

This review attempts to look at all research done on the family of origin, but will deal most thoroughly with the few well-planned projects that have tried to validate and quantify their data with the use of control groups. The articles are broken down into three sections based on the methodology used. The first section includes clinical or empirical articles in which the authors have proposed their clinical impressions and theories, but have made no attempt to quantify or compare their data. The second section also includes empirical studies, but those in which there was some attempt to quantify the data for the purposes of comparison and validation but which did not include control groups. The third section includes all studies that in addition to quantifying the data also contained control groups. The resources drawn upon for the present study included: MEDLINE, (a bibliographic searching service provided by the National Library of Medicine that extends from 1970 to 1973 and includes over 1,000 biomedical journals), MEDLAR (the same service, but extending back to 1966), a complete review of all *Family Process* journals, all references obtained from Rutger's University Center for Alcoholism Control, references from the Addiction Research Foundation in Toronto, and the bibliographies of articles that were found in the above sources. Several articles concerning drug abuse in families were reviewed, but were not considered to have enough useful information to include in the paper and these are listed in the bibliography (Faigel, 1969; Guze et al., 1967; Kendall, 1972; Norton, 1968; Pittel et al., 1971; Randall, 1972; Smart et al., 1972; Vincent, 1972; Wheeler and Edmonds, 1969).

One of the most consistent family constellations identified in many of the research articles with a variety of methodological approaches is the combination of an overprotective, indulgent mother with an absent or emotionally distant father. This finding was in addition to the very frequent occurrence of an absent parent in the childhood of the addict. These results, however, are not very specific and point to a need for increased analysis of the methodology used in these articles as well as a study of what might be needed in future research. This paper presents the development of family research as it pertains to a specific symptomatic behavior, i.e., compulsive drug abuse. The methodological evolution of family research presented here can be helpful not only in understanding and creating present and future approaches to the study of drug abuse but also in being applied to family studies of other maladaptive behavior.

Clinical Studies

Some of the earliest literature that has significance for drug abusers and their families concerns the work done with delinquents and their families. This research into parent-child relations doesn't deal specifically with drug abusers, but drug abuse can be seen as an example of delinquent behavior, and threfore the research yields useful information. One of the first theoretical formulations that attempted to identify specific family causal factors for delinquency was the work of A. Johnson (1949). Johnson described some of the mechanisms by which adolescents developed their acting out of antisocial impulses. She hypothesized, based on her clinical work with adolescents and their parents, that the identified patients were acting out unconscious impulses of the parents. The parents were seen as ambivalent about certain impulses or societal restrictions, transmitting this ambivalence through inconsistent setting of limits. The acting-out behavior of the child served two needs of the parents: the vicarious gratification of their wishes and the displacement of parental self-punishment through the expression of hostility to the child. Several case examples illustrated these dynamics. It was pointed out that treatment is usually not successful and may be contraindicated if the parents are not involved or if the adolescent cannot be separated from the family during the treatment.

Another article dealing with delinquency of adolescents and their parents is by O. Carek et al. (1961). The authors of this paper have had experience with over 400 adolescents in which the parents sanctioned the delinquency, usually unconsciously. Again, this paper does not deal with drug abuse as the specific delinquent behavior. Carek et al. delineated several different mechanisms in the parent-child relationship that seemed to lead to the development of acting out forbidden impulses for the parent: (a) an overly determined negative reaction that may provide pleasure for the child; (b) imbalance of restrictions and permissiveness, with an overly reactive punishment coming after previous sanctions of the delinquent behavior; (c) conscious sanction of the behavior as long as the child is not caught by external authority; (d) displacement of the real issues to irrelevant subjects in order to avoid confronting the probelm; (e) no real moves by the parents to limit the acting out, despite frequent claims of doing so; (f) "anticipation of delinquency in the semblance of emphatic prohibition"; and (g) "consistent inconsistency" in parental reactions to the delinquent's behavior.

One of the early articles that looked at the parents of drug abusers from a treatment as well as a research view is by Hirsch (1961), who had three mothers and one father of adolescent drug abusers in group therapy. He had no selection criteria; the parents studied were the ones that chose to remain in the group for a prolonged period of time. Hirsch presented his general impression of the psychodynamics involved with these parents as well as case histories of each one. He identified narcissistic mothers who rejected their addict children when they didn't return their love. The mothers were seen as masochistic and infantilizing and as creating a core of masochism in the child. The fathers wre considered weak and ineffectual, providing a poor model for identification. All of the parents were seen as guilt-ridden and having a tendency to project the guilt when under stress. There were some examples of parents promoting the drug use by buying the drugs or by giving the adolescent money for the drugs. Because there were no selection criteria for the parents studied and no consideration of demographic factors such as socioeconomic status, it would be difficult to apply these impressions to other families of drug abusers.

A study by David Wellish et al. (1970) looked at the dyadic relationship of heroin addicts. The authors work at the Haight-Asbury Free Medical Clinic and have treated nearly 1,000 heroin addicts. They identified several interpersonal patterns for the addict couples and looked to the family background as a source for the patterns. Through interviews and histories taken from the addicts, the parental figures were reconstructed. The fathers of the female half of the addict couples were frequently either inept or alcoholic and were sexually and aggressively abusive to their daughters. The mothers were seen as the silent, masochistic figures who could manipulate the father and who were in competition with their daughters for the father. The fathers of the male addicts were described as usually absent from the home or passive-aggressive, emotionally distant figures. The mothers were portrayed as overprotective and highly dependent on their sons. Both groups of addicts were seen as recreating the nuclear family of origin within the dyadic relationship. In both the Hirsch and Wellish articles there is a tendency to use broad, loosely-defined terms such as narcissistic, masochistic, and passive-aggressive, terms too general to be of any specific use when applied to a large range of psychopathology. Another criticism of the data in this article is that the information about the family of origin was obtained only through interviews of the addicts. This diminishes the objectivity of ascertaining the actual family dynamics and interactions.

In 1961, Wolk and Diskirk reported on 344 parolees from the New York state prisons who had been involved with heroin abuse. Their findings put great emphasis on the role mothers play in the patients' addictions: "The mother—frequently a neurotic, overprotective, masochistic individual who must maintain her child's emotional illness for her own emotional survival—contributes largely to the poor adjustment of the drug addict." The father was portrayed as a "weak or absent father whose efforts toward discipline are blocked by the mother." This article was more critical of the mother than any other in the series. Although some direct access to the families of the addicts was included in the research, the methodology used to study these families is not clear.

In 1968, Whelpton studied ten chronic LSD users; significant to his findings were markedly disturbed family patterns. The mothers were found to be excessively involved with the patients to compensate for a poor relationship between the parents. Further, the families "had been split into rivalrous factions with the subjects and their mothers on one side and their fathers and siblings on the other." The patients "viewed their fathers as rivals who had disappointed their mothers and were not to be imitated." The author found further that the patients had difficulty separating from their home environment. This is the only study in the review concerned with LSD users, whose family dynamics are probably different from those of heroin users. The criteria for compulsive drug abuse is not clear because seven of the patients had taken LSD between six and 30 times, and this does not constitute compulsive drug abuse.

In this section we also include the only review article that could be found dealing with families of addicts. Seldin (1972) approached the family of the addict from the sociological, psychological, psychiatric, and social work perspectives. Most of the articles reviewed from a sociological view are general works and theoretical constructions about family systems, not specific to drug-abusing families. The few sociological studies that deal directly with addicts found a high incidence of disruptive family background through divorce, separation, or overt hostility between parents. One article reviewed hypothesized drug addiction as learned through peer-group association. In Seldin's review of works approached from the psychological, psychiatric, and social work view, he reported several emerging themes about the family background of addicts. The family was usually unstable and marked by divorce or separation. The mother was seen as the dominant figure who was ambivalent about her role. She was reported as overindulgent and highly interdependent with the addict child. The father was usually described as absent either through emotional detachment or actual physical separation. The addict's marriage repeated the nuclear family dynamics. Seldin, however, did not attempt to view the literature in terms of assessing the methodology used. The research results that may have been well controlled and validated are presented without differentiating them from the more speculative ones. Also, many of the articles reviewed deal only with the general theory about social systems or individual psychodynamics, and one has to infer some relevance for drug addicts. We therefore do not find Seldin's review very helpful in determining what research models need to be constructed and in what areas they should be applied.

Clinical Studies with Quantitative Results

The second group of studies includes those that make an attempt to quantify data but in which no control groups were used in this research design. In 1954, Gerard and Kornetsky studied the families of 32 adolescents admitted to the Public Health Service Hospital in Lexington, Kentucky. With regard to characteristics of the families of the patients, the results showed that the mothers were either excessively controlling and stern (40 percent) or excessively indulgent and nondisciplinary. Twenty-four percent of the mothers were classified as seductive. The fathers, on the other hand, were shown to play a minimal role in the patients' lives through absence, divorce, separation, or disinterest (60 percent), to be excessively punitive and moralistic (30 percent), or to be paranoid and controlling (twenty percent). An interesting finding and one to be repeated in other studies was the absence of one of the parents from the home environment. In 41 percent of the absence cases, parents were separated before the patients reached age ten, in 25 percent, after age ten. This study used carefully constructed criteria for compulsive drug addiction. Some of the families were interviewed directly by social agencies, but it is not clear how other families were studied.

Hawks et al. (1969) reported on 74 amphetamine abusers (both male and female). Again, an unstable family situation was prominent. Overall, 34 of the 74 patients had "suffered parental bereavement or separation before age sixteen." In addition to these findings, the authors reported high pathology among the other family members. It was found among the fathers that 21 percent had difficulties with alcohol or other drugs, five percent had criminal records, and ten percent had a history of psychiatric hospitalizations or had consulted a psychiatrist. Seven percent of the mothers were alcohol and drug abusers, and fourteen percent had a history of a psychiatric disorder. There was a 23 percent incidence of siblings with a history of abusing alcohol or other drugs. Twelve percent had a history of a psychiatric disorder. The reliability of these figures is impaired somewhat because the families were not interviewed directly.

A study in 1970 by Chambers et al. of narcotic addiction in females found that of 168 admissions to the U.S. Public Health Services Hospital in Lexington, 54.8 percent had been raised in homes that had been broken by age sixteen.

In a report to the Committee on Problems of Drug Dependence in 1971 by Crow et al., eight heroin addicts from a suburban community were studied. In the eight families, there were three divorces and remarriages, one two-year separation, and one common-law marriage. All eight patients "saw themselves as extremely weak and ineffectual as males. This resulted primarily from poorly developed father-son relationships." The importance of the fathers was emphasized in this study, with the finding that "the absence of a warm, masculine model with which to identify may be one of the common bonds which the suburban addict shares with his inner city counterpart." This study had reliable screening of the addicts, and all were compulsive heroin abusers. Also, the families were interviewed directly.

Rosenberg, in 1971, reported on the families of 35 adolescent patients (26 male and nine female) who were hospitalized for a variety of addictions in Sydney, Australia. Either the mother or father was interviewed alone and sometimes the family together. However, there was no standardization of the interviews or observations made on the families. It was reported that 63 percent of the addicts had not had positive relationships with their fathers. The fathers were described as being brutal or as exercising little or erratic control or as being absent. By contrast, 55 percent of the patients' brothers and 60 percent of their sisters were described as having had a good relationship with their fathers. Furthermore, over 90 percent of the addicts and their siblings had positive relationships with their mothers. It was found further that over one-third of parents or older siblings were in some way disturbed so that psychiatric treatment was required. The author concludes there is "the heightened degree that a personality disturbance shown by the addicts appears to be related more to their intense hostility towards their fathers, with whom they could not identify in a positive way, coupled with an over-dependent bond with their mothers" and that the "drug addiction is not only a manifestation of the adolescent's personality disturbance, but is symptomatic of a wider family problem."

A brief study by R. L. Linder et al. (1972) measured 839 college students' degree and type of drug use and correlated this with their birth order in their family of origin. The only significant difference found was that the only-children used tranquilizers more often. There were non-statistically significant trends that showed only-children using barbiturates, cocaine, and nitrous oxide more often.

An article by P. A. Carney et al. (1972) reported on 50 adolescent drug abusers in Dublin of which 42 were male. The method of study was through a precoded questionnaire about family data and the Cattell 16 Personality Factor Questionnaire. The type of drug taken varied, with only 30 percent using heroin intravenously. The family background showed that "only 40 percent of the families had both parents alive, living together, and free of incapacitating psychiatric illness." The results showed that twenty percent of the fathers were treated by psychiatrists and that 42 percent of the mothers had had treatment for psychiatric problems. The siblings also showed a high degree of disturbance, with twelve percent receiving psychiatric treatment, fourteen percent having a delinquent history, and 16 percent reported to be drug abusers. This study reveals patterns similar to previously reviewed studies, but it suffers from some of the same methodologic flaws: (a) the family results were obtained only through interviews with the addict; (b) there was a lack of specificity in the type of drug abuser tested; (c) there were no clear criteria for compulsive drug users. Again, the results tell us something about the general disorganization of the family system but nothing specific about the interaction of the family members.

A study by Noble and Barnes (1971) followed 100 control girls and 227 drug-using girls (both narcotic and nonnarcotic) who were in a London remand home from 1966 to 1968 to determine their presnt-day drug use. Out of this population of adolescent girls three groups of 30 girls each were matched for age and year of admission: (a) narcotic group—girls that were taking narcotics on admission; (b) progresser group—girls taking nonnarcotics on admission but narcotics later; (c) nonprogresser group—nonnarcotic on admission and no narcotics later. There were no well-defined differences between the families of these three groups. Some of the families were interviewed directly, but the manner in which information was obtained is not clear. It was felt that the families were marked by "disruption, parental separation, poor discipline, and hostility." There was little evidence found for overprotection, and only a few parents were seen as having psychological difficulties. This study is noteworthy in that drug-use criteria are well defined and it is one of the few prospective sudies done. However, the methodology for studying the family is unclear, and the terms used for description of the family are vague and too general.

A study by S. Haastrup et al. (1971) was conducted with the parents of young (less than 25 years old) drug abusers who had been hospitalized in Copenhagen for a diagnosis of either drug dependence or psychosis with drug intoxication. The parents of 187 drug abusers were interviewed by the same social worker about six to twelve months after the patients were admitted to the hospital. The drug group was compared with a normal group of adolescents who were evaluated in another study. The whole group of drug addicts included soft and hard drug users and were represented mostly by high and low socioeconomic levels. The chief findings for the whole group were an increased number of broken homes, increased age of father, increased psychiatric admissions for the mother, increased misuse of alcohol for the fathers, and increased use of psychoactive medicines for the mothers. There was a correlation between the increased soft drug use of the addicts and the psychoactive drug use of the mothers. However, this study did not differentiate compulsive drug abusers from more sporadic users. Also, the family dynamics were crudely measured, and it is difficult to ascertain the reliability of the data.

Cancrini et al. (1970) approached the adolescent drug user from several different levels. This research model used clear criteria for identifying compulsive drug abusers and interviewed directly the families of 80 adolescent drug addicts. For each family, two interviewers and a supervisor recorded their observations separately and then synthesized them. The results showed a high disruption of family life with 40-45 percent of the patients having an absent parent or no family at all. The teenagers' drug problem was seen to be the result of a series of maladaptive solutions and certainly not the initial problem. This study was one of the few that reported on family therapy with drug abusers; it was found to be a useful approach.

Controlled Research Studies

This section includes six articles and two books on studies that had either "normal" or dysfunctional patient control groups. Most of these articles explored circumscribed areas, but the results of each allow some interpretation of the significant family dynamics.

A brief study by Kurtzberg et al. (1966) measured the responses of 59 incarcerated male heroin addicts and 60 incarcerated male nonaddicts to a Draw-A-Person Test. The results demonstrated a significant difference between the two groups: a greater number of male addicts drew the female figure first and, also, larger. These results are interpreted as confirming the theories of the male addict's overidentification with and dependence on his mother. Although this study is brief and does not deal with the family directly, it complements the clinical impressions gained in previously mentioned studies.

A study by Torda (1968) consisted of giving psychological tests and evaluation forms to 30 heroin addicts and 30 nonaddict psychiatric patients. These two groups were matched for age, interest, background, and psychiatric diagnosis. The tests given were the Biological Personality Assessment Test, Roth's Mother-Child Relationship Evaluation Test, and the Family Adjustment Test of Elias. The questionnaires were filled out by the patients and some family members, but, unfortunately, there is no mention of how many or which family members participated. Statistically significant differences showed addicts coming from homes in which the mothers were dominant and where very aggressive behavior was devalued. The mothers were not aware of the infants' needs and tended to feed them before they were hungry. Passivity was rewarded, and there was a tendency toward intellectualization, daydreaming, omnipotence, narcissism, and magical thinking in the child. The fathers were seen as weak, distinterested, absent, or alcoholic. The addicts were frequently described as "easiest to raise" and the "favored child." Again, in this work, the whole family was not studied directly.

Oltman and Friedman (1967) measured the amount of parental deprivation in a large number of psychiatric inpatients with a variety of diagnoses and compared this to a control group of normals. For a comparison, parental deprivation was subdivided into three areas: (a) parental death; (b) parental separation (due to divorce, desertion, separation); (c) prolonged absence of the parent secondary to psychiatric hospitalization. For 69 white drug addicts, the overall amount of parent deprivation was 43.5 percent—higher than the control group but not statistically significant. However, for parental separation alone, the drug addicts had a statistically significant increase second only to the level reached by psychopathic personalities. This study contained patients addicted to a variety of drugs, including heroin. The results were obtained via interviews with individual patients but not their familes.

A study by Mead and Campbell (1972) is one of the few in which the addict and parents were tested together. Twenty family triads including both parents and one drug-abusing child were matched with twenty normal families for age, race, and socioeconomic status. The families were given decision-making tasks based on a modification of Ferreira and Winter's test items. Family members were tested individually and then as a group, during which the time it took for family agreement on decisions was measured. The results confirmed some of the authors' hypotheses but rejected others. There was a significant increase in the amount of "spontaneous agreement or value consensus" for the normal families. With all families it was found that the children tended to have greater agreement with the parent of the same sex. There was no significant difference found for increased spontaneous agreement between mother-child dyads and father-child dyads in the drug abuser's family. The results did not lend weight to findings in many previous studies of a symbiotic tie of male drug abusers with their mothers. The lack of identity of the sex of the child in Mead and Campbell's measurements of the parent-child dyad is confusing. It would be helpful to know this in order to evaluate the results, which seemingly contradict many of the previous studies. The results were interpreted, however, as confirming that families of drug abusers were similar in their lack of spontaneous agreement with families of schizophrenic, maladjusted, and delinquent children. For the family with a drug-abusing member, there was evidence that discussion of disagreement tended to be avoided even though present and that discussion time was spent inefficiently talking about areas already agreed upon. This study, overall, is well constructed and significant in the attempt to measure the dynamics of the interacting family. Unfortunately, it is difficult to generalize from the results since no criteria are listed for what constitutes drug abuse; thus, it is not known if the abusers are compulsive drug users or merely occasional users.

Another well-constructed and controlled study was made by Attardo (1965). Twenty-eight mothers of drug addicts, 41 mothers of schizophrenics, and 60 mothers of normal adolescents were matched for demographic variables. The author created a symbiosis or "S" scale based on M. Mahler's concepts of symbiosis and separation-individuation (Mahler et al., 1975). The mothers were tested retrospectively as to their propensity for symbiotic relating during three different age spans of their own offspring. These age spans of their children were, years zero to five, years six to ten, and years eleven to 16. In addition to this interpersonal scale of symbiotic relating, "S" scale, another scale "0" measured the intrapsychic dynamics of the mother. The results showed all three groups of mothers as having similar levels on the symbiotic scale relating to their offspring during ages zero to five. However, in the age group six to ten, the mothers of drug abusers were significantly higher on the symbiotic scale than the other two groups of mothers. In the eleven to sixteen age group, the mothers of drug abusers were again statistically higher than the other two groups of mothers on the "S" scale, but the mothers of schizophrenics were also significantly higher than the normals in this age level. Moreover, on the "0" scale, mothers of drug abusers showed greater symbiotic needs than the others. The results tend to confirm the overprotectiveness of mothers of drug addicts found in previously reviewed research. Again, there are no criteria listed for what constitutes a drug abuser, nor does the study measure directly the family interaction, but tests only one family member.

Blum and his associates (1972) have attempted to explore the family factors that lead to drug risk in children and adolescents. The research undertaken by Blum was well planned and systematic. He attempted to measure many family variables of adolescents who were identified as low, middle, or high drug risks. The drug classification system is the key to the research and is presented here. He considered the use of all psychoactive drugs (excluding alcohol and tobacco) and the manner and outcome of the usage to be important in determining drug risk. The different drugs were weighed as to severity of risk, with opiates and hallucinogens having a higher score than marijuana. The exact system of classification for each type of drug use was not given in the book. Intact families were obtained predominantly from random sources in the community (not through medical or psychiatric referrals) and were controlled for socioeconomic variables. Middle-class, blue-collar, white and black, Mexican-American, and hippie families were studied. The investigative tools were questionnaires about value systems, family roles and interactions, drug use, and religious and social views. Also, the interviews of individuals and the whole family were held. The results were voluminous, and there were many statistically significant differences found between high and low drug-risk families. The results of the bulk of the study identified psychosocial styles for high and low drug-risk families. The increased drug use of the high-risk families fit into a general constellation of values that tended to be more permissive and less authoritarian than low-risk families. It is not relevant to present here all the detailed results found, but an attempt will be made to assess the methodology used. It is the belief of the authors that these research data are not clinically useful because the drug-risk classification system does not separate addicting and nonaddicting drugs. Also, the compulsive drug users are not separated from the adolescents who are merely experimenting with, or occasionally using, drugs. There is no way of determining which of the drug-using adolescents in the high-risk category actually go on to be compulsive drug abusers. Two chapters in the book do attempt to explore the family interaction from a more clinical viewpoint, and the most clinically relevant material is obtained from these. However, the families are again compared on the basis of the original drug-risk classification system. Blum does point out that it was found from the intensive clinical study that drug use alone does not necessarily mean the adolescent is in trouble. In view of this, it would seem to be more important to try to ascertain the family interactional characteristics of adolescents with real drug problems. The actual compulsive drug users and their family dynamics cannot be identified in this large study. Possibly, some adolescents from the middle or low drug-risk families might become compulsive drug users, and it would be important to know exactly what the family dynamics of this group are. Blum's work seems to hold more value as a sociological study that is too broad in its identification of drug risk in adolescents to be useful for clinicians hoping to treat drug abusers.

Chein et al. in 1964 reported in a comparison of 30 male compulsive drug abusers with 29 normal controls that "some of the most striking contrasts in the experiences of our addicts and controls occurred in the relationship of the boy with the father or father figure." In 80 percent of the addicts as compared with 45 percent of the controls, there was an extremely weak father-son relationship. In 48 percent of the addicts, as compared with 17 percent of controls, the father figure was absent for a significant part of the addict's early childhood. In 97 percent of the addicts' families as, compared with 41 percent of controls, the parents had a disturbed relationship. The relationship between mother and addict, compared with the controls, showed "little evidence of an atypical or unusual relationship between them." There was a special group of mothers of addicts, however, that did differ from the controls and the remaining group of mothers of addicts. This special group of mothers was described as having, like the fathers of addicts, a distant and hostile relationship with their sons. This study, using a control group of normals and interviewing the entire family as opposed to only the addict, seemed quite well done.

Rosenberg, in a study reported in 1969, compared 50 neurotics, 50 drug abusers, and 50 alcoholics in Sydney, Australia. He found that the alcoholics and drug addicts had a higher incidence of broken homes than did the neurotics. Thirty-one alcoholics and 28 addicts reached their fifteenth birthday without their natural fathers in the home, as compared with only twelve of the neurotics. The fathers of the alcoholics and addicts were described as uninterested, rejecting, or rendering erratic and unjust punishment. The fathers of the neurotics were described as strict and emotionally detached. The mothers of the three groups were similar in most respects except that, with the alcoholics and drug addicts, there was a greater incidence of separation from the mother than with the neurotics. This study further confirms the finding of a high degree of parental deprivation, but suffers from a lack of normal controls. Also, the actual families of the patients were not interviewed, only the patients themselves.

Discussion

In this section, we discuss and summarize our findings as well as indicate future areas for research. The results show that family dynamics are instrumental in the development and maintenance of pathological drug use. There appears to be a general pattern of interaction between compulsive drug abusers and both their mothers and fathers. The mothers are most often described as indulgent and overprotective. The mothers had "special" relationships with their sons and tended to be involved with their addictions. There are, however, some notable exceptions to this. Mead and Campbell (1972) found that there was no increased agreement between mother-child dyads in drug abusers' families. This is contrary to what might be expected. Chein et al. (1964) found, too, that there was a smaller group of mothers of addicts who had "emotionally distant or hostile relationships with their sons" and that the other mothers of addicts seemed similar to mothers of the controls. They concluded, however, that "there is reason to believe that the mothers of the addicts were much more involved in the development of their sons' addiction than indicated by the categories included in the indexes." The fathers were seen in most studies as being weak and ineffectual. There were exceptions to this, too. Chein et al. (1964) and Rosenberg (1969) found that often fathers who were in the home were hostile and punitive. It seems useful to note, though, that throughout all the studies the addict did not have a male figure he could identify with positively. Overall, it seems that the overprotectiveness of the mother and the absence of a positive identification with the father tend to be viewed as separate variables in their contribution to the development of drug-abusing adolescents. The mothers' pathogenic presence seems to be granted more significance as a causal factor. This may or may not be a correct assumption. In any case, this is inconsistent with family systems theory, which views these parental characteristics as interdependent. The one finding that was observed to occur in all studies was an increased percentage of absence of one of the parents in the addict's childhood and early adolescence. This appears to be significant in the development of compulsive drug abuse. A special problem arises in the consideration of the female addict and her family. The only three articles dealing solely with the female addict found the same high incidence of the absence of one parent from the home. Most of the studies have been with males, and those that dealt with both sexes made no differentiation of results according to sex. One exception was Wellish et al. (1970) who reported the fathers of female addicts to be inept, alcoholic, and sexually aggressive to their daughters. Their mothers, instead of being indulgent, were described as being in competition with the daughter.

A critique of the particular methodology used in the various studies seems helpful in assessing their usefulness. The articles in our first section were the most theoretical and provided the greatest in-depth formulation as to family interactional dynamics, but because there was no attempt at quantification and control, their validity remains only speculative. The insight produced by these works, however, does provide a useful beginning for evaluating more family dynamics systematically. In our second section were articles attempting to quantify and validate certain family patterns, but here the lack of controls raises the question of the specificity of the findings for families with compulsive drug abusers.

The studies that have controls contain the most reliable research data. The comparison of normal families with families containing a drug-abusing, schizophrenic, and neurotic member provides a beginning for identification of specific interactional patterns within these various types of families. In our third section, as in the previous two, there were several articles in which criteria for the types of drug abuse were unclear; in certain of these articles, the patients appeared to be occasional and not compulsive drug abusers. It is reasonable to assume that family dynamics are different for compulsive drug users and occasional users. Hence, the two groups should be dichotomized in order to obtain a clear view of what is taking place in the family.

In the discussion thus far, we have presented the pathological family patterns that have emerged as well as a critique of methodology. What follows is a discussion of more specific methodological problems common to all three types of studies.

A major difficulty is that in only a few of the studies were the actual family members other than the addict interviewed and the interactional patterns viewed directly. This method is of some value in understanding the drug abuser's perceptions and fantasies of his family. The approach, however, inhibits a clear and objective appraisal of the actual family interactions, since the reality of family life is subject to distortion by any single family member. This distortion is also applicable to the few studies in which only the mother of the addict was interviewed. In the future, for a clearer understanding of families with a drug-abusing member, research should no longer involve only one family member. Also lacking in many of these studies is specification of socioeconomic status, race, and sex among the experimental groups. We have attempted to present these factors when they were clearly defined in the articles.

The most consistent family pattern identified in the literature about compulsive drug abusers is the overprotective, indulgent mother coupled with the absent or emotionally distant father. However, this pattern has been suggested for many different types of families where there is an identified psychiatric patient—homosexuals (Kardiner, 1963), school-phobic children (Eisenberg, 1958), and schizophrenics (Freedman and Kaplan, 1967, pp. 610-611), for example. The application of this pattern to such a wide variety of psychiatric syndromes suggests that further refinement of the descriptive terminology and methodology is needed. Levy (1966) attempts further refinement by classifying overprotective mothers into four different types. This lack of specificity is likewise seen in the frequent use of such vague terms as narcissism, masochism, and aggression throughout the articles mentioned in this study. The terminology used in the research thus far is particularly inapplicable to interpersonal transactions. At this point, it might be asked whether it is presumptuous to assume that further specificity does exist for types of families with a drug-abusing member. In view of past findings of more specific dynamics, for example, the double bind in schizophrenia, it is reasonable to assume that, unless otherwise refuted, specificity may exist.

Conclusions

In conclusion, it seems useful to outline certain factors that need to be included in any future studies:

(a) Exact criteria for the type of drug use and abuse are essential to the achievement of reliable research data. These include the type of drug, whether amphetamines, cocaine, heroin, etc. Also, the frequency and duration of drug use are important in order to assess the compulsivity of use. The compulsive drug users are considered to have the most severe problem and are more likely to have disturbed family relations.

(b) The sex of the drug user should be identified, for it is likely that there are different family dynamics for the male and female addict.

(c) The socioeconomic background of the families studied should be similar so as to differentiate specific interactional dynamics for families of various cultures.

(d) The entire family of origin should be directly involved in any research study. This can include any significant parental figures (such as grandparents) as well as siblings in order to assess all parts of the family's functioning, both pathological and healthy.

(e) It is worthwhile to consider specific family styles that may be relevant to the development and maintenance of a drug-abusing child. For example, a child's attitude may be determined by the parents' views toward the child's use of inanimate objects. The parents might constantly encourage the child to satisfy frustrations through relatedness to inanimate objects, i.e., pacifier, toys, medication, in place of interpersonal investments. The child would thus learn that the most consistent and safe way to satisfy internal needs and conflicts is to rely on nonhuman objects. With this set, the individual may turn in later life to drug abuse to resolve conflict.

Drug abuse as a symptom may be maintained by the individual to serve family functions. For example, an addicted adolescent may use his drug abuse as a means of maintaining involvement with the family. As long as he continues to use drugs, the family remains concerned about the addict's fate. Similarly, the parents may encourage continued drug abuse (e.g., giving money to the addict to purchase drugs) as a means of maintaining control of the addict. As long as the abuser continues to use drugs, he is dependent on the family for support. This prolonged parent-child involvement may serve to mask not only marital discord but also latent psychopathology in the parents.

Another relevant area to explore is the use of psychotropic drugs by the addict's parents. It may be speculated that the parents would tend to resolve their own conflicts by the use of such drugs. This potentially maladaptive usage would probably involve a somatization of psychic conflicts as well as a lack of a reliance on personal relatedness to resolve such frustrations.

(f) A control or comparison group is essential in assessing the nature and degree of pathology in drug-using families. Comparison groups, such as families with a schizophrenic member, with an occasional drug user, with a neurotically disturbed member, etc., can enhance the identification of specific family dynamics of compulsive drug users.

If all these research factors can be accounted for, it is likely that future family studies will contribute much more understanding of the family's contribution to this maladaptive symptom. We hope this survey of family research will help form a comprehensive view of the many factors essential to developing and maintaining compulsive drug abuse.

References

Attardo, N. (1965), Psychodynamic factors in the mother-child relationship in adolescent drug addiction: A comparison of mothers of schizophrenics and mothers of normal adolescent sons. *Psychother. Psychosom.*, 13:249-255.

Blum, R. H. et al. (1972), *Horatio Alger's Children*. London: Jossy-Bass.

Cancrini, L. et al. (1970), Social and family factors of teenager drug addiction. *Europ. J. Toxicol.*, 3:397-401.
Carek, O. J., Hendrickson, W. J., & Holmes, O. J. (1961), Delinquency addiction in parents. *Arch. Gen. Psychiat.*, 4:357-363.
Carney, P. A. et al. (1972), The social and psychological background of young drug abusers in Dublin. *Brit. J. Addict.*, 67:199-207.
Chambers, C., Hinesley, R.K., & Moldestad, M. (1970), Narcotic addiction in females: A race comparison. *Internat. J. Addict.*, 5:257-278.
Chein, I., Gerard, D., Lee, R., & Rosenfeld, E. (1964), *The Road to H*. New York: Basic Books.
Clinard, M. B. (1957), *Sociology of Deviant Behavior*. New York: Rinehart.
Crow, L. et al. (1971), *Report to the Committee on Problems of Drug Dependence*, 11:1893.
Dolc, V.P., Nyswander, M.E., & Warner, A. (1968), Successful treatment of 150 criminal addicts. *JAMA*, 206:2708-2711.
DuPont, R. L. (1973), Coming to grips with an urban heroin addiction epidemic. *JAMA*, 233:46-48.
Eisenberg, L. (1958), School phobia: A study in the communication of anxiety. *Amer. J. Psychiat.*, 115:712-718.
Faigel, H. C. (1969), Teenage drug abuse—what should you do when one of your adolescent patients says he is a drug addict? *Clin. Pediat.*, 8:123-125.
Freedman, A. M. & Kaplan, H. I., eds. (1967), *Comprehensive Textbook of Psychiatry*. Baltimore: Williams & Wilkins.
Gerard, D. & Kornetsky, C. (1954), A social and psychiatric study of adolescent opiate addicts. *Psychiat. Quart.*, 28:113-125.
Guze, S. B., Wolfgram, E. P., & McKinney, J. K. (1967), Psychiatric illness of the families of convicted criminals: A study of 519 first degree relatives. *Dis. Nerv. Sys.*, 28:651-659.
Haastrup, S. et al. (1972), The social background of young addicts as elicited in interview with their parents. *Acta Psychiat. Scand.*, 48:146-173.
Hammond, A. L. (1971), Narcotic antagonists: New methods to treat heroin addiction. *Science*, 173:502-506.
Hawks, O. et al. (1969), Abuse of methamphetamine. *Brit. Med. J.*, 2:715-731.
Hirsch, R. (1961), Group therapy with parents of adolescent drug abusers. *Psychiat. Quart.*, 35:702;710.
Johnson, A. M. (1949), Sanctions for superego lacunae of adolescents. In: *Searchlights on Delinquency*, ed. K. R. Eissler. New York: International Universities Press, pp. 225-245.
Kardiner, A. (1963), The flight from masculinity. In: *The Problem of Homosexuality in Modern Society*, ed. H. M. Ruitenbeck. New York: Dutton, pp. 17-39.
Kendall, R. F. (1972), Life history antecedents of subjective contentment and dysphoria in a hippie culture. *J. Psychedelic Drugs*, 5:89-93.
Kurtzberg, R. L., Eavior, N., & Lipton, O. S. (1966), Sex drawn first and sex drawn larger by opiate addicts and non-addict inmates on the Draw-A-Person Test. *J. Project. Tech.*, 30:55-58.
Levy, D. (1966), *Maternal Overprotection*. New York: Norton.

Linder, R. L. et al. (1972), Self-medication: An only-child syndrome. *J. Psychedelic Drugs*, 5:62-66.

Lindesmith, A. R. (1968), *Addiction and Opiates*. Chicago: Aldine.

Mahler, M. S., Pine, F., & Bergman, A. (1975), *The Psychological Birth of the Human Infant*. New York: Basic Books.

Mead, O. E. & Campbell, S. S. (1972), Decision-making and interaction by families with and without a drug-abusing child. *Fam. Proc.*, 11:487-498.

Noble, P. & Barnes, G. (1971), Drug-taking in adolescent girls. *Brit. Med. J.*, 2:620-623.

Norton, W. A. (1968), The marijuana habit: Some observations of a small group of peers. *Canad. Psychiat. Assn. J.*, 13:163-173.

Oltman, J. E. & Friedman, S. (1967), Parental deprivation in psychiatric conditions, III. *Dis. Nerv. Sys.*, 28:298-303.

Pittel, S. et al. (1971), Development factors in adolescent drug use. *J. Amer. Acad. Child Psychiat.*, 10:640-660.

Rado, S. (1933), The psychoanalysis of pharmacothymia (drug addiction). *Psychoanal. Quart.*, 2:1-23.

Randall, H. (1972), Drug use and abuse and the family. *Woman Physician*, 27:70-

Rosenberg, C. M. (1969), Determinants of psychiatric illness in young people. *Brit. J. Psychiat.*, 115:907-908.

——— (1971), The young addict and his family. *Brit. J. Psychiat.*, 118-469-470.

Seldin, N. E. (1972), The family of the addict: A review of the literature. *Internat. J. Addictions*, 7:97-107.

Smart, R. et al. (1972), Drug use among adolescents and their parents: Closing the generation gap in mood modification. *J. Abnorm. Psychol.*, 79:153-160.

Torda, C. (1968), Comments on the character structure and psychodynamic processes of heroin addicts. *Percept. Mot. Skills*, 27:153-156.

Vincent, C. (1972), An open letter to the caught generation. *Addictions*, 19:64-79.

Wellish, D. K., Gay, G. R. & McEntre, R. (1970), The easy rider syndrome: A pattern of hetero- and homosexual relationships in a heroin addict population. *Fam. Proc.*, 9:425-430.

Wheeler, K. & Edmonds, E. (1969), A profile of drug takers. *Med. J. Austral.*, 2:291-294.

Whelpton, D. F. (1968), Psychodynamics of chronic lysergic acid diethylamide use. *J. Nerv. Ment. Dis.*, 147:377-385.

Wolk, R. L. & Diskirk, M. (1961), Personality dynamics of mothers and wives of drug addicts. *Crime and Delinquency*, 7:148-152.

Disturbed families, more than healthy families, exhibit violence, hurtful to themselves and others. The author reviews studies on violent families and offers a theory to explain violence at home, embracing psychological, social, and cultural perspectives.

Violence at Home: A Review of the Literature

MARY HANEMANN LYSTAD

If the function of the family is to love and to nurture and to support its members, then violence in the family would seem to be incompatible with its function. Why does violence occur? How often does it occur, and who are its victims?

For the purpose of this paper, violence in the family is defined as a mode of behavior involving the direct use of physical force against other family members. The "family" referred to is primarily the nuclear family of mother, father, and children. Physical force in the family varies in severity from homicide at one extreme to mild spankings at the other. It also varies by intent; in some cases the intent is to control people's behavior, in others it is to vent personal hostility, and in still others it is a mixture of both. In addition, family violence varies by societal interpretation; homicide is rarely considered legitimate in any society, while spankings are considered by some to be necessary to the socialization process.

This paper will review several types of studies relating to family violence: those raising theoretical issues; incidence studies of family violence; studies of violence as it relates to particular family members—husband

---

Mary H. Lystad, Ph.D., is Special Assistant to the Director, Division of Special Mental Health Programs, National Institute of Mental Health. Views expressed in this paper are the author's and do not necessarily reflect those of NIMH. Reprinted from the *American Journal of Orthopsychiatry*, vol. 45, no. 3, April, 1975.

and wife, parent and child, siblings; studies of violence related to social structure; and finally, studies concerning needed services, and their effectiveness—services to discordant families employing a wide variety of professional help, from neighborhood policeman to emergency-ward physician.

Theoretical Studies

Theoretical studies have explored many different types of variables—psychological, sociological, and cultural. A number of the studies interrelated several types of variables, but the majority analyze only a single type.

In terms of psychological and psychopathological variables, many factors have been studied, particularly that of intimate social contact in the family. Goode (1969) pointed out that one reason intimates commit violence against one another is that they are in each other's presence a lot, and few others can anger one so much as those who are close. Goode maintained that it is probable that intimate emotional links among human beings have their own effects independent of pervasive pressures from the larger culture. A number of other authors (Eron, 1959; Kopernik, 1964) noted the feeling of rejection that aggressive children have in the family situation because of separation from parents, birth of another sibling, or parental indifference.

Several studies point to a special interpersonal relationship between murderers and their victims in which violence is the result of antagonisms that have been tolerated for years while the victim teased, taunted, or suppressed his eventual murderer until a breaking point was reached. On the other hand, the killers are sometimes described as submissive and passive, desiring to avoid conflict whenever possible, particularly if playing a masochistic role results in gaining their affection (Houts, 1970; Schultz, 1968). Wolfgang (1969) pointed out the suicidal nature of some homicide victims who so aggressively provoke attack upon themselves that they can be viewed as suicides. As for children who murder, Sargent (1971a) supports the hypothesis that sometimes the child who kills is acting as the unwitting lethal agent of an adult, usually a parent, who unconsciously prompts the child to kill so that the adult can vicariously enjoy the benefits of the act.

In discussing child abuse, a number of authors point to the presence of psychoses among parents (Editorial, 1970; Pohlen, 1968; Richette,

1969; Editorial, 1973). Zalba (1966) reported that child battering and severe child abuse are inflicted by parents with a variety of difficult problems, from violent and episodic schizophrenia to impulse-ridden character disorder. These parents displace and act out their anger over marital conflicts onto their children, the common element among them being that children are used as targets of abuse and injury in the process of displacing and denying interpsychic and other-object-oriented hostility and aggression.

On the other hand, Gelles (1973) criticized those who look on the phenomenon of child abuse strictly from a psychopathological model. He thought a more fruitful approach to this problem is to focus on sociological and contextual variables associated with abuse: since unemployment and social class are important contextual variables, then strategies to prevent child abuse should aim at alleviating the disastrous effects of being poor in an affluent society; because there appears to be an association between child abuse and unwanted pregnancy, programs should be developed to aid in planned parenthood.

By far the most frequently discussed social-structural theory of family violence is that involving the socialization of aggression. The theory states that parents who punish more severely produce children who are more aggressive. And *they* in turn tend to punish *their* children more severely. This is particularly well documented in the study of child abuse—the abused child often becomes the abusing parent. Punishment both frustrates the child and provides him a model (Ilfeld, 1970; Lefkowitz et al., 1963; Silver et al., 1969).

On the other hand, Yarrow et al. (1968), in analyzing theories and correlates of child aggression, concluded that many of the hypotheses relating the child's aggression to punishments and rewards in rearing practices of the mother are not supported in interview studies. The authors cautioned that several methodological factors complicate interpretation of such studies of child rearing: the unknowns and inadequacies in instruments and the nonstandard, uncertainly equivalent, and uncertainly suitable conceptual labels in the data. The authors concluded that interpretations of consistency between research findings of a number of studies have slighted a great deal of evidence and have given theoretical expectations too compelling an influence.

Not all groups in our society socialize children to the same degree by means of violent behavior. Gelles (1973) and Gil (1970) found a higher incidence of violence against children among families with lower educational achievements and lower socioeconomic status, among broken families, and among families with four or more children. Eron (1963), to the contrary, did not find class differences.

Why do some parents socialize their children more aggressively? Eron et al. (1963) cited evidence that those who do have fewer upward-mobility aspirations for their children. Straus (1971) found that such punishment varies with the sex of the child and with the traits parents value in their children. His findings are interpreted as supporting a "linkage theory" explanation of the use of physical punishment. This theory holds that the use of physical punishment by parents is influenced by the parents' conception of the roles the child is to play as an adult. If the child is expected to become an aggressive, competitive adult, to be upwardly mobile, he is encouraged to be aggressive, to win as a child, and he is not punished for aggressive behavior.

Two other social-structural aspects of family violence that have been explored are power structure of the family and power structure of the larger society. With regard to power structure of the family, Curtis (1963), Goode (1971a), Phillips (1966), and Reiss and Sheriff (1970) pointed out that the family, like all social groups, consists of a hierarchy of interpersonal relations, with superordinate and subordinate roles, rivalries, and use of force. These variables can be measured and analyzed in the study of the family as a social group. Straus (1973), offered a general-systems-theory approach to the study of violence between family members. His paradigm begins with family-group characteristics affecting violence in the family, including organization, position in the social structure, values, and belief. Straus carried his analysis through individual characteristics of family members, precipitating factors, societal values of opportunity and power, and the violent act and its consequences for child, family, and society.

In discussing roles between family members and inevitable conflict situations, a number of family sociologists point out that conflict is itself not bad; it can be a positive force in making for equitable exchange of rewards and benefits (Scanzoni, 1972)). Sprey (1969, 1971), asserting that the conventional treatment of family harmony and conflict is inadequate, suggested as an alterative and more fruitful theoretical approach a view of the family as a system in conflict.

Unlike the social theories of violence, which hold that the source of the problem lies within the family, the cultural theories hold that the source of the problem lies outside of the family. Gil (1970) focused on the power structure within the society as it affects violence in the family, and drew attention to what he considers massive societal abuse of children as a more serious problem than individual abuse of children. Societal abuse, Gil wrote, is manifested in the statistics on infant hunger and malnutrition, mortality, poverty, inadequate medical care, poor education, and officially sanctioned abuse in schools, correctional institutions, childcare facilities, and juvenile court.

Abrahamsen (1972) and Gil (1971) discussed the cultural attitudes and values that sanction violence as a way of life. Gil wrote that the reason there is considerable child abuse in American society is because our cultural norms of child rearing allow the use of a certain amount of physical force toward children by adults caring for them. Such use tends to be encouraged by some professional experts in child rearing, education, and medicine, and by some members of the press, radio, and television. Furthermore, Gil pointed out, children are not protected by law in our society against bodily attack in the same way adults are.

Owens and Straus (1973) discussed the complementarity of social and cultural theories of violence. These authors did, however, point out the implications of each for the reduction of violence. The culture-of-violence theory assumes that there is a system of values which justifies and supports violent behavior among segments of the society with high levels of violence; the implication: an educational program designed to change these values is needed. The structural theory of violence assumes that the more violence present in the social structure during childhood, the more the person learns to use it; the implication: alteration of this underlying social behavior of violence is needed. Both of these needs, the authors argued, are actually involved in the reduction of family violence.

Incidence Studies

Data on frequency of violence among family members are hard to come by. No one wants to admit to such behavior, and, of course, except for homicide and severe child abuse, it is relatively easy behavior to hide.

At the extreme end of the spectrum—homicide—a number of investigators have found a high proportion of victim-offender pairs to be relatives. Boudouris (1971), in a study of homicide cases in Detroit over a 42-year period, found that 30% of the pairs were related. Voss and Hepburn (1968) found that almost half of the victims in the city of Chicago in 1965 were related to their offenders. Willie (1970) found a high proportion of relationships in the state of Michigan, as did Field and Field (1973) in a study of murders in the United States as a whole. Wolfgang (1958) found that friends, relatives, and acquaintances made up the major types of specific relationships between this nation's homicide victims and offenders—69% of violence-precipitated homicide. Outside of this country, Maldonado (1968), in a study in northern and central Portugal, found that 71% of those who committed murder did so in their place of residence; McClintock (1963), in a study in London, accounted for 30% of homicides as domestic disputes; Siciliano (1968), in a study in Denmark, found a predominance of murders occurring among family members, as did McCarthy (1974), who analyzed murders committed by children in Ireland.

Wolfgang (1957) broke down the frequency of homicidal relationships in the United States by race (and found that whites are more likely to be slain by relatives) and by sex (and found that primary group contact amounts to 59% of all victim-offended relatives for males and 84% for females).

The statistics on frequency of child abuse vary considerably, partly of course because of the wide differences in definition of child abuse among researchers. For some researchers, child abuse is defined as severe battering; for other researchers, child abuse involves any use of physical force or acts of omission causing physical injury to a child.

Kempe (1971) estimated that child abuse may occur as often as six times for every 1000 births. Zalba (1971) estimated conservatively that, of 200,000 to 250,000 children in need of protective services in the United States each year, 30,000 may have been badly hurt. Gil and Noble (1967) asserted that reported cases in this country are only a fraction of the actual number, which they estimated at between 2.5 and 4.1 million per year. A nationwide study of child abuse in New Zealand by Fergusson et al. (1972) showed that 41% of the abused children were under five years of age; the largest number were children under one year old. Younger age groups as more frequent victims were also reported by Gil (1968).

With respect to other violent crimes, some interesting differences are found. As the degree of violence decreases, the percentage of strangers committing the offense increases. Mulvihill et al. (1969) reported that, among recent violent crimes in this country involving strangers, 16% were homicide, 21% aggravated assault, 53% forcible rape, and 78% armed robbery. The widely held fear that an attacker will be a stranger is therefore strongly justified for robbery and relevant for rape, but is much less valid for aggravated assault and generally inappropriate for homicide.

Violence between Husbands and Wives

The occurrence of adult violence in the home usually involves males as aggressors toward females. It is repeatedly cited as a cause for marital unhappiness and discord and for divorce (Chester and Streather, 1972; Cormier, 1962; Snell et al., 1974). In analyzing complaints of husbands and wives seeking divorce, Levinger (1966) wrote that wives complain about neglect, physical or verbal abuse, lack of love, or other matters included under the catch-all term of "mental cruelty." While husbands are also disturbed by neglect, emotional cruelty, and lack of love, they are more prone to express complaints about in-law intervention or sexual mismatching. Whitehurst (1971a) reported that one reason for increasing jealousy among husbands is the trend toward economic and social equality of women, which often leads the male to feel threatened. A further problem arises with the wife who violates the sexual norms of a double-standard society.

Bergen (1958) gave a detailed account of the effect upon a child of violence between parents. A four-year-old child observed the killing of her mother by her father. In a way she had been prepared for this event by her father's previous threats to her mother, and had therefore to deal less with the unexpectedness of the murder than with its confirmation of her fears and anxieties. The effect on children of violence between parents has not really been explored to any significant extent, even though it is in itself a form of child abuse and is also a part of the socialization process.

Abuse of Children

The first thing to be learned from the literature is that child abuse is not a unique product of our time and place. Kellum (1974) discussed the existence of massive infanticide during the Middle Ages. Langer (1974) wrote that, except among Christians and Jews, infanticide has from time immemorial been an accepted procedure for disposing not only of deformed or sickly infants, but of all such newborns as might strain the resources of the individual family or the larger community. Langer noted that infanticide is still employed by so-called "underdeveloped peoples" in an effort to keep the population in reasonable adjustment to the available food supply.

In the nineteenth century, the Society for the Prevention of Cruelty to Animals succeeded in removing a maltreated child from his parents on the grounds that he was a member of the animal kingdom and entitled to protection under the laws against animal cruelty (Redbill, 1968). This action precipitated the formation in 1871 of the Society for Prevention of Cruelty to Children. More recent interest in child abuse, particularly in the battered-child syndrome, has its origin in the discipline of pediatric radiology, begun in 1906. From x rays it is possible to document repeated injuries to a child over time and to confirm suspicions of abuse.

A number of typologies have been developed in relation to child abuse; some focus on the degree of battering—i.e., controllable abuse to enraged battering—(Boisvert, 1972), some on the reasons for child abuse—i.e., altruistic to revenge—(Flammang, 1970; Resnik, 1969; Scott, 1973), and some on the effect of child abuse on the child—i.e., psychological and physical—(Birrell and Birrell, 1968; Bloch, 1966). Many studies point out clearly that child abuse occurs with other forms of dysfunction in the family. From within the family, there is marital conflict between parents (Johnson and Morse, 1968a; Editorial, 1971; Terr, 1970); from without, there are social pressures of economic adversity and social isolation (Brown and Daniels, 1968; Holter and Friedman, 1969).

Some studies have found socioeconomic differences among abusers of children, a preponderance of abusers being lower class (Editorial, 1969; Cohen et al., 1967; Zuckerman et al., 1972). Others (Galdston, 1965; Helfer and Kempe, 1968) have not found such differences. Reliable data on socioeconomic differences are difficult to obtain because, as a number of studies have pointed out, upper-class persons are able to get help from private doctors who are sometimes willing to let the abuse go unreported, while lower-class persons must go to the public hospital, which is required to make a report (Caffey et al., 1972).

What, then, are some of the real problems in family functioning, particularly in child care, that cause parents to abuse their children? There are, first of all, emotional problems. Because of confusion in identities between the mother and the baby, postpartum depression can lead to infanticide in place of suicide (Asch, 1968). The relationship of infanticide to later actual or attempted suicide of parents is mentioned by a number of investigators (Harder, 1967; Lukianowicz, 1972; Mohr and

McKnight, 1971; Uskiewiczowa, 1971). Severe personality problems of parents are discussed, and psychoses, including both manic-depressive and schizophrenic behaviors, are reported (Bennie and Sclare, 1969; Editorial, 1969; Flynn, 1970). Other socio-psychological problems referred to are alcoholism (Fontana, 1971a, 1971b; Pawlikoski, 1972; Stetic, 1966) and drug addiction (Fontana, 1971a, 1971b). Finally, Elmer (1971b) and Grumet (1970) mentioned a combination of physical and emotional problems of parents leading to child abuse.

Some studies point to problems between mother and father as related to child abuse (Becker, n.d.; Holter and Friedman, 1969; Johnson and Morse, 1968a; Terr, 1970). The husband or wife displaces hostility onto the child. Still other researchers have found child abuse to be related to the stress of mothering. Elmer (1967a, 1971a, 1971b) and others (Giovannoni, 1971; Editorial, 1971; Editorial, 1973) pointed out that child abuse is usually the result of accumulated stresses within the family, often associated with the lower socioeconomic classes. Among factors involved in the stress are the birth of several children close together, prematurity, and special physical or emotional problems of children. With the increasing isolation of the nuclear family from relatives and the increasing number of one-parent families, parents, most often mothers, are on call 24 hours a day, seven days a week, 52 weeks of the year. When there is no relief from the pressures of this job, the stresses result in blowups of one sort or another.

Researchers in this field have noted still another problem leading to child abuse: parental ignorance (Johnson and Morse, 1968b; Spinetta and Rigler, 1972). Many parents do not know about age-appropriate behavior for young children. They also have mistaken notions of how to rear children, how to encourage and guide them at different ages. They see recalcitrant behavior as willful naughtiness. Laury (1970) and Steele and Pollock (1968) noted that battering is often the result of the child's failure to meet various parental expectations.

A number of studies of child abuse have found a generational pattern to exist. The battered child tends to become a battering parent in the classical battered-child syndrome. Social anthropologists and psychologists have long recognized that patterns of child rearing, both good and bad, are passed from one generation to the next in relatively unchanged form. Psychologically speaking, one could describe this phenomenon as an identification with the aggressive parent, this identification occurring despite strong wishes of the person to be different (Jenkins et al., 1970;

Kempe et al., 1962; Lascari, 1972; Meinick and Hurley, 1969; Oliver et al., 1971; Spinetta and Rigler, 1972; Steinhausen, 1972). Some mothers who beat their children have themselves been beaten not only during childhood, but, as adults, in weeks immediately prior to their own battering behavior (Weston, 1968). Some children likewise batter other younger children after their own battering.

Abuse by Children

Extreme violence by children occurs rarely. When it occurs, it is viewed primarily as a pathological response to very poor relationships between parent and child. A number of studies show that children who kill or attempt to kill usually choose parents as victims (Campbell, 1967; Katz, 1973; Mecir, 1968; Sadoff, 1971). Hellsten and Katila (1965) reported that such children are encouraged by one parent to aggress against the other. Duncan and Duncan (1971) reported cases where a history of parental brutality is a significant consideration in cases of homicidal adolescents' abrupt loss of control.

In addition to abusing adults, children also abuse other children. Adelson (1972), in his study of homicide by children eight years old or younger, reminded us that the preschool child is capable of homicidal rage when he is provoked by what he considers to be a threat to his position in the family unit or in the immediate human environment. Sargent (1971b) presented a case study of two children who killed siblings and who, it is suggested, were the recipients of both overt and covert commands from adults in their environment to commit murder. In all the studies mentioned, the child abuser is viewed as the recipient of poor models of social behavior and of overstressful social situations which cause him to lash out as he has been told or in the only way he can.

Family Violence and Social Structure

The majority of empirical work in the area of family violence has focused upon social structural variables hypothesized to be related to such family disharmony. These include not only the demographic variables of sex, race, and class, but also functional variables of relationships within and outside of the family. In terms of sex, research on family groups (Lansky, 1961; Toby, 1966; Whitehurst, 1971b) and on television and fiction portrayals of family groups (Gecas, 1962; Gerbner, 1972; Halloran and Croll, 1972) show men to be more violent than women. Women may be verbally aggressive, and such behavior is related to the masculine ideal of violence in Western culture. Feshbach and Feshbach (1973) have also found six-year-old boys to be more physically aggressive than six-year-old girls in our society. Whiting (1965) analyzed both non-Western and Western societies and found a higher frequency of physical violence, as a form of protest masculinity, in those societies where the male has lower salience in infancy but higher prestige and salience from childhood on. Levine (1962) found Yoruba students' memories of childhood rewards and punishments more heavily related to physical punishment for boys than for girls.

Information on the difference in the amount of family violence between racial groups is scanty. Rosenberg and Silverstein (1969) reported violence among Puerto Ricans in New York to be present because of family relationships—parents hit to punish children; parents and children fight to defend one another against outsiders. Campbell (1969) stated that the impact of slavery and segregation on the black family has often had a debilitating effect on its ability to socialize its children. The shattering of family control typically causes the family to be replaced as the primary norm-setter by the street culture—in the streets of a crime-ridden, violence-prone, and poverty-stricken world. Erlanger (1971) wrote that, insofar as differences in social patterns are found between races, they are at least in part related to social class—working-class whites and blacks report more frequently that they were spanked as children than do middle-class whites and blacks.

Class differences in family violence are frequently reported. These differences have to do primarily with differences in socialization practices among middle- and lower-class persons. Brody (1968) pointed out that middle-class mothers tend to use a more stimulating and emotionally warm mode of child rearing, with emphasis upon the child's achieving through satisfactions from his own efforts rather than through material rewards and punishments. Working-class mothers, on the other hand, tend to play a more passive and less stimulating role with the child, with more emphasis upon control through rewards and punishments. Brofenbrenner (1958), Coles (1968), and Lewis (1971) reported similar class differences in patterns of socialization. Cooney (1967) found middle-class mothers more permissive than lower-class mothers.

Why are middle-class mothers gentler and more permissive than lower-class mothers? Kohn (1969) related the differences in disciplinary practices to the degree of self-direction valued in the two classes, which is in turn related to characteristics of their occupations—middle-class occupations demanding self-direction and creativity, lower-class occupations demanding conformity. Steinmetz and Straus (1974), agreeing with Kohn, focused on a methodological issue in the study of class differences. They asserted that the widespread practice of using social class as an independent variable in socialization research suppresses important relationships between occupational groups and socialization practices. Her own findings suggest that differences in the verbal, interpersonal, and attitudinal tasks and orientations required by an individual's occupational roles are related to differences in his socialization techniques and personality outcomes. Her findings indicate, furthermore, that these occupational requirements are better indexed, not by social class, but by a system of "Occupational Environments" which cuts across social classes to directly index the types of occupationally induced behaviors and values that are only indirectly indexed by social class.

A number of researchers emphasize the necessity of giving children some controls in the process of socializing them. Havens (1972), in looking at recent trends in family structure, concluded that there is a need for a better combination of the balance between parental firmness and gentleness. Campbell (1969) found that parents of delinquents tend to be more punitive than do parents of nondelinquents, although they do not differ in extent of firmness of socialization and home demands. Gallenkamp and Rychlak (1968) reported that delinquents tend to see their parents as more sanctioning of antisocial behavior than the parents see themselves. In measuring aggression in children, Gordon and Smith (1965) found that (1) the stricter the girl's mother, the more aggressive the daughter, if the mother uses physical punishment; and (2) the stricter the boy's mother, the less aggressive the son, especially if physical punishment was not used. Winder and Rau (1962), in a study of social deviance among preadolescent boys, found aggression, dependency, withdrawal, depression, and likability correlated with certain parental attitudes. Low self-esteem and high ambivalence in mothers, high punitiveness and physical punishment in fathers, were associated with deviance among children.

Still another structural element that has been explored in the study of family violence is the process by which parent and adolescent are separated. In discussing parent-youth conflict, Goode (1971b) maintained that even when much of the argument centers upon the sexual behavior of the adolescent, the youngster is not disobeying old rules merely because of temptation. Rather, he or she is asserting the right to behave in that fashion; hence, the conflict may be fierce, and often breaks, either temporarily or permanently, the attachment of parents and children. Edwards and Braubruger (1973) also discussed the breakdown of exchange between parents and adolescent children which can lead to violent conflict. He asserted that such breakdown can also lead to more social independence from parents when children accept fewer benefits and rewards from them. Peer groups, in particular, serve as alternative suppliers for a variety of services needed by adolescents.

Finally, nontraditional and changing family structures have been studied in relation to family violence. In a study of six communes, Leigh (1974) wrote that a large majority of commune members report much less hostility and competition and much more cooperation and meaningful communication between men and women in the communal situation than in their former situation. Whitehurst (1974) suggested that alternative family structures, those which contain more people than the traditional husband-wife-children combination, may reduce the potential for family violence. He based his discussion on the assumption that alternative family systems allow more autonomy to the individual than does the nuclear family system. Such an assumption is still to be tested.

Services to Violent Families

There is a considerable amount of literature on delivery of services to adult family members who are in physical combat. A number of articles discuss family-crisis intervention using police teams (Bard, 1969; Bard and Berkowitz, 1969; Bard and Zacker, 1971; Barocas, 1973; Katz, 1973, Newman, 1972; Parnas, 1971. Parnas, 1973; U.S. National Institute of Law Enforcement and Criminal Justice, 1970). They focus upon the application of sociopsychological principles to increase the policeman's effectiveness in handling such disputes and to increase the policeman's own safety. There is an emphasis, too, on improving police-community relations, especially in minority-group communities. Many of the articles discuss training programs designed to sensitize police workers to social problems and help them resolve conflict, rather than carry out traditional police roles of authoritarianism and arrest.

In addition to this material on services to adults in violence, there is a considerable amount of material related to child abuse. A number of authors point out that parents who abuse children present themselves in many different ways (Alexander, 1972; Court and Kerr, 1971). Most often, the child is brought as the problem, and the parents may sincerely believe the difficulty rests with him. No matter how the parents appear, their expectations are that they will be used, attacked, and accused of being bad parents. The worker's immediate and continuing response must be to the underlying fear, hurt, and frustration that the parents are feeling.

A number of authors point out the diversity of problems and of solutions (McCaghy, 1968; Newberger et al., 1973; Raffalli and Christian, 1970; Zalba, 1967). Treatment, it is urged, must be related to both the child's needs and the basic family situation. Most of the writers suggest the need for interdisciplinary teams to provide services to the whole family, the abuser as well as the abused (American Humane Association, 1967; Holter and Friedman, 1968; Kempe and Helfer, 1972; Savindo and Sanders, 1973). Many services are needed, including emergency medical services and legal counseling. As Wasserman (1967) pointed out, battering families generally suffer from community exclusion and require intervention by community agencies to break the cycle of reciprocal aggression in the family.

The most important services mentioned are, of course, those that relate to prevention. Educational programs in parenthood are suggested strongly, since it has been amply documented that parents who abuse children often are woefully ignorant about child development (Gil, 1969; Light, 1973; Editorial, 1974). Gil (1969, 1970) and others (Gelles, 1973; Harder, 1967) also urge certain basic social reforms, such as comprehensive family planning programs, the elimination of poverty, and the assurance of economic security as a right to all individuals and families by means of mother's wages, children's allowances, a negative income tax, or some other mechanism. No doubt such reforms are only a partial answer to the complex issue of preventing violence toward children, but perhaps a very important part of the total answer, and certainly that part without which other preventative efforts may be useless.

Intervention programs are also discussed. Paulson and Blake (1969) stated that preventive intervention requires that the caseworker or therapist consider not only the abused child but the relationship of the parent to this child and the relationship of the family to the community. The caseworker must be able to identify high-risk families and take steps to help the parents. Bean (1971) described a group-therapy demonstration project designed to aid parents in families showing patterns of child abuse. The major treatment method is group therapy, with parent participation encouraged in supervised child day care.

Finally, legal matters are discussed by a number of authors. Elmer (1967b) mentions the need for sufficient personnel to back new child-abuse laws. Polier et al. (1972) wrote that the authority of the juvenile court or family court should be invoked when there is evidence of abuse and when voluntary cooperation of the parent is inadequate to safeguard the welfare of the child. The court has a twofold responsibility at the initial fact-finding hearing. It must see that the constitutional rights of the parent are protected, and it must also safeguard the welfare of the child. When a fact-finding hearing warrants a finding, the court must be able to call upon the probation officers for a full investigation and to call upon its psychiatric staff for an evaluation of the parents, when that is indicated, before disposition is made. Above all, the court must be committed to determining, in accordance with all available information, what is truly in the best interest of the child.

Discussion

Studies on family violence have explored the phenomenon from psychological, social, and cultural levels of analyses. Examination of psychological variables indicates the importance of the factor of long-term, intimate social contact, which can evoke anger, and the factor of psychopathology, which can result in uncontrollable social behavior. Social factors found to have a high relationship with violence at home include demeaning and debilitating social statuses such as unemployment and poverty, and the socialization of aggression, in which the child learns aggressive behavior from an aggressive parent or caretaker. Cultural analysis points to cultural norms of the society, which allow violent behavior, and to attitudes and values, which sometimes condone and sometimes extol violent behavior.

By and large, the available evidence is not contradictory, leading to the conclusion that a comprehensive theory of violence at home must take into account factors at these several levels, placing individual functioning within the social group and within the culture norms by which the group operates. Thus, violence at home occurs when the individual's social needs and expectations are unsupported by either the family or by other social institutions, and when such a mode of expression seems eminently available and legitimate to the individual.

Study of violent behavior in the family should begin with a focus on basic individual needs. What are such needs? What is the role of the family in responding to such needs? What is the interplay (or lack of interplay) of the family with other social institutions in responding to needs? From such a perspective one may ask further questions on how the frustrations and stresses on the individual of economic insecurity, community isolation, illness, and overwork contribute to child abuse and to violence between husband and wife; why there is violence rather than passive withdrawal or some other mode of displacement; what are the processual modes of development leading to the violent act; how the participants define the situation.

There is need for study of the changes in relationships between individuals in the family and changing relationships of the family with support institutions of church, school, and work. Not only new family forms but the restructuring of old forms should receive attention. Of particular importance is study of the child-rearing function in our society. Who is to care for the child, attend to his physical needs, socialize him, teach him? Who is to love the child?

There are difficult methodological issues in the study of family functioning. While it is relatively easy to obtain basic demographic data of families, especially those that are not functioning well and are being seen by public agencies which collect records, it is not easy to obtain data on the interpersonal relationships, attitudes, and values among a community sample of families. Important in this research is the analysis of data by class, occupational, racial, and ethnic groups, for such groups receive different societal opportunities and rewards, and they also share different social beliefs and goals. Clear definitions of what constitutes violent behavior, particularly with regard to child abuse, are required of all such research. Sensitive instrument measures that achieve both reliability and validity, and adequate measures for protecting human subjects in this research, still must be devised.

Even though methodological problems exist, it is essential that research be continued on family functioning and on family violence as a major form of dysfunction. It is important not only for theoretical reasons but for the humane reasons of defining and evaluating services that the society should be providing all families, and those it should be providing special families in distress. For it is within the family that societal stress affects each individual most immediately. It is here that the child's capacity to grow and develop is nurtured. And it is here that the child learns future adult roles of a violent or nonviolent character.

References

Abrahamsen, D. (1972), *Our Violent Society*. New York: Funk & Wagnalls.

Adelson, L. (1972), The battering child. *JAMA*, 222:159-161.

Alexander, H. (1972), The social worker and the family. In: *Helping the Battered Child and His Family*, ed. C. Kempe & R. Helfer. Philadelphia: Lippincott, pp. 22-40.

American Humane Association (Children's Division) (1967), *The Protective Services Center*. Denver. American Humane Association.

Asch, S. (1968), Crib deaths: Their possible relationship to post-partum depression and infanticide. *J. Mt. Sinai Hosp.*, New York, 35:214-220.

Bard, M. (1969), Family intervention police teams as a community mental health resource. *J. Crim. Law, Criminol. Police Sci.*, 60:247-250.

——— & Berkowitz, B. (1969), Family disturbance as a police function. In: *Law Enforcement Science and Technology—II*, ed. S. Cohn. Chicago: I.T.T. Research Institute, pp. 238-250.

——— & Zacker, J. (1971), The prevention of family violence: Dilemmas of community intervention. *J. Marr. & Fam.*, 33:677-682.

Barocas, H. (1973), Urban policemen: Crisis mediators or crisis creators? *Amer. J. Orthopsychiat.*, 43:632-639.

Bean, S. (1971), The parent's center project: A multiservice approach to the prevention of child abuse. *Child Welfare*, 59:277-282.

Becker, W. (no date), The problem of maltreatment of the child. *Therapie der Gegenwart* (Berlin), 107:135-136, 138-140, 142-144, 147-149.

Bennie, E. & Sclare, A. (1969), The battered-child syndrome. *Amer. J. Psychiat.*, 125:975-979.

Bergen, M. (1958), The effect of severe trauma on a four-year-old child. *The Psychoanalytic Study of the Child*, 13:407-429. New York; International Universities Press.

Birrell, R. & Birrell, J. (1968), The maltreatment syndrome in children: A hospital survey. *Med. J. Austral.*, 522:1023-1029.

Bloch, D. (1966), Some dynamics of suffering: Effect of the wish for infanticide in a case of schizophrenia. *Psychoanal. Rev.*, 53:31-54.

Boisvert, M. (1972), The battered-child syndrome. *Soc. Casewk.*, 53:475-480.

Boudouris, J. (1971), Homicide and the family. *J. Marr. & Fam.*, 33:667-676.

Brody, G. (1968), Socioeconomic differences in stated maternal child-rearing practices and in observed maternal behavior. *J. Marr. & Fam.*, 30:656-660.

Brofenbrenner, U. (1958), Socialization and social class through time and space. In: *Readings in Social Psychology*, ed. E. Maccoby et al. New York: Holt, Rinehart & Winston.

Brown, J. & Daniels, R. (1968), Some observations on abusive parents. *Child Welfare*, 47:89-94.

Caffey, J. et al. (1972), Child battery: Seek and save. *Med. World News*, 13:21-25, 28, 32, 33.

Campbell, J. (1969), The family and violence. In: *Law and Order Reconsidered:*

A Staff Report to the National Commission on the Causes and Prevention of Violence, vol. 10, ed. J. Campbell, J. Sahid, & D. Strong. Washington, D.C.: U.S. Government Printing Office.

Campbell, R. (1967), Violence in adolescence. *J. Anal. Psychol.*, 12:161-173.

Chester, R. & Streather, J. (1972), Cruelty in English divorce: Some empirical findings. *J. Marr. & Fam.*, 34:706-710.

Cohen, M., Philbrick, E., & Mulford, R. (1967), *Neglecting Parents: A Study of Psychosocial Characteristics*. Denver: American Humane Association, Children's Division.

Coles, R. (1968), Violence in ghetto children. In: *Annual Progress in Child Psychiatry and Child Development*, ed. S. Chess & A. Thomas. New York: Brunner/Mazel, pp. 273-280.

Cooney, N. (1967), Control of aggression in child rearing in Puerto Rico: A study of professed practices used with boys and girls in two socioeconomic urban groups. *Dissert. Abstr.*, 28-A:777.

Cormier, B. (1962), Psychodynamics of homicide committed in a marital relationship. *Corrective Psychiat. J. Soc. Ther.*, 8:187-194.

Court, J. & Kerr, A. (1971), The battered child syndrome—2. *Nursing Times*, 67:187-194.

Curtis, G. (1963), Violence breeds violence—perhaps? *Amer. J. Psychiat.*, 120:386-387.

Duncan, J. & Duncan, G. (1971), Murder in the family: A study of some homicidal adolescents. *Amer. J. Psychiat.*, 127:74-78.

Editorial (1969), Battered babies. *Brit. Med. J.*, 5672:667-668.

Editorial (1970), M.D. has role in child-abuse case. *Penn. Med.*, 73:102.

Editorial (1971), The battered-child syndrome. *J. Tenn. Med. Assn.*, 64:346-347.

Editorial (1973), High-risk-abuse children should be identified in clinical setting. *U.S. Med.*, 6-7.

Editorial (1974), The abused child. *Today's Ed.*, 63:40-43.

Edwards, J. & Braubruger, M. (1973), Exchange and parent-youth conflict. *J. Marr. & Fam.*, 35:101-108.

Elmer, E. (1967a), Child abuse: The family's cry for help. *J. Psychiat. Nursing*, 5: 332-341.

——— (1967b), Abused children and community resources. *Internat. J. Offender Ther.*, 11: 16-23.

——— (1971a), Child abuse: A symptom of family crisis. In: *Crisis of Family Disorganization*, ed. E. Pavenstedt. New York: Behavioral Publications, pp. 297-308.

——— (1971b), Studies of child abuse and infant accidents. In: *The Mental Health of the Child*. U.S. National Institute of Mental Health. Washington, D.C.: U.S. Government Printing Office, pp. 343-370.

Erlanger, H. (1971), *The Anatomy of Violence: An Empirical Examination of Sociological Theories of Aggression*. Ann Arbor, Mich.: University Microfilms.

Eron, L. (1959), Symposium: The application of role and learning theories to the study of the development of aggression in children. *Proceedings of the Rip Van Winkle Clinic*, 10:3-61.

——— et al. (1963), Social class, parental punishment for aggression, and child aggression. *Child Develop.*, 34:849-867.

Fergusson, D., Fleming, J., & O'Neill, D. (1972), *Child Abuse in New Zealand*. Wellington: A.R. Shearer, Government Printer.

Feshbach, N. & Feshbach, S. (1973), The young aggressors. *Psychol. Today*, 6:90-95.

Field, M. & Field, H. (1973), Marital violence and the criminal process: Neither justice nor peace. *Soc. Serv. Rev.*, 47:221-240.

Flammang, C. (1970), The neglected child. In: *The Police and the Underprotected Child*. Springfield, Ill.: Charles C Thomas, pp. 18-24.

Flynn, W. (1970), Frontier justice: A contribution to the theory of child battery. *Amer. J. Psychiat.*, 127:375-379.

Fontana, V. (1971a), Social manifestations. In: *The Maltreated Child*, ed. V. Fontana. Springfield, Ill.: Charles C Thomas.

——— (1971b), Which parents abuse children? *Med. Insight*, 3:16-21.

Galdston, R. (1965), Observations on children who have been physically abused and their parents. *Amer. J. Psychiat.*, 122:440-443.

Gallenkamp, C. & Rychlak, J. (1968), Parental attitudes of sanction in middle-class adolescent male delinquency. *J. Soc. Psychol.*, 75:255-260.

Gecas, V. (1962), Motives and aggressive acts in popular fiction: Sex and class differences. *Amer. J. Sociol.*, 77:680-696.

Gelles, R. (1973), Child abuse as psychopathology: A sociological critique and reformulation. *Amer. J. Orthopsychiat.*, 43:611-621.

Gerbner, G. (1972), Violence in television drama. Trends and symbolic functions. In: *Television and Social Behavior: Reports and Papers*, vol. 1, ed. G. Comstock & E. Rubinstein. Washington, D.C.: U.S. Government Printing Office, pp. 28-187.

Gil, D. (1968), *Nationwide Survey of Legally Reported Physical Abuse of Children*. Waltham, Mass.: Brandeis University.

——— (1969), Physical abuse of children: Findings and implications of a nationwide survey. *Ped. Suppl.*, 44.857.

——— (1970), *Violence Against Children: Physical Child Abuse in the United States*. Cambridge: Harvard University Press.

——— (1971), Violence against children. *J. Marr. & Fam.*, 33:637-648.

——— & Noble, H. (1967), Public knowledge, attitudes and opinions about physical abuse in the U.S. *Papers in Social Welfare*, No. 14. Florence Heller Graduate School for Advanced Studies in Social Welfare, Brandeis University, Waltham, Mass.

Giovannoni, J. (1971), Parental mistreatment: Perpetrators and victims. *J. Marr. & Fam.*, 33:649-657.

Goode, W. (1969), Violence among intimates. U.S. National Commission on the Causes and Prevention of Violence. Task Force on Individual Acts of Violence. *Crimes and Violence*, 13:941-977.

——— (1971a), Force and violence in the family. *J. Marr. & Fam.*, 33:624-636.

——— (1971b), Family disorganization. In: *Contemporary Social Problems* (Third Ed.), ed. R. Merton and R. Nisbet. New York: Harcourt Brace Jovanovich, pp. 479-552.

Gordon, J. & Smith, E. (1965), Children's aggression, parental attitudes, and the effects of an affiliation-arousing story. *J. Pers. Soc. Psychol.*, 1:654-659.

Grumet, B. (1970), The plaintive plaintiffs: Victims of the battered-child syndrome. *Fam. Law. Quart.*, 4:296-317.

Halloran, J. & Croll, P. (1972), Television programs in Great Britain: Content and control. In: *Television and Social Behavior: Reports and Papers*, vol. I, ed. G. Comstock & E. Rubinstein. Washington, D.C.: U.S. Government Printing Office, pp. 415-492.

Harder, T. (1967), The psychopathology of infanticide. *Acta Psychiat. Scand.*, 43:196-245.

Havens, L. (1972), Youth, violence and the nature of family life. *Psychiat. Annals*, 2:18-21, 23-25, 29.

Helfer, R. & Kempe, C., eds. (1968), *The Battered Child*. Chicago: University of Chicago Press.

Hellsten, P. & Katila, O. (1965), Murder and other homicide by children under 15 in Finland. *Psychiat. Quart. Suppl.*, 39:54-74.

Holter, J. & Friedman, S. (1968), Principles of management in child abuse cases. *Amer. J. Orthopsychiat.*, 38:127-136.

——— ——— (1969), Etiology and management of severely burned children: Psychosocial considerations. *Amer. J. Disturbed Child*, 118:680-686.

Houts, M. (1970), *They Asked for Death*. New York: Cowles, p. 241.

Ilfeld, F., Jr. (1970), Environmental theories of violence. In: *Violence and the Struggle for Existence*, ed. D. Danield, M. Gilula & F. Ochberg, Boston: Little, Brown, pp. 79-95.

Jenkins, R. et al. (1970), Interrupting the family cycle of violence. *J. Iowa Med. Soc.*, 60:85-89.

Johnson, B. & Morse, H. (1968a), Injured children and their parents. *Children*, 15:147-152.

——— ——— (1968b), *The Battered Child: A Study of Children with Inflicted Injuries*. Denver: Colorado Welfare Department.

Katz, M. (1973), Family crisis training: Upgrading the police while building a bridge to the minority community. *J. Police Sci. Admin.*, 1:30-35.

Kellum, B. (1974), Infanticide in England in the later Middle Ages. *History of Childhood Quart.*, 1:367-389.

Kempe, C. (1971), Pediatric implications of the battered-baby syndrome. *Arch. Dis. Childhood* (London), 46:28-37.

——— et al. (1962), The battered-child syndrome. *JAMA*, 181:17-24.

——— & Helfer, R., eds. (1972), *Helping the Battered Child and His Family*. Philadelphia: Lippincott.

Kohn, M. (1969), *Class and Conformity*. Homewood, N.J.: Dorsey Press.

Kopernik, L. (1964), The family as a breeding ground of violence. *Corrective Psychiat. J. Soc. Ther.*, 10(6).

Langer, W. (1974), Infanticide: A historical survey. *Hist. Childhood Quart.*, 1:353-367.

Lansky, L. (1961), Sex differences in aggression and its correlates in middle-class adolescents. *Child Develop.*, 32:45-58.

Lascari, A. (1972), The abused child. *J. Iowa Med. Soc.*, 62:229-232.

Laury, G. (1970), The battered-child syndrome: Parental motivation, clinical aspects. *Bull. N.Y. Acad. Med.*, 46:676-685.
Lefkowitz, M., Walder, L., & Eron, L. (1963), Punishment, identification and aggression. *Merrill-Palmer Quart.*, 9:159-174.
Leigh, M. (1974), The peaceful communities. In: *NATO Conference on "Determination and Origins of Aggressive Behavior,"* ed. J. De Wit and W. Hartup. The Hague: Mouton.
Levine, B. (1962), *Yoruba Students' Memories of Childhood Rewards and Punishments*. Ibadan: Ibadan University Press.
Levinger, G. (1966), Sources of marital dissatisfaction among applicants for divorce. *Amer. J. Orthopsychiat.*, 36:803-807.
Lewis, R. (1971), Socialization into national violence: Familial correlates of hawkish attitudes toward war. *J. Marr. & Fam.*, 33:699-708.
Light, R. (1973), Abused and neglected children in America: A study ofalternative policies. *Harvard Ed. Rev.*, 43:556-598.
Lukianowicz, N. (1972), Attempted infanticide. *Psychiatria Clinica*, 5:1-16.
Maldonado, M. (1968), Study of certain socio-criminological aspects of a group of homicides. *Boletim Da Administracao Penitenciaria E Dos Institutos De Criminologia*, 23:5-34.
McCaghy, C. (1968), Drinking and deviance disavowal: The case of child molesters. *Soc. Problems*, 16:43-49.
McCarthy, P. (1974), Summary for assessment by "papers committee": Youth who murder. In: *NATO Conference on "Determinants and Origins of Aggressive Behavior,"* ed. J. De Wit & W. Hartup. The Hague: Mouton, pp. 588-594.
McClintock, F. (1963), *Crimes of Violence*. New York: St. Martin's Press.
Mecir, J. (1968), Homicidal behavior of minors directed against their parents. *Ceskoslovenska Psychiatrie* (Praha), 64:319-325.
Meinick, B. & Hurley, J. (1969), Distinctive personality attributes of child-abusing mothers. *J. Cons. Clin. Psychol.*, 33:746-749.
Mintlerer, L., Gunning, K., Holloway, M., & Peterson, C. (1974), The peaceful communities. In: *NATO Conference on "Determinants and Origins of Aggressive Behavior,"* ed. J. De Wit & W. Hartup. The Hague: Mouton, pp. 489-499.
Mohr, J. & McKnight, C. (1971), Violence as a function of age and relationship with special reference to matricide. *Canad. Psychiat. Assoc. J.*, 16:29-53.
Mulvihill, D., Tumin, M., & Curtis, L. (1969), The interpersonal relationship between victim and offender. In: *Crimes of Violence: A Staff Report to the National Commission on the Causes and Prevention of Violence*, Vol. 11. Washington, D.C.: U.S. Government Printing Office, pp. 216-220.
Newberger, E., Haas, G., & Mulford, R. (1973), Child abuse in Massachusetts. *Mass. Physician*, 32:31-38.
Newman, C. (1972), Police and families: Factors affecting police intervention. *Police Chief*, 39:25-26, 28, 30.
Oliver, J. et al. (1971), Five generations of ill-treated children in one family pedigree. *Brit. J. Psychiat.*, 119:473-480.
Owens, D. & Straus, M. (1973), The social structure of violence in childhood

and approval as an adult. Presented to the 1973 annual meeting of the American Orthopsychiatric Association, New York.

Parnas, R. (1971), Police discretion and diversion of incidence of intrafamily violence. *Law & Contemp. Prob.*, 36:539-565.

——— (1973), Prosecutorial and judicial handling of family violence. *Crim. Law Bull.*, 9:733-769.

Paulson, M. & Blake, P. (1969), The physically abused child: A focus on prevention. *Child Welfare*, 48:86-95.

Pawlikoski, A. (1972), Fates of children from families of alcoholics. *Problemy Alkoholizmu* (Warszawa), 7:4-6.

Phillips, C. (1966), Power relationships in marital discord. *Dissert. Abstr.*, 27-A:1457-1458.

Pohlen, M. (1968), The psychosis of a family. *Zeitschrift fur Psychosomatische Medizin Und Psychoanalyse* (Gottingen), 14:257-274.

Polier, J. & McDonald, K. (1972), The family court in an urban setting. In: *Helping the Battered Child and His Family*, ed. C. Kempe & R. Helfer. Philadelphia: Lippincott, pp. 208-224.

Raffali, H. C. & Christian, H. (1970), The battered child: An overview of a medical, legal, and social problem. *Crime and Delinq.*, 16(2):139-150.

Redbill, S. (1968), A history of child abuse and infanticide. In: *The Battered Child*, ed. R. Helfer & C. Kempe. Chicago: University of Chicago Press.

Reiss, D. & Sheriff, W., Jr. (1970), A computer-automated procedure for testing some experiences of family membership. *Behav. Sci.*, 15:431-433.

Resnik, P. (1969), Child murder by parents: A psychiatric review of fillicide. *Amer. J. Psychiat.*, 126:325-334.

Richette, L. (1969), Cheated out of childhood. In: *The Throw-Away Children*. Philadelphia: Lippincott, pp. 79-100.

Rosenberg, B. & Silverstein, H. (1969), Fighting. In: *The Varieties of Delinquent Experience*. Waltham, Mass.: Blaisdell, pp. 89-96.

Sadoff, R. (1971), Clinical observations on parricide. *Psychiat. Quart.*, 45:65-69.

Sargent, D. (1971a), Children who kill—a family conspiracy? In: *Theory and Practice of Family Psychiatry*, ed. J. Howells. New York: Brunner/Mazel, pp. 734-744.

——— (1971b), The lethal situation: Transmission of urge to kill from parent to child. In: *Dynamics of Violence*, ed. J. Fawcett. Chicago: American Medical Association, pp. 105-113.

Savindo, A. & Sanders, R. (1973), Working with abusive parents: Group therapy and home visits. *Amer. J. Nursing*, 73:482-484.

Scanzoni, J. (1972), Marital conflict as a positive force. In: *Sexual Bargaining: Power Politics in the American Marriage*. Englewood Cliffs, N.J.: Prentice-Hall., pp. 63-89.

Schultz, L. (1968), The victim-offender relationship. *Crime and Delinq.*, 14:135-141.

Scott, P. (1973), Parents who kill their children. *Med. Sci & Law*, 13:120-126.

Siciliano, S. (1968), Homicide in Denmark. *Annals Internationales De Criminologie* (Paris), 7:403-435.

Silver, L., Dublin, C., & Lourie, R. (1969), Does violence breed violence? Contributions from a study of the child-abuse syndrome. *Amer. J. Psychiat.*, 126:152-155.

Snell, J. et al. (1974), The wifebeater's wife: A study of family interaction. *Arch. Gen. Psychiat.*, 11:107-112.

Spinetta, J. & Rigler, D. (1972), The child-abusing parent: A psychological review. *Psychol. Bull.*, 77:296-304.

Sprey, J. (1969), The family as a system in conflict. *Marr. & Fam.*, 31:699-706.

——— (1971), On the management of conflict in families. *J. Marr. & Fam.*, 33:722-730.

Steele, B. & Pollock, C. (1968), A psychiatric study of parents who abuse infants and small children. In: *The Battered Child*, ed. R. Helfer & C. Kempe. Chicago: University of Chicago Press, pp. 89-133.

Steinhausen, H. (1972), Sociomedical aspects of physical maltreatment of children. *Monatsschrift f. Kinderheilkunde* (Berlin), 120:314-318.

Steinmetz, S. & Straus, M., eds. (1974), *Violence in the Family*. New York: Dodd, Mead.

Stetic, D. (1966), Treatment of alcoholics at the Pakrac Medical Center. Psihijatrijska Njega; *Casopis Za Srednje Medicinske Kadrove* (Zagreb), 1:23-25.

Straus, M. (1971), Some social antecedents of physical punishment: A linkage theory interpretation. *J. Marr. & Fam.*, 33:658-663.

——— (1973), A general-systems-theory approach to a theory of violence between family members. *Soc. Sci. Information*, 12:105-125.

Terr, L. (1970), A family study of child abuse. *Amer. J. Psychiat.*, 127:665-671.

Toby, J. (1966), Violence and the masculine ideal: Some qualitative data. *Annals Amer. Acad. Polit. Soc. Sci.*, 364:19-28.

U.S. National Institute of Law Enforcement and Criminal Justice. (1970), *Training Police as Specialists in Family Crisis Intervention* (submitted by Morton Bard, project director). Washington, D.C.: U.S. Government Printing Office.

Uskiewiczowa, L. (1971), Child murder by parents in the light of medicoforensic material. *Psychiatria Polska* (Gdansk), 5:125-132.

Voss, H. & Hepburn, J. (1968), Patterns in criminal homicide in Chicago. *J. Crim. Law Criminol. Police Sci.*, 59:499-508.

Wasserman, S. (1967), The abused parent of the abused child. *Children*, 14:175-179.

Weston, J. (1968), The pathology of child abuse. In: *The Battered Child*, ed. R. Helfer & C. Kempe. Chicago: University of Chicago Press, pp. 61-86.

Whitehurst, R. (1971a), Violently jealous husbands. *Sexual Behav.*, 1:32-38, 40-41.

——— (1971b), Violence potential in extramarital sexual responses. *J. Marr. & Fam.*, 33:683-691.

——— (1974), Alternative family structures and violence reduction. In: *Violence in the Family*, ed. S. Steinmetz & M. Straus. New York: Dodd, Mead, pp. 315-320.

Whiting, B. (1965), Sex identity conflict and physical violence: A comparative

study. *Amer. Anthropol.*, 67-2:123-140.
Willie, W. (1970), Citizens who commit homicides. *Revista Inter-Americana De Psicologia* (Buenos Aires), 4:131-144.
Winder, C. & Rau, L. (1962), Parental attitudes associated with social deviance in preadolescent boys. *J. Abnorm. Soc. Psychol.*, 64:418-424.
Wolfgang, M. (1957), Victim precipitated criminal homicide. *J. Crim. Law Criminol. Police Sci.*, 48:1-11.
——— (1958), *Patterns in Criminal Homicide*. New York: John Wiley.
——— (1969), Who kills whom. *Psychol. Today*, 3:54-56, 72-75.
Yarrow, M., Campbell, J., & Burton, R. (1968), Theories and correlates of child aggression. In: *Child Rearing: An Inquiry into Research and Methods*. San Francisco: Jossey-Bass, pp. 55-93.
Zalba, S. (1966), The abused child: I. A survey of the problem. *Soc. Wk.*, 11:3-16.
——— (1967), The abused child: II. A typology for classification and treatment. *Soc. Wk.*, 12:70-79.
——— (1971), Battered children. *Transaction*, 8:58-61.
Zuckerman, K., Ambuel, J., & Bandman, R. (1972), Child neglect and abuse: A study of cases evaluated at Columbus Children's Hospital in 1968-1969. *Ohio State Med. J.*, 68:629-632.

Sex reassignment is a potentially traumatic event in family life. Seven male-to-female sex reassignments are examined as events in family sociology, with special reference to social stigmatization, publicity, and concealment.

Families of Seven Male-to-Female Transsexuals after Five to Seven Years: Sociological Sexology

JOHN MONEY, FLORENCE CLARKE, and TOM MAZUR

The social mirror of sex in our culture is tarnished with taboo, making it exceedingly difficult for people—conventional people at least—to admit openly to sexual problems. Among the most difficult for conventional families to admit as problems are those related to gender identity, and erotic behavior which society has branded as immoral, perverse, and punishable. To admit to such problems is to be stigmatized in much the same way that to admit to devil possession during the Inquisition was to be stigmatized—imprisoned, tortured, and burned at the stake as a penalty for the content of one's sexual fantasies, dreams, and nightmares. The penalties of stigmatization are not so cruel today, but they are severe enough. They pose a difficult dilemma for a family confronted with transsexualism in one of its members.

Transsexualism is a very public phenomenon when it involves hor-

---

Supported by USPHS Grant HD00325 and by funds from the Grant Foundation and the Erickson Educational Foundation.

John Money, Ph.D., Florence Clarke, B.S., and Tom Mazur, A.B., are from Johns Hopkins University School of Medicine and Hospital, Baltimore, Maryland.

Reprinted from: *Archives of Sexual Behavior*, vol. 4, no. 2, 1975.

monal, surgical, and legal sex reassignment. It is hardly something that a family can easily conceal, even by the extreme measure of disowning or disinheriting the transsexual member. Moreover, most parents are not so lacking in compassion that they would sever all connection with a transsexual son or daughter.

Description of Sample

The sample represents all seven cases of male-to-female surgical sex reassignment performed five to seven years ago on transsexuals whose families live in the Baltimore-Washington area. That is, they were living within commuting distance for follow-up visits and interviews to supplement those done at the time of surgery.

Four of the families are black and three white. The black families are working class and inner city. They were headed by a woman most of the time when the patient was growing up. The woman is still the head of the household, except for one who has died. Her place as next of kin is taken by the patient's much older half-sister. One patient, though knowing her mother, who was sixteen when the patient was born, was reared by a childless cousin who is still her primary relative. A third, whose mother was thirteen when the patient was born, was raised by her grandmother and mother, who continue to be her dual mothers. The fourth black patient was reared by the parents in infancy, and by the paternal grandmother until age fourteen; she then lived at the mother's residence until three years after reassignment surgery. This patient is the first son and third child in a sibship of eight. In another family, there were four older brothers and a half-sister. Two families had an only child.

The white families were working-class to middle-class suburban. They were nuclear families, two with three children, one with six. The largest family included also the invalid maternal grandfather, and in another family the maternal grandmother lived with them permanently.

In both the black and white families, there was no recurrent pattern to either the sex ratio of siblings or the ordinal position of the patient. All seven patients were born to young parents: two of the black mothers were unmarried teenagers who conceived with teenaged boyfriends. The other five mothers were young adults in their twenties when the patient was born. Their husbands were of like age, except for one, aged 29 when his child was born, who was eight years older than his wife.

The four black patients were known to one another, having met by reason of their social pastimes and entertainments in the gay community. Two of the white patients were friends, having met in the same way; the third patient knew none of the other six. All seven knew something of the Christine Jorgensen case, which, through the media, was virtually the sole source of public information about transsexualism. Either directly or indirectly, they were influenced by this case to try to resolve the dilemma of their own lives in the same way. Those who knew one another shared information, together and with other transsexual friends, concerning physicians and clinics hospitable toward the transsexual patient. Independently of their families, and with indeflectible determination, they set sex reassignment as a goal, stopping at neither deceit nor subterfuge, on occasion, if either seemed likely to bring the goal closer. Thereby, they gave tacit recognition to the stigma that our society places on anomalies of gender identity. Stigmatized themselves, they had no choice under certain circumstances but to hide their transsexual decision even from parents and physicians, disclosing it only to those who had already proved sympathetic or trustworthy.

At the time of surgery, the seven patients ranged in age from 23 to 33. Two were 23 and two were 24 years old.

Procedure

The parents, or those who stood in their place, were tape-recorded in solo interviews at the hospital or, if they failed to keep appointments, interviewed at home. In one case, information was obtained from a telephone call to the mother, who did not wish to be interviewed in person. The patients also were seen for a long-term, follow-up taped interview, except for one, last interviewed three years ago, who now resides at a far distance.

From the transcripts of interviews, the appropriate data were abstracted onto prepared data sheets, and then summarized into Tables 1, 2, and 3.

Findings

Concealment vs. Disclosure

In all seven cases, the families knew about their son's effeminacy when he was a teenager, far in advance of sex reassignment. They knew that he dressed on occasion as an impersonator in women's clothes, though seldom so as to be seen by family members.

By late teenage or young adulthood, five of the seven patients had managed to achieve sufficient economic independence to live separately from their families. Some had the support of friends. Some had been able to find employers sympathetic to their condition, and so could work as women. They maintained contact with their families, but initially did not disclose the extent of their dressing and living as a woman. On home visits, they defeminized their clothing and cosmetic appearance so as to pass as masculine. One black patient eventually dropped all pretense and visited the family (siblings, nieces, nephews) as a woman years before she obtained hormonal feminization and reassignment surgery. Pretense was also dropped by the two patients, both black, who did not leave home. One dressed as a girl exclusively from age fourteen.[1] The other did not transfer full-time to the feminine role until after embarking on feminizing hormonal therapy—reassured, no doubt, by having the support of a sympathetic physician. The other four patients, since they were not living at home, did not need to confront their families with their living and dressing full-time in the feminine role, but they did have to get their parents' agreement to their surgical sex reassignment, this being one of the clinic's requirements and a safeguard for effective rehabilitation. These families had an option, which the other three did not, of acting so as to conceal or attempt to conceal the stigma of transsexual reassignment from some of its members. These families also had an option as to whether they would inform friends and neighbors who could not see the evidence for themselves and might not pick it up from hearsay. Publicity that would inform strangers was an option to be taken up by either the patient or the family or both.

Table 1 is designed to show for each of the seven patients how information about the sex reassignment was either concealed from or disclosed to kin and community. The four black families were the most open, especially with kinfolk and family friends. One family followed the lead of their transsexual child when she publicized her reassignment to the community at large, by having her story featured with pictures in a local

[1] The baby of the family, a half-sister, had always known this transsexual exclusively in the feminine role, with a feminine nickname and wearing women's clothes, although sometimes referred to as "he."

TABLE 1
FAMILY'S CONCEALMENT VS. DISCLOSURE OF SON'S SEX REASSIGNMENT, FIVE TO SEVEN YEARS LATER (N = 7)

People informed or not	Black families				White families		
	A	B	C	D	E	F	G
Siblings	0[a]	+	+	+	±	±	+
Kinfolk	+	+	+	+	±	±	±
Family friends	+	+	+	+	±	±	±
Neighborhood	+	±	±	±	±	±	±
Patient's in-laws	+	–	–[b]	–[b]	–	–	–
Patient's workmates	–	–	–	–	–	–	–
Patient's key advisors	+	+	+	+	+	+	+

[a]Only child.
[b]Not legally married, but had long-term living arrangement with boyfriend.

newspaper on the occasion of her wedding. The other three families were selective in informing friends and neighbors.

The black transsexuals themselves, once they became established in life as women, withheld their stories from selected people, including fellow employees and relatives of the husband or boyfriend. One had to rebuild social and occupational privacy a second time after receiving unwanted publicity following an arrest on a minor charge. To a variable extent, all four broke the privacy of their new lives to fraternize with old friends who knew their past, but they kept the two sets of people socially and/or geographically separated (Kando, 1972).

The three white transsexuals, like their black counterparts, were, in variable degree, concerned to keep their past concealed from friends, neighbors, employers, and workmates who knew them only in their new life. They discontinued contact with many but not all who knew their transsexual history, and kept them safely separated from those who did not.

The three white families felt the stigma of transsexual reassignment so burdensome that they tried to conceal the information from some of even the closest relatives. In two cases, younger siblings were not informed and were required to grow up never questioning the fiction that the one-time elder brother was working in a distant state too far to visit. In another case, a similar fiction was given to the paternal grandparents. One father's attitude toward other relatives was reported by his transsexual daughter thus: "My father said, 'This is the way it is; if you don't like it, don't come over'—and hung the phone up."

The three white families were selectively close-mouthed with friends and neighbors, as well as with relatives, leaving many people to find out what they could through the grapevine. They were not harassed by gossip as a result, but they were left in the uncomfortable position of not knowing what various people knew or surmised, and of not knowing when something might be said or done that would prove embarrassing in public.

These three white families were unable to fraternize, for fear that the past would out, with the families of their sons-in-law when their daughters by reassignment got married. One black family was in the same position. The transsexual daughters themselves were guarding their secret from their husbands' families.

Of the five weddings, black and white, three were civil ceremonies without relatives present, one was a big church wedding without publicity about the bride's transsexual status, and one was a big home wedding with transsexual publicity. The brides did not and could not conceal the truth about themselves coitally from their husbands, though they may have told edited stories about the diagnosis in those cases where the first meeting was after surgical reassignment (in two cases, the husbands were rather scrupulously kept away from the hospital by their wives.) The husbands all met their parents-in-law. In the white families, there was a low level of fraternization with the son-in-law, and it may well have been that his visits were kept to a minimum by his wife. The two black families with a son-in-law fraternized more freely with him.

Families concealed information from the transsexual's current workmates and friends only in the sense that they did not fraternize with them. Families belonged to the transsexual's old life and, though far from being disowned by the transsexual, were discreetly kept separate from people who knew her only in her new life.

Families shared the secret of their son's transsexualism openly with key advisors, including clergy and legal, medical, and educational professionals, as needed. No family members consulted a psychologist, psychiatrist, or psychotherapist out of personal need, but only in connection with their transsexual child's treatment and follow-up.

Type of Family Contact

The amount and type of continued contact that a reassigned transsexual maintains with the family relates directly to the family's and the transsexual's policy of disclosing or concealing the fact of reassignment from relatives and friends who used to know today's daughter as yesterday's son.

Table 2 shows that none of the seven transsexuals abandoned her family and lost all contact. During the early stages of cross-dressing in defiance of family, transsexuals who had left home would write or phone fairly regularly. Reassignment in defiance of family was not acceptable to the clinic, so that all seven are cases in which the family had become reconciled to the child's demand to be surgically reassigned. This reconciliation opened the way to postreassignment visiting. Though not exclusively one way, most visiting was by the transsexual to the family. Reciprocal visits by the family have been, apparently by silent consent, not desired by either party. For the transsexuals who wanted nothing known of their early life as a boy, family visits ran too much risk of inadvertent disclosure of the past.

In the five- to seven-year post-follow-up period, all seven transsexuals have at some time or another made day visits home while living within commuting distance. One of the black transsexuals, recovering from a severe attack of illness, now lives at the home of her half-sister. Another made an extended visit home at the time of getting a second-stage vaginoplasty. The other two visit home, staying overnight as desired. The three white transsexuals have recently lived too distant for day visits; two have returned home for vacations (without their husbands), and the third has only written or phoned.

The two transsexuals whose reassignment has been left unmentioned to younger siblings are both white. One of these is the transsexual who

TABLE 2
TYPE OF FAMILY CONTACT: SEVEN REASSIGNED TRANSSEXUALS

In absentia (letters and/or phone calls)	7/7
Day visits to family	7/7
Extended visits to family	6/7

does not visit home in person at the present time; when she did visit, the younger siblings were given the story that because she had no home she had been adopted into the family, though not legally. As they grew older, these younger children knew from the framed chart of the family tree that the oldest sibling is a brother, of whom it is said only that he lives in another state.

In the other case, the transsexual does visit and spend vacations at home. Of her brother, aged eleven, who was six at the time of surgery, she said: "I think he knows that there was an alteration in the identity, but I don't think he knows exactly what's going on." She planned one day to tell him, but had no idea when.

Parental Reaction Categorized

In cases of sex reannouncement or reassignment associated with intersexuality in infancy, not the child but the parents have the decision-making responsibility. In the present study, the parents (or their substitutes) were cast in the role of agreeing to a policy of sex reassignment commanded by their child (Table 3). "Commanded" is the appropriate term, for, as is typical of transsexuals, all seven were uncompromisingly imperious and manipulative in their determination to live as women. The responsible relatives had the choice only of consenting or not consenting to the decision. They would have preferred to be rid of transsexualism altogether, and to have a normally masculine son. Failing this, they were relieved that their son's condition had come under the purview of medicine instead of the penal system. They saw in sex reassignment a resolution of at least part of the family's, as well as of the son's, dilemma. Nonetheless, they were in the position of making a forced choice, in which sex reassignment was the lesser of two evils, rather than an unambiguously positive decision. The decision could not be unambiguous because the parents recognized the social stigma attached to sex reassignment, because they knew it was a method of rehabilitation rather than cure, or because they ruminated on possible self-blame for not having been able to prevent the child's condition.

Eventual resolution of the ambiguity present at the time of consenting to sex-reassignment surgery was more complete in the black parents (or their substitutes) than the white. In Table 3, those classified as finding the outcome of reassignments fully acceptable were the families of the

TABLE 3
SON'S REASSIGNMENT: PARENTAL REACTION CATEGORIZED
(N = 7)

Acquiesced to reassignment policy set by son	7/7
Outcome fully acceptable	4/7
Outcome ambivalently acceptable	3/7

four black transsexuals, whereas all three white families were ambivalently accepting.

The most probable explanation of this difference is that the black families felt under no great social pressure to conceal transsexualism from kin and friends, so that the sex-reassigned member of the family could continue to be a participant family member in person. The black family did not fraternize with their sex-reassigned member under the threat of anxiety of embarrassment and of exposure.

The white families, with their cultural heritage of more prudish and punitive sexual mores, were at a disadvantage. Neither they nor their transsexual member could be completely open with all their kin and friends about sex reassignment. Death would probably have been easier for them to deal with, socially, though not personally. When their sex-reassigned child returned home, it was something like having a live skeleton in the closet.

The long-term ambivalence of one white father emerges even in the following endorsement: "Well, I think it was, definitely—everybody made the right choice. This individual, I think, is a completely happy person, pursuing her own life, without any qualms that she definitely would have had if this operation had not taken place." This same father had earlier said of his son: "I would rather he had the sex reassignment than be a homosexual."

The long-term ambivalence of one white mother was revealed on the occasion of telephoning her to request a follow-up interview. Fortuitously, the transsexual daughter was home on vacation and insisted on joining the telephone interview on an extension phone. She engaged her mother in a yelling-weeping tantrum, interspersed with Pollyanna statements by both of how wonderful everything was, and insisted that neither the mother nor the father need give any further information. They failed to respond to subsequent correspondence.

By contrast, the mother of a black transsexual said of the reassignment: "It was quite a relief to me . . . I would recommend other people to have the operation even if it is a long drawn-out affair." The maternal grandmother who reared this child said: "I feel she is happier since she's been changed. That's my feeling about it. I feel better about it since she feels better herself . . . since she's had an operation and she can do as she always wanted to do."

Miscellaneous

Sex reassignment of one of its members brought no legal repercussions on the family. Nor were there adverse financial repercussions. Families helped with medical expenses only insofar as they were able.

In the seven families, there was no recorded instance of health problems, somatic or psychiatric, following the one member's sex reassignment. One father reported a heart attack, said to be mild, the timing of which may or may not have been fortuitous, a month after his transsexual daughter's wedding.

There were no reported instances of disturbances of sleep and dream life in family members following the one person's sex reassignment. If parents had dreams of their reassigned child as a girl, they either did not remember them or did not single them out as noteworthy and worth reporting, except for one grandmother who said she always dreamed of her transsexual grandchild as a girl, and one mother who reported dreaming of her child's death as a girl and wondering how to announce her death.

The sex reassignment of one child did not lead to a breakup of the parents' marital relationship in the three cases in which the nuclear family had always been intact. By contrast, the experience strengthened the bond between husband and wife, according to the testimony of one or both of them.

Discussion

Before it became an acceptable medical procedure for the rehabilitation of adult transsexuals, sex reassignment was known only in connection with rare cases of intersexuality or hermaphroditism. In such cases, the change might be elective or by edict—in neonates and young children, always by edict.

Regardless of age or diagnosis, the experience for the family of reannouncing or reassigning the sex of one of its members is difficult and socially threatening. There is no routine formula, ceremony, or social institution to resort to when the sex of one family member has to be revoked and declared anew. There are no firm and universally applicable legal precedents and procedures. Instead, there is the stigma of deviating from one of society's most cherished verities, namely, the absoluteness of the dimorphism of the sexes.

In the absence of prior experience as a guide, the instructions given to families regarding the public relations of sex reassignment in the present seven cases were deliberately unauthoritative. Thus, the families each formulated pretty much their own policies. They were advised that privacy lost by too much publicity might be unretrievable and that it would be wise to take all close family members into confidence, but they did not necessarily heed the advice. They were also advised that a family's complete cover-up of a sex reassignment of one of its members is well nigh impossible, even if the family emigrates and attempts to sever all communication with relatives and friends. None of the families did in fact move.

In the management of hermaphroditic sex reassignment, the now outmoded policy used to be a recommendation that the father change his job and move the family geographically. However, the personal cost of a family's total concealment of the sex reassignment of one of its members is too great in terms of severed communication with all relatives and old freinds. Moreover, there is no total protection against future discovery and disclosure, so that the family lives on a precipice of anxiety.

The new and successful policy in the reannouncement or reassignment of the sex of a hermaphroditic baby or child (Money et al., 1969) is to inform and educate members of the family or community on the medical and behavioral rationale for the change. Their curiosity satisfied, they are then asked, for the sake of the child in the future, to discontinue all further mention of the topic. There is a special need to give a suitable explanation to children in the family and the community who will know of the change. This method of dealing with a sex reassignment is amazingly effective. People do indeed accept it and stop talking about it.

Recently, we have had one sex-reassigned transsexual who followed a similar policy. In this case, the transsexual placed in the local, small-town newspaper a notice of his proposed surgical and legal change to female. So informed, the townspeople accepted the change without much ado.[2]

The seven cases of the present study point to the conclusion that the less a family attempts concealment of a sex reassignment, the better—the four black families were less harassed than the three white ones because they did not feel vulnerable to exposure and emotional blackmail. The black transsexuals themselves had less need to be defensive, defiant, and deceitful, and were less manipulative.

In the future, families of transsexuals will be well advised to adopt a public-relations policy of not attempting to conceal the fact of sex reassignment. One might even go to the extent of saying that there should be some sort of ceremony or celebration that formally marks the occasion of a redeclaration of sex, analogous to that which marks a change of citizenship.

References

Kando, T. (1972), Passing and stigma management: The case of the transsexual. *Sociol. Quart.*, 13:475-483.

Money, J., Potter, R., & Stoll, C.S. (1969), Sex reannouncement in hereditary sex deformity: Psychology and sociology of habilitation. *Soc. Sci. Med.*, 3:207-216.

[2] The four-year-old nephew of this transsexual patient provided an example of how well even a child of this age can handle a frankly admitted sex reassignment. He asked his dad: "Why is Aunt Judy Uncle Jim?" When given the answer, "Because Uncle Jim wants to become a woman," the boy accepted his aunt's identity without ever questioning again.

The author reports, with commentary, an unusual phenomenon: five suicides in a family, mainly through the instrument of burning. The collectiveness of the events suggests a family will to suicide, or "family suicide," as the author terms it.

Family Suicide

FAKHRI DABBAGH

The phenomenon of suicide is one facet of a complex of psychiatric, cultural, and social variables which should be considered to understand its dynamics (Veevers, 1973). By this approach one might be able to look into the phenomenon free from the traditional influences of the well-known theories. Nevertheless, depression of various types and grades remains the highest and foremost causative psychiatric disorder behind suicidal behaviour. El-Gaaly (1974) found that the severity of depression was not as important as the degree of social dysfunction present, such as the need for self-satisfying activities, lack of community activities, and adoptive rigidity.

Self-directed aggression—suicide—seems a satisfactory method of resolving depression (Hirsch, 1960a). Various family situations play their part in enhancing suicide and attempted suicide. The so-called "suicidal family" has been a topic of interest to workers in the field of suicidology (Richman and Rosenbaum, 1970). Among such family-suicide potentials, these authors mentioned: an intolerance for separation, a preoccupation with death, a symbiosis without empathy, crisis intolerance, and a pattern of role disturbances and role failure in every area of social and personal functioning.

The agents and methods of suicide have been regarded by some

Fakhri Dabbagh, M.B., Ch.B., M.R.C. Psych., is Assistant Professor of Psychiatry, College of Medicine, Mosul University, Iraq.

Reprinted from the *British Journal of Psychiatry*, vol. 130, pp. 159-161, 1977.

psychiatrists as part of the dynamics and symbolization in the process of self-destruction rather than being overlooked or regarded as incidental and governed by chance (Hirsh, 1960b). The communication of suicidal ideas is usually more frequent with suicides than with attempted suicide (Yessler et al., 1960). The ritualistic types of suicide and of "dying together" (or suicide pacts) bear several mutual psychodynamics that might play their part in what I am inclined to call family suicide.

Case History

A female patient (Y.T.), 50 years old, married, with six children, had been suffering from severe depression for three months before she consulted me in May, 1974. Her main symptoms were depression with anxiety and mild agitation, tearfulness, weight loss, forgetfulness, insomnia (difficulty in falling asleep plus all-night restlessness), suicidal ideas and attempts (by burning), sense of feeling inadequate, weakness, tremors in the legs, headache, and occasional acroparaesthesia in the hands. She had no guilt feelings and no persecutory delusions or ideas of reference. There were no real hallucinations, but inner thoughts of committing suicide with a temptation to do it in the same manner as her sisters and relatives had already done.

Before her illness, she had been pleasant, kind, social, very conscientious, and attached to her children. She is of asthenic build and enjoyed physical good health. Her menses stopped ten years ago when she was 40.

No gross or convincing factor was advanced by her or her relatives, apart from the usual daily family-life inconveniences. She made two suicidal attempts by pouring kerosene on herself before setting fire, but she stopped immediately of her own will. She had such clear insight that she begged for help and protection against her potent impulsive tendency to commit suicide as her relatives had done.

Family History

The patient's parents both died of natural illness and had good relations with their children. There was no history of suicide in their families.

The patient had seven brothers and three sisters, of whom two sisters and one brother committed suicide. Two more suicides had occurred among her nephews: a sum of five suicides, four performed by burning and one by gunshot. The intervals between those suicides ranged from one to five years.

Brief notes of each are given below, and the family pedigree is shown in Figure 1.

1. Mrs. S.T. (II, 4), 48 years old, a sister of the patient, a widow with two sons, living in good family conditions, financially and morally. She committed suicide by burning herself with kerosene in the presence of the patient Y.T., on the balcony of the house. She suffered from depression and guilt feelings, had previously attempted suicide by drowning in the river, and had given several suicidal warnings. She had recived psychiatric treatment with ECT and antidepressants.

2. Mrs. B.T. (II, 8), 38 years old, a sister of the patient, a housewife with one son. She committed suicide by burning herself with kerosene on the roof of the house (in 1960). Nobody was present at the time. She suffered from anxiety and worry about the forthcoming marriage of her son and had guilt feelings as well. She had not received psychiatric treatment.

3. Mr. M.T. (II, 2), 34 years old, a brother of the patient, single, a merchant. Committed suicide by gunshot after locking himself inside a room. He left a note saying that he was fed up with life. He had serious business troubles.

4. Mr. K.L. (III, 6), 26 years old, single, a nephew of the patient and a military pharmacist. He committed suicide by burning with benzine. At the time it was suspected that it occurred by chance while he had been cleaning his clothes. He had really been suffering from signs of

FIGURE 1

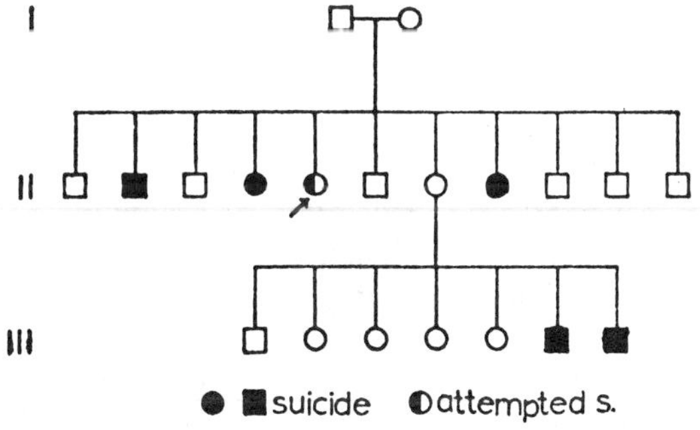

The Family Pedigree Showing Five Suicides

depression, agitation, loss of weight, and lack of interest for a few months.

5. Mr. L.L. (III, 7), 45 years old, a nephew of the patient and brother of K.L., married, a lecturer in the College of Science. He committed suicide by burning himself with kerosene on the roof of his house. Nobody was present at home. He left a letter explaining his boredom with life; he fixed this under a stone to prevent it from being blown away. There were no definite exogenous motives for his depression.

The Common Pattern

It was thus found that the suicides were all performed in clear consciousness, with serious intent, clever planning, either preceded by warning or accomplished silently and abruptly, but still leaving a note or brief letter. One of them (Mrs. S.T.) had a severe depression for which she had been given psychiatric treatment. The rest did not have psychiatric treatment, but were definitely reported to be unhappy, anxious, or in distress.

The burnings were conducted in a semiritualistic manner. The subjects used kerosene (one used benzine), carried it in a small bowl, poured it on their head and clothes, and set fire. They all went outside the house to a balcony or a roof so as not to harm the house or members of the family.

Some (two of them) committed suicide in the presence of other members of the family at home, but only when the latter were distracted or busy. The rest had done it while absolutely alone. Only one of them (S.T.) had made suicidal attempts before the final one.

Discussion

Detailed case histories of the suicides reveal in each case a clear or concealed depressive episode preceding the suicidal act. The warnings or notes did not carry any hints of accusations against or attaching blame to others. The safety measures taken in self-burning indicate that there were no appreciable hostile or retaliatory motives. These signs all point to an endogenous, self-depreciating, "harmless" suicide. Moreover, the insignificance of exogenous causes (except in one case—M.T.) confirms the endogenous character of the depression that ended in suicide.

Atypical features were the presence of anxiety, mild agitation, clear insight, and the difficulty in falling asleep, and restless nights.

The interesting points about this study are the repetition of the same method of suicide (burning in four out of five) and the ritualistic character of the actions of sisters, brothers, and sons of one sister who was herself normal. The burnings were performed by the endogenously depressed patients, while the gunshot suicide was done by the exogenously depressed one. The whole scene was rehearsed and related by my patient (II, 5) who had twice been on the verge of committing suicide by burning and who sought psychiatric help from fear of doing it.

For those reasons—the obvious hereditary and familial relations, the marked similarities of the subjects' behavior and common clinical features—one may with justification use the term "family suicide." The events of suicide did not occur within such a short period of time as to allow one to consider them as "epidemic" or "mass" suicide (Meerlo, 1962), but the ritualism, close family ties, absence of suicidal behavior on the mother's side of the first pedigree are all in favor of "family" suicide.

References

El-Gaaly, A. A. (1974), Social dysfunction in depressives and attempted suicides. *Acta Psychiat. Scand.*, 50, 341-345.

Hirsh, J. (1960a), Methods and fashions of suicide—Part 2, *Ment. Hyg.*, 44, 3-11.

——— (1960b), Dynamics of suicide—Part 3. Ment. Hyg., 44, 274-280.

Meerlo, J. (1962), *Suicide and Mass Suicide*. New York: Grune & Stratton.

Richman, J. & Rosenbaum, M. (1970), The family doctor and the suicidal family. *Psychiat. in Med.*, 1:27-35.

Veevers, J. E. (1973), Parenthood and suicide: An examination of a neglected variable. *Soc. Sci. & Med.*, 7, 135-144.

Yessler, P. G., Gibb, J. B., & Becker, H. A. (1960), The communication of suicidal ideas. *Arch. Gen. Psychiat.*, 111, 612-631.

A group of workers from the children's field explores family psychopathology as it relates to the development of severe psychosomatic disorders in children. They comment on treatment of the families based on their conceptual model.

A Conceptual Model of Psychosomatic Illness in Children: Family Organization and Family Therapy

SALVADOR MINUCHIN, LESTER BAKER, BERNICE L. ROSMAN, RONALD LIEBMAN, LEROY MILMAN, and THOMAS C. TODD

In a century, the study of psychosomatic illness, which began with the simplest accumulation of clinical anecdotes, has evolved to the use of the most sophisticated techniques of laboratory and behavioral science. Speculation based on the hypothesis that certain psychological dynamics are specific to certain somatic diseases has been replaced by systematic studies of the complex interrelationships of psyche and soma. Many important contributions have been made in interpreting the mediating mechanisms whereby emotions cause bodily changes.

Unfortunately, this progress in understanding the causes of psycho-

---

Salvador Minuchin, M.D., Lester Baker, M.D., Bernice L. Rosman, Ph.D, Ronald Liebman, M.D., Leroy Milman, M.D., and Thomas C. Todd, Ph.D., are with the Philadelphia Child Guidance Clinic and the Children's Hospital of Philadelphia.

Reprinted from the *Archives of General Psychiatry*, vol. 32, August, 1975.

This investigation was supported in part by National Institute of Mental Health Grant 21336 and Research Resources Division, National Institutes of Health Grant RR-240.

somatic syndromes has not invariably been accompanied by increased effectiveness in treatment.

It is our contention that both research and therapy in psychosomatic medicine have been severely handicapped by the prevailing conceptual model of psychosomatic illness. This linear model links the individual's life situations to his emotions to bodily illness, in a causal chain. But the illness is seen as contained within the individual. Consequently, research and treatment approaches are focused on the individual, and this is far too limited a target.

Research governed by the linear model has made many important contributions to the study of the central nervous system, the autonomic nervous system, and the endocrine system, as well as to the study of how these systems respond to emotions. These investigations range from the very early studies of Cannon (1920), who showed the physiological accompaniments of fear and range, to the more sophisticated study of Mason (1968).

The personality structure of the psychosomatically ill patient has also been intensively explored under the aegis of the linear model. Dunbar (1935) made early observations on whose basis a personality specific theory of psychosomatic disease was formulated. Similarly, Ruesch (1948) defined an infantile personality as a basic problem in psychosomatic illness.

Some investigators began to look past the field circumscribed by the artificial boundary around the individual. Alexander and French (Alexander, 1961, Alexander and French, 1948) expanded the focus of their investigations to include the onset situation. They believed that the individual's situation at the time of onset, coupled with the personality of that individual, was critical in the development and maintenance of psychosomatic symptoms. Mirsky (1960) and Weiner and co-workers (1957) introduced the concept of social stress into their formulations. They studied the interrelationship of constitutional factors, psychological predisposition, and social stress in the precipitation of psychosomatic illness. Holmes and Rahe (1967) extended the study of life stresses epidemiologically, relating major life stresses to the onset of serious illness.

Some researchers focused on the relationship between the stressful situation, the response to stress, and the development of the symptom. Wolff (1961) was able to provide substantial evidence for the relationship of environmental stressors to physiological changes. Hinkle and Wolf (1952) studied the relationship of life stresses to fluctuations in diabetic control, tying the situation and the way the individual coped with that situation into an analysis of the physiological response to that stress. Grinker and Robbins (1954) also explored the relationships between external stresses and individual emotions.

Senay and Redlich (1968), in a broad review of the topic, drew attention to the variety of social contexts that influence the emergence and patterning of psychosomatic illness. These contexts range from the largest scale-differing cultures to intermediate subcultural or social-class related environmental phenomena to small groups, such as the family. These authors consider disturbances within the familial context to be the most intimately linked to psychosomatic illnesses.

Many investigators have explored the family context in their search for explanations of psychosomatic illness, particularly in children. A disturbed mother-child relationship has frequently been postulated as an etiological factor (Alexander, 1961; Alexander and French, 1948; Bastiaans and Groen, 1955). Ulcerative colitis has been studied extensively from this point of view, and particular family constellations have been observed to be associated with this illness (Finch and Hess, 1962; Lidz and Rubenstein, 1959). Many authors have focused on disorganizing events within the family, particularly the loss of important persons (Long et al., 1958; Lieberman et al., 1959; Wahl, 1960). Meyer and Haggerty (1961), and Schmale (1958) were able to cite family disturbances preceding the onset of illness in their studies of large numbers of patients. Pinkerton (1967) has studied the interaction of parental attitudes with the personality structure of the asthmatic child, and his schematic representation of his model could be a paradigm for the sophisticated exploration of the juvenile patient's family context.

However, therapy based on the linear model has retained the focus on the individual. Individual personality factors are seen as major determinants of psychosomatic illness, and, as a logical corollary, the therapeutic focus is on the individual. The importance of the individual's context is recognized, but there has been a curious dearth of therapeutic attempts to modify that context. This is particularly striking in the case of children, who can be assumed to be deeply involved with some form of family group. Yet the child is apparently seen as a passive recipient of noxious environmental influences. Consequently, the general therapeutic response has been only to separate him from those influences, either by individual psychotherapy, or by behavioral therapy, or "parentectomy." All of these treatment approaches place the burden of change on the patient alone.

In the past decade, we have begun to look beyond the individual to the individual in his social contexts and to the feedback processes between individual and context. As a result, a less restricted conceptual model, here called the open systems model, is evolving. It has directed investigators to a better understanding of psychosomatic syndromes and to the discovery of more effective treatment techniques.

Pinkerton's (1967) work with asthmatic children represents a transitional phase. His evaluation of the impact of family stress on the child has resulted in therapeutic efforts at "identifying and ultimately resolving the underlying aura of tension or [promoting] a more favorable adaptation to it . . ." (p. 19).

Mara Selvini-Palazzoli (1970), an Italian psychiatrist who reported on the treatment of over 60 anorectic children, more specifically exemplifies this change in the field. When she began her clinical work with anorexia, she concentrated on the relationship between the sick child and the pathogenic mother. Later, she began to wonder, "could [anorexia nervosa] be the only possible means of psychic survival for a given subject in the context of a given type of family functioning? . . . The mere fact of becoming aware of the existence of the problem led me to adopt the new work methods . . . " (p. 321). She began to insist on seeing all the members of an anorectic child's family together. Approaching the problem in this way, she discovered that there were family components quite directly and specifically related to the anorexia syndrome, and that these could be modified by family therapy.

The Open Systems Model

Broadening the focus from the sick child to the sick child within the family redefines the nature of pathological disorder and the scope of therapeutic change. This shift is facilitated by a conceptual model that postulates (1) that certain types of family organization are closely related to the development and maintenance of psychosomatic symptoms in children, and (2) that children's psychosomatic symptoms play a major role in maintaining family homeostasis. In the open systems model, a psychosomatic crisis is held to consist of two phases that encompass both psychological and physiological measurements. There is the "turn on" phase: some family conflict situation induces emotional arousal in the child, triggering physiological response. Then there is the "turn off" phase, or return to base-line levels. Turn off may be handicapped by the nature of family members' involvement with each other around the conflict. Since family interactions affect the psychophysiology of the child in the psychosomatic crisis, disorder is seen as situated in the feedback processes of child and family. The artificial boundary between individual and context no longer handicaps therapeutic efforts. These can be directed toward the child, the family, and the feedback processes of the family system's transactional patterns in whatever combinations seem most promising.

In other words, family interactional patterns may trigger the onset or hamper the subsidence of psychophysiologic processes, or both. The resulting psychosomatic symptoms function as homeostatic mechanisms regulating family transactions. Therefore, therapy must be directed toward changing the family processes that trigger and maintain the child's psychosomatic symptoms and toward changing the use of these symptoms within the family.

This concept of the open systems model is not dissimilar from one discussed by Mishler and Waxler (1968; Waxler and Mishler, 1970) in their review of different etiological models of psychopathological disorder such as schizophrenia. They describe a nonlinear system maintained through a variety of feedback mechanisms so that single causal sequences cannot be identified. The complexity of such a model could account for the lack of verified simple relationships between family constellation and psychopathological disorder, including psychosomatic illness. It is important to note that the hypotheses we are advancing here do not imply symptom specificity in relation to a given family constellation; rather, we will describe a more general type of family process that encourages somatization. Within this conceptual scheme we do not suggest a single or simple etiological factor, but describe a cluster of important related determinants.

The Family Model

Our studying and treating families of psychosomatically ill children has led to the development of an exploratory model of the structure and functioning of such families. This model holds that three factors in conjunction are necessary for the development of severe psychosomatic illness in children. First, the child is physiologically vulnerable; that is, a specific organic dysfunction is present. Second, the child's family has the following four transactional characteristics: enmeshment, overprotectiveness, rigidity, and lack of conflict resolution. Third, the sick child plays an important role in the family's patterns of conflict avoidance; and this role is an important source of reinforcement for his symptoms.

Vulnerability

The diabetic and asthmatic children we have treated are so defined by pediatric evaluation. The presence of physiological vulnerability in anorexia nervosa is debatable, but we have followed the literature in treating it as a psychosomatic disease.

It may be important to distinguish here between "primary" and "secondary" psychosomatic symptomatology. In primary psychosomatic symptomatology, a physiological disorder is already present. These include metabolic disorders like diabetes, allergic diathesis such as that found in asthma, and so forth. The psychosomatic element lies in the emotional exacerbation of the already available symptom. In the secondary psychosomatic disorder, no such predisposing physical disorder can be demonstrated. The psychosomatic element is apparent in the transformation of emotional conflicts into somatic symptoms. These symptoms may crystallize into a severe and debilitating illness like anorexia nervosa.

Symptom choice may be differently determined in these two instances. However, our work indicates that the "psychosomatogenic" family organization described here is applicable across these varieties of psychosomatic illness.

Family Transactional Characteristics

The four characteristics—enmeshment, overprotectiveness, rigidity, and lack of conflict resolution—can be observed in a family's behavior during family testing, diagnostic interviews, and in family therapy sessions. They appear to be representative of a general type of family organization and functioning. (A description of the family task may be found in *Families of the Slums* [Minuchin et al., 1967]. The diagnostic interview is discussed in *Families and Family Therapy* [Minuchin, 1974].)

Enmeshment

A pathologically enmeshed family system is characterized by a high degree of responsiveness and involvement. This can be seen in the interdependence of relationships, intrusions on personal boundaries, poorly differentiated perception of self and of other family members, and weak family subsystem boundaries.

In a highly enmeshed family, changes in one family member or in the relationship between two reverberate throughout the family system. Dialogues are rapidly diffused by the entrance of other family members. A dyadic conflict may set off a chain of shifting alliances within the whole family as other members get involved.

Internal structures within a highly enmeshed family system are characteristically fluid. The boundaries that define individual autonomy are so weak that an individual's life space is impinged on. This may be reflected in lack of privacy, excessive "togetherness," and sharing. ("Why do you change the furniture around in my room all the time when I'm not there?" a fifteen-year-old complains to his mother.) Family members also intrude on each other's thoughts, feelings, and communications. One family member may relay messages from another family member to a third, blocking direct communication. There are often many interruptions; family members may finish each other's sentences.

Problems of enmeshment are also reflected in family members' poorly differentiated perceptions of each other. Parents asked to tell what they like about each of their children often can speak of them only as a group.

In enmeshed families, subsystem boundaries are weak and easily crossed. As a result, executive hierarchies are confused. Children may join one parent in criticizing the other. The children often take inappropriately parental roles toward each other. In the absence of a clearly defined and effective parental subsystem, it is common for the parents to work at cross purposes in relation to the children. A parent frequently enlists a child's support in struggles with the other parent.

Overprotectiveness

In families with a psychosomatically ill child, family members show a high degree of concern for each other's welfare. This concern is not limited to the identified patient or to the area of illness. Nurturing and protective responses are constantly elicited and supplied as family members interact. A sneeze sets off a flurry of handkerchief offers; complaints and queries about fatigue or discomfort punctuate the flow of communications. Critical remarks and demands are often accompanied by pacifying behaviors. Signs of distress frequently cue family members to the approach of dangerous levels of tension or conflicts. For example, a mother's weeping as she anticipates father's criticism may galvanize the children into distracting behavior. A symptomatic child's emotional outburst may elicit comforting and help to avert exploration of family conflicts.

Family members' perceptions of each other are structured around protective concerns, particularly where there is a sick child. (When family members are asked to tell what pleases them and displeases them the most about each other, they may, for example, reply, "I like it when you don't overdo." "I like it when you rub my chest." "I don't like it when he gets sick all the time.") In such families, the parents' overprotectiveness retards the children's development of autonomy and competence. (A father tells his two adolescent diabetic daughters, "If Mommy and I could only take the needles for you, everything would be all right.")

In turn, the children, particularly the psychosomatically ill child, feel great responsibility for protecting the family. For the sick child, the experience of being able to protect the family by using his symptoms may be a major reinforcement for the illness.

RIGIDITY

The pathologically enmeshed families are heavily committed to maintaining the status quo. During periods when change and growth are necessary, they experience great difficulty. For example, when a child in an effectively functioning family reaches adolescence, his family will be able to change its rules and transactional patterns in ways that allow for age-appropriate increased autonomy while still preserving family continuity. But the family of a psychosomatically ill child operates like a closed system. When events that require change occur, family members insist on retaining accustomed methods of interaction. Consequently, avoidance circuits must be developed, and a "symptom bearer" is a particularly useful detouring route. When the family's low threshold of tolerance for conflict is approached, the sick child becomes ill, allowing family members to detour their conflict via concern for him. The family reinforces his development of deviance and rewards its continuance because of its usefulness in maintaining the pathogenic system's precarious equilibrium.

As a result of their inappropriately summoned homeostatic mechanisms, these families live in a chronic state of submerged stress. Issues that threaten change, such as negotiations of individual autonomy, are not allowed to surface to the point where they could be explored. Typically, these families represent themselves as normal and untroubled except for the one child's medical problem. They deny any need for change in the family.

Lack of Conflict Resolution

The rigidity and overprotectiveness of the family system, combined with the constant mutual impingements characteristic of pathologically enmeshed transactional patterns, make such families' thresholds for conflict very low. Often a strong religious or ethical code buttresses and provides a rationale for avoiding conflict. As a result, there can be no explicit negotiation of differences. Problems are left unresolved, to threaten again and again and continually activate the system's avoidance circuits.

Each family's idiosyncratic structure and functioning dictate their ways of avoiding conflict resolution. Often one spouse is an avoider. The non-avoider brings up areas of difficulty, but the avoider always manages to detour confrontation that would lead to the acknowledgment of conflict and, perhaps, its negotiation. A man may simply leave the house when his wife tries to discuss a problem.

Other families bicker continually, but the constant interruptions and subject changes typical of an enmeshed system obfuscate any conflictual issue before it is brought to salience. Other families simply deny the existence of any problems whatsoever.

The four transactional characteristics typical of families with psychosomatically ill children—enmeshment, overprotectiveness, rigidity, and lack of conflict resolution—provide the context for using illness as a mode of communications.

The Use of the Sick Child

The third condition postulated in this family model is that the ill child plays an important role in the family conflict avoidance and that this is an important source of reinforcement for his symptoms.

The results of our experimental work using a controlled interview designed to elicit parental conflict in the index child's presence suggest that there are characteristic patterns of conflict-related behavior that involve the child and affect him in different ways. Families commonly move into several of these patterns in the course of the interview, but one tends to predominate. These conflict-avoidance patterns have been grouped according to whether they facilitate or handicap turn off.

Three patterns of involvement seem to handicap turn off severely, and, therefore, are related to psychosomatic illness. In the first two patterns, triangulation and parent-child coalitions, the spouse dyad is frankly split. The child is openly pressed to ally with one parent against the other. In *triangulation*, the child is put in such a position that he cannot express himself without siding with one parent against the other. Statements that impose coalition, such as "Wouldn't you rather do it my way?" are used in the attempt to force the child to take sides. (For example, one demonstrative father was finally able to express his covert criticism of his wife, accusing her of coldness to the children. Both parents then pressed their anorectic daughter to say whether she preferred her father's ways and wanted her mother to change. Stuck between the two adults, she was unable to speak.) In the second pattern, *parent-child coalition*, the child tends to move into a stable coalition with one parent against the other. The role of the excluded parent varies to the degree that he tries to disrupt the coalition. (A mother was unable to express her rage at her husband's refusal to protect her from his mother's attacks. The asthmatic son was highly involved as the mother's protector, and he could state her complaints. He urged his father to protect her from her mother-in-law. The father tried to persuade his son to reject the mother's "childish" demands, but the wheezing boy maintained his adult stance.)

In the third type of pattern, called *detouring*, the spouse dyad is united. The parents submerge their conflicts in a posture of protecting or blaming their sick child, which is defined as the only family problem. In several such families, the parents required that the children reassure them that they were good parents or join them in worrying about the family. The parents occasionally vacillate between their concerns for the child and exasperation over the burdens he imposes by "not trying to help himself." In most cases, parental concerns absorb the couple, so that all signs of marital strife or even minor differences are suppressed or ignored.

It is important to note that these patterns of involvement are not intended to represent a classification of families. They describe transactional sequences occurring in response to family conflict. Such sequences often occur in the transactions of effectively functioning families; they are within the wide range of methods used to cope with conflict. However, families in the normal range can shift into other modes of conflict confrontation and negotiation. The rigid families with psychosomatically ill children are more likely to enact maladaptive sequences again and again. As they are usually operating under conditions of stress and tension, the child is frequently involved in his role as avoider circuit.

To summarize, we hypothesize that the family with a psychosomatically ill child is characterized by the transactional patterns of enmeshment, overprotectiveness, rigidity, and lack of conflict resolution. The sick child is involved in parental conflict. We have been testing this model in three ways. First, we are comparing the interactional characteristics of families having psychosomatically ill children with those of families having nonpsychosomatic but chronically ill children. Second, we have designed a structured family interview that permits the physiological assessment of family members' responses to psychological family stress. The assessment of turn on and turn off is of particular interest. We shall present our data in these two areas in other communications. In this report, we address ourselves to our third test, the examination of whether or not changing the specified family behavior patterns through structural family therapy results in improved management and substantial alleviation of psychosomatic symptoms.

Family Therapy Program—Methods and Results

Over the past seven years, this team has been involved in an interdisciplinary research project designed to identify the elements of family structure and functioning that are related to the development and reinforcement of psychosomatic symptoms in children. A concomitant program of family therapy oriented toward changing these elements of family organization has treated children with anorexia nervosa (Minuchin, 1974; Minuchin et al., 1973; Liebman et al., 1974a), children with superlabile diabetes (psychosomatically triggered recurrent ketoacidosis) (Baker et al., 1975; Minuchin and Barcai, 1969), and children with intractable asthma (Liebman et al., 1974b). Almost all these children were seriously ill at the time of referral. The anorectic group had suffered a mean weight loss of 30 percent; the diabetic group had an average of twelve hospitalizations a year; and most of the asthmatic group were steroid-dependent. All the patients described were diagnosed as psychosomatic and referred for family therapy on the basis of independent pediatric criteria rather than psychiatric evaluation. Hospital admissions for the *superlabile diabetic* group were occasioned by severe bouts of ketoacidosis; chronic acetonuria patients were diagnosed on the basis of daily urine testing as well as symptoms. In all cases, careful screening and control studies were carried out under pediatric supervision to rule out other physiological disorders and instances of insulin omission. Similar criteria were applied during follow-up. Similarly, in the case of the *asthmatic* patients, independent pediatric assessment by members of an allergist team verified the physiological severity of the illness and the necessity for special treatment (i.e., steroid therapy) prior to psychiatric referral. School loss for diabetic and asthmatic children was determined on the basis of pediatric chart review and was directly related to incidence of medical symptoms; improvement in this area reflected true symptom remissions. *Anorectic* patients were diagnosed solely on the basis of medical criteria, i.e., severe weight loss and amenorrhea, after other medical conditions were ruled out. In evaluating recovery, major emphasis again was placed on pediatric criteria (weight gain). The only psychiatric evaluation of recovery may be seen in the clinical assessment of the anorexia group and was based on behavioral rather than psychological data. Families were referred to the study group and for family therapy by the pediatricians and were free to receive treatment without participating in the study, or to refuse referral and remain in pediatric care only. Pediatricians and family therapists worked in close collaboration throughout the treatment period.

The results of this pediatric-family therapy treatment approach have been highly encouraging, as may be seen in Tables 1 through 4.

Dramatic improvements or remission of psychosomatic symptoms or both, have been achieved in most of these cases. We believe that the effectiveness of our therapeutic procedures can be traced to the use of the open systems model of psychosomatic illness in the development of therapeutic strategies. This conceptualization directs the therapist's attention toward the context in which the psychosomatic event was initiated and is maintained. Therapeutic strategies are directed toward modifying that matrix.

(Tables 1- 4 on pp. 328-331)

TABLE 1
SUMMARY OF 13 CASES OF SUPERLABILE DIABETES

Case No.	Presenting Problems	Family Treatment, mo	Follow-Up
1*	30 hospital admissions in 3 yr	9	4 admissions in 3 yr 8 mo, 3 associated with infection
2*	14 hospital admissions in 2½ yr	5	No admissions in 2 yr 4 mo
3*	35 hospital admissions in 20 mo	9	1 admission in 3 yr 1 mo
4*	18 hospital admissions in 4 yr	12	No admissions in 5 yr 11 mo
5*	24 hospital admissions in 20 mo	9	No admissions in 6 yr 7 mo
6*	6 hospital admissions in 6 mo	9	No admissions in 2 yr 6 mo
7*	20 hospital admissions in 2 yr	7	No admissions in first 4 yr 7 mo, 2 admissions in past 21 mo
8†	Recurrent ketosis, nausea, & frequent school absence	3	Free of recurrent ketosis, no associated school absence 2 yr 8 mo
9†	Chronic acetonuria, 6 hospital admissions in 2 yr to evaluate poor diabetic control, & frequent school absence	9	2 hospital admissions in 2 yr 3 mo; free of chronic acetonuria, school attendance excellent (2 days' absence per year)
10†	Poor diabetic control, & 1 hospital admission for vomiting and 3 for diabetic regulation in 1 yr	3	Good control, no vomiting for 2 yr, lost contact 1 yr 9 mo, no problems reported
11†	Chronic acetonuria, headaches, nausea, & vomiting for 12 mo	5	Acetonuria well controlled, 1-day absence for vomiting, no problems for 4 yr 6 mo
12*	15 hospital admissions in 4 yr	15	No admissions in 15 mo
13†	Lethargy, nausea, vomiting, frequent school absence, & 3 hospital admissions in 3 yr to evaluate poor diabetic control	2	For first 6 mo, less frequent nausea & school absence, 1 incident poor control associated with cold; for past 20 mo, no problems, good control

* One of eight cases of severe relapsing diabetic acidosis.
† One of five cases of chronic acetonuria.

TABLE 2

SUMMARY OF 10 CASES OF INTRACTABLE ASTHMA

Patient No.	Referral Time: Sex-Age, yr	Age at Onset	Steroid Dependent	Clinical Severity, Grade*	Duration Family Therapy	Current Status, Grade*	Follow-Up Posttherapy
1	F-8	3 yr	Yes	3	7 mo	1	2 yr 8 mo
2	F-12	3 yr	Yes	3	6 mo	1	2 yr 2 mo
3	F-12	15 mo	Yes	3	9 mo	1	1 yr 8 mo
4	M-16	11 yr	No	3	5 mo	1	3 yr 2 mo
5	M-14	18 mo	Yes	4	22 mo	2	2 yr 2 mo
6	M-8	6 yr	Yes	3	8 mo	1	1 yr 2 mo
7	M-11	3½ yr	Yes	3	6 mo	1	2 yr
8†	F-11	1 yr	Yes	3	11 mo	1	1 yr 11 mo
9	M-12	18 mo	Yes	4	Ongoing	2‡	10 mo
10	F-6	6 yr	No	2	Ongoing	1‡	9 mo

* Pinkerton (1970) Scale for Evaluation of Clinical Severity of Asthma[37]: Grade 1, no school loss, mild attacks, occasional need for use of bronchodilator; grade 2, days off school, mild to moderate attacks, need for regular use of bronchodilator; grade 3, weeks off school, more prolonged and severe attacks, steroid plus bronchodilator therapy; grade 4, more than 50% school loss, persistent symptoms, need for special schooling, regular steroid therapy.

† Asthma-free for past 17 months.

‡ Treatment continuing for other problems.

TABLE 3

CHARACTERISTICS OF 25 ANORECTIC PATIENTS PRIOR TO PARTICIPATION IN FAMILY THERAPY PROGRAM

Patient No.	Age at Onset, yr-mo	% Weight Loss	Interval: Onset-Referral	Therapy Previous to Admission to this Program
1	9-0	32	2 mo	None
2	13-9	32	3 mo	1 yr individual therapy; 2 weeks inpatient
3	9-0	26	2 mo	None
4	11-8	30	2 mo	None
5	15-0	42	9 mo	1 yr inpatient; 2 yr psychiatric outpatient
6	13-1	26	18 mo	None
7	12-0	36	2 weeks	None
8	14-4	23	1 yr	None
9	15-5	56	27 mo	2 mo psychiatric ward; individual psychiatrist & social worker
10	14-2	30	6 mo	None
11	14-0	42	15 mo	None
12	9-5	22	3 mo	None
13	13-0	35	5 mo	Therapy
14	12-0	44	7 mo	Previous hospitalization; earlier child therapy
15	15-0	29	5 mo	Family counseling
16	16-0	28	6 mo	None
17	14-6	41	6 mo	None
Outpatients:				
18	15-0	25	1 yr	None
19	14-0	30	7 mo	Brief psychotherapy
20	13-0	39	6 mo	None
21	9-0	41	18 mo	None
22	15-6	18	3 mo	None
23	13-0	29	4 mo	None
24	12-0	Unavailable	6 mo	None
25	15-0	21	3 mo	Brief therapy with psychologist

TABLE 4

SUMMARY OF TREATMENT AND FOLLOW-UP OF 25 ANORECTIC PATIENTS

	Treatment Duration		Current Statistics				
Patient No.	Inpatient, Days	Family Therapy	Weight, kg	Weight Gain	Duration Follow-up	Anorexia	Clinical Assessment*
1	11	1 yr	31.8	14.1	2 yr 9 mo	Recovered	Recovered
2	21	1 yr	50.5	17.3	2 yr 5 mo	Recovered	Recovered
3	8	4 mo	25.5	5.0	1 yr 9 mo	Recovered	Recovered
4	13	6 mo	40.9	24.1	2 yr 5 mo	Recovered	Recovered
5	16	4 mo	33.6	10.9	2 yr 5 mo	Fair	Recovered
6	15	6 mo	50.0	11.4	1 yr 2 mo	Recovered	Recovered
7	14	9 mo	35.9	14.1	1 yr 2 mo	Recovered	Recovered
8	7	10 mo	. . .	. . .	. . .	Dropped program	
9	13	3 mo	43.2	14.1	1 yr	Recovered	Recovered
10	13	7 mo	51.1	14.8	11 mo	Recovered	Recovered
11	15	. . .	. . .	. . .	. . .	Dropped program	
12	20	7 mo	28.6	10.9	1 yr	Recovered	Recovered
13	22	7 mo	39.5	9.5	1 yr	Recovered	Recovered
14	24	7 mo	51.8	18.6	2 yr 5 mo	Recovered	Recovered
15	25	6 mo	37.3	6.4	5 mo	Recovered	Recovered
16	14	9 mo to date	49.1	10.9	Continuing	Recovered	In treatment
17	14	6 mo	46.8	15.9	11 mo	Recovered	Recovered
Outpatients:							
18		1 yr	52.3	11.4	4 yr	Recovered	Recovered
19		6 mo	61.4	18.2	3 yr 9 mo	Recovered	Recovered
20		1 yr	63.6	27.7	3 yr 9 mo	Recovered	Recovered
21		2 mo	53.6	31.4	2 yr 9 mo	Recovered	Recovered
22		4 mo	46.4	10.9	2 yr 9 mo	Recovered	Recovered
23		14 weeks	46.8	19.5	1 yr 9 mo	Recovered	Recovered
24		. . .	35.9	9.5	. . .	Dropped program	
25		1 yr	52.3	16.4	Lost contact	Recovered	Recovered

* Social, school, and family adjustment.

Development and Maintenance of Psychosomatic Symptoms

The open systems model explicitly differentiates the symptom choice, the precipitating event, and the maintenance of the symptom in its current manifestation. Our framework of analysis is similar to that suggested by Redlich and Freedman (1966) for the cause of psychosomatic illness. This framework requires elucidation of the predisposing factors (biological, psychological, and environmental), precipitating events, the homeostatic importance of the symptom, and the consequences for the patient in terms of limitations in coping and growth. Our orientation in this case is to explicate the cause in terms of the family system.

Symptom Choice

Symptom choice is related to the family history and organization. Frequently, other members of a family have psychosomatic complaints. Hypochondriacal fears and excessive concern with bodily functions are common. In the secondary psychosomatic disorders, symptom choice may relate to family members' excessive preoccupation with normal areas of bodily functions. In families with an anorectic child, other family members often worry about table manners, become overconcerned with diet, have food fads, and so on. In the primary psychosomatic conditions, a child with a physiological vulnerability grows up within a family system that uses his illness as a point of concentration or as a method of diffusing system stresses or both. For instance, the allergic diathesis of asthma is a true physiological condition. However, only some of the children thus affected grow up in a family that encourages and maintains psychosomatic responses. It is this group that develops attacks that challenge medical management. In other words, in the primary cases, symptom selection is determined by the physical illness; in the secondary cases, symptom selection is idiosyncratic for each family. In contrast to psychodynamic workers, we are less concerned with the specifics of symptom selection, and analysis of the symptom does not form a basis for therapy.

We have found that in both cases the child grows up in a family organization that is fertile ground for the development and utilization of the symptom. The child's autonomy is curtailed by the other family members' intrusive concern. Areas of his psychological and bodily functioning remain subject to others' control long after they should have become automatic or unattended or both. This control is maintained under the cloak of concern and protection and therefore cannot be challenged without impugning the motives of the concerned one.

Denial of self for others' benefit and high value for self-sacrifice and family loyalty characterize the context in which the child develops. Family members make their wishes known indirectly and "unselfishly"—"I want this because it is good for you." Initiative and competence in areas not dictated by the family become acts of betrayal. The concern for mutual accommodation without friction produces an environment in which differences are submerged.

Precipitating Event

This pattern of family homeostasis, with its emphasis on loyalty, protection, and avoidance of conflict, is challenged at different stages of family and family members' development, particularly in those normal developmental crises in which family members must make life decisions about issues that threaten the stability of the family unit. This unavoidable disequilibrium is frequently the *precipitating event* for the psychosomatic episode. All the family members are mobilized to protect the system and to protect or coerce the member whose distress or need for change is threatening accustomed transactional patterns. The child, feeling the stresses within the system, responds with symptoms that may be utilized as a detouring mechanism. The family unites in concern and protection, and thus rewards the symptom.

At each crossroad, when a family member meets conflicting demands from the familial and extrafamilial, the stress in the family may be expressed in psychosomatic terms by the sick child. A psychosomatic episode, therefore, will have different characteristics at different periods of a family's life because the family context in which the child experiences his illness is organized around different life tasks.

The developmental stages of the family in treatment have consequences for the selection of treatment strategies. For instance, when working with families in which the identified patient is a preadolescent child, the therapist will help to increase the parents' sense of competence and support their executive function. When working with families in which the identified patient is an adolescent, the therapist will challenge the parents to grow up too so that they can support the child's right to explore the extrafamilial world. In each instance, the therapist will encourage an age-appropriate differentiation of the child.

Symptom Maintenance

Once it has appeared, the psychosomatic symptom becomes embedded in but also changes the family organization. Challenged by the chronicity, the unpredictability, and the life-threatening quality of the illness, the family members respond by increasing their protective control of the sick child and by establishing strong dependency on the pediatrician. The concentration on the symptomatic child maximizes his self-appraisal as a patient, with consequent utilization of his illness as a substantial coin for interpersonal transactions. Parents and siblings feel exploited by the demands of the "child and his illness" and increase their controlling protection. The child feels protected and scapegoated and increases his dependency on the parenting members. If this process continues for a substantial period of time, the child may be rendered incompetent in many areas of life functioning and consequently increase his dependent demands.

The change in family organization goes beyond the dynamic needs of detouring family conflict. The family feedback to the child's symptoms becomes an autonomous process that maintains the symptom.

Initial therapeutic strategies that challenge these processes may sometimes result in rapid improvements of the child's symptomatology and an additional clarification of family dynamics. For example, the therapist may concentrate on the manipulative aspect of the child's behavior, pointing out how the child controls family transactional patterns. A child who has been seen as weak and sick and in need of family protection is relabeled a disobedient child who is using his illness to control the family. The parents will then develop a demanding attitude that evicts the child psychologically from his roles in the enmeshed system. As a result of the maneuver (which may seem unfair), the child moves from an "I am sick" stance to a stance of "I am controlling the situation." This increases distance between the child and the family by enhancing his autonomy.

Such a maneuver also challenges the family's conflict-avoidance patterns. The child and parents begin to enter into areas of conflict, and these become the center of therapy. This strategy has been successful in a number of cases of anorexia where the child's control of his symptom is more apparent. In other cases, the strategies of concentrating on the behavior of other siblings who transitionally become the sick members serves intially to move the child out of the central position. Intertwined with these strategies, the basic therapeutic procedure is directed toward changing the four characteristics of the family system: enmeshment, overprotection, rigidity, and lack of conflict resolution.

It is beyond the scope of this report to describe the many particular techniques employed; these have been elaborated elsewhere (Minuchin, 1970, 1974; Minuchin and Barcai, 1969; Liebman et al., 1974b, 1974c). Rather, our concern has been to outline the therapy approach in relation to the open systems family model developed above.

Therapy with many families with psychosomatic children supports our impression that when family organization is changed, the psychosomatic child improves greatly. These conclusions are based not only on the results reported in the tables but on our work with other psychosomatic conditions, i.e., psychogenic vomiting, headaches, gastrointestinal disorders, and so forth.

Independent verification of changes in our patients' family organizations must await the final analysis of data from our current study. However, we believe that evaluation of family therapy outcomes, as indicated by pediatric improvement as well as improvement of other adjustment problems, offers support for the conceptual schema underlying the goals and strategies employed with this framework.

SUMMARY

We have explored the importance of a theoretical model in framing a methodology of research and treatment. A conceptual model maps areas for exploration, but it tends to limit data collected to those data that fit within the framework of the model. Psychosomatic medicine has been handicapped by an inadequate model that focuses on the individual and does not take into account the transactions in a patient's life context. This gap in the model may account for much of the inadequacy of previous treatment techniques.

We have suggested that the open systems model of psychosomatic illness is a more effective guide to exploration and therapy. This circular model does not preclude work with physiological mediating mechanisms, pharmacological, and biofeedback intervention techniques based on better understanding of these mechanisms. These techniques may be easily incorporated into the open systems framework.

A number of points have been highlighted in our presentation. First, interventions that modify the life context of the psychosomatically ill patient seem to achieve a faster and more sustained remission than interventions that focus exclusively on the individual. The need for prolonged hospitalization for nonphysiological reasons disappears because the patient will move from the controlled institutional environment to a natural environment that is changing according to therapeutic goals. The model of the psychosomatogenic family pinpoints dysfunctional areas within the child's most important life context, short-cutting much of the necessary exploration and opening areas for intervention. This knowledge of family organization and functioning predisposing to psychosomatic problems can also be used in preventive programs.

References

Alexander, F. (1961), *The Scope of Psychoanalysis*. New York: Basic Books.

——— & French, T. M. (1948), *Studies in Psychosomatic Medicine*. New York: Ronald Press.

Baker, L., Minuchin, S., Milman, L., et al. (1975), Psychosomatic aspects of juvenile diabetes mellitus: A progress report. *Modern Problems in Pediatrics*, 12:332-343. Basel: Karger.

Bastiaans, J. & Groen, J. (1955), Psychogenesis and psychotherapy of bronchial asthma. In: *Modern Trends in Psychosomatic Medicine*, ed. D. O'Neill. New York: Paul B. Hoeber, pp. 242-268.

Cannon, W. B. (1920), *Bodily Changes in Pain, Hunger, Fear and Rage*. New York: Appleton-Century-Crofts.

Dunbar, H. F. (1935), *Emotions and Bodily Changes: A Survey of Literature on Psychosomatic Interrelationships*, 4th ed. New York: Columbia University Press, 1954.

Finch, S. M. & Hess, H. H. (1962), Ulcerative colitis in children. *Amer. J. Psychiat.*, 118:819-826.

Grinker, R. R. & Robbins, F. P. (1954), *Psychosomatic Casebook*. New York: Blakiston.

Hinkle, L. E. & Wolf, S. (1952), A summary of experimental evidence relating life stress to diabetes mellitus. *J. Mt. Sinai Hosp.*, 19:537-570.

Holmes, T. H. & Rahe, R. H. (1967), The social readjustment scale. *J. Psychosom. Res.*, 11:213-218.

Lidz, T. & Rubenstein, R. (1959), Psychology of gastrointestinal disorders. In: *American Handbook of Psychiatry*, Vol. 1, ed. S. Arieti. New York: Basic Books, pp. 678-689.

Lieberman, M. A., Stock, D., & Whitman, R.M. (1959), Self-perceptual patterns among ulcer patients. *Arch. Gen. Psychiat.*, 1:167-176.

Liebman, R., Minuchin, S., & Baker, L. (1974a), An integrated treatment program for anorexia nervosa. *Amer. J. Psychiat.*, 131:432-436.

——— ——— ——— (1974b), The use of structural family therapy in the treatment of intractable asthma. *Amer. J. Psychiat.*, 131:535-540.

——— ——— ——— (1974c), The role of the family in the treatment of anorexia nervosa. *Child Psychiat.*, 13:264-274.

Long, R. T., Lamont, J., Whipple, B., et al. (1958), A psychosomatic study of allergic and emotional factors in children with asthma. *Amer. J. Psychiat.*, 114:890-899.

Mason, J. W. (1968), Organization of psychoendocrine mechanisms. *Psychosom. Med.*, 30:791-808.

Meyer, R. J. & Haggerty, R. J. (1962), Streptococcal infections in families: Factors altering individual susceptibility. *Pediatrics*, 29:539-549.

Minuchin, S. (1970), The use of an ecological framework in the treatment of a child. In: *The Child in His Family*, ed. E. J. Anthony & C. Koupernik. New York: John Wiley, pp. 41-57.

——— (1974), *Families and Family Therapy: A Structural Approach*. Cambridge, Mass.: Harvard University Press.

——— Baker, L., Liebman, R., et al. (1973), Anorexia nervosa: Successful application of a family therapy approach. Abstracted in *Pediatr. Res.*, 7:294.

——— & Barcai, A. (1969), Therapeutically induced family crisis. In: *Science and Psychoanalysis*, vol. 14, ed. J. Masserman. New York: Grune & Stratton, pp. 199-205.

——— Montalvo, B., Guerney, B. G., et al. (1967), *Families of the Slums: An Exploration of Their Structure and Treatment*. New York: Basic Books.

Mirsky, I. A. (1960), Physiologic, psychologic, and social determinants of psychosomatic disorders. *Dis. Nerv. Sys.*, 21:950-956.

Mishler, E. G. & Waxler, N. E. (1968), *Interaction in Families: An Experimental Study of Family Processes and Schizophrenia*. New York: John Wiley.

Pinkerton, P. (1967), Correlating physiologic with psychodynamic data in the study and management of childhood asthma. *J. Psychosom. Res.*, 11:11-25.

——— (1969), Patho-physiology and psychopathology as co-determinants of pharmaco-therapeutic response in childhood asthma. In: *Psychotropic Drugs in Internal Medicine*, ed. A. Pletscher & A. Marino. Amsterdam: Excerpta Medica, pp. 115-127.

Redlich, F. C. & Freedman, D. Z. (1966), *The Theory and Practice of Psychiatry*. New York: Basic Books, pp. 403-458.

Ruesch, J. (1948), The infantile personality. *Psychosom. Med.*, 10:134-144.

Schmale, A. H., Jr. (1958), Relationship of separation and depression to disease: A report on a hospitalized medical population. *Psychosom. Med.*, 20:259-277.

Selvini-Palazzoli, M. (1970), The families of patients with anorexia nervosa. In: *The Child in His Family*, ed. E. J. Anthony & C. Koupernik. New York: John Wiley, pp. 319-332.

Senay, E. C. & Redlich, F. C. (1968), Cultural and social factors in neuroses and psychosomatic illnesses. *Soc. Psychiat.*, 3:89-97.

Wahl, C. W. (1960), The psychodynamics of hypertension. *Calif. Med.*, 92:336-337.

Waxler, N. E. & Mishler, E. G. (1970), Sequential patterning of family interaction: A methodological note. *Fam. Proc.*, 9:211-220.
Weiner, H., Thaler, M., Reiser, M. F., et al. (1957), Etiology of dudoenal ulcer. *Psychosom Med.*, 19:1-10.
Wolff, N. G. (1961), *Stress and Disease*. Springfield, Ill.: Charles C Thomas.

In the early work on family process, particularly in the United States, a major part of theorizing on family dynamics and family therapy was devoted to families with schizophrenic members. It is still an unanswered question whether family psychopathology causes schizophrenia in a family member, whether it arises as a reaction to a disorder whose cause lies elsewhere, or whether family psychopathology and schizophrenia are coincidental. What is termed schizophrenia is crucial. The author reviews this field. He suggests that the study of normal and abnormal perceptual development might be a meeting ground for researchers in the areas of the biological and familial theories of schizophrenia.

The Family and Schizophrenia

DAVID REISS

The last decade has been full of exciting advances in the study of schizophrenia, and the present review represents a samplying of these new findings. Although the data are new, this group of papers displays the familiar Cartesian split: two papers represent the Cartesian "mind," now called "psychosocial varibles," and most of the other papers represent the "body," now given such labels as "genetic mechanisms," "creatine phosphokinase," and "synaptic transmission." This dualism reflects the structure of our field, which in turn reflects the continuing dualism of our conception of mental illness and human development. Each of us must develop proof of the validity of our variables and their specific role in the etiology of schizophrenia. We have applied to this work a set of increasingly rigorous scientific standards that seem only to have increased the

---

David Reiss, M.D. is Professor, Departments of Psychiatry and Behavioral Sciences and of Medicine, George Washington University School of Medicine, 2300 Eye St., N.W., Washington, D.C. 20037.

austerity and solitude of our pursuits. Why should we not now enjoy some of the fruits of our work by joining our efforts in an attempt to formulate a unified concept of the evolution of schizophrenia?

In this brief review of the role of the family in the etiology of schizophrenia, I present first my opinion of how far our field, working in relative isolation from other areas of investigation (chiefly biologic), has advanced in proving the etiologic role of the patient's family and then speculate on how this work on the family might relate to the biologic investigations.

Recent Research on Family Variables in Schizophrenia

The role of the family in the etiology of schizophrenia can be assessed by the same general scientific principles as the role of biologic variables. First, the hypothesized variables must be clearly defined and measured by reliable and objective methods. Second, the causal role of the variable must be assessed by demonstrating that it (1) is specifically linked with schizophrenia as opposed to other conditions and states, (2) has an impact on the individual before the onset of schizophrenia, and (3) is not confounded with a covarying or concomitant variable that is the "true" etiologic variable.

I shall discuss the relevant work that has been done in each of these areas and the research strategies that have been developed to carry out this work.

Identification and Measurement

The major impetus for family research in the area of schizophrenia was the early work of Theodore Lidz at Yale University, Gregory Bateson at the Mental Research Institute, Palo Alto, California, and Lyman Wynne at the National Institute of Mental Health. Mishler and Waxler (1965) have critically reviewed these ground-breaking concepts.

Lidz' work stimulated interest in two aspects of relationships between the parents of the schizophrenic—the quality of their emotional ties and the relative power of the parents. Lidz found intense discord and distrust in the marital relations of parents of schizophrenics, particularly females. He also suggested that in the case of male schizophrenics, the father is abnormally submissive and the mother is abnormally dominant. In recent years a variety of techniques have been developed to measure affective quality and power balance in marital relations.

Bateson and Wynne, on the other hand, stimulated interest in communication between parent and child. Bateson noted profound logical inconsistencies in the communications of parents of schizophrenics, and Wynne observed blurring, fragmentation, and disqualification in communication. In response to these early observations and ideas, researchers have developed various ways of measuring clarity of speech, the capacity of family members to understand one another, and the quantity of information and flexibility in verbal exchanges.

Many of these variables meet scientific standards reasonably well. They are all assessed by direct, quantitative measurement of family interaction, often in well-controlled laboratory settings. A few of these measurements meet quite exacting psychometric standards: they possess concurrent, discriminatory, and predicitive validity, as well as adequate interrater reliability and stability over time. Unfortunately, there have also been weaknesses in these variables. Particularly in their application to actual studies, they do not match the sophistication or complexity of the theories from which they are derived. This is especially true for those measuring conflict, dominance, and affect. A second weakness is that the variables depend too heavily on rater judgments: an independent judge observes a family interacting, listens to a tape, or codes a typescript and then scores the family. These judgments, however reliable, leave too much room for bias and subjectivity. Riskin and Faunce (1972) have reviewed problems of validity and reliability in family interaction research methods.

In the past few years there have been some exciting new trends in identifying and measuring family variables that have not yet been systematically applied to schizophrenia. I believe, however, they are fully applicable and will briefly mention two of them. The first trend resulted from the application of ethology and structural linguistics to family life, which has stimulated an interest in the structure of rules each family seems to develop for itself over time. These rules govern the family's relationships with other families and the wider social community. Both clinical and laboratory evidence indicate that families of schizophrenics have peculiar or idiosyncratic relationships with the wider social community. Our laboratory has reported one method for assessing these relationships: repeated measurements of families interacting with one another in a multiple family group (Reiss et al., 1975). A second trend is the increasing recognition that behavior of family members during family interaction is tightly coordinated on a microscopic level. For example, Condon and Ogston (1967) observed that during a dinner table conversation the movement of every individual was carefully regulated by the phonemic structure in the speech of the family member who was talking. These and many similar observations suggest a vast unseen continent of family interaction processes completely invisible to the unaided observer and measurable only with precise instruments in laboratory situations. It seems entirely possible that the most devastating and enduring influences of the family may be manifest on this microscopic level of family interaction.

Controlled Study of Family Variables as Etiologic Factors

Specific, Concurrent Links between Family and Schizophrenia

Despite substantial advances in the identification and measurement of family variables, their specific links to schizophrenia are modest at best (Jacob, 1975; Goldstein and Rodnick, 1975). The results in the areas of power, affect, and conflict have been inconsistent. For example, some studies have shown more evidence of abnormal affect in normal families than in families of schizophrenics; others have reported just the reverse. Studies of parental submissiveness have generally been inconclusive. However, studies of communication clarity have yielded consistently reproducible results. More than twenty separate studies in at least ten different laboratories have demonstrated that communications between parents of schizophrenics and one or another of their children are blurred, poorly understood, inconsistent, poorly focused, wandering, disruptive, and illogical. The differences between families of schizophrenics and those of normal individuals is often large. More important, this abnormality of family communication seems specifically linked to families of schizophrenics and occurs much less frequently, if at all, in families that include individuals with other serious psychiatric disorders such as impulsive character disturbances. These findings seem reproducible in a variety of conditions; for example, several findings from middle-class families can be replicated among lower-class families, and findings with well siblings repeat those with the identified patient present.

The Time of Impact of Family Variables

There are two fundamentally different explanations for the finding that family abnormalities are regularly associated with schizophrenia. The first is that the family abnormalities precede the schizophrenic disorder (and presumably are one of its causes). The second is that the onset of schizophrenia may come first; in that case, abnormal communication might represent the family's response to the disorganizing impact of the schizophrenic member. To my knowledge, there have been three approaches to assessing these alternatives: experimental models, follow-back and follow-up studies, and longitudinal studies.

In the experimental model, investigators have tried to drastically shorten the time course of the evolution of schizophrenia. They have experimentally introduced an abnormality in either parental or sibling interaction and observed the impact on the normal children and parents respectively. For example, Haley (1968) exposed normal children to audiotapes of parents of schizophrenic children, and Waxler (1974), in a problem-solving experiment, included two groups of pseudofamilies (parents and child drawn from different families), one with parents of schizophrenics and a normal child and the other with parents of normal children and a schizophrenic child. In our laboratory, we used secobarbital to induce a temporary thought disturbance in an offspring and observed the impact on family interaction (Reiss, 1973).

In the follow-back studies, school or clinic records of schizophrenics from periods before they were overtly ill are compared with similar records from control subjects. Little data on families are available from these studies. In the follow-up study, the twenty- to 30-year-old records of contrasting groups of children are located and compared. A search is made for these adults, and the follow-up data in terms of psychopathology are correlated with the childhood records (Ricks, 1970; Ricks and Berry, 1970; Waring and Ricks, 1965).

In the longitudinal studies (there are two in progress focusing particularly on the family) a high-risk sample of children is identified and followed for some years (Goldstein and Rodnick, 1975). Family and other variables are measured at regular intervals. These variables are correlated with later pathologic outcome.

The findings from the longitudinal studies are just becoming available. Findings from the laboratory model and follow-up and follow-back studies have been published in the last few years. The combined evidence suggests that a number of the family abnormalities are unlikely to be a consequence of (i.e., occur after) the onset of the schizophrenia. The basic pattern of evidence suggests that family abnormalities exist before the onset of the illness. Not all of these studies examined communication in families. Haley (1968) and Reiss (1973) studied some of the specific communication variables that seem so promising at present, whereas Ricks (1970) and Waring and Ricks (1965) reported the establishment of more global family abnormalities, such as symbiotic relationships and withdrawal of the family from the community in the years before the onset of schizophrenia.

Separation from Confounding Variables

Even if we can ascertain that a family abnormality (e.g., a communications deficit) precedes the onset of schizophrenia, we cannot say that it is either a necessary or sufficient cause of schizophrenia. It is entirely possible that abnormalities in parental behavior reflect an underlying, preclinical genetic disturbance, in which case schizophrenia in the offspring would be the result of genetic transmission. Disturbed communication would in this model be considered epiphenomenal, not causal. In other words, genetic and family variables may be confounded because they covary. Through the years, there have been many attempts to disentangle these two variables. Most scholars in the field agree, however, that this has only been possible in the last eight years since the publication of the Oregon and Danish adoption studies (Heston and Denney, 1968; Kety et al., 1968; Rosenthal et al., 1968; Wender et al., 1968). Most family researchers who have carefully reviewed the data from the earlier studies regard them as strong support for the role of a genetic mechanism. We did not, however, believe they provided strong evidence for or against the necessary or sufficient role of family variables. A more recent report from the Danish adoption studies, specifically investigating family variables, demonstrates a small but distinct role for family variables. Rosenthal and associates (1975) found significant correlations between disordered family relationships and pathologic outcome in adoptees whose biologic parents were not schizophrenic. This suggests that family abnormalities may produce a pathologic outcome in the absence of pathogenic genes, but may have no appreciable effect when the genes are present. However, this finding is limited by the design of the study, which required the investigator to recreate the early family life of adoptees from their comments and recollections as adults.

Major Research Strategies

Each of the three separate groups of investigators has a very special role to play in the elucidation of the family's role and its relationship to other variables (including the biologic one). The *cross-sectional group* use laboratory and other precision methods for measuring interaction processes in families with a schizophrenic member. They usually conduct measurements during a single time period. Their two distinct tasks are identifying variables that are likely correlates of schizophrenia, which requires the development of careful and comprehensive theory as well as precise and reliable methods, and systematically testing the specific relationship between these variables and schizophrenia. They note distinctions between various subtypes of schizophrenia and contrast family patterns associated with schizophrenia with those associated with other psychiatric syndromes, other nonpsychiatric disabilities, and with those in families whose members are physically and mentally healthy. Their work has yielded and should continue to yield variables specifically linked with schizophrenia or one of its several subtypes.

The investigators who conduct *adoption studies* use two basic approaches: either the parents are directly observed (e.g., Wender et al. [1968] compared parents biologically related to a child who becomes schizophrenic, parents raising an adopted child who becomes schizophrenic, and parents raising adopted children who remain healthy), or the adopted children are studied. Rosenthal et al. (1975) and Heston and Denney (1968) compared children who had different biologic and rearing experiences, for example, the mental health of a group of adoptees whose biologic parents were schizophrenic was compared with a group whose biologic parents were healthy. Recently, a third comparison group of children has been added—adoptees whose biologic parents were healthy but whose adopting parents were schizophrenic (Wender et al., 1974). In the study of adopted children, the parents are rarely (if ever) available for direct study. The investigator must thus depend on the adopted offspring (usually an adult at the time of the study) to reconstruct his/her childhood from memory.

Those investigators who conduct *longitudinal studies* follow the course of children and their parents from a period of time before the child became schizophrenic. In order to improve the chances of finding schizophrenics in their sample, these investigators select children at risk (i.e., either their parents are schizophrenic or the children display some suspicious abnormality). These researchers are in a unique situation in that they can determine the time of onset of schizophrenia and observe whether it precedes or follows the family abnormalities. They have the special role of determining how successfully an investigator, by using data available after the disorder has appeared, can reconstruct the family life of a schizophrenic before the disorder was developed.

There is an important system of exchanges between the three groups of investigators. The consistent correlates found in the cross-sectional studies can be used in the longitudinal and the adoption studies. Because these variables require direct observation of parents, they cannot be extended to the studies of adopted children. However, the longitudinal studies can determine which of the consistent correlates hold up over time and which can be reconstructed by other means (e.g., retrospective accounts by adults of their childhood). These purified variables become most salient for studies of adopted children.

Possible Relationships between Family and Biologic Variables

We need some assurance that the purified variables that may emerge from a conglomerate of cross-sectional, longitudinal, and adoption investigations relate in some way to a general conception of schizophrenia that can integrate both biologic and social findings. I shall focus on the communication abnormalities, which have proved to be consistent family correlates of schizophrenia. According to present odds, if you like to wager, these are the family variables most likely to emerge from the multidesign studies as a consistent correlate of schizophrenia, as preceding its onset, and as a necessary etiologic agent for at least a subset of the schizophrenias. In relating these findings to biologic studies, I will make one major assumption—that biologic and family abnormalities will be found in the same population of schizophrenics (i.e., that we do not have a situation in which biologic variables without influence from family variables produce one subset, and family abnormalities unrelated to biologic factors produce another quite distinct subset). Rosenthal et al.'s recent research (1975) does not, in my view, seriously challenge this assumption because of the methodologic limitations of their study.

Parental communication patterns serve in a very fundamental way to shape and mold the basic perceptual functions of young children. Clear parental communication patterns tend to highlight and amplify the child's stimulus world; they vividly convey the breadth and variety of the parent's experience of his own existential universe (Jones and Gerard, 1967; Hess and Handel, 1959; Reiss, 1971). As research by Mishler and Waxler (1968) strongly suggests, flexible communication patterns permit the child to insert his own percepts and observations into the family interaction when he is ready. Ambiguous and inconsistent parental communication patterns blur the stimulus world for the growing child. He is unable to grasp his parents' experience of the world, and his own experience is often disqualified and undercut (Wynne, 1968). Inflexible communication patterns between his parents may prevent him from presenting his own observations to others or requesting help. We can understand, then, how family interaction patterns—particularly the communication variables so specifically linked with schizophrenia—can have a profound effect on the growing child's capacities and styles for processing stimuli: his attentional capacities and his styles or habits of regulating stimulus intensity and of integrating, differentiating, and giving meaning to stimuli. I emphasize these elementary capacities and styles of stimulus processing because recent evidence has indicated that there may be very specific deficits in these processes that underlie many, if not most, of the cardinal symptoms of schizophrenia (Buss and Lang, 1965; Marshall, 1973). Furthermore, these psychological processes have strong biologic roots: they seem to have a genetic component (Holzman et al., 1974), they can be studied with biologic tools such as the average evoked response (Buchsbaum et al., 1974; Buchsbaum and Silverman, 1968), and they can be altered by psychotropic drugs (Saleter et al., 1973). Thus these elementary psychological processes of stimulus processing are important intervening variables. As we purify family variables to determine their etiologic significance in schizophrenia, we should pay special attention to their influence on these elementary perceptual processes. Biologic investigators may benefit from the same strategy; they can examine the relationship between measurements of enzymes, synaptic physiology, and neuropharmacology, on the one hand, with assessments of elementary perceptual processes, on the other. Wyatt and I have discussed such a strategy in detail elsewhere (Reiss and Wyatt, in press). The fundamental point is that the Cartesian split is poor scientific strategy. "Mind" and "body" researchers need to join forces and find variables both can love. Schizophrenia may be conceptualized as a special form of human development shaped by deficits or distortions of specific and elementary psychologic variables that (according to present evidence) are vulnerable to both social and biologic influences. The perceptual variables that I and others have emphasized may not be the final meeting ground for psychosocial and biologic investigators, but they do permit a strategy worth pursuing.

References

Buchsbaum, M., Coppola, R., & Bittker, T. E. (1974), Differential effects of "congruence" stimulus meaning and information on early and late components of the average evoked response. *Neuropsychologia*, 12:533-545.

——— & Silverman, J. (1968), Stimulus intensity control and the cortical evoked response. *Psychosom. Med.*, 30:12-21.

Buss, A. H. & Lang, P. J. (1965), Psychological deficit in schizophrenia: II. Interference and activation. *J. Abnorm. Psychol.*, 70:77-106.

Condon, W. S. & Ogston, W. D. (1967), A segmentation of behavior. *J. Psychiat. Res.*, 5:221-235.

Goldstein, M. J. & Rodnick, E. H. (1975), The family's contribution to the etiology of schizophrenia: Current status. *Schiz. Bull.*, 14:48-63.

Haley, J. (1968), Testing parental instructions of schizophrenic and normal children. *J. Abnorm. Psychol.*, 73:559-565.

Hess, R. D. & Handel, G. (1959), *Family Worlds*. Chicago: University of Chicago Press.

Heston, L. L. & Denney, D. (1968), Interactions between early life experience and biological factors in schizophrenia. In: *The Transmission of Schizophrenia*, ed. D. Rosenthal & S. S. Kety. New York: Pergamon Press, pp. 363-376.

Holzman, P. S., Proctor, L. R., Levy, D. L., et al. (1974), Eye tracking dysfunctions in schizophrenic patients and their relatives. *Arch. Gen. Psychiat.*, 31:143-151.

Jacob, T. (1975), Family interaction in disturbed and normal families: A methodological and substantive review. *Psychol. Bull.*, 82:33-65.

Jones, E. F. & Gerard H. B. (1967), *Foundations of Social Psychology*. New York: John Wiley.

Kety, S. S., Rosenthal, D., Wender, P. H., et al. (1968), The types and prevalence of mental illness in the biological and adoptive families of adopted schizophrenics. In: *The Transmission of Schizophrenia*, ed. D. Rosenthal & S. S. Kety. New York: Pergamon Press, pp. 345-362.

Marshall, W. L. (1973), Cognitive functioning in schizophrenia III. The relationship between conceptual performance and information processing capacities. *Brit. J. Psychiat.*, 123:428-433.

Mishler, E. G. & Waxler, N. E. (1965), Family interaction processes and schizophrenia: A review of current theories. *Merrill-Palmer Quart.*, 11:269-315.

——— ——— (1968), *Interaction in Families. An Experimental Study of Family Processes and Schizophrenia*. New York: John Wiley.

Reiss, D. (1971), Varieties of consensual experience: 1. A theory for relating family interaction to individual thinking. *Fam. Proc.*, 10:1-35.

——— (1973), Resilience of family process. *Arch. Gen. Psychiat.*, 28:425-433.
——— Costell, R. et al. (1975), The multiple family group as a small society. Presented at the 128th annual meeting of the American Psychiatry Association, Anaheim, Calif., May 5-9.
——— & Wyatt, R. J. (1975), Family and biologic variables in the same etiologic studies of schizophrenia: A proposal. *Schiz. Bull.*, 14:64-81.
Ricks, D. F. (1970), Life history research in psychopathology: Retrospect and prospect. In: *Life History Research in Psychopathology*, ed. M. Roff & D. F. Ricks. Minneapolis: University of Minnesota Press, pp. 288-307.
——— & Berry, J. C. (1970), Family and symptom patterns that precede schizophrenia. In: *Life History Research in Psychopathology*, ed. M. Roff & D. F. Ricks. Minneapolis: University of Minnesota Press, pp. 31-50.
Riskin, J. & Faunce, E. E. (1972), An evaluative review of family interaction research. *Fam. Proc.*, 11:365-455.
Rosenthal, D., Wender, P. H., & Kety, S. S. (1975), Parent-child relationships and psychopathological disorder in the child. *Arch. Gen. Psychiat.*, 32:466-476.
——— ——— ——— et al. (1968), Schizophrenics' offspring reared in adoptive homes. In: *The Transmission of Schizophrenia*, ed. D. Rosenthal & S. S. Kety. New York: Pergamon Press, pp. 377-391.
Saleter, B., Saleter, M., & Itil, T. M. (1973), The relationships between psychopathology and evoked responses before, during and after psychotropic drug treatment. *Biol. Psychiat.*, 6:45-74.
Waring, M. & Ricks, D. F. (1965), Family patterns of children who became adult schizophrenics. *J. Nerv. Ment. Dis.*, 140:351-364.
Waxler, N. E. (1974), Parent and child effects on cognitive performance: An experimental approach to the etiological and responsive theories of schizophrenia. *Fam. Proc.*, 13:1-22.
Wender, P. H., Rosenthal, D., & Kety, S. S. (1968), A psychiatric assessment of the adoptive parents of schizophrenics. In: *The Transmission of Schizophrenia*, ed. D. Rosenthal & S. S. Kety. New York: Pergamon Press, pp. 235-250.
——— ——— ——— et al. (1974), Crossfostering. A research strategy for clarifying the role of genetic and experiential factors in the etiology of schizophrenia. *Arch. Gen. Psychiat.*, 30:121-128.
Wynne, L. C. (1968), Methodologic and conceptual issues in the study of schizophrenics and their families. In: *The Transmission of Schizophrenia*, ed. D. Rosenthal & S. S. Kety. New York: Pergamon Press, pp. 185-199.

This is a follow-up study of 100 children first observed and diagnosed as childhood schizophrenics at the Bellevue Children's Service between 1935 and 1952; the outcome of their condition was related to family patterns. The subjects' ages on first observation were two and a half to twelve years and on follow-up, in 1969, were 22-46 years. Study showed that about three-fourths of the children's family patterns could be considered severely pathological, with psychotic, disturbed, or inadequate fathers or mothers, or both. About one-third of the children, on reaching adulthood, adjusted more or less well to society, the largest group coming from homes in which the mother functioned effectively, but all the children still retained schizophrenic traits and vulnerability.

The Family Patterns of 100 Schizophrenic Children Observed at Bellevue, 1935-1952

LAURETTA BENDER

There have been several follow-up studies of 100 children observed at the Bellevue Children's Service, New York City, between the years 1935 and 1952, the most recent one having been conducted in 1969 (Bender, 1970; Bender and Faretra, 1973).

Classified by onset, 32 of the 100 children had shown features of infantile autism in the first year of life. Another 27 had shown features of infantile psychosis with symbiosis in the second and third years, although eighteen of these had had some autistic symptoms in the first

---

Lauretta Bender, M.D., wrote this when associated with the New York State Psychiatric Institute, New York.

Reprinted from the *Journal of Autism and Childhood Schizophrenia*, vol. 4, no. 4, 1974.

year. For 28, onset was in early childhood, ages three and a half to six years; for thirteen, onset was at puberty, ages ten to eleven years.

Classified by outcome in 1969, 63 were found to have been placed in institutions for the mentally ill or mentally retarded because they had become chronically disabled to various degrees; eight of these had died and the remaining 55 were still institutionalized. Thirty-seven were in the community and had been there for two to 30 years.

Definition of Childhood Schizophrenia

My concept of childhood schizophrenia is that it is a psychobiological entity determined by inherited predisposition and precipitated by an early physiological and organic crisis, persists for the life of the individual, but exhibits different clinical, behavioral, and psychiatric features during the different epochs in the individual's development, and is modified by compensating defenses. Autistic (Kanner, 1973) and symbiotic disorders (Mahler and Furer, 1968) occur in early infancy and childhood; typical psychoses occur in middle and late childhood, with remissions in puberty; and pseudoneurotic and pseudopsychopathic features appear in adolescence. A wide range of regressive, psychotic, and ambulatory conditions appear in adulthood. The specific features of childhood schizophrenia are a developmental lag and embryonic plasticity and a lack of differentiation of pattern formation and of boundaries in various areas of functioning, i.e., autonomic, motor, perception, cognition, affect, and social behavior. The direct response is anxiety, which calls forth a variety of defenses.

Follow-up Studies

Our follow-up studies showed that childhood schizophrenia represents the early onset of a lifetime of schizophrenia of any possible type. For six of our patients, the diagnosis was not confirmed after they had left Bellevue. Three patients proved to be mentally defective with organic brain disease or congenital defect. I agreed with these diagnoses. But I did not agree that two other patients with early encephalitis were not also schizophrenic or that one patient diagnosed as having a psychopathic personality disorder was not primarily schizophrenic with pseudopsychopathic features.

On follow-up, 63 or two-thirds of the patients were found to have been placed in institutions because of chronic incapacitation. The unfavorable circumstances were (a) an associated organic disorder or (b) a predominant picture of infantile autism without language and with an untestable or very low level of intellectual development but no symbiotic features or tendency to develop defense mechanisms. The favorable circumstances for the 37 who were able to make a community social adjustment in adulthood seemed to be (a) symbiotic features in early childhood, (b) testable intelligence which tended to show variability in childhood but generally rose at least above a verbal IQ of 70 and (c) responsiveness to available treatment programs appropriate to each age period, such as special social and educational facilities and drug therapy in childhood, group experiences in adolescence, and a total rehabilitation program involving drugs and socializing activities in adulthood. We had also hoped that the influence of supportive homes and social agencies after discharge would make a critical difference. It was for this reason that this study was planned.

Some Literature Concerning Family Impact on Schizophrenic Children

The literature on the families of schizophrenics, both adults and children is extensive. Some of it represents efforts to explain the etiology of schizophrenia in childhood, especially infantile autism. Kanner's (1973) description of the cold, obsessive, intelligent, "refrigerator" type of parent has been exploited, not so much by Kanner himself as by some of his followers, as an explanation for primary infantile autism. The concept of the schizophrenogenic mother and the lack of communication in families with a schizophrenic member have been emphasized. Goldfarb (1961) has suggested that bewildered parents seem to account for schizophrenia in children who are not organically damaged. Wynne (1977, 1978) discussed family communication and its relationship to schizophrenia. He accepted the combination of genetic predisposition and some form of organic brain damage as a primary etiological factor at least for nuclear schizophrenia. He stated that sociocultural factors including family relationships were not of primary importance, but tended to potentiate the other etiological factors. His research indicated that parents of schizophrenics showed more communication deviancies with an impact on their schizophrenic offspring than did controls, even though the parents were apparently not schizophrenic themselves.

Frank (1965), in discussing the role of the family in the development of psychopathology, reported that the families of schizophrenics in his series were apparently characterized by aggressive mothers and passive fathers and by considerable family disharmony. He found that the mothers were overprotective and overcontrolling, but he felt that they were basically rejecting. However, each family characteristic that was found to be typical of schizophrenics also existed in the families of neurotics and those of controls. Moreover, he said, it would be hard by blind analysis to distinguish a family that produced an emotionally disturbed child from one that produced a so-called normal or well-adjusted child. He also said that there was no such thing as a schizophrenogenic mother.

Ethnocultural and Economic Backgrounds of 100 Families with a Schizophrenic Child

Nearly half (44%) of the families of the 100 children observed at Bellevue in the 1930's and 1940's were of Jewish derivation, the parents or grandparents having emigrated from Middle European countries. In 19 percent of these families, at least one parent had a profession. Only nine families were black; in two of these, one parent was a professional (see Tables 1 and 2). This distribution was a result of the cases having been found among families who sought out Bellevue as one of the few places that cared for schizophrenic and similarly deviant children. Of the families, 45% were dependent on social welfare agencies, and for the most part their children had been referred by these agencies. This distribution was not representative of the nonschizophrenic children referred to the hospital during the same period. Of the welfare families, 30-40% were nonwhite, fewer than 10% were Jewish, and the majority were of low economic level.

An epidemiological study (Bender and Grugett, 1956) was made of 30 schizophrenic children compared to 30 nonschizophrenic children with neurotic and behavioral disorders under observation at Bellevue at the same time. The problems of the children with neurotic and behavioral disorders seemed more closely related to family and cultural situations, while the schizophrenic children had more endogenous and hereditary problems. Of course, the latter could be influenced both favorably and unfavorably by environmental factors.

At Bellevue we found that the schizophrenic children referred to us

TABLE 1
ETHNIC AND RELIGIOUS DERIVATION OF SUBJECTS AND TYPE OF ONSET

Religious or ethnic group	Infantile autism without symbiosis (1–2 yr)	Symbiotic syndrome (2–3 yr)	Onset in childhood (3½–6 yr)	Onset at puberty (9–10 yr)	Totals
Jews	16	13	9	6	44
Catholics	9+[a]	7	7++	5	28+++
Protestants	7+	5+	4+++	2+	18++++++
Mixed	0	2	8	0	10
Blacks	2	1	5	1	9
Totals	32	27	28	13	100

[a]Plus signs indicate the number of black children in the Catholic and Protestant groups.

TABLE 2
SOCIOECONOMIC STATUS OF PARENTS AND TYPE OF ONSET

Status	Infantile autism without symbiosis (1–2 yr)	Symbiotic syndrome (2–3 yr)	Onset in childhood (3½–6 yr)	Onset at puberty (9–10 yr)	Totals
Professional	8	9	1	1	19
Employed and small business	10	10	12	4	36
Marginal and dependent	14	8	15	8	45
Totals	32	27	28	13	100

came from every type of home. We did not find any convincing evidence for etiological factors in the home. We, too, saw the "refrigerator" type of parents, six in this series, some having been referred by Kanner. Some anxious, uncommunicative, and symbiotic-type mothers were seen. Of the mothers, fifteen had been diagnosed as schizophrenic and 25 had other types of serious personality disturbance. Of the fathers, 40% had been diagnosed as mentally ill. We also had very good mothers who undoubtedly were able to contribute to their children's better adjustment.

Social Studies of Families

Three social workers assigned to the children's service in Bellevue studied 40 families of schizophrenic patients on the ward during the 1940's.

Bay (1941) reported that all but one of the families she studied were Jewish immigrants; the one exception was a black family from the British West Indies. Her families consisted of a dominant, aggressive mother and a passive, inadequate father who was overattached to and dependent on his own mother. There was considerable marital strife and tension. Seven of the children had not been wanted by their mothers, as evidenced by the use of abortifacients in the early months of pregnancy. The schizophrenic child was very dependent on his mother, a relationship that she fostered, seeing in this child a special need that she wanted to meet and not being able to find a satisfying relationship with her inadequate husband. Still, she often was unwilling to recognize the severity of her child's illness and often resisted separation by removing the child from the hospital, against advice, only in most cases to return him later.

Baer's (1943) seven families included four Jewish and three Italian Catholic families, all immigrants and all economically dependent. In these families, five of the fathers tended to be more dominant. In four families, the mother was overprotective in response to her recognition of her child's serious illness. Four of these mothers had attempted abortion. These families, too, resisted hospitalization and removed their children at least once, often returning them to Bellevue or arranging other hospitalization after they found that they could not care for them.

Frostenson (1944) was impressed with the number of mentally sick or inadequate, neurotic parents and other relatives in all but one of the families she studied. She found that the resulting disturbed family life affected both the sick child and his normal siblings and suggested that this emphasized the genetic factor. She believed that there was a need for more social work and community facilities to support families under stress and patients when out of the hospital. There was a wide distribution of ethnic, cultural, social, and economic backgrounds for the group of nine families that made up her final report: two Irish, one English, two Polish, two Italian, one Austrian, and one American black. There were four Catholic families, two Jewish, two Protestant, and one Lutheran. Four were of the middle socioeconomic level; the rest were economically dependent.

Kety et al. (1966) studied the incidence of mental illness in the biological and adoptive families of known schizophrenic adopted children. They found a continuum of schizophrenic disorders in the biological families but not in the adoptive families. They concluded that the genetic factor is important in the transmission of schizophrenia and that there is still no evidence for specific causative environmental stress factors.

We studied (Bender and Faretra, 1973) the schizophrenic stress disorders in the families of 50 of these children, excluding out-of-wedlock children when there was no paternal family history, and combining two or more siblings into one family unit (see Table 3). The control group consisted of 50 nonschizophrenic children observed at Bellevue at the same time for whom the same criteria were used, including an adequate follow-up. I found that the schizophrenic children had 39 schizophrenic relatives in all categories of relationship, and the nonschizophrenic children had none. There were also 50% more sociopathic, neurotic, and inadequate personalities among the relatives of the schizophrenics. There was no significant difference between the two groups in the number of relatives having other mental illnesses, retardation, organic brain disorder, or criminal behavior.

Present Studies of Family Patterns

One hundred individuals, schizophrenic since childhood when they were observed at Bellevue and diagnosed so, were studied in terms of their family patterns and whether they were able to adjust socially in the community or remained chronically incapacitated in institutions. Analysis of the family patterns in this group led to the classification of each family under one of the five headings shown in Table 4 and discussed below.

Family Pattern I: "Immigrant" Family with a Dominant Mother and a Passive, Inadequate Father

The dominant, aggressive mother and the passive, dependent father have been thought of as typical of an immigrant family. Indeed, parents so classified constituted for the most part first- and second-generation immigrants. In these families, the pattern had apparently been exaggerated by pathology. Fathers were described as passively dependent on their own tyrannical, possessive, and often paranoid mothers, and this interfered with their marital adjustment. These fathers were often withdrawn and uncommunicative and related poorly to their children. Periods

TABLE 3

SCHIZOPHRENIC SPECTRUM DISORDER IN FAMILIES OF SCHIZOPHRENIC CHILDREN: TOTAL DATA ON ALL RELATIVES BY DIAGNOSIS

	50 control subjects		50 schizophrenic subjects	
	N	%	*N*	%
Family history of mental illness denied	12		3	
Schizophrenia diagnosed in hospital	0	0	39	28
Other diagnosis in hospital or other institution	26	32	23	16
Nonhospitalized, organic brain disorder or retardation	5	6	6	4
Sociopathic personality	19	24	30	21
Neurotic or inadequate personality	30	38	44	31
Totals	80	100	142	100

TABLE 4

FAMILY PATTERNS AND OUTCOME OF 100 SCHIZOPHRENIC CHILDREN

	37 patients in social adjustment in community		63 patients in chronic institutional care		Total
Family pattern	*N*	%	*N*	%	*N*
I. "Immigrant"-type family: mother dominant, father passive-dependent	15	41	15	24	30
II. Disturbed family: father psychotic, mother inadequate	10	27	16	26	26
III. Disturbed family: mother psychotic, father tried to keep up home	0	0	8	12	8
IV. Substitute family: foster or adoptive home from infancy	6	16	4	6	10
V. Good intact home supportive of patient all his life	6	16	20	32	26
Totals	37	100	63	100	100

of actual mutism and disappearance from home were described. During the early life of their schizophrenic children, five fathers were absent from the home either because they had died (one committed suicide), were mentally ill, or had deserted.

Children Who Became Socially Adjusted Adults

Of the 100 patients, 37 were found on follow-up to be socially adjusted adults. Five had been in residential care at Bellevue for only a few months during their childhood before they were removed by their mothers, and their whole lives thereafter had been organized and controlled by their mothers with the help of social agencies, special schools, protective workshops, and outpatient psychiatric services. Four of these men were gainfully employed outside of the family for part of the time.

Of the others, ten had been hospitalized for periods ranging from seven to 24 years, although they had often been at home for various lengths of time. They have all received modern treatment with psychiatric drugs and some form of rehabilitation since adulthood. Their mothers had typically devoted themselves to visiting their sons in the hospital and taking them home as soon as possible. In six of these families, there were other mentally ill children also dependent on the mother. She organized her home on public welfare, or sometimes with the help of a small family business, or employed healthy children. Her sick child or children and sometimes her passive, dependent husband were the nucleus of the family life. Community assistance was sought when the sick child became unmanageable at home and possibly needed further hospitalization, or when any other member of the family faced a crisis. None of these ten men who had been schizophrenic since childhood had had employment other than odd jobs arranged within the family.

Children Who Became Chronically Incapacitated

Of the 63 patients who were chronically incapacitated and institutionalized, fifteen belonged to an immigrant-type family: eight Jews from Middle European countries; five Catholic, Irish, Italian, Polish, or mixed; one black West Indian; one German Lutheran. Four had had small businesses or low-salaried positions. The rest were economically dependent or partially so. Seven of the fifteen patients had one or more mentally ill siblings.

Although all fifteen were chronically institutionalized as adults, twelve had tried living at home after treatment at Bellevue for at least six months, and seven had been out of the hospital for three to eight years during adolescence. All had frequent home visits, modern drug treatment, and open hospital privileges. They were never abandoned by their devoted mothers. Two died in the hospital.

The family pattern of these chronic patients seems to have been similar to that of the immigrant families whose sons were able to make an adult social adjustment. The difference seems to have been that the illness was less severe in the latter group.

Family Pattern II: A Disturbed Family with a Psychotic Father and an Inadequate Mother

Children Who Became Socially Adjusted Adults

Twenty-six families were seriously disturbed because the father (or stepfather) was disturbed, psychotic, or absent and the mother was inadequate and could not cope. Ten schizophrenic children from such homes were able to make a social adjustment as adults. Three fathers had died in mental hospitals during the patients' childhood, but not without traumatizing these children both physically and mentally. Seven of these children had other mentally ill siblings. Two girls are included in this group who were sent back to their unstable homes after receiving treatment with psychoactive drugs and rehabilitation as adults. Both had recurring stormy periods. Both had illegitimate children and became dependent on social agencies for the care of their babies and themselves.

Four mothers succeeded in making protective homes for their moderately improved but dependent sons, two after the boys were ten years old and their fathers had died in mental hospitals. Four other men have adjusted away from their disturbed and broken homes: one successfully, as far as we know, in the Navy; one marginally with the help of social agencies; and two as dependent homosexuals.

Children Who Became Chronically Incapacitated

Sixteen or 26% of the chronic patients came from homes that were disturbed because the father was disturbed, psychotic, or absent and the mother inadequate. In nine families, the father was entirely absent because of death or abandonment. Five other fathers were psychotic, and in and out of the hospital and the home. When at home they were often disruptive; three of the fathers had battered their sick children. Six of these families had another psychotic child. Five mothers were able to maintain a home with the help of welfare agencies and keep their normal children with them; in two of these families, there was another psychotic child. Five other homes were disrupted by the mothers' negligent and erratic behavior, and five mothers were mentally ill.

Seven in this group were girls, none of whom had a stable home. Two remained in the hospital after being sent there from Bellevue at seven and ten years of age. Nine of the twelve boys were six to thirteen years old when first admitted to Bellevue. Three were admitted directly to an institution, where they remained, abandoned by a single inadequate parent. One attempted escape and self-rehabilitation without success. Six had devoted if inadequate mothers who tried repeatedly to care for them at home. They were out of hospital for six months to five years during adolescence, and were in and out, but mostly in, during adulthood.

Family Pattern III: A Disturbed Family with a Psychotic Mother and a Concerned Father

None of the patients who made adult social adjustment came from a home in which the mother was psychotic and the father adequate. There were eight chronically institutionalized patients who came from a family disturbed because the mother was psychotic and the father tried but was unable to keep the ill child home even when he was able to keep the home together. He often used the help of relatives and agencies.

Five of the mothers had been hospitalized chronically with mental illness. Three mentally ill mothers remained out of the hospital, cared for at home by the adequate father, but they battered their children. Two families also had another psychotic child. Four were economically independent, including one in which the father had a profession; the rest were marginal.

This group included four girls and four boys. Once hospitalized, these patients spent very little time at home. Concerned fathers kept two of the girls at home when they were eight to fourteen years old. One boy was in a residential treatment center from age thirteen to fifteen and at home with his father and disturbed mother from age fifteen to seventeen. One boy stayed out of the hospital with the help of an aunt and his father and had a successful military training period, but has been in veterans hospitals since. The remaining four have been chronically institutionalized since they were four and a quarter to ten years old.

This group with mentally ill mothers seemed to be the most seriously affected in the entire series. A chronically sick mother seems to be more destructive to the home than a chronically sick father. An adequate and interested father does not seem to be able to compensate for the mother in the care of a mentally ill child. On the other hand, seven of the eight families had other normally adjusted children for whom the father-centered home was evidently adequate.

Rogler and Hollingshead (1965) made a study of families of low social and economic status in Puerto Rico in which one parent (or spouse) was schizophrenic. If the father was schizophrenic, the mother could compensate and function as both father and mother, and the family did not become disorganized. But if the mother was schizophrenic, the father could not compensate for her, and the family became disorganized. Rogler and Hollingshead accounted for this as the result of the cultural ideology of Puerto Rico, in which the male is dominant and cannot demean himself by performing the functions assigned to the female.

Family Pattern IV: Substitute Families and Foster Homes

Children Who Became Socially Adjusted Adults

Ten of the schizophrenic children in this series were raised in substitute homes, and six of them have made a social adjustment as adults. Four were raised in foster homes arranged by agencies, and two by relatives—an aunt and a grandmother. Four mentally ill mothers of these children were hospitalized at their birth; two mothers had died.

Four of these children experienced many changes in foster placement and institutions, most often necessitated by their own disturbed and maladapted behavior. After a period of hospital care at Bellevue as children and state hospital care later with drug and social therapy, they have been able to remain in the community since their late teens or early twenties. There they have been unproductive and dependent on collateral relatives, foster homes, and social agencies, with occasional minor conflicts with the law.

Children Who Became Chronically Incapacitated

Four boys were chronically institutionalized after having been raised in substitute homes. All four were illegitimate, abandoned by their mothers and cared for in a number of foster homes. Nothing was known of the natural families of two of these boys. The other two were known to be offspring of disturbed and mixed-mated parents. All these children had stormy infancies, physically and emotionally. Two had many changes of foster homes until they were admitted to Bellevue at seven and a quarter and ten years of age and then transferred to chronic institutional care. Two had permanent devoted foster parents who continued to take an interest in them, visiting them in hospitals and taking them home for necessarily brief visits whenever possible. They had both been hospitalized at age seven.

Family Pattern V: Good Intact Home, Supportive of Child Throughout His Life

Children Who Became Socially Adjusted Adults

Six men, socially adjusted as adults, had the benefit throughout their lives of good stable homes. These families were economically independent, although two were nearly marginal. The parents' marriages were stable. They had the knowledge, the financial resources, and the determination to organize their lives and all available medical and social facilities to do the best they could for their mentally ill children. There were three Jewish families, one Irish Catholic, one Italian Catholic, and one black American Protestant. Three families included a parent with a profession, and the parents were active on behalf of other emotionally disturbed children as well as their own.

These families were not without other pathology, although the family life was never crippled. Five parents received some psychiatric guidance or therapy other than that connected directly with their sick child. Three children were only children and the other three had normal siblings. Of these six boys, two were of superior intelligence, two were average, and two were retarded.

Three of the boys were quite ill mentally, and were hospitalized, with frequent home visits, until they were seventeen, 21, and 30 years old. They then responded to psychiatric treatment with psychoactive drugs and rehabilitation programs. After that, they remained at home as dependents and received drugs from aftercare clinics. Their families know that they may again have to return to a hospital.

The other three were in residential care only at Bellevue as children. Since then, they have been in special schools and rehabilitation programs.

They have received maximum education for their individual capacities, and two have finished college with advanced degrees. All three have been employed in good positions, and all have received psychiatric supervision in the community. They live away from home but under the immediate and continuous supervision of their concerned families. One of them in the last two years has left his position, his wife, and his children to live alone under psychiatric care.

Children Who Became Chronically Incapacitated

While six patients were able to make an adult adjustment (16% of the socially adjusted), twenty of the chronically institutionalized patients (32% of this group) were unable to adjust to or use the good intact homes from which they came. There were finally twice as many institutionalized adults as socially adjusted adults from this group that had home situations which seemed essentially similar.

Seven of these families had at least one parent with a profession, e.g., college president and professor, teacher, engineer, social worker. Nine were economically independent and of medium to high social level, self-employed or salaried. Three were marginal and, at times during the childhood of the patient (1930's and 1940's), had been on welfare. Of the twenty families, eight were Jewish, six Catholic (four Italian, one Irish, one black Haitian-Panamanian) and six Protestant. The marriages were stable, and there were other normal children except for three families in which the patient was the only child and one family with two other psychotic children.

The hereditary incidence was particularly low in this group. Nine of the families gave a negative family history. There were two mentally ill children in one family. Three fathers were disturbed, two with what we might call Kanner's syndrome—cold, withdrawn, and obsessive—and one diagnosed as neurotic. Of the mothers, one was neurotic and one had suffered a postpartum depression. There were twelve collateral relatives reported to be variously mentally ill. This is a total of eighteen relatives for the twenty families; the incidence rate was 0.9 percent. For the total 100 patients in this study, the incidence rate was 2.15% (Bender, 1970).

Two families were disturbed during the infancy of the patient due to temporary illnesses of the mothers, but the children were adequately cared for in their own families. Twelve children had early infantile autism without any apparent exogenous factors.

All but two families had arranged for private medical consultation or psychotherapy in special schools, residential treatment centers, sanitaria, or other special programs, either before bringing their children to Bellevue, after the children left Bellevue, or later during periods interrupting the state hospital care. More than half of the parents were involved in parent groups organized by them at that time, or were in parent group therapy, or were volunteers in programs for deviant children.

Twelve of these patients were admitted directly to state institutions from Bellevue as children or after a short token trial at home. Six were at home or in private boarding schools for two to four years as adolescents. One girl was at home in a nonfunctioning condition until she was 31, when her mother died. Many of these chronically ill patients had frequent visits at home and were often visited in the hospitals by their parents. One family moved to a distant part of the state to be near the patient's institution.

It is striking that in the apparently favored group twenty children were unable to utilize the many treatment programs and family support and became chronically incapacitated in institutions. This is 32% of the total 100 cases under study and the highest incidence of chronic illness. It can probably be accounted for by the fact that many of these parents were professionals, intelligent, and with some means, and had "shopped around" at many other medical and therapeutic facilities before bringing their very sick children to Bellevue as a last resort. Similar families whose schizophrenic children responded to treatment did not need the Bellevue facility.

Discussion and Conclusions

Follow-up studies have already shown (Bender, 1970) that childhood schizophrenia in this series of patients was the beginning of lifetime schizophrenia with a great variety of clinical manifestations. The patients made various types of adjustments during adolescence and into the fourth and fifth decades of life, although all continued to be vulnerable. Excessive dependency characterizes the schizophrenic individual at all ages. Remissions occurred in one-third to one-half of the patients, during adolescence in boys and starting at latency in girls. These remission periods could be used to educate and socialize the patient, usually in the community. Recurrences of disturbed and psychotic states often led to subsequent rehospitalization. Drug and rehabilitation programs used since the mid-1950's proved to be effective, leading to community adjustment for 22 of these patients, who otherwise probably would have been chronically hospitalized.

This study of family patterns confirms the following conclusions:

1. A schizophrenic child becomes a schizophrenic adult and retains the schizophrenic vulnerability.

2. About one-third of such patients can be expected to make a social adjustment as adults but still be dependent on families, agencies, or new-found friends.

3. Recent drug therapy and rehabilitation programs in adulthood seem to be able to improve these expectations.

4. About three-fourths of the patients' families are severely pathological, with psychotic, disturbed, or inadequate mothers or fathers or both.

5. The degree of endogenous pathology in the patient seems to be the dominant factor in determining the capacity to make a social adjustment.

6. The highest percentage of successes came from mother-centered homes. The lowest percentage came from father-controlled homes where the mother was mentally ill.

7. Good intact homes supportive of the patients could not prevent twice as much chronic incapacitation as social adjustment in adulthood.

References

Baer, E. J. (1943), Study of seven schizophrenic children: Inquiry into the family background and current adjustment of seven children who were patients in the Bellevue Children's Ward. Unpublished.

Bay, E. (1941), A study of family constellation in nine cases of childhood schizophrenia. Unpublished.

Bender, L. (1970), The life course of schizophrenic children. *Biolog. Psychiat.*, 2:165-172.

——— (1975), Schizophrenic spectrum disorder in the families of schizophrenic children. In: *Genetic Research in Psychiatry*, ed. R. R. Fieve, H. Brill, & D. Rosenthal. Baltimore: Johns Hopkins University Press, pp. 124-134.

——— & Faretra, G. (1973), The relationship between childhood schizophrenia and adult schizophrenia. In: *Genetic Factors in Schizophrenia*, ed. A. R. Kaplan. Springfield, Ill.: Charles C Thomas, pp. 28-64.

——— & Grugett, A. E. (1956), A study of certain etiological factors in a group of children with childhood schizophrenia. *Amer. J. Orthopsychiat.*, 26:131-145.

Frank, G. H. (1965), The role of the family in the development of psychopathology. *Psychol. Bull.*, 64:191.

Frostenson, H. M. (1944), A familial study of nine children diagnosed as schizophrenic in the Children's Ward of Bellevue Hospital. Unpublished.

Goldfarb, W. (1961), *Childhood Schizophrenia*. Cambridge, Mass.: Harvard University Press.

Kanner, L. (1973), *Childhood Psychosis: Initial Studies and New Insights*. New York: Halstead Press.

Kety, S. S., Rosenthal, D., Wender, P., & Schulsinger, F. (1966), The types and prevalence of family illness in the adoptive and biological families of known adopted schizophrenics. In: *Transmission of Schizophrenia*, ed. D. Rosenthal & S. S. Kety, *Suppl. 1, J. Psychiat. Res.*, 6:345-362.

Mahler, M. & Furer, M. (1968), *On Human Symbiosis and the Vicissitudes of Individuation*. New York: International Universities Press.

Rogler, L. H. & Hollingshead, A. B. (1965), *Trapped: Families and Schizophrenia*. New York: John Wiley.

Wynne, L. C. (1977), Schizophrenics and their families: Research on parental communication. In: *Developments in Psychiatric Research*, ed. J. M. Tanner. London: Hodder & Stoughton, pp. 254-286.

——— (1978), Communication disorders and the families of schizophrenics. In: *The Nature of Schizophrenia*, ed. L. C. Wynne, R. Cromwell, & S. Matthysse. New York: John Wiley, pp. 499-511.

Family Psychotherapy

Strictly defined, Family Therapy is a term that embraces any procedure of the therapy (treatment) of the family. Family Psychotherapy, one of its procedures, utilizes the psyche of the therapist, or therapists, as the instrument to effect change in the psychopathology of the family. One technique, family group therapy (conjoint family therapy), is of overwhelming importance. Conjoint family therapy has exploded into clinical practice in the last twenty years and can be compared only with the similar rapid development of individual psychotherapy earlier in the century; its fulcrum lies within the United States, and its influence has spread from there throughout the world.

The choice of contributions in this field is vast. Nevertheless, thoughtful contributions based on clear rationale are rare. Enthusiasm is not an adequate substitute for precision. Discerning therapists are critical and cautious, and these notes are struck in the first five contributions from five noted therapists. The remaining papers explore special aspects of family group therapy—multiple family therapy and intergenerational family therapy.

The author presents a constructive, critical re-evaluation of family therapy, drawing from his rich experience and the literature.

Family Therapy: Clinical Hodgepodge or Clinical Science?

GERALD H. ZUK

I propose to summarize my position in the field of family therapy, a position which I believe comprises a comprehensive theory and technique. My summary will be a statement of basic principles, assumptions, propositions, and inferences. It is, somewhat paradoxically, often difficult in a lengthy clinical essay, monograph, or book to discern the basic elements that underlie a theory and technique. Such material may contain inconsistent or contradictory claims which, because of the method of exposition, are not apparent. For example, there is the claim in recent years of contributors to family therapy who—obviously deeply imbued with psychoanalytic notions—still insist they are really systems-oriented workers. This has resulted in a corruption of the term systems-oriented so that it has become more or less meaningless—or even misleading.

I would like to summarize the principles, et cetera, that appear to me to reflect more or less accurately my viewpoint in family therapy, thus offering the reader an opportunity to assess the consistencies and inconsistencies therein, omissions (or erroneous commissions), validity of claims, and the capacity of the position to generate meaningful hypotheses. I hope in so doing to encourage other claimants to duplicate

---

Gerald Zuk, Ph.D., is Director of Training, Family Psychiatry Department, Eastern Pennsylvania Psychiatric Institute, Philadelphia, Pa. 19129.

my effort. In my judgment, this would be a constructive step in the process of comparing the values espoused by the various claimants. By boiling down claims and putting them in a summary form, it should be easier to make constructive comparisons and might help discourage a major criticism of family therapy: namely, that it consists of a hodgepodge of techniques and part-theories espoused by a variety of "schools" whose ardent followers are sometimes given to excess because they either ignore or disregard suggestions that they subject claims to rigorous test. Due to the presence of such advocates, the field has become perhaps unduly politicized.

Recently, in major psychiatric journals, such prominent spokesmen for psychiatry as Brown (1976) and Marmor (1975) stated that in psychotherapy it is the wisdom and experience of the therapist that really count, not theory or technique. Brown in particular says that while "There has been an increment of knowledge in the area of marital and family therapy . . . the critical variable today is the same as it was 20 years ago—the maturity and wisdom of the helping person" (p. 493). In a recent article in a newspaper distributed to most United States psychologists, Keebler (1976), a journalist, does much to convey the impression of family therapy as a hodgepodge done by well-meaning but freewheeling therapists. The main message to the uninitiated or beginner by Keebler is *caveat emptor*.

There is more than a small measure of truth in what the critics are saying. Glick and Kessler (1975) and Olson (1975) have recited the methodological gaps and conceptual weaknesses in family therapy research. There continues to be an overreliance on the successful case to support a particular technique or theory. These deficiencies have indeed tended to the development of what may be more properly called part-techniques and part-theories. Although in many respects a useful book and one that accurately reflects a rich diversity of viewpoints, one cannot help but come away from reading *The Book of Family Therapy*, by Ferber, Mendelsohn, and Napier without agreeing with the critics.

As one who has been engaged over the past fifteen years in the rather frustrating business of trying to develop a comprehensive theory of family therapy (Zuk, 1972) and a method of teaching it (Zuk, 1975) that does not require the student to emulate my personal style or idiosyncrasies, I am deeply concerned by efforts to picture the field as simply an art form. Without denying the importance of artistry, I believe there is an obligation to subject the various concepts and techniques that have emerged in the field to increasingly rigorous research, and that those found inadequate, deficient, or ineffective, should be discarded.

During the past few years I have—although not without some trepidation—had my viewpoint subjected to such a rigorous test by two workers, Garrigan and Bambrick (1975, 1977), in what I believe is the most carefully controlled series of studies available in the field. Reports of successful cases have been useful, even in instances where the evaluation of success has been done by the therapist himself. But what is especially needed in the field today is precisely the kind and quality of research undertaken by Garrigan and Bambrick. Using rigorous experimental design, adequate controls, and valid and reliable measures, they were able in a brief time to train relatively unsophisticated graduate students in counseling in my technique and theory of family therapy. These "therapists" then conducted a time-limited series of interviews with families having children at a school for the emotionally disturbed. In replicated studies, groups of emotionally disturbed children showed improved behavior in the classroom and at home; and parents and children showed better attitudes toward each other. The "therapists" did not become fully experienced family therapists, but they were able to absorb some basics of a particular method in a relatively brief time and utilize what they learned to the benefit of their patient-families.

I believe studies such as those of Garrigan and Bambrick are absolutely essential to the progress of the field at this time. The ardent advocacy by members of "schools" has reached a point of diminished or zero returns, and credibility must now be established by hard-nosed evaluation.

What follows now is a summary of my viewpoint, which contains what I believe are the essential elements. I offer it to serve as a stimulus for others to do the same in order that critical comparisons may be made without the complexities or diversions or distractions that lengthy essays, monographs, or book material often interpose between reader and author. I also hope that, along with other such summaries, it may especially stimulate researchers to test assumptions that are held to be basic or fundamental by their authors. Only in this way can the validity of claims made by the various "schools" be fairly and properly determined on a scientific rather than purely adversary basis.

I. Some General Propositions

(A) The family is a bundle of values derived in large measure from the institutions in which it claims membership, such as church, civic associations and fraternal orders, labor unions, and so on. Its ethnic, racial, religious, and neighborhood affiliations are important considerations in defining its "identity," and therefore the therapist will take pains to discover them and generally support them.

(B) The therapist is interested in family history, but focuses on current family functioning and activities. His style of relating to the family may be bold and confrontational, or reserved and nondirective, depending on his evaluation of the status of the family, e.g., its background, its expectations about therapy, how many interviews have been held, the nature of pathogenic relating that exists, and the progress that has been made.

(C) The therapist is interested in all conflicts experienced by the family, but focuses on three: (1) that between husband and wife; (2) that between parents and children; (3) that between the nuclear family and other larger social combinations, such as the neighborhood.

(D) The therapist employs all established therapeutic techniques or devices to effect useful change, but emphasizes the special set of leverages available to him because he is working with a unique group, namely, the family. In the next section(s) that set will be defined.

II. Role Functions of the Therapist

(A) The Go-Between: The therapist exerts leverage as a go-between by facilitating communications among family members, by negotiating conflicts, and by limit setting.

(B) Side-Taker: The therapist exerts leverage as a side-taker by siding with some members against others in a dispute, or with or against the family as a whole in a dispute with an outside source, such as the neighborhood.

(C) Celebrant: The therapist exerts leverage as a celebrant by offering or being asked to officiate at an event deemed important by the family, such as a run-away or divorce or job loss.

III. Values Expressed by Therapist and Families

(A) Neither the therapist nor family is value free. In interviews they express many values which may be categorized as follows: (1) "continuity" values; or (2) "discontinuity" values. "Continuity" values espouse the goodness of compassion, justice, equality, and relatedness, e.g., between the generations or neighbors. "Discontinuity" values espouse the goodness of systems of controls, of rational approaches to problems, of law and legal codes, of orderly procedures, and discipline. In conflict between husband and wife, wives usually espouse the "continuity" values. In conflict between parents and children, children usually espouse the "continuity" values. In conflict between the nuclear family and neighborhood, the nuclear family usually espouses the "continuity" values. Thus, values are not randomly communicated in these conflicts, by and large, and the therapist, depending on his evaluation, may side with or against "continuity" or "discontinuity" values as expressed in family conflict.

IV. Pathogenic Relating in Families

(A) Pathogenic relating refers to those inflammatory, malevolent processes the therapist directly observes in family interviews, such as silencing of members by others, open or covert threats, scapegoating of other kinds, or other systematic efforts to control or manipulate members' behavior that in the judgment of the therapist are destructive to the functioning of a member or members.

(B) The general goal of the therapist is to reduce pathogenic relating or eliminate it, using those role functions described in Section II, while expressing differentially those values described in Section III. Pathogenic relating tends to erupt after an impasse in competing values, thus the therapist must also address the underlying value conflicts.

V. Some Types and Practical Goals of Family Therapy

(A) There are four types of contracts families make with therapists: (1) for the purpose of crisis resolution, lasting one to six interviews; (2) for the purpose of short-term therapy, lasting ten to fifteen interviews; (3) for the purpose of middle-range therapy, lasting 25-30 interviews; (4) for the purpose of long-term therapy, lasting 40 or more interviews.

The goal of each is somewhat different—from tension-reduction in (1) to increased family solidarity but with better acceptance of individual liberties in (4).

(B) Whereas the effort of the therapist is to evaluate and reduce or eliminate pathogenic relating in the family, his practical goals are those described above—tension-reduction, symptom-reduction, improved family cooperation, and so on. These changes are measured on an individual, not family, level for two main reasons: (1) because *families* will evaluate the success of therapy in terms of its effect on individual members; and (2) because valid, reliable measures of family change are still nonexistent.

VI. The Phases of Family Therapy

(A) The engagement period, lasting roughly the first four or five interviews, is the first phase of family therapy because it is the first critical issue raised between therapist and family. The engagement is actually the prototype of all critical issues, and each subsequent issue as it arises may be considered a phase of therapy.

(B) Termination is the final critical issue in therapy which, like the engagement, contains the potential for significant positive therapeutic movement. It occurs when therapist or family, jointly or unilaterally, decides that a satisfactory goal has been achieved, or that such a goal is unattainable under present circumstances.

(C) *Since the majority of families limit the time the therapist has to work to six months or less*, it is of little or no value to the therapist to distinguish between "deeper" and "superficial" critical issues.

VIII. Limitations and Contraindications

(A) There are numerous limitations in family therapy, as in other psychotherapies, starting with simple lack of motivation to appear for interviews, which often stems from lack of readiness to undertake the stress of the program. Certain types of presenting problems are not favorable prospects, e.g., families with an alcoholic member or chronic drug abuser. Single-parent families with very young children are often not favorable because it often turns into an individual therapy of the parent in the presence of the young children.

(B) While there are numerous practical limitations, there is only one principle of contraindication which is evoked in those relatively few instances where the therapist is trapped into serving as an agent of a referral source for the purpose of carrying out a disciplinary action, such as occurs once in a while in a court or school referral. In such instances, to undertake a course of therapy is to produce more harm than good.

References

Brown, B. S. (1976), The life of psychiatry. *Amer. J. Psychiat.*, 133:489-495.

Garrigan, J. J. & Bambrick, A. F. (1975), Short-term family therapy with disturbed children. *J. Marr. and Fam. Counseling*, 1:381-388.

——— (1977), Family therapy for disturbed children: Some experimental results in special education. *J. Marr. and Fam. Counseling*, 3: 83-93.

Glick, I. & Kessler, D. (1975), *Marriage and Family Therapy*. New York: Grune & Stratton.

Keebler, N. (1976), Family therapy: A profusion of methods and meanings. *APA Monitor*, 4: 4-5.

Marmor, J. (1975), The nature of the psychotherapeutic process revisited. *Can. Psychiat. Assn. J.*, 20: 557-565.

Olson, D. H. (1975), Marital and family therapy: A critical overview. In: *Couples in Conflict*, ed. A. S. Gurman & D. G. Rice. New York: Aronson, pp. 7-62.

Zuk, G. H. (1972), *Family Therapy: A Triadic-Based Approach*. New York: Behavioral Publications.

——— (1975), *Process and Practice in Family Therapy*. Haverford, Pa.: Psychiatry & Behavior Science Books.

It augurs well for the future of family therapy that leading therapists can openly embark on an examination of their own work. The direct, relaxed style of the author adds conviction to the valuable narrative.

Personal Reflections of a Family Therapist

JAMES L. FRAMO

I would like to share some of my thoughts and experiences with the field of family therapy over the past sixteen years, especially since the publication of *Intensive Family Therapy* (Boszormenyi-Nagy and Framo, 1965).

THE EARLY YEARS

Let me start with telling you a little bit about where I've come from. For about six years after I got my Ph.D. I was a conventional clinical psychologist who gave several thousand Rorschachs and Wechslers, looked for signs of psychopathology, and sat in case conferences where everybody argued about diagnoses. (I can no longer sit in the same room where this is happening.) I did some research, individual psychotherapy, and group therapy, but always with a sense of vague unease about the worthwhileness of what I was doing.

When I joined Ivan Nagy at the Eastern Pennsylvania Psychiatric Institute in 1957 on a schizophrenia project, and we started working with families, we felt a sense of excitement of discovery of a wholly new way

James L. Framo, Ph.D., is Professor, Department of Psychology, Temple University, Philadelphia, Pa. 19122. He is on the faculty of The Family Institute of Philadelphia.

of viewing and conceptualizing emotional difficulties. For us it was somewhat akin to the discovery of the microscope in that phenomena were revealed that had never been seen before. We couldn't wait to get out of bed in the morning to get to work to see what we'd find out that day. We were sure then, as I am even more convinced today, that we had hold of something damned significant in the transpersonal-intimate view of man. Revelation of the phenomenon of interlocking, multiperson motivational systems was a genuine breakthrough. Many heretofore inexplicable paradoxes and symptoms began to make sense; the family systems approach helped decode age-old human dilemmas. How to *change* a family was another story. There was nobody around to teach us, of course; we watched each other and supervised each other, and we used co-therapists to keep from getting overwhelmed. In the light of what we know today about working with families, our efforts were crude and fumbling, but I will always remember the exhilaration and joy of creation of those days. It was pretty lonely in those days, too, especially when we wanted to share ideas with colleagues. I remember we had to be surreptitious about seeing families; we'd whisper to friends at conventions in hallways, "I'm seeing families; what about you?" In those days, it just wasn't done; there were both professional and cultural taboos.

Since those early days there has been a tremendous growth in the field. The literature has expanded enormously, training programs have proliferated, local family institutes have been organized around the country (although family therapists for various reasons still resist forming a national organization), and workshops and seminars on family therapy at conventions continue to be crowded. Family therapy is being used in many different settings. I myself have given over a hundred workshops around this country and in Italy, the Netherlands, and Mexico. There is no question that family therapy is here to stay; it is now even listed in traditional textbooks as an "acceptable" form of treatment. Many mental health professionals latched on to family concepts and practices because of the ring of truth that it is very difficult to change individuals solely through the one-to-one relationship with a professional; it is necessary to change contexts, especially intimate ones. For the first time, practitioners dissatisfied with puzzling treatment failures using traditional approaches found a way to deal with the *real* problems of people, the relationships with those who matter most to them. A son, for example, could work directly on his real relationship *with* his father rather than talk *about* this relationship to professionals or make a father out of the therapist. A wife could deal directly with her real husband rather than "a paid friend." Symptoms came to be viewed as by-products of pathological relationship events.

The situation, however, is much more complicated and tricky than the picture I've just painted. Paradoxically, in the midst of all this growth and acceptance and admiration, a systems approach is still quite threatening to the psychiatric, psychologic, and social work establishment—those who have the power to give grants, establish policy, train, set salaries, and appoint to positions. For example, I wrote up an NIMH grant to establish the first family therapy unit in the country as an independent service within a community mental health center. The grant was approved in 1969, but took three years to be funded. I could write a book on the hurdles that were placed in the way of this grant, at the federal, state, and local levels, from the medical university, and even from the community mental health center where I worked. Those resistances ranged all the way from the federal government wanting to know why I couldn't rewrite the grant and orient it toward children or drugs because there was money there; through the state office that said they couldn't give matching funds to a program that violated the CMHC act, which requires treatment for psychiatric illness; through a message from the city office of mental health that local matching funds could be granted only to proven treatment programs, and, besides, why have an independent service for a specific form of treatment? If they set up a unit for the family, why not set up one for group therapy? At the medical university I was called in by the person who set my salary; I was told that some of my publications implied that established psychiatric practices were sometimes less than therapeutic, and would I please tone down my papers. As I was leaving the office, I was told, "By the way, Jim, I've begun doing family therapy, and have been doing it for years." I might mention that, although I was chief of the unit, my assistant chief, a psychiatrist, was paid a much higher salary. Within the CMHC it was difficult to get referrals from other services, so we had to go outside the center and deal with such people as the clergy, nonpsychiatric physicians, the courts, schools, welfare and child-protective agencies, and so on. The ambivalence of the other services in the CMHC about our unit was striking. On the one hand, the unit was viewed with envy as the glamour outfit, but the sabotaging was fascinating to observe—the unit was used as a dumping ground for all the impossible situations. You know the story: "Send them to family therapy; it can't do them any harm." We rarely got fresh crisis situations.

I used to think it was just the psychiatric establishment that was responsible, but later I joined the faculty of an academic department of psychology, and at one of the case conferences of the psychological service center I suggested that the patient be seen with her family. Despite the fact that this staff had recruited me because they wanted a family therapist on the staff, it was interesting to observe all the dubious and evasive remarks that followed my suggestion.

Family therapy can't be ignored, but it can't be digested either. Someday I'll take Murray Bowen's advice and suggest to my staff that they go around "bad-mouthing" family. I have learned that one should not try to sell this approach; what I find happening is that people come over to observe treatment sessions through the one-way mirror, and then they get hooked.

Family Therapy Today

Pressure from students is forcing some departments of social work to give a course on family therapy; as far as I know there are only a few doctoral programs in clinical psychology that offer a course, but the most interesting development is occurring in psychiatric training. Because family therapy is "in" these days, it is felt it ought to be included in psychiatric residency training programs, but this gesture is often merely lip service. When some of the full implications of the systems viewpoint begin to seep through—in terms of its effect on diagnosis and treatment procedures, admission policies, status, and so forth—we may witness the termination of these training programs. It is a mystery to me why the new medical discipline of family medicine rarely includes any teaching about family dynamics in its training programs.

One wonders in this connection whether it's best for family therapy to exist in a setting of competing viewpoints or mixed models, or if it should do what psychoanalysis did and set up its own institutes and standards. That course led to psychoanalysis becoming isolated, and you can note how psychoanalysts are trying to get back in; for instance, the movement of analysts into universities, medical schools, and community psychiatry. I can see the validity of the arguments on both sides, and I don't have an answer for that question. In fact, at the present time practically all training in family therapy is being done by local family institutes in the major cities around the country. While there are a few service centers that are exclusively family oriented, most family therapy is practiced in settings that use many treatment modalities.

I do see the family approach as a philosophy and an orientation to the human condition, not as just a technique or a form of therapy. I've even wondered if this work is therapy at all and whether it isn't a special form of experience, one that belongs outside the framework of the helping professions, perhaps in education. A lot of people are hopping on the bandwagon; some have overbought the family approach and use it inappropriately. For instance, bringing a family together in one room to talk about the patient is considered family therapy by some people. Viewed as a theoretical orientation, it matters less who is actually in the treatment room; the Bowen group does family-oriented work with individuals. Virginia Satir has said she can find out in 30 seconds' discussion of a family whether someone understands the systems approach. I do not mean to imply that there is only one right way to treat families. Indeed, one of the main developments in the field is the existence today of many schools of family therapy, all the way from work with single family members (Anonymous, 1972) to social networks (Speck and Attneave, 1973) and Auerswald's focus on ecological systems and the interfaces between systems (1968). Already there is talk of the old and the new family therapies. In a paper on "The Future of Family Therapy" (1970) John Bell correctly predicted that the field would move into working with black-ghetto families, communal families, and the multifamilies created by divorce and remarriage, and foresaw the field moving into industry and business (not only with families dislocated by reassignments but with work systems themselves); he envisioned more transcultural family work, and movement into a variety of settings and institutions such as prisons, homes for the aged, foster homes, and group living homes, as well as movement in the direction of preventative and family life education programs.

Speaking for myself, changing a family system is the ultimate professional challenge; it is perhaps the most difficult of all therapeutic tasks, but also has the greatest pay-off. My own therapeutic philosophy is to learn as many kinds of treatment approaches as possible in order to have a full repertory of techniques available to shift the system. Consequently, I go to workshops in transactional analysis, gestalt therapy, encounter techniques, behavior therapy, rational-emotive therapy, existential therapy, as well as to those using methods of working with families that are outside my own orientation, such as family sculpting. I use techniques from psychodynamic theory, communication theory, group therapy, paradoxical instructions, audio and video playback—whatever I need to use to move a system. Shifting a family system just a notch increases by multiple ratio, much like a pebble dropped in water has a rippling effect. In my training programs I try to acquaint students with as many different schools of family therapy as possible; after being exposed to many different ways of working with families, the trainees can eventually develop a style that is most comfortable for them.

We've learned a lot about the nature of working with families as the years have gone by. Following those early years of working with schizophrenics and their families, we moved into work with many family types and throughout the range of manifest symptoms. Most family therapy today is of the short-term crisis variety, I would suspect; I'm uncomfortable when I remember that the first family I saw was seen for five years. Undifferentiated families usually will come forever without significant change beyond symptom improvement, but the more differentiated families seldom stick beyond the crisis resolution. Perhaps this is as it should be, in that families should only be helped to the point where they can rely on their own self-corrective mechanisms. The drop-out rate in family therapy is quite high, but there are good reasons for this, I think. First of all, the sources of resistance in families (as compared with individuals) are greater and can come from many more directions. A family can drop out or prematurely terminate for reasons that have nothing to do with the way the therapy was conducted: A husband and wife can have a fight before a session, and one refuses to attend; a child might not want to return, and the parents go along with the refusal; the parents may have too much invested in scapegoating a child and sense from the first session that this mechanism might change; an extended family member or outside psychiatrist, lawyer, or clergyman may dissuade the family from returning, and so on. Events go on outside sessions that the therapist knows nothing about. Another reason for early dropouts, in my judgment, testifies to the very power of family therapy. *Because* it can bring about fundamental changes (and this can happen as a result of just one session) many families are very threatened by the anxiety of change, and therefore don't come back. *When people don't really want things to change, they find methods other than family therapy to deal with them*. This high early drop-out rate or "no-shows" is a source of disappointment that beginning family therapists have to learn to deal with. I'm intrigued by Murray Bowen's experimentation with nonregularity of sessions, whereby sessions are timed to system changes or gauged by the anxiety level, rather than being spaced for the convenience of the therapist's schedule. Such a procedure may cut down on dropouts. Family process is a continuous dynamic force that may not be geared to once-a-week intervention. We have a lot to learn about the timing of sessions as well as many other matters that bring about change.

I still struggle with one of the oldest dilemmas in family therapy, namely, that the different family members come in with varying secret agendas and expectations, and these often clash with each other and with the goals the therapist sets for them, at least implicitly. Perhaps part of the skill of the therapist resides in finding the appropriate balance between the clash of goals and expectations of all the family members as well as those of the therapist. This problem existed in individual therapy when the patient wanted to stop his suffering but did not really want to change his exploitation of others. With whole families, it gets more complicated because motivations vary; people come in for somebody else and not for acknowledged help; some members are dragged in, others act out their problems through other people, and they are either not suffering or they endure bearable hurts. Some family members give family therapy superficial commitment, go along with it for a while, and then later on say, "Yes, Doc, we understand we have a part in this, but what about Johnny, really?" It's true that most of the time the designated patient is the first to change, but sometimes he's the last, or doesn't seem to change at all, even when a part of the system has changed (e.g., the marriage relationship is better). As Tony Ferreira once said, we first had to discover that the family is a system, before we could recognize that it does not always behave as a system.

Most families are very fearful of coming to sessions, but there are some I've seen who asked for family therapy and were eager for it; some of these families use its very rationale to subvert the therapy. They'll say, "It's a family problem," but nobody takes responsibility for anything. When I see families or couples, I make clear my expectation that each person has to take responsibility for his own life; yet this is a paradox in a way, because asking them to come in together implies shared responsibility, that all their fingers are in this pie. When are you responsible for someone else, and when only for yourself? I wrote a long time ago that families essentially come to therapy to restore or maintain the status quo, despite their words and their pain, and I still think this is so. A key question I ask myself is: Why, since the problem has usually existed for some time, is the family coming in *now*? What in the system is not working? The presented problem usually has little to do with the real problem. (For example, the presented problem may involve concern about a teenager's school problems or loneliness, whereas, actually, the teenager's growing autonomy is perceived by the parents as rejection of them.)

I still occasionally get feelings of failure and helplessness when I've tried everything I know, and they are still stuck. So you bring in a cotherapist as a consultant, advise a break in treatment, or refer them elsewhere. When do we let families go—when their games are better than ours? When you're tired of them? When you realize that you want more for them than they want for themselves? When your case load is high, do you increase your expectations with the families who are dragging? You cannot always expect appreciation for your efforts; as a matter of fact, there are times when expressed appreciation is a sign that no change has taken place. There are some people you just can't connect with, and you realize later when you listen to the tapes that you just didn't like them, or sensed they didn't like you, and that you kicked them out. I've wondered—those families or couples who do change a lot—are they the ones we liked?

Another phenomenon I've noticed is that some people cannot tolerate success (e.g., one father said, "I can't stand it; my wife is nice to me and even my car is working.") Occasionally one has to work with families around the issue of accepting the improvement. For example, when the marital relationship improves, sometimes the children (who presumably have much to gain) become more resistive in family therapy. The parents, who wanted medals for their progress, are then disappointed. What will be provided as replacement for the unhappiness? While the family or couple are regrouping and finding new ways, depression may follow the stopping of the "acting out"; this phenomenon has a parallel in the way the psychoanalysts speak of the sense of regret over the loss of symptoms.

Evaluation—Success and Failure

I'd like to discuss briefly this question of success and failure because it's related to the important question of research evaluation of family therapy. Does family therapy work, and what do we mean by working? The question is enormously complicated, and I'll just touch on a few aspects. On what level should we look for change? On the level of symptom relief? (This is the least of the family therapist's goals.) Do we seek greater differentiation among family members, greater intimacy, less family distress and unhappiness, more open and clear communication? Do we seek changes in attitudes, in behavior, on the level of deep needs, homeostatic balance, shifts in alliances? Do we pursue better social functioning outside the family? If we help resolve interpersonal conflicts, will interpsychic conflicts become lessened; if we resolve intrapsychic conflicts, will the relationships improve?

Incidentally, on this question of the interplay between family-group and individual defenses against depression and anxiety, I see the real task of the psychological sciences over the next century as a deepening understanding of the extraordinarily intricate relationship between the intrapsychic and the transpersonal. I've made a tentative beginning along this line in my paper, "Symptoms from a Family Transactional Viewpoint" (1970) where I explored Fairbairn's object relationship theory as a link between the personal and the social.

Continuing with this question of evaluation of family therapy results, we have to keep in mind parameters of social class, types of families, and the all-important factor of the particular stage of the family life cycle the family is in when they come to us. We plug into a continuous family natural force at a particular phase of the family development, and only deal with pieces of a larger context at any given point in time. How many of us in dealing with a given family wish we could have seen them years ago, before the patterns became calcified? (How many of us, for that matter, have wished family therapy had been in existence when we ourselves were children, and felt that if we'd had it for ourselves, our lives might have been different?)

Nat Ackerman has commented on still another dimension of this evaluation problem. Unlike most forms of therapy, family therapy does not aim so much at merely taking something away, such as pathogenic conflicts, but often achieves a surplus, positive, actualizing sense of enrichment in family life (1966, Chapter 2). How do we go about measuring this dimension? Many families report that they really enjoy each other more and get more out of life than was ever thought possible. What about the bad and good side-effects of family therapy on extended members? For example, should we include in our evaluation the fact that we produced no change with a given family, but that the married sister who originally came to sessions to help her delinquent brother reported that her own marriage got so much better as a result of attending sessions? On the other hand, doesn't it sometimes happen that somebody has to lose for the rest of the family to gain? For example, a grandparent who has been tyrannizing a whole family may lose out to the autonomy forces of her children and grandchildren, and she may end up in an institution for the aged. Or a man finally gets to the point where he can leave his suffocating, widowed mother and get married; from his and the therapists' point of view he is better, but from his mother's point of view he's worse. Under what circumstances is a divorce an indication of improvement or growth, and when is it not? In any discussion of favorable or unfavorable results, you get involved with questions of values, not only value conflicts between the family members but between the therapist and various family members, as well as societal value dissonances. Take, for example, how the current social revolutions creep into the treatment room—the black militant teenager castigating his "Uncle Tom" parents, the woman who wants to change her traditional housewife role and have an open marriage, the therapist struggling with his old value system when treating couples engaged in the swinging, group-sex scene.

Recent Methods of Treatment

Shifting the topic a bit now, I'd like to discuss some of the treatment methods I have come to use in recent years. Take this question of combining other forms of treatment with family therapy. For instance, I have found that when one member of the family is in individual therapy or analysis outside the family sessions, this arrangement forces the family therapy to labor under a handicap. That individual usually reserves the most significant material for his "own doctor" and filters his productions for the family sessions. I have found concurrent peer group therapy for adolescents or other family members helpful and not interfering with the family therapy. Also, I have occasionally sent obsessive and up-tight people to encounter or marathon weekends in order to loosen them up, and this is done for the overall purposes of the family therapy. Now and then I work with sibling subsystems without the parents, as well as other combinations of family members. Occasionally I will see individuals; for instance, when working with a married couple who cannot tolerate being in the same room with each other or cannot interrupt a repetitive interaction pattern, I will temporarily see them separately and then bring them back together, when, as individuals, they have changed. I have used the structured separation method for couples where one or both partners cannot tolerate living together; the spouses live apart, continue to come to therapy sessions, and each person works on family of origin (Toomim, 1972). My method of working with adults and their families of origin will be discussed later.

Although in particular situations I believe it is necessary to do *family* therapy throughout the course of treatment (i.e., including the children), I have moved more in the direction of working with the marriage relationship of the parents once the originally symptomatic children have become defocused. Most of my family therapy these days, then, becomes marital therapy. In addition, of course, I see couples in marriage therapy who come in explicitly for marital problems; some of these couples do not have children and some with children do not present their children as the problem. I still believe a statement I wrote years ago that "whenever you have a disturbed child you have a disturbed marriage, although all disturbed marriages do not create disturbed children" (Boszormenyi-Nagy and Framo, 1965, p. 154)—i.e., some partners do manage to keep the kids out of their difficulties.

The next direction I moved into was to start doing couples group therapy, and I did this as a matter of clinical expediency. There are some couples who work beautifully by themselves, and utilize the therapeutic setting so effectively that the best thing you can do is stay out of the way and not do something stupid. With other couples I found myself boxed in by their triangulating efforts, or I couldn't tone down the emotional accusations to each other, or they'd move for a while and bog down, and I found my freedom of action blocked by feelings of anger, boredom, and frustration. So in the beginning I put couples together in order to handle my own feelings and free myself. Another reason I organized couples groups is that, as with a family, you need an ally, the most differentiated one, to help you deal with the system. I frankly felt I needed allies to help me deal with some of the couples. These "assistant therapists" serve a different function from that of a formal cotherapist. Like a lot of things that you do for one reason you find has serendipitous effects, I discovered that couples group therapy is a powerful form of treatment in its own right. As a matter of fact, I've come to believe that couples group therapy is the treatment of choice for premarital, marital, separation, and divorce problems (Framo, 1973).

This all leads to a major, most recent dimension of my work, family therapy involving adults with their family of origin. Before I deal with this clinical method, I'd like to make a few observations about some dynamics of family life. People are constantly repeating relationship struggles from their family of origin and they seek through marriage, children, friends, enemies, work colleagues, encounter groups, and psychotherapists the kinds of responses that will enable them to correct, master, or continue old, unfinished family business. The relational environment is manipulated so that others are maneuvered into being nurturant parents, servants, tormentors, or what have you, in order that more primitive conflicts will not come to the surface. In this sense, painful symptoms can be avoided by selective choice of relationship. But no one has any choice when it comes to relatives, to parents and siblings, grandparents, uncles and aunts; these are captive relationships. One's parent may not be the sort of person one would have chosen to have as a friend; even if one's father is a weak, lovable, neglectful failure and one's mother is unreal, unreachable, and always depressed, one cannot easily give up parents the way one can give up an acquaintance. Friends and mates are replaceable; nothing can change the fact that one's mother and father will always be one's mother and father.

The stakes are higher and the consequences graver when one deals with one's family members because they have the wherewithal to affect the core of one's being. Families are where we live, and, as Carl Whitaker said, "The family is the place where you are dealing with life and death voltages." These realizations help explain why disappointment, hostility, and frustration are so much more intense in the family setting, the rejection much more hurting, the loyalty and sacrifices so compelling, and the gratification so fulfilling. There is a special, real quality in dealing with one's parents, brothers and sisters, spouse, and children, which does not apply to other social relationships. The psychology of intimate relationships is unique, has laws of its own, and reduces all people, whatever their station in life, to the same common denominator. For instance, when Franklin Roosevelt got married, his mother bought two contiguous houses in New York City, had the walls between the two houses knocked down, and lived on one side while Franklin and Eleanor lived on the other. In this way she could control every aspect of the newlywed's lives. One wonders where Franklin, one of the four world leaders and a president of the U.S., was in all of this?

We family therapists are in possession of a great and powerful secret. The Chinese Communists who brainwashed their enemies knew this secret; they forced prisoners to confess the wrongs they'd done their parents in order to put them in a more vulnerable position. In family therapy sessions, dealing with the most powerful needs in the human realm, the most commanding, socially influential people can be reduced to the status of a sobbing child.

Family influence persists through space and time, kept alive by "programming" and family ghosts of the past, and lived through other people in the present. Family primacy does not affect geography, as adults discover when they try to break off contact and put physical distance between themselves and their families of origin. One pretty much *has* to be involved with one's family whether one wishes to or not, even if one doesn't actually see the family very often or at all. The long arm of family loyalty, loves, and hates stretches beyond death and grave unto succeeding generations, creating unseen forces which influence the destiny of many lives.

I began bringing in families of origin on the basis of my clinical experience with family and marital therapy. Of all the methods I have used, involvement of the family of origin is the most effective; I've found that one session of any adult with his family of origin can take the place of many regular therapy sessions. I should mention that people usually strenuously resist bringing in their families of origin initially, and it takes considerable therapeutic preparation before they are ready to deal with their families.

Early in my experience with families and couples it became apparent that the relationship problems that adults have with their mates, children, and others are reconstructions of earlier conflicts with their families of origin. It seems almost naïve to state this truism, but when I began searching the literature for those who had a systematic theory for using family of origin as a therapeutic resource there was no one to add to Murray Bowen (Anonymous, 1972). My method of involving adults with their families of origin differs from Bowen's. Murray Bowen sends his adult clients home on timed visits to their families of origin and coaches them in their differentiating efforts. He uses the same method in training family therapists, supervising his trainees to conduct family voyages. Whereas Bowen rarely has the adult bring in his family of origin for therapy sessions with him, I do just that, since I'm working toward somewhat different goals.

This practice has been so productive that now I routinely have at least one session, if at all possible, with each adult and his or her family of origin. I have found this procedure to be valuable, in a different way, for the married adult who is overinvolved with family of origin, the one who has infrequent superficial contact, and the adult who is totally alienated from his parents or siblings. In these sessions the mate or children are not present, I usually do not allow much talk about the adult's marriage to take place when he or she is meeting with the family of origin (another method of triangling which diverts from the main purpose). The focus is on that adult's past and present relationship with his parents and siblings—what went on in the history of that family, how the roles were distributed, the alliances formed, nodal events, tragedies, secrets—in short, the usual things looked for in a family diagnostic interview. Important diagnostic information is obtained on how past family problems are being acted out in the present. More to the point, however, in these sessions, opportunities are available for genuine corrective experiences, clarifying of old misunderstandings, and the possibility of establishing an adult-to-adult relationship with one's parents. This kind of experience gives people the chance to get to know their parents as people rather than as fantasy figures who have to be inflated or deflated.

Incidentally, in recent years I have been doing family, marital, and couples group therapy with my wife as cotherapist. In these family-of-origin sessions, her presence has come to be especially meaningful, particularly for the parents and siblings as well as for the adults who had been in treatment. Her being a woman and parent gives her a special role that helps ease the natural gap between generations and sexes.

The Subjective Side of Doing Family Therapy

Turning now to the subjective side of doing family therapy: Back in 1968 I went through some personal experiences whereby the boundary between my work with clinical families and my relationship with my family of origin and my wife and kids was becoming more and more permeable and diffuse. It was becoming increasingly difficult for me to keep the two separate. One way I handled this struggle was to write a paper. It was called, "My Families, My Family" and was published in *Voices*, the *Journal of the American Academy of Psychotherapists* (1968). I wrote this paper in four days, and I wrote it in blood. I think it's the most honest piece of writing I've ever done. The paper has had a strange reception. I've received many letters about it from all over the world, it has been xeroxed hundreds of times for training programs around the country, yet it has never been cited in any reference list. This phenomenon is a mystery to me. I wrote in this paper:

> I don't know when I first became aware of the phenomenon that treating families not only revives the specters of one's own past family life, but also has subtle, suffusing effects on the therapist's current family relationships. After doing family therapy, and seeing what emotional systems can do to people, I take my own family life more seriously. In the living presence of a mother, father, brothers, and sisters, the constellation in which most of us grew, one finds oneself transported back to old thoughts, longings, disharmonies, and joys in a way which can be more moving and reintegrative than one's own personal therapy or analysis. Each family we treat contains a part of our own. As I saw more and more families I have become used to reliving each stage of my own family life cycle during sessions, in a series of flash-backs at once compelling and fearsome, fascinating and despairing, growth-promoting and regressive. While I am conducting treatment sessions, with my surface calm and important, hiding behind my degrees and the trappings of my profession, evaluating the dynamics of the family before me, figuring out the strategy, avoiding the traps, I communicate to the family only a small portion of the emotional connections I make with them, the places where we touch.

The rest of the paper consists of statements made by family members during sessions with different families, and then, in parentheses, my personal and verbally uncommunicated associations to the material, (such as the time I heard a teenager tell his parents, "Go fuck yourselves," and I got the uncanny feeling that his parents suddenly looked like my parents and I wondered if this boy was saying for me what I never dared to say.) And I also recounted moments of tenderness, nostalgia, regrets, loving feelings, disappointments, and lost opportunities, culminating in the realization that I was trying to refashion all my clinical families into the kind of family I always wanted mine to be. When a family member said to me, "Doc, I keep getting the feeling that you have some kind of ideal family image you expect us to live up to and that somehow we should be like your family," I shuddered with the thought, "My God, can it be true?" But my point in bringing up this paper is that I barely scratched the surface, then, on the personal side of being a family therapist.

Family therapists are a curious, distinctive breed among mental health professionals. They have broken down a number of professional taboos, especially concerning secrecy and confidentiality, and they practice openness, direct observation of therapy and each other, live supervision, the sharing of experiences, and they treat people as persons rather than as patients. They view symptoms as epiphenomena of relationship struggles, and they focus on the human context rather than on psychopathology. They keep looking for some word other than "patients" to describe the people they see professionally and some word other than psychotherapy to describe the process. Mavericks that they are, they are relatively unconcerned with the degrees its practitioners have. Most try to practice what they preach, and are relatively frank about their own family struggles, thereby decreasing the usual distance between professional and seeker of help. Family therapists have strong convictions about the validity of their work and firmly believe that they are where the action's really at. Innovative and creative in theory, therapy techniques, and methods of training, they nonetheless run into trouble at times in their professional and personal lives. Professionally, they are concerned with such questions as: Should family therapists be certified or licensed; should anyone who has a feel for this work practice it; and what kinds of standards should there be? Are family therapists born and not made? Should they have had prior experience in individual and group therapy? What is the best way to train family therapists, assuming they have the necessary personality equipment? (I find that some mental health professionals can never become family therapists no matter how much training they get.) How much do we really know about changing families: How comprehensive are our theories, how effective our techniques, and why is there so little systematic research on family interaction or therapy outcome studies? Do we need a national organization or confederation of local family institutes?

The personal side of treating families and couples is even more important because these private matters have a strong effect on professional and treatment issues even if they are not recognized and acknowledged. I'll plunge directly into one of the touchiest. My sampling is limited and may be off, and I do not know the statistics for other mental health professionals, but among the family and marital therapists I know of, I see a high rate of divorces, separations, accidents, emotional crises, and even premature deaths. Assuming that the frequency of these events is beyond chance, one wonders why? I have speculated about several possible explanations. Foremost, I think there is a selective factor in people going into this kind of work. Although all family therapists, I believe, continue their struggles with their own families of origin with their clinical families, some have mastered or resolved or have come to terms with (or whatever words you want to use) their own past so that they can use the experiences adaptively. Others, I fear, do use families in order to work out their own problems. (I am not discussing here the kind of highly sophisticated way that Carl Whitaker exposes his child self and asks the family to take care of him; he knows exactly what he's doing). What I'm trying to identify here is that those family therapists who become casualties of one sort or another probably have serious family problems themselves, either from the old family or with their current family, and it's likely these events would have occurred even if they had never become family therapists.

Another factor may have to do with the fact that treating couples and families is extraordinarily stressful work. How hazardous is this occupation? While the transactions of a family session may sustain us, at the same time they drain and exact a toll. I'm sure you've all had the experience of having observers behind the one-way mirror needing a reentry experience with you at the conclusion of a treatment session; they are often so overwhelmed with feeling that nobody has anything to say. Have you also noticed how, during sessions, observers behind the one-way mirror will joke, laugh at, kibitz, and make hostile remarks about the family members or therapist? Do observer therapists need this release to get back at families for what they do to us? Many a time after a particularly heavy session I need a drink or need to unload with my cotherapists, a friend, a group of observers, or I need to talk with my wife at night when I can let all the feelings out and get feedback that I did the right thing or that I didn't fail or that I'm a pretty wonderful guy. Sometimes I work it out vicariously with a good TV show, play, or movie, or by chopping wood or gardening on weekends, writing an article, building a bookcase, painting an oil, making love.

A wide range of support systems, personal and professional, for doing this work is vital, and when these support systems are not working there's going to be hell to pay (Whitaker et al., 1965). When your own marriage is seriously troubled, or you're having difficulty with your kids, or if you haven't worked out a self with your family of origin, or if your work system is hostile to a systems approach, it's going to be especially difficult to conduct marital or family therapy sessions. This whole question of whether therapists in deep distress can be of help to others is a very intriguing one. I've seen therapists whose own marriages and families were falling apart who nonetheless managed to be effective as professional therapists; somehow they were able to disassociate themselves from their own personal lives and still be objective. Others, of course, bring their own personal unhappiness, biases, and distortions into the treatment room—with uncertain effects. But who's to say? Sometimes the sharing of a personal tragedy or a vulnerability can be just the thing that establishes a human contact.

A great book on psychotherapy was written in the 1950's by Carl Whitaker and Tom Malone called *The Roots of Psychotherapy* (1953). Some important things were said in that book, but I don't think therapists were ready for them. The book dealt with something that is coming up now in family therapy, the subtle interplay of professionally helping people and being helped by them. Are some family therapists getting divorced because they discover with clinical couples what expanded dimensions of relationship are possible, and they decide they want more than they themselves have? As you know, all marriages go through up and down phases. What do you do during a down phase in your own marriage when you're treating a couple whose marriage relationship is in better shape than your own? Or this can go the other way: you are likely to write optimistic articles about the viability of marriage or set different standards for treatment couples when your own marriage is in an up phase. How unsettling is it when couples or families or individual family members you are treating are way ahead of you and working on their growth better than you are? How do you deal with your jealousy when you help kids get more from their parents than you yourself got from your own parents? What do you do when you see a man being cruel to his attractive wife and you feel you wouldn't treat her that way if you were married to her? How more often are you able to have moments of authenticity with clinical families than you are able to with your own family? How do you handle observing a man on his knees crying and begging his wife not to leave him? How tough is it for you to deal with incest or parents who have literally murdered their children, or a dying father who's mean to his family because he doesn't want them to miss him when he's gone? *Does tragedy toughen you or chip away at you?*

How many of us are amateurs who carry over into our own personal lives the turmoil of the families we treat, and is a true professional one who learns to take distance and cut off? Although in general I have pretty good control over my own feeling system, there are family phenomena I still have difficulty handling: marriages where one partner desperately wants out and the other just as desperately wants to hold on; men who smile at everything; snotty kids; stagnation; lying and dishonesty; dealing with child abuse; cloudlike vagueness in people; people who make you feel helpless or those who appreciate nothing you do or who are too appreciative; overly suspicious people; valid family secrets; men humiliated by their wives and wives humiliated by their husbands; letting my theories get in the way of my listening; massive scapegoating; passive-aggressive people; depressed families; parents destroying children and children destroying parents; families where someone in the family is dying, especially a child.

Family phenomena I enjoy dealing with: resuscitating a dead marriage to the point where they are really married and "in love"; helping kids get unhooked; bringing together an alienated father and son or mother and daughter and observing the "high" when they become more real to each other; helping a mother or father feel like a parent for the first time; watching a whole family move from despair to an enriched life; seeing dangerous or painful symptoms disappear; getting baby-card announcements; seeing people make use of their potential; enjoying children who cut right through adult pretensions; realizing that the beneficial effects of the family therapy today may carry over into the next generation; sensing a real system change; doing a follow-up and learning that the changes lasted.

Professional psychotherapists are just like anybody else when it comes to dealing with their own families, and some people say they handle intimate relationships even worse than others. One family therapist I knew used to tell couples all the time how important it was to go to marital therapy together, yet when his own marriage was breaking up he and his wife went to two therapists separately. One therapist I knew told of how her children used to slip notes under the door to her office at home, asking for an appointment. I believe that the first obligation of a therapist is to improve his own functioning and get his own house in order.

This discourse leads to the question of whether family therapists should get family therapy for themselves; should it be a requirement, as the analysts require analysis to be a psychoanalyst? Although I'm not certain whether it should be a requirement, I do feel it's highly desirable. I can tell you first hand that it's damned important to know what it's like to be on the other side. In the family sessions I've had with my own current family I came to appreciate the fear and anxiety that people have when the system is under examination. Before the sessions started, I fooled myself into thinking I would not be a therapist in that situation, that I'd just play from myself, be open and sincere, be a husband and a father. I realized later that I'd had it all planned how the sessions should go. But it went in unexpected directions, as I learned what my kids and wife really thought about some things. When I heard the tape later, I heard myself telling everyone what they *should* think. And I discovered that 48-hour, delayed anxiety response that other family therapists have mentioned. Believe me, it's real and it's scary; you get to identify what's really going on, and it can really change things, and by change I don't mean just feeling better. In that situation you are like every other family member who comes for help. If you really want to find out what family therapy is all about, try it yourself.

References

Ackerman, N. W. (1966), *Treating the Troubled Family*. New York: Basic Books.

Anonymous (1972), Toward the differentiation of a self in one's own family. In: *Family Interaction: A Dialogue Between Family Researchers and Family Therapists*, ed. J. L. Framo. New York: Springer, pp. 111-173.

Auerswald, E. H. (1968), Interdisciplinary versus ecological approach. *Fam. Proc.*, 1:202-215.

Bell, J. E. (1970), The future of family therapy. *Fam. Proc.*, 9:127-141.

Boszormenyi-Nagy, I. & Framo, J. L. (eds.) (1965), *Intensive Family Therapy*. New York: Medical Department of Harper & Row.

Framo, J. L. (1968), My families, my family. *J. Marr. & Fam. Counseling*, 1:15-28.

——— (1970), Symptoms from a family transactional viewpoint. In: *Family Therapy in Transition*, ed. N. W. Ackerman et al. Boston: Little, Brown, pp. 125-171.

——— (1973), Marriage therapy in couples group. In: *Techniques of Family Psychotherapy: A Primer*, ed. D. A. Bloch. New York: Pantheon, pp. 87-97.

Speck, R. V. & Atneave, C. (1973), *Family Networks*. New York: Pantheon.

Toomin, M. K. (1972), Structured separation with counseling: A therapeutic approach for couples in conflict. *Fam. Proc.*, 11:299-310.

Whitaker, C. A., Felder, R. E., & Warkentin, J. (1965), Countertransference in the family treatment of schizophrenia. In: *Intensive Family Therapy*, ed. I. Boszormenyi-Nagy & J. L. Framo. New York: Medical Department of Harper & Row, pp. 323-341.

——— & Malone, T. P. (1953), *The Roots of Psychotherapy*. New York: Blakiston.

Here the family therapist concentrates on his own group-activating techniques in handling family aggression and on elaborating the absurd—a new development.

Psychotherapy of the Absurd: With a Special Emphasis on the Psychotherapy of Aggression

CARL A. WHITAKER

TYPES OF PSYCHOTHERAPY

Any discussion of psychotherapy must begin by defining the character of psychotherapy one intends to present. Are we talking about *reparative psychotherapy*? Are we talking about the *relief of symptoms*? Are we talking about *character restructuring*? Are we talking about a *growth-accelerating experience*? Qualitatively, the character of psychotherapy patterns may take many forms. A classification could include:

(a) Interpersonal feedback as in group psychotherapy, some sensitivity training experiences, and communication training.

(b) The development of self-induced feedback—a kind of recycling experience with content and affect rediscovered or re-experienced, as in the psychoanalytic pattern.

(c) Psychological education, as in rational psychotherapy and the late phase in the usual transference kind of treatment. This psychotherapeutic

---

Carl A. Whitaker, M. D., is Professor, Department of Psychiatry, University of Wisconsin Medical School.

Reprinted from *Family Process*, vol. 14, no. 1, March, 1975.

process is very much like the parent-child conference with a late adolescent offspring.

(d) A here-and-now experience with a professional who can share in activating and accelerating the feedback to the patient by his own nonrational participation and by his here-and-now growth process.

This later mode, which includes family therapy, has elements of the play that makes child therapy different from insight therapy. It requires control by power in the early part of treatment and makes broad use of the symbolic aspects of the total relationship, including body language, now sometimes labeled gestalt techniques or nonverbal communication. There is also a freedom to see therapy include a manipulative process, as with children and psychotics. This facilitates the ability of the therapist to shift from a peer give-and-take to an authoritative position of making decisions like sending the psychotic back to his bedroom or interrupting the child's play to end the hour. This model assumes the therapist will also push to experience his own craziness, his own LSD kind of turn-on, and a nonrational exposure of himself. (A rational pattern in the therapist's function doesn't help the patient break his own prison of reason.) It also assumes the use of deliberate paradox, a kind of chess-playing with the patient—a sense that therapy is not just being sincere and honest and open and even crazy with the patient, but is also the freedom to shift back and forth between being intimate and crazylike to being deliberately manipulative and managerial.

The author and T. Malone (1953) have previously presented the concept of individual therapy as a forced, regressive process or as induced regression. This approach assumed that the psychotic is himself also playing at being an adult and therapy is an effort to force him into becoming fully crazy, fully infantile, regressing to the year-and-a-half or two-year-old point at which he began distorting his growth process.

Psychotherapy structure, of course, is not a variant of social relating. "Love is not enough"—unless the patient has sufficient maturity and integration to carry most of the initiative for the process. Dr. Barbara Betz says the quality of all psychotherapy is profoundly dependent upon the therapist as a person: his inherent freedom to share and his inherent capacity and freedom to care. A noncaring therapist may be useful to a patient who is fairly well along in his growth process, but is probably not of much use to the more immature patient.

The process of family psychotherapy is generally characterized by a transference phase in which there is established a symbolic generation gap and a suprasystem in which the family becomes part of an extended family, including the therapeutic team. With this structuring, there develops an *induced regression* of the component parts of the subsystem, that is, the individuals, the dyads, the triangles, and the two generations. The therapeutic process then begins to establish the integrity of the individual components of the system. Given this integrity, the individual components of the family system develop a specific autonomy and become capable of functioning without the need for the suprasystem—its control and its integrative power. There emerges because of this regression a gradual restructuring of the family system itself with greater mobility and greater flexibility.

The second phase of the process of this psychotherapy I label the existential phase. This develops later, although it of course overlaps the transference phase, and consists of the establishment of a peerlike balance between the patient group and the therapist group with the autonomy of the components. It has an adult-to-adult character with contributions from each side to the other and from each unit to the whole system.

The Family Hostility System

As defined by Partridge (1959), aggression really arises out of two components, assertiveness and hostility. Assertiveness relates to words meaning to get fed, to get together with, to walk toward, whereas hostility has two aspects, one to assail and one to destroy.

Culturally, aggression wins hands down in the competition with sex for what is *most unacceptable* in our interpersonal living pattern: assault and battery is taken much more seriously by the authorities than rape or incest. Furthermore, most crimes of violence take place within the family rather than on the sidewalk. Such aggression is usually an effort to be a personal savior to a Significant Other and best defined by a famous schizophrenic, not a patient of mine, who said in defining his therapeutic effort to save us all, "I come not to bring peace but a sword," translated as "You've got to fight to get to heaven." Furthermore, Dr. Winnicott, a London child analyst, in an exceptional paper called "Hate in the Counter-Transference" (1949), said, "If you haven't been hated by your analyst, you've been cheated," and at another time, "The psychotic patient can't tolerate his own hatred unless the analyst hates him." Even the Old Testament participates, saying, "He that hideth with smiling lips is a fool."

THE THERAPIST'S MADNESS

Constructive aggression by the therapist is one way of defining his integrity as a person. It's a modeling process and, not so secondarily, is also a way to destroy the myth of the omnipotent parent. Although our overt aggression early in therapy may be clinically inappropriate, aggression, once it does develop, may be hidden by the doctor's famous bedside manner or by that poker face that hints indifference or a fear of involvement. We may even repress our anger until the patient in his transference loyalty acts it out for the therapist like a child stealing cars for his pre-delinquent father's sake. Sometimes a therapist dare not admit his simple ambivalence lest his aggression explode. Thereby, we also conceal our free associations, mis-hearing, slips of tongue, and even creative fantasies. Such suppression of self will hide our own night dreams and anger at our real world, as well as any love for, and identification with, the family.

How does the modern therapist express this therapeutic anger? The four simple ways are pigmy versions of the patterns that are detailed in the standard American psychiatric classification of "madness': First, the *sneer or snarl* that they label in its extreme form paranoid psychosis. It's the open style and at least an interpersonal turn-on. More powerful is the *poker-face freeze* that, carried to an extreme, they call catatonia. Still more serious is that contentless *inner boredom* called by Baudelaire (1968) the worst crime. If carried to its extreme, they label it simple psychosis. Finally, and most destructive, that *derisive laughter* that, carried to its ultimate, is the hebephrenic system for withdrawing from the interpersonal world. If the patient (family) is personal enough, these withdrawal models may fail and the therapist is forced to come alive. Then his madness explodes into the family.

THE PATIENT'S MADNESS

The patient's madness may become growth-accelerating and creatively rechanneled when aided by the therapist, either through direct intervention or by indirect means. Those who have practiced psychotherapy for long usually become exponents of indirect methods. I should like to list several that seem definable within the usual ongoing treatment process:

(a) Handling aggression by forgiveness—the typical mother support pattern which may result in an induced regression and a return to childlike directness and openness.

(b) The second type I call counterattack. It's a kind of *judo* approach to aggression that tends to neutralize the anger or the bitterness or the physical assault. It's an interpersonal retraining in which, because of superior strength and superior confidence, the therapist is able to shunt the aggression out of its escalation or render it impotent without seriously threatening the aggressor, whether an individual or the family as a whole. For example, a curt command to "Sit down" can prevent a physical attack.

(c) A third method is to one-up the situation rather than the person. One-upmanship is like *akaido*—a method of judo-like character except that it does not involve any aggressive response to the attacker but rather prevents him from doing damage with his aggression. It renders the aggression futile—for example, the therapist who doesn't notice a murderous look.

(d) A fourth method is to justify the aggression, to go with it, thus reducing the guilt and producing a loss of the aggressive affect. One day, in an initial interview with an adult veteran, I became terrified lest he kill me there and then. I excused myself, went across the hall and got Dr. John Warkentin and brought him back into the interview; I told him and the patient of my fear. He said to the patient with a perfectly straight face and in a serious tone, "I don't blame you a bit; I've often wanted to kill Whitaker myself." This confused me, but it made the patient's anger much more controllable, and we went on with a comfortable interview.

(e) Still another way of handling aggression is to defuse or redirect it. For example, one can help the patient project anger at his father onto the therapist or redirect hatred against his wife back into the residual hatred for mother or father or big sister.

(f) It is also possible to handle aggression by direct attack. Thus, the therapist can dominate the patient psychologically, making him suppress his anger. This is similar to *karate*—the therapist can defeat the patient and thus render his anger something he dare not use.

Psychotherapy of the Absurd

Finally, I should like to talk at some length about a method that I seem to have developed in spite of myself. It's a method of augmenting the unreasonable quality of the patient's symptom or situation to the point of absurdity. It includes a kind of tongue-in-cheek attitude—a kind of put-on by the therapist, but is surprisingly useful if it's a natural component of the ongoing relationship. The therapist may so augment or escalate the incongruity of a symptom or bit of the patient's behavior that the absurdity is easily apparent to the patient and he enjoys the implications, as one does after a slip of the tongue. Success with this maneuver demands that it be lovingly done, and this caring is the anesthesia for the amputation of pride that takes place. A most elementary example would be responding to a child's angry scream by pseudo screaming back at him. With enough of these imitation screams that echo his screaming, he feels impotent and stops because nothing is happening the way he expected it to, or he joins the therapist and the two of them laugh at what's happening.

When working with a grossly aggressive patient or family, bits of absurdity may serve as a quantum jump from rational psychotherapy to an effective tactic that reduces aggression and establishes a creative craziness in the therapeutic group. The therapist may expose his own absurd behavior or respond to his own boredom by a flight into absurdity via minute, incongruous bits of behavior—e.g., (a) give the top of an old coffee percolator to college sophomore schizoid without comment when she leaves interview; (b) identified patient is accused by parents of having poor ego boundaries—therapist offers blank sheet of paper with large X to "use as ego boundary as needed"; (c) unannounced exit from office and return five minutes later without excuse and with inane reason—"My foot itched"; (d) write a letter during hour to your cotherapist entitled "Why this family won't make it"—offer it to family if anyone questions the behavior.

The use of the absurd may be a fragment, as described, or it may become an ongoing process. When it is the latter, it resembles the leaning tower of Pisa. The patient comes in offering an absurdity, and the therapist accepts the absurdity, builds upon it, escalates it until the tower has become so high and so tilted that it crashes to the ground. The steps in this seem fairly clear:

Step 1. The patient or the family presents an absurdity—for example, "I can't stand my husband." The therapist agrees, "Men are pretty difficult."

Step 2. He then extends the inference "Why haven't you divorced him?" or "Why not try an interim boyfriend?"

Step 3. The therapist then expands the absurdity by escalating the patient's feedback to the original interaction. She says, "But, I love him." The therapist says, "Of course, that's why you'd have an affair—to prove your love and to stimulate his love 'till it equals yours." The patient says,

"But I love my kids," and the therapist says, "Well, if you do, then you should make a sacrifice by leaving them so they'll learn that father also loves them." "But he'll neglect them." "Then you can prove your love of them by suing him for child neglect."

Step 4. The patient or the family attempts to break this escalation, to take off the top floors of the tower as it were. The patient says, "This is silly." Therapist: "No, it's very logical and loving and human, and I'm only trying to help you. I believed you when you said you couldn't stand him, and I was trying to help you find and figure out ways of making things work out right." Although this pattern may seem ridiculous when looked at in this verbal and logical framework, it may develop quite naturally and become an extremely powerful force. This raises the question of what happens when it goes on for most of the hour or for week after week.

Step 5. It seems as though the fifth step emerges when the patient's attempt to break the escalation does not pay off. There is then a break in the patient's integration and his imprinted thought pattern. This resembles a Zen enlightenment experience. The tower of absurdity comes crashing down. This may happen in three different ways: (a) By sudden development of a profound dependency so that the patient reports, "We've had a very good week, and I don't understand it"; (b) The crash may be experienced as a flare of rebellion. The patient says to the co-therapist or to her partner, "Let's get out of here; I can't stand this screwball and the way he talks"; (c) The break and crash may come by transcendence. The patient says, "Carl, you're crazy, but I think I see what you're talking about. I really couldn't stand my husband, the rat. I would have left him long ago, but there must be something about him that makes me go on loving him."

Step 6. The sixth step, of course, is the therapist's acceptance of the patient's flight into health or enlightenment experience. I call this the benediction and just say, "Have fun."

Let me give another example. The patient presents with a fear of sex. The therapist says, "Yes, I understand sex is a very frightening experience." Thus accepting the absurdity, he begins to escalate it to step three. "Do you find sometimes that you also have difficulty eating, that after eating you get the feeling of being very full and maybe you shouldn't eat more or that maybe it would be better if you didn't eat at all and then you wouldn't feel so full? There is also the possibility of choking or of getting some food that has glass in it. I read recently of a boy who ate something and was so badly poisoned he almost died." In the fourth step, the patient attempts to break the sense of absurdity. "I have started eating less. The other day I had to throw away a whole TV meal because it didn't look right." Or he says one day, "We really had a great orgasm last night," or in a transcending way, "I'm feeling all sexed up this week."

Let me give still another example. This is a real family story: There is father, mother, thirteen-year-old daughter, and six-year-old son. Wife insists husband is unfaithful and that, anyway, he lies all the time. Husband says the affair is over and that, anyway, she shouldn't complain because he is working two jobs and giving her all the money. The therapist suggests that if he's not careful and she stays suspicious she may hold back his allowance. He says, "Well, she has already held back some of it." The therapist notes that the wife looks very happy and asks *her* if she has expressed appreciation to her husband for stimulating their relationship by this affair. The wife is quite indignant but a little confused. Therapist explains that it's his belief that when these things happen the two of them have done a long-range planning project with great care and that the result is a concealed decision that he should have an affair. It obviously worked out well since she looks very pretty and both had agreed she has been a better wife since the affair. The therapist then asks if mother's mother believes the affair should be tolerated, or should the wife get a divorce. The wife explains that her mother thinks she shouldn't split from her husband. The therapist then suggests to the husband that since the wife is so happy maybe he should be careful not to go back to his wife. Had he thought about having several girls—then he could get an allowance from each of them. If he should decide to do this, he should add on one at a time because girls are very apt to get jealous of each other. A man must learn how to handle a team of girls when each of them is paying him an allowance from her earnings. At this point father attempts to break the escalation of the tower by getting sarcastic with the six-year-old son who is gently restless. Father also backs off after he explodes, so the boy does not modify the behavior. Finally, the father snarls, "Fool," at the son with great bitterness. The son is as unimpressed by this apparent viciousness as father is unimpressed by mother's verbal attack. Son, like father, keeps a poker face. As the entire absurd episode explodes the wife's organized coping process, she begins to cry and yet wonders why she's crying. The success of the break is further signaled by the wife's willingness to return for another appointment and the husband's agreeing to come back and to bring the only surviving grandparents, his father and her mother, for the next interview.

Gus Napier suggests a different explanation for the above episode. The couple is deliberately mystified by the therapist, who then escalates the confusion by his seeming serious attitude. He denies the couple's effort to demystify by repeated affirmation of good faith ("I'm just trying to help you"). As he does this, he encourages rebellion against previous mystification. Furthermore, as the process escalates, the therapist, in contrast with the spouse or mother, encourages rebellion by the couple and thereby joins them in a low-profile game of teasing each other.

A marital counselor and his wife came as patients to two cotherapists with whom they had had previous interviews. They requested help for their marital relationship. It seemed that each had developed an affair with the full awareness of the other partner. The affairs were doing well on each side, but they had decided to spend six months trying to clarify their marital relationship before they decided about divorce. The therapists requested a 24-hour delay while they considered a possible plan. Next day they suggested that there were two ways to go on with treatment. One, the cotherapists would begin couple psychotherapy with a contract specifying no sexual relationships during the therapy so as to potentiate the affective relationships with the two therapists. The couple must also contract to have no sexual experiences with their two affair-partners. An alternate plan specified that the husband and wife bring in their girlfriend and boyfriend and the spouses of those two partners so that the cotherapists could work with all six. Both offers were declined, but a letter six weeks later indicated that the couple were doing much better and appreciated the help we had given them.

This multiple triangle was presented to the cotherapists with a request that was itself absurd—mystifying?—double-binding? The therapists took the absurd task and escalated the absurdity—mystification?—double bind?—paradoxical intention? They further encouraged the rebellion by offering an alternative escalation of the original absurdity: multiple triangles. The couple did rebel and indicated the success of the process in a letter.

Possible Mechanism

Why does the theater of the absurd have such a popular hold on audiences? Esslin (1969) talks about this question, as does Bogard and Oliver (1965). Oliver believes this attraction derives from its relation to our general problem in living—our world is absurd, our culture is absurd, my life is absurd, my reason is absurd. Is psychotherapy, like this drama, a microcosm of the process of our living?

The drama critics state that man's thinking is absurd to his senses, and his senses are absurd to reasoned thought. Paradoxically, we attain power at the sacrifice of reason. When we try to act reasonably, we deny our personhood. Furthermore, as we struggle to "be" who we are, it is impossible to stop acting. These are the self-defeating paradoxes of our lives. They portray our power and our impotence but also our knowledge and ignorance, our attunement and alienation. In essence, we are both tragic and farcical. This Janus mask is thus our absurdity. Absurdity is both metaphilosophical and the existential summation of man. Our absurdity is ironic and a fragment of our craziness. The drama of the absurd says, "This is not life I express, this is a work of art about life." The logic of the drama of the absurd is never directly stated but indirectly and symbolically expressed. The use of deliberate obscurantism makes it necessary for the audience not only to *recognize* a body of thought but also to *learn* it. In contrast, direct presentation many times leads to recognition but results in a failure to learn. Obscurity is one method to activate learning, and models the absurdity we find in life. In contrast, realism in drama and, I think, in psychotherapy reduces the actor or the patient or the therapist to a puppet, and furthermore, one then lives in a perpetual distrust of language.

Many times the process of relating to patients consists of moving in for an experience of belonging and then asserting the freedom to move out. *Most therapists develop empathy. They learn to move in, but they stumble as they try to move out*, i.e., *to individuate without leaving the patient rejected*. One possible method is to utilize this process of activating the absurd. For example, a therapist makes some derogatory remark about the patient's appearance and then says, as the patient is about to counter, "Isn't it silly of me, since I'm not your husband," or, "I was only kidding." The therapist may also move in with a note of affection such as, "You look pretty," or, "I'm sorry you had this scheduling problem," and then moves to a note of absurdity. "I'm glad I don't look pretty," or, "I slept in the office last night, so getting here was no problem for me." The therapist thus establishes a bond—a "we"—with the patient (or couple or family) and then breaks it. Since he identifies with the patient, he does so with a roguish touch that seems enjoyable and not rejecting. There is even the maternal voice tone— "Just you wait, I'll be right back."

By this microcosmic experience, the patient evolves a kind of immunity to the strange assault of the absurdity in our living process and some experience in how to zig and zag with the absurdity of his life. Hopefully, the patient also gets a kind of objective distance by participating in the therapist's distancing. Subsequently, he expands his capacity to tolerate the anxiety and the stress and even chaos of his ongoing life.

There is, of course, a similarity between this process and Don Jackson's prescribing the symptom or his forcing the development of a "runaway" within the family, thereby reducing to absurdity the escalating process of the family struggle. There is also a similarity to advising the family to augment the confusion of psychotherapy and to try *not* to understand psychotherapy as a process but allow themselves to experience it more fully by not objectifying it or talking about it, even among themselves, outside the interview.

If psychotherapy is indeed a pilot plant to try out patterns of living different from those we are imprinted with in our childhood, then psychotherapy of the absurd can be a deliberate effort to break the old patterns of thought and behavior. At one point, we called this tactic the creation of *process koans*. It's a constant, exaggerated extension of the patient's self-concept, a constructed elaboration, an effort to help the patient develop a caricature of the implicit stance he has been assuming or the life style that he has presented by his symptoms or by his effort to explain himself. It is as though the therapist stretches the inferences the patient makes by manipulating the transference until the therapist's credibility is at the breaking point and the patient must either develop a new gestalt that excludes the therapist or regress to keep the transference gestalt alive—that is, to keep the therapist magic, keep him the God of their joint reality from which the "therapist-as-a-person" has now withdrawn. The therapist then develops a deviant quality or fantasy that excludes reason and impugns, or at least threatens, the rational aspects of the patient's daily life. The therapist may even escalate the absurdity to the ultimate of credibility and then beyond it. It's as though an individual patient comes with a leaning tower of Pisa, and the therapist, instead of trying to straighten the tower, builds it higher and higher and higher until, when it falls, the entire building falls rather than just the construct that the therapist has helped with.

Why then would we want to use the family as a whole for this kind of process? William Taylor (1970) notes that the single deviant produces an emotional income for each member of the family—that is, each member of the family looking at the deviant feels so much better about each of the other members and so much better about the group as a whole, excluding the deviant, that it makes a very sensible way of handling family stress. Just so, if in family psychotherapy everyone is present, the emotional income for each person, because of his investment of affect in the family treatment effort, produces a large total investment by the family. The family thereby makes a sizeable down payment toward changing the entire system with an increased flexibility or induced chaos of the total ecosystem—that is, the increased chaos, the increased craziness makes it possible for the deviant to re-enter the family and for the whole system to develop, thereby increasing flexibility.

This brings us to a conclusion in contrast to the older, direct therapy in which the effort was to reconstruct in a rational way. This psychotherapy of the absurd, or what Wolf and Schwartz (1958) years ago called irrational psychotherapy and which Malone et al. acknowledged as nonrational therapy (1961), *is a way of saying that the therapeutic problem is to increase the complexity of the situation rather than restore order*. Following the second law of cybernetics as defined by Lynn Hoffman (1971), we are trying to induce chaos and craziness rather than restore order. May I stretch your patience to include three more examples of this kind of psychotherapeutic approach.

Mary F. arrived at the inpatient service after a very serious suicidal attempt. After being on the ward for several days, her family was invited for a family conference. With the seven of them there and with a general history of the family's way of living and some effort to establish for them a sense of whole so that it was clear we were dealing with a systems problem, I asked her who in the family wanted her dead. She was not able to answer this, but a younger brother got around to saying that he felt Dad would be happier if sister were out of the way. We moved from there to a discussion that activated her fantasy about what would have happened if she had been successful in her suicide attempt. How big a funeral, how expensive a casket, how many flowers, how long would Dad mourn, how long would Mother cry, what would happen to her belongings, her room, her boyfriend's picture, her old clothes? In each case, the therapist made considerable point of his own fantasy about this, wondering if mother could wear the patient's clothes, wondering if they would throw all her old letters from boyfriends into the garbage or burn them, wondering whether boyfriends would come to the funeral, whether the family could live in that house, who would sleep in her room, would they have to repaper it, etc. A by-product of this strategem is the discovery that when the patient goes through a full-fledged fantasy of this nature, the suicidal threat seems much reduced. The therapist may participate at great length, and what appears on paper like ridiculous expansions are well tolerated and surprisingly useful. The usual suicidal fantasy—"They'll be sorry when I'm dead and gone," or, "I'll fix the bastards"—is thereby so contaminated that the exquisite pain of isolation is hard to maintain. I wonder if they'll really burn all my clothes? Would Bill go back to making it with Mary Jones? I'll bet Mother would leave Dad within a month.

Jane W., a 50-year-old mother in ongoing family therapy, had been picked up drunk on the street and brought to the hospital. She declared the problem was her younger daughter. She must make this daughter either marry her boyfriend or get rid of him. Her efforts to resolve the problem were becoming increasingly painful since daughter and boyfriend were sleeping in his car in the driveway and daughter would come each morning to get breakfast for the boyfriend and take it out to the car. Later, mother had to rap on the car window and yell at them to back their car out, so she could get her car out and go to work. The therapist suggested that she was not loving enough. She really should invite them in to sleep in the basement—the car was very cold, and such treatment would run down their battery. She did this and came back the next month to report that she went down to the cellar one morning, found the boyfriend in his undershorts, and "I ordered the daughter out of the house, but they have just gone on doing the same thing in the car." The therapist then suggested that she might alternate nights with them. She could sleep in the car one night and they in the house, and they could sleep in the car the next night and she in the house. Or she could at least get their breakfast so that the daughter wouldn't have to get out of the warm car and come in to make breakfast for him. Simultaneously, the therapist expressed his admiration for her getting drunk—something she had never done before. He encouraged her to continue that process, since it would undoubtedly help her alcoholic husband whom she had been neglecting for so many years. He might very well have to quit drinking if she got picked up for being drunk like this because he'd have to take care of her, and it might even cure her daughter, who would begin to worry about mother and the extreme cost of being hospitalized every night for being drunk on the street. This kind of induced confusion and expansion of the absurdity brought about a diminution of anger by an overlay of confusion and chaos. Surprisingly enough, although the retelling of this kind of experience sounds ridiculous, the patient is able to utilize a tremendous amount of absurd initiative from the therapist, as the next case will show.

Susie Q., 29, who came from a foreign country, had survived two abortions and one missed abortion. That one was now five years of age and was called "It." Her husband was a square of the first caliber, and the problem as stated was that they wanted to get a divorce shortly, and therefore he'd brought her for couples therapy. The therapist suggested that they could also put off getting divorced until they were older, and psychotherapy would be one way of delaying it. The secondary problem seemed to be that each time she became pregnant she was convinced that she was so immature she couldn't possibly raise a child and therefore would get an abortion, and each time the abortion would leave her so guilty that she would immediately want to get pregnant. The assistant professor husband was passively cooperative in all this, unconcerned about the $250 per abortion or her impulse to get pregnant again. He was glad to help in any way he could. After living through two more of these episodes, the cotherapists had developed a constant pattern of kidding in dead seriousness. They finally suggested the couple really try to have at least three abortions a year, and in the twenty years remaining of her childbearing life she probably could have sixty abortions and establish a world record. This was taken so seriously that three weeks later the husband suggested to the wife that she must get pregnant within the next six weeks or she wouldn't have her third pregnancy for that current year and thus not have her third abortion.

Conclusions

Clinical observation would indicate that insight psychotherapy may well be even more useless in growth-activating family treatment than in one-to-one therapy. The need for power tactics suggests that many group therapy techniques may be valuable. Responding to aggression in one or more of the family members, the author is increasingly free to use these group-activating tactics and the power politics of his own intervention.

An attempt is made to describe a method for activating the tendency to resolve behavior paradoxes through transcendence by elaborating the absurd.

If the therapist is a caring person, he can frequently modulate aggression by cutting diagonally across the affect through use of a tongue-in-cheek humor or a nonrational extension of the situation that leaves the aggressor off balance and often amenable to more open family interaction.

Aggression is an overt or covert component in all family interaction. Family homeostasis is such a powerful component of family therapy that the therapeutic team must be able to manipulate the group dynamics or the family will not change in spite of intense effort on his part and theirs. Therefore, power techniques become a central factor in the process of treatment. The paradoxes so characteristic of their now instrumental, now symbolic, interaction can many times be resolved by positive feedback to the point of absurdity. The saber-tooth tiger starved to death when mother nature overdid the blessing of that absurd tooth.

Craziness is the only real solution to boredom, as with the chimpanzees who generate territorial wars to amuse themselves.

References

Baudelaire, C. (1968), Au Lecteur [from *Les Fleurs du mal*]. In: *The Voyage and Other Versions of Poems*, ed. R. Lowell. New York: Farrar, Strauss & Giroux.

Bogard, T. & Oliver, W. (1965), *Modern Drama*. New York & Oxford: Oxford University Press.

Esslin, M. (1969), *The Theatre of the Absurd, Revised*. Garden City, N.Y.: Anchor Books.

Hoffman, L. (1971), Deviation-amplifying processes in natural groups. In: *Changing Families*, ed. J. Haley. New York: Grune & Stratton, pp. 285-311.

Malone, T. P., Whitaker, C. A., Warkentin, J., & Felder, R. E. (1961), Rational and non rational psychotherapy. *Amer. J. Psychother.*, 15:212-220.

Partridge, E. (1959), *Origins*. New York: Macmillan.

Taylor, W. (1970), Research on family interaction. *Fam. Proc.*, 9:221-232.

Whitaker, C. & Malone, T. (1953), *The Roots of Psychotherapy*. London: Blakiston.

Winnicott, D. W. (1949), Hate in the counter-transference. *Internat. J. Psycho-Anal.*, 30:69-74.

Wolf, A. & Schwartz, E. K. (1958), Irrational psychotherapy I, II, III. *Amer. J. Psychother.*, 12:300-314, 508-521, 744-759.

This chapter embraces a review of family strategies and techniques.

Strategies and Techniques of Family Therapy

LARRY B. FELDMAN

Strategy is defined (Webster's 1969) as a careful plan or method for achieving an end. Applied to the family therapy situation, a therapist's strategies are his or her general and specific plans and methods for promoting change in the family and its members. In order to productively *formulate* such plans and methods, the therapist must first have in mind one or more *theories* of behavioral change from which the plan or strategy is derived. In order to productively *implement* his or her strategy, the therapist must be able to interact with the family in certain specific ways. The specific behaviors by means of which the therapist's strategies are put into practice are the *techniques* of family therapy.

It should be noted that in clinical practice most experienced family therapists use different strategies and techniques with different types of families and with different types of problems. Wynne has stated (1969) that he is aware of not being the same therapist (a) " . . . when I am seeing an upper-middle-class urban Jewish couple and their drug-taking college drop-out son and (b) when I am meeting with a lower class Southern Protestant family with two hebephrenic children. The therapist-family

Larry B. Feldman, M.D., is Assistant Professor, Division of Family Studies, Department of Psychiatry, Northwestern University Medical School. Mailing address: 10 East Huron, Chicago, Ill. 60611.

I gratefully acknowledge the assistance of Charles H. Kramer, M.D., Jean Goldsmith, Ph.D., and John Schwartzman, Ph.D., whose comments and critiques were extremely valuable.

Reprinted from *American Journal of Psychotherapy*, vol. 30, no. 1, pp. 14-28, January, 1976.

system is different in these instances; . . . the impact of the family upon [the therapist] will differ and what he does in response to their impact will differ" (p. 327).

Family therapists' approaches to families also vary with the progressive phases of the ongoing therapy process. A strategy employed at the beginning of the process may be replaced with a somewhat different strategy once the family has become engaged. This second strategy may then be replaced in turn as termination approaches.

In spite of these complications, it is my belief that certain general principles about family therapy strategies and techniques can be distilled from the writings of family therapists and that these principles will prove useful to the practicing clinician. In addition, the elucidation of an overall scheme of family therapy strategies and techniques is an essential step in the development of much needed research investigations of the process and outcome of family therapy.

Before entering into a detailed review of family therapy strategies and techniques, some discussion of the overall family therapy system is in order. Just as the notions of wholeness, nonsummativity, and mutual influencing processes (Buckley, 1968) are applicable to the family system, they are also applicable to the family *therapy* system. In order to understand the workings of the family therapy system it is essential to view it as a unified whole, which is more than the sum of its parts. Nonetheless, one must know what the parts are before one can understand how they function together as a unified whole. In the presentation to follow, strategies and techniques will be discussed one at a time, stripped of their relationships to each other and to the context of the ongoing therapy situation. This is a necessary simplification which need not lead to misunderstanding, provided the artificial nature of the simplification is kept in mind. At the end of the review, I shall attempt to relate the individual strategies and techniques to the concept of a unified family therapy system.

Manner of Relating

At the outset, a distinction needs to be made between the therapist's overall manner of relating to the family and the particular strategies and techniques that he or she employs. By the term *manner of relating*, I intend to convey the notion of dimensions of relating which transcend strategies and techniques while at the same time are essential for their successful implementation. This notion is exemplified in Whitaker's (1973) statement that "techniques are not enough . . . [they] cannot be a substitute for the therapist's being a person or for his being personally involved in the psychotherapy" (pp. 3-4).

In reviewing the writings of a wide variety of family therapists, four aspects of the therapist's overall manner of relating were most often highlighted: empathy, respect, concern, and genuineness. It is of interest that these qualities are the same ones that were articulated by Rogers in his attempt to understand the process of individual and group therapy (1957). Since Rogers' initial writings, a large number of research studies (Truax and Mitchell, 1971) have confirmed the idea that empathy, respect, concern, and genuineness are essential for therapeutic success in both individual and group therapy. As yet, there are no such studies for family therapy, but in theory these dimensions should be just as important here as in other forms of therapy.

Empathy

Empathy, the interpersonal process of one person "tuning in" to another's feelings or ideas and then communicating an understanding of both the surface and deeper feelings and meanings which are expressed (Carkhuff, 1969), is viewed by many family therapists as a fundamental aspect of family therapy technique. Ackerman (1966) suggests that the family therapist's "primary responsibility is to mobilize a useful quality of empathy and communication" (p. 92). Paul (1967) highlights the critical importance of "the therapist's ability to empathize with the subject reviewing and exposing his intense inner feelings" (p. 189).

Minuchin (1974) notes that, in order to function effectively, the family therapist must "experience the family's transactional patterns and the strength of those patterns. That is, he should feel a family member's pain at being excluded or scapegoated, and his pleasure at being loved, depended upon, or otherwise confirmed within the family" (p. 123). Liberman (1970), though writing from a behavior modification point of view, places great emphasis on the importance of a "positive therapeutic alliance," one ingredient of which is "accurate empathy" (p. 333).

In applying the empathy concept to the family therapy situation, it is important to consider the therapist's behavior with *each* family member and with the family as a unitary whole. The therapist's empathy must extend equally to all the members of the family or a serious stumbling block to effective therapy will be created, Also, the therapist must be "tuned in" to the mood of the family as a whole. This requires responding to the group as a unit, rather than to individual family members in isolation.

RESPECT/CONCERN

Carkhuff (1969) conceptualizes respect as a condition in which one person "communicates to the second person that the second person's feelings and experiences are worthy of consideration and that the second person is capable of acting constructively" (p. 317). Closely related to respect is concern, defined by Carkhuff (1969) as a condition in which one person "communicates that who the second person is and what he does matter to the first person" (p. 318). At the highest levels of concern, the first person communicates "a very deep caring for the feelings, experiences, and potentials of the second person" (p. 318).

Respect and concern are cited by a number of family therapists as important ingredients in the successful family therapy process. Ackerman (1966) emphasizes the need for the therapist to offer acceptance, concern, and "affirmation of worth" to the family members and to the family as a whole. Whitaker (1973) focuses on the therapist's personal involvement with the family: "If there is no involvement on the part of the therapist, there is no real teaching possible" (p. 4). He adds: "A family that is worth treating is worth loving" (p. 27). Satir (1967) stresses the nonjudgmental aspect of concern and the need to label the family's assets and strengths. She urges the frequent use of "I value you" comments.

As with the "empathy" dimension, the application of the "respect" concept to the family therapy situation requires a consideration of the therapist's mode of relating to *each* family member and to the family as a unitary whole.

GENUINENESS

To be genuine is to communicate in such a way that what is expressed is sincerely and honestly felt or experienced (Carkhuff, 1969). Ackerman (1966) repeatedly stresses the importance of the family therapist's being open, earnest, and honest in his or her interactions with the family. Whitaker (1973) emphasizes the significance of the therapist's "presence and the quality of his person" (p. 5). He notes that specific techniques cannot be a substitute for the therapist's "being a person" (p. 4). Satir (1967) emphasizes the importance of congruence in the therapist's communications. Her definition of a congruent communication (p. 82) is one in which the different levels of communicated meaning (verbal, nonverbal, contextual) do not seriously contradict each other.

Strategies and Techniques

Within a context of empathy, respect, concern, and genuineness, therapeutic strategies and techniques can be successfully formulated and carried out. In reviewing family therapists' descriptions of their approaches to therapy, I have become aware that conceptualizations of therapeutic strategy occur at two different levels. On one level, therapists address themselves to issues of *global* strategy. Here, concepts are broad and general and can be visualized as strategies for "structuring" the therapy process. At the second level, theorizing is directed toward *specific* strategies which are designed to accomplish specific and limited ends. These two levels of therapeutic strategy will now be presented and discussed, along with the techniques by means of which the strategies are implemented.

Global Strategies

Control

To be in control of a situation is to exercise restraining or directing influence over it (Webster's, 1969). The importance of the therapist's assuming and maintaining control of the family therapy situation is stressed by many family therapists. Bell (1961) suggests that the effective family therapist "does not hesitate . . . to assert authority over the conduct of the conferences, for this is his domain—the aspect of treatment for which he is clearly responsible" (p. 45). Whitaker (1973) tries to set up a treatment framework "such that it is clear in me and to the family that this is my operating room and that I intend to be in charge" (p. 11). Examples of areas in which control needs to be exerted include defining how the therapy process will take place, who shall be present, scheduling the time, and having one or more consultants. In general, the therapist needs to be "the rulemaker for the interview setting" (p. 11).

Zuk's (1971) approach to family therapy is based on the notion that the therapist must be in the role of "go-between" in relation to the family.

He notes that in this role the therapist is constantly structuring and directing the treatment situation. Examples of ways in which the therapist might do this include: (a) selecting specific disagreements between family members as "especially worthy of discussion," rejecting others as "unworthy," and resisting the family's expected efforts to establish its own rules of priority; (b) refusing to allow family members to interrupt each other; (c) indicating who should speak if there seems to be a therapeutic reason for one family member to speak rather than another.

Bowen (1967) maintains control by paying careful and continuing attention to "defining his self" to the family. A crucial aspect of this is the therapist's action stands in which he presents to the family in a clear and consistent manner what he will and will not do.

An important aspect of the control dimension is the distinction between maintaining control of the interview and trying to maintain control of the family's life outside of the interview room. The same therapists who emphasize the importance of trying to accomplish the former emphasize equally strongly the importance of *not* trying to do the latter. Bell (1961) indicates that the therapist should remain "outside the problem-solving and decision processes of the family for the most part. . . . In essence, he keeps telling the family that control of its life outside the conference is its own business" (p. 45). Whitaker (1973) tries to communicate to the family that "the ball is in their hands and although I can coach, I cannot carry the ball of their living and their efforts to make that living more successful" (p. 12).

Balance

In dealing with a family, the therapist is faced with the dilemma of trying to balance his or her interventions among the various family members so that the formation of disruptive coalitions between the therapist and one or more family members is avoided. Ackerman (1966) notes that the therapist must "move his influence from one part of the family to another, following the shifting core of the most destructive conflict" (p. 95). By so doing, the therapist is able to "minimize destructive rivalry" (p. 95). Haley (1963) suggests that in relating to the family, it is not possible for the therapist to be neutral or nondirective: " . . . his voice, his expression, the context, or the mere act of choosing a particular statement to inquire about introduces directiveness into the situation. When the therapist is being directive, coalition patterns are being defined and redefined" (p. 138). What the therapist can and must do if he or she is to be effective, is to work in such a way that the coalition patterns between therapist and family members are continually changing. Also, the therapist, should look for opportunities to side with "all at once by finding a level where he is placing all factions within a single class. For example, he might side with the parents because the child is misbehaving but also side with the child because he is being provoked into misbehaving" (p. 170). Minuchin (1974) utilizes the technique of joining into temporary alliances with family members as a means of restructuring the family. He notes that "this type of entrance into the family structure requires careful planning and an ability to disengage, so that the therapist is not sucked into the family war. . . . When a particular sequence finishes, because a goal has been attained or the threshold of endurance has been reached, the therapist must shift his position and ally with the former target" (pp. 148-149).

Focus

In family therapy, it is essential that the therapist's major focus be on the family as a unitary whole made up of interacting parts, rather than on individual family members in isolation. In order to do this, it is often necessary to "defocus" from an individual to the family group.

Ackerman (1966) suggests that one function of the family therapist is to "neutralize prejudicial assault and scapegoating" (p. 97). When successful, this technique enables the therapist to "retranspose the underlying conflict to its place of origin in the family group" (p. 97). Whitaker (1973) tries to "defuse the scapegoat ploy by suggesting that we already know he [the identified patient] is depressed or he is delinquent and let's find out about the rest of the family" (p. 10).

Jackson and Weakland (1971) attempt to define the focus of the therapy as quickly as possible. In the initial session, they communicate to the family that "we are here to work together on better understanding one another so that you all can get more out of your family life" (p. 23). They also announce that all members of the family are privileged to all information about any contacts that a family member might choose to make in between sessions. If parents try to focus exclusively on their child's "illness," the therapists "politely interrupt." If, on the other hand, the child tries to utilize the "I am the sick one, so I am not responsible" ploy to refocus attention back on himself or herself, the therapists immediately intervene.

Specific Strategies

In an earlier paper (Feldman, 1975), I delineated four models or paradigms of change in family therapy: (a) The Insight/Working-Through Paradigm; (b) The Conditioning/Reinforcement Paradigm; (c) The Modeling Paradigm; and (d) The Paradox Paradigm. Each of these models was found to be supported by research or clinical evidence, or both. In the present section, the specific therapeutic strategies and techniques which are derived from these four models will be presented and discussed.

Strategies Derived from the Insight/Working-Through Paradigm

CONFRONTATION

Confrontation is the process of bringing family members face to face with some aspect of their behavior (Webster's, 1969). There are many different ways to do this, including verbal feedback, family sculpture, spatial manipulation, and videotape playback.

Verbal Confrontation. Ackerman (1966) suggests that the successful family therapist "makes free use of the device of confrontation. . . . He calls attention to the inefficiency, inappropriateness, and harmfulness of certain sickness-inducing defenses. . . . He tickles the defenses by exposing dramatic discrepancies between [the family members'] self-justifying rationalizations and their subverbal attitudes" (p. 97). Bell (1961) urges that the family therapist verbalize his observations on the current state of family affairs and especially on the immediate occurrences in conferences. Zuk (1971) exposes and otherwise resists the family's efforts to deny or disguise disagreement.

Satir (1967) emphasizes the importance of showing people how they look to others. As with Ackerman, she points out significant discrepancies in communication (for example, when a depressed patient says he feels fine, Satir says, "you look awful").

Experiential Confrontation. Family sculpture is a confrontation technique in which relationships are portrayed in space and time so that events or attitudes may be perceived and experienced simultaneously (Duhl et al., 1973). In asking family members to portray their perceptions of the family in action, rather than describe them in words, the therapist anticipates that all family members will be confronted with a new experiential awareness of the family system. The actual technique of family sculpture consists of the following steps (Duhl et al., 1973):

Asking the family to think of the spaces between people as representative of emotional closeness, the therapist asks one family member to be sculptor and to position the other members in space, in relation to himself, and each other.

As the sculptor begins to position people, the "monitor" (usually the therapist) asks clarifying questions, for example: "How do you see them not only in relation to yourself, but also in relation to each other?" "How does Mother touch Father?" "Does Susan only reach Father through Mother?" and the like.

When family members try to interject their views of the situation (for example, "that's not how it is") the monitor freezes the family in their positions and reminds them that each member will have a turn to position the family as he or she experiences it. In this way, the therapist underscores the idea that there are multiple perceptions of reality in all families, and that each person's perception is worthy of consideration.

The therapist and the family discuss what has been revealed by their family sculptures, and attempt to integrate the total experience.

Minuchin (1974) has described the use of another form of experiential confrontation, which he calls "manipulating space." Basically, the technique consists of positioning family members in ways that either strengthen or weaken particular subsystem boundaries: "If the therapist wants to create or strengthen a boundary, he can bring members of a sub-system to the center of the room and have other family members move their chairs back so that they can observe but cannot interrupt. If he wants to block contact between two members, he can separate them, or he can position himself between them and act as go-between. Spatial manipulation has the power of simplicity. Its graphic eloquence highlights the therapist's message" (p. 143).

Videotape playback has been described by Alger (1973) as "a method of introducing system-specific feedback during the ongoing [family therapy] process so that immediate corrections and alterations can be made, and new resolutions for that particular system can be achieved" (p. 65). Alger lists four ways in which videotape playback can be used with families in therapy:

A family session may be recorded, then played back in its entirety immediately following the session or just before the next session. An arbitrary ten- or fifteen-minute segment of a session may be recorded, and then the remainder of the time spent in a playback review of that segment. The playback review is limited to those segments that the therapist has selected as particularly meaningful. Specific replay during a session is available on an "ad-lib" basis. That is, the therapist or any family member may interrupt the sessions at any time and request an instant replay of a particular segment.

INTERPRETATION

Interpretation is a concept which originated in the psychoanalytic situation. According to the American Psychoanalytic Association's *Glossary* (Moore and Fine, 1968), interpretation is a form of intervention whose aim is to achieve therapeutic results by adding to the patient's knowledge of himself through making him aware of psychic content and conflict which had been warded off. The golssary distinguishes dynamic interpretations, which refer to psychic forces operating to produce a particular effect on mental life at any given time, from genetic interpretations, which are concerned with indicating or clarifying the connections between past mental states and present ones.

In the family therapy situation, interpretation is more broadly defined. Bell (1961) delineates four types of interpretation, which he calls reflective, connective, reconstructive, and normative. Reflective interpretations are essentially equivalent to confrontations. Connective interpretations are statements that "point out unrecognized links between acts, events, attitudes, and experiences." Of particular importance are unrecognized reciprocal behaviors between family members—"role matched with role, feeling touching feeling, conception meeting conception" (p. 47). Reconstructive interpretations are those in which the therapist "recalls the history of the family, its relationships, and its peculiar ways of reacting. The reconstituted past provides a context for the present" (p. 47). Normative interpretations are statements in which the therapist compares the behavior of the family in treatment to that of other families or to "most families." Bell cautions that "this is a form of interpretation to be used sparingly because such statements are usually received by the family as instructions or expectations of them" (p. 47).

Strategies Derived from the Conditioning/Reinforcement Paradigm

BEHAVIOR REHEARSAL

Behavior rehearsal is the strategy of providing family members an opportunity to practice "more desirable responses . . . under the supervision of the therapist" (Eisler and Hersen, 1973, p. 112). Through practice, family members gradually acquire new responses which then feed back into the family system to promote changes in other family members. The technique of behavior rehearsal consists of the following steps (Eisler and Hersen, 1973):

Clarification of the changes desired by each family member, stated in precise behavioral terminology.

Discussion of which of the proposed changes the family would be willing to "try."

Creation of a hypothetical situation which the family can role-play in order to practice the agreed-upon new modes of behavior.

Feedback from the family members to each other and from the therapist to the family in regard to whether their behavior is, in fact, different from before.

Positive reinforcement from the therapist and family members for changed behavior.

BEHAVIOR CONTRACTING

A behavioral contract is a "negotiated agreement detailing . . . the condition under which individual X will do something for individual Y." In applying the strategy of behavior contracting to family therapy, reciprocal contracts are negotiated in which two or more family members agree to change some aspect of their behavior in exchange for a reciprocal agreement to change on the part of the other. A crucial aspect of the strategy of behavior contracting is reciprocal reinforcement. By selecting behavior changes that are positively reinforcing, family members learn that "compromise and reciprocal positive reinforcement . . . [are] effective methods of mediating interpersonal discord" (Eisler and Hersen, 1973, p. 113).

The specific technique of behavior contracting is as follows: an explanation to the family of the benefits of positive reinforcement, with examples of the effects of reciprocal reinforcement; clarification of the needs and expectations of discordant family members, stated in precise behavioral terminology; specification of what responses to changed behavior would constitute a reward for each family member; creation of a contractual agreement (oral or written) between the members of the family in which each family member agrees to: try to change a specific aspect of his or her behavior, with the expectation of being rewarded by the other family members; reward other family members for their achieved behavioral changes.

Strategies Derived from the Modeling Paradigm

In a certain sense, everything that a family therapist does can be related to the modeling paradigm. Whether the therapist is listening, talking, role-playing, expressing anger, or crying, he or she is always functioning as a model for the family. However, two particular modeling strategies, self-disclosure and role-playing, are cited so often that they merit separate discussion.

SELF-DISCLOSURE

Ackerman (1966) states that in his opinion "true healing does not take place unless the understanding of emotion goes both ways. . . . The analyst must sift out his own emotions and selectively inject those which the patient needs to experience in order to become well" (p. 104). Whitaker (1973) proposes that "it is not fair to expect the family to expose itself while the therapists sit by as peeping Toms. Just as the therapist in the one-to-one relationship can prove his humanness by sharing his own free associations and the patient will not be terrified to expose himself, so it is important that the therapist in the family expose his own feelings and his own person to the family" (p. 17). Satir (1967) notes that the therapist's lack of fear in revealing himself may be the first experience the family has had with clear communication.

ROLE-PLAYING

Role-playing in the family therapy situation provides an opportunity for the therapist and/or family members to model modes of behavior that are different from the usual familial patterns. By observing the model's behavior, family members gradually acquire new responses, which then feed back into the family system to promote reciprocal changes in others. In practice, modeling is often combined with behavior rehearsal and reciprocal reinforcement (Eisler and Hersen, 1973). The steps of the modeling technique are as follows:

As in behavior rehearsal, the first step is the clarification of the changes desired by each family member, stated in precise behavioral terminology. The therapist and family reach an agreement regarding which change to work on first. The therapist or a family member is selected to role-play the person whose behavior is to be changed. With the "target" family member observing, the therapist and family play out a hypothetical situation in which the model reacts in a way that is different from the usual pattern. Specifically, the model reacts in a way that the family has agreed to as a desirable change. The family gives the model feedback about his or her performance (that is, was the model's behavior in fact different from the usual pattern?). The process is repeated, with the other members of the family each having the experience of being in the observer position.

Strategies Derived from the Paradox Paradigm

RELABELING

Relabeling is a strategy in which the therapist defines or labels some aspect of a family's behavior in a way that is *different* from the way the family had been defining or labeling it. Haley (1963) advocates that "in general, whenever it can be done, the therapist defines [labels] the couple as attempting to bring about an amiable closeness but going about it wrongly, being misunderstood, or being driven by forces beyond their control" (p. 139). For example, if a husband is protesting his wife's constant nagging, the therapist might comment that the wife seems to be trying to reach her husband and achieve more closeness with him. If the wife protests that her husband constantly withdraws from her, the husband might be defined as one who wants to avoid discord and achieve an amiable relationship. "Particularly savage maneuvers will not be minimized but may be labeled as responses to disappointment (rather than the behavior of a cad)" (p. 139).

In some instances, the opposite form of relabeling (namely, labeling positive behavior as negative) is indicated to "shake up the system." Jackson & Weakland (1971) note the importance of the therapist's reframing and reinterpreting the messages of family members. "By this means, the positive side of difficult or provocative behavior in the family can be shown, sense made out of craziness, and congruence out of incongruence" (p. 27). Whitaker (1973) focuses on the redefinition of behavior that the family has seen as problems as efforts for growth. For example, when a wife accuses her husband of infidelity, Whitaker tells the couple that the two of them had become desperate about the coolness of their marriage, that they had agreed implicitly and covertly that something had to be done to heat up the marriage, and that the husband was elected to help raise the thermostat. Whitaker adds that if they had not been ready for change, they would not have dared the pain of exploding out of their impasse. Satir (1967) emphasizes relabeling hostile behavior and feelings (for example: "So you felt unlovable"; "So you felt attacked").

In this way, the hurt that she believes underlies all hostility can be examined and resolved.

PARADOXICAL DIRECTIVES

A paradox is a statement in which self-contradictory conclusions are derived by seemingly valid deduction from acceptable premises (Webster's, 1969). In the family therapy field, the therapeutic use of paradoxical statements has been particularly emphasized by Jackson, Haley, Weakland, Watlawick, and their colleagues at the Mental Research Institute in Palo Alto. Haley (1963) suggests that "encouraging a couple [or family] to behave in their usual way is paradoxically one of the most rapid ways to bring about a change" (pp. 143-144). To illustrate this technique, Haley cites the example of a therapist treating a family in which the mother insists on being the group leader. To break up this habitual pattern, he suggests that the therapist ask the mother to take charge of the family, either in general, or in a session, or for a particular task. Haley's rationale is that, in the wake of such a statement by the therapist, the only way the mother can attempt to control the therapist (which she will be very much inclined to do) is by permitting other family members to take the lead, thus changing the pattern of family interaction.

A variation of this technique consists of the therapist's directing one member of the family to encourage another member to exhibit usual behavior. Jackson and Weakland (1971) conceptualize the technique of paradoxical instructions in the following way: "We are apt to choose an apparently minor matter—which still will be involved in some significant pattern of interaction—and give an instruction to do A, expecting that the person, from our knowledge of his reactions, will in fact do B, which will cause change C in a family relationship" (p. 27).

The Therapist(s)—Family System

As stated earlier, the family therapy situation is a system and therefore is governed by the general system properties of wholeness, nonsummativity, and mutual causality (Buckley, 1968). In considering therapeutic strategies and techniques, it was necessary to discuss individual elements of the family therapy process in isolation, without considering their relationships with each other. (The one exception to this was the delineation of therapist empathy, concern, respect, and genuineness as prerequisites for the effective implementation of *any strategy*.) However, in actual practice, nothing occurs in isolation. Everything that the therapist does is related to the events that preceded his or her behavior, and this behavior in turn influences subsequent events. Also, causality is a two-way street—the therapist is influenced by the family as well as influencing it. Because of this aspect, it is important for family therapists to become aware of the ways in which they are influenced by different types of people and different types of families.

In order to really understand the process of family therapy, strategies and techniques must be seen in relation to each other, as well as in relation to the therapist's manner of relating. Different strategies can combine and interact in a variety of different ways. Their effects might be simply additive, in which case the combined effect is equal to the sum of the individual effects. Or, they might be synergistic, in which case the combined effect is *more* than the sum of the parts. Another possibility is that two different strategies might interfere with each other, in which case there is a net loss. Still another possibility is that there might be an *interactive* effect. For example, strategy A and strategy B might work synergistically in the presence of strategy C, but might interfere with each other in the presence of strategy D.

In addition to the relationships among individual strategies, one must also consider the relationships between particular strategies and particular types of families. What works well for one type of family may be disastrous for another. Also, the effects of particular strategies may vary with the phase of the therapy process. The same approach may promote positive changes at the beginning of therapy but retard progress at the end. As with the relationships among strategies, there may also be interactive effects between particular strategies, type of family, and phase of therapy. For example, strategy A may have positive effects with family type A if used early in the therapy process, but have negative effects with this type of family if used late in the process. On the other hand, the reverse may be true for family type B.

In order to unravel the relationships between family therapy process and outcome, research investigations of ongoing therapy cases are urgently needed. While awaiting the results of such research investigations, I would recommend that therapeutic strategies and techniques be viewed as tools which, in the hands of a therapist who is empathic, respectful, concerned, and genuine, can help to promote changes in familiar behavior patterns. The therapist who becomes familiar with a wide variety of approaches and then applies them selectively with particular types of families at particular stages of the family therapy process has the greatest chance of succeeding.

Summary

A variety of global and specific strategies and techniques of family therapy have been reviewed and discussed, along with the more basic issue of the therapist's overall manner of relating to the family. Attention has been drawn to the complex relationships between the family therapist's manner of relating, the strategies and techniques which he or she employs, the type of problem or problems which the family presents, the particular characteristics of the family in treatment, and the developmental phases of the family therapy process. Precise delineation of the relationships among these variables must await the results of much needed research investigations of the process and outcome of family therapy.

References

Ackerman, N. (1966), *Treating the Troubled Family*. Boston: Little, Brown.

Alger, I. (1973), Audio-visual techniques in family therapy. In: *Techniques of Family Psychotherapy*, ed. D. Bloch. New York: Grune & Stratton, pp. 65-75.

Bell, J. (1961), *Family Group Therapy*. Public Health Monograph No. 64. Washington, D.C.: U.S. Department of Health, Education and Welfare.

Bowen, M. (1967), Toward the differentiation of a self in one's own family. In: *Family Interaction*, ed. J. L. Framo et al. New York: Springer, pp. 111-166.

Buckley, W., ed. (1968), *Modern Systems Research for the Behavioral Scientist*. Chicago: Aldine.

Carkhuff, R. (1969), *Helping and Human Relationships*. New York: Holt.

Duhl, F. et al. (1973), Learning, space, and action in family therapy: A primer of sculpture. In: *Techniques of Family Psychotherapy*, ed. D. Bloch. New York: Grune & Stratton, pp. 47-65.

Eisler, R. & Hersen, M. (1973), Behavioral techniques in family-oriented crisis intervention. *Arch. Gen. Psychiat.*, 28:111-116.

Feldman, L. (1975), Processes of behavioral change in family therapy. Chicago: The Family Institute of Chicago.

Haley, J. (1963), *Strategies of Psychotherapy*. New York: Grune & Stratton.

Jackson, D. & Weakland, J. (1971), Conjoint family therapy: Some considerations on theory, technique, and results. In: *Changing Families*, ed. J. Haley. New York: Grune & Stratton, pp. 13-36.

Liberman, R. (1970), Behavioral approaches to family and couple therapy. *Amer. J. Orthopsychiat.*, 40:106-118.

Minuchin, S. (1974), *Families and Family Therapy*, Cambridge, Mass.: Harvard University Press.

Moore, B. & Fine, B., eds. (1968), *A Glossary of Psychoanalytic Terms and Concepts*. New York: American Psychoanalytic Association.

Paul, N. (1967), The role of mourning and empathy in conjoint marital therapy. In: *Family Therapy and Disturbed Families*, ed. G. Zuk & I. Boszormenyi-Nagy. Palo Alto, Calif.: Science & Behavior Books, pp. 186-206.

Rogers, C. (1957), The necessary and sufficient conditions of therapeutic personality change. *J. Consult. Psychol.*, 21:95-103.

Satir, V. (1967), *Conjoint Family Therapy*. Palo Alto, Calif.: Science & Behavior Books.

Truax, C. & Mitchell, K. (1971), Research on certain therapist interpersonal skills in relation to process and outcome. In: *Handbook of Psychotherapy and Behavior Change*, ed. A. Bergin & S. Garfield. New York: John Wiley, pp. 299-345.

Webster's Seventh New Collegiate Dictionary (1969), Springfield, Mass.: Merriam.

Whitaker, C. (1973), Process techniques of family therapy. Unpublished manuscript.

Wynne, L. (1969), Comments on family therapy: A view. *Fam. Proc.*, 8:326-328.

Zuk, G. (1971), Family therapy. In: *Changing Families*, ed. J. Haley. New York: Grune & Stratton, pp. 212-226.

Family group therapy has similarities with and differences from the traditional individual therapies. The author describes the ideas that distinguish family group therapy from the individual therapies.

Basic Concepts in Family Therapy: A Differential Comparison with Individual Treatment

LEON R. ROBINSON

In the course of several years of experience as an organizer and teacher of family therapy training programs developed for a variety of psychiatric professionals, I have become aware of some of the conceptual problems that confront the individually oriented practitioner who attempts to adjust to a frame of reference in which the family becomes the unit of pathology and treatment. The purpose of this paper, therefore, is to set forth briefly those ideas which I think are most fundamental to the practice of family treatment and which distinguish it from other forms of psychotherapy.

Family therapy may be differentiated from individual therapies (defined here as any form of psychotherapy in which treatment is confined to a dyadic relationship between a therapist and a patient or client) by making use of the fact that all individual therapies share a common perception of the nature and location of the forces most active in the formation of personality, the appearance of symptoms, and the production of change. In this paper I hope to demonstrate that this common perception is recognizably different from the perceptions and perspectives underlying family treatment.

Leon R. Robinson, M.D., is Associate Director, Family Psychiatry Department, Eastern Pennsylvania Psychiatric Institute, Henry Avenue and Abbotsford Road, Philadelphia, Pa. 19129.

All approaches to psychotherapy are based on certain fundamental assumptions regarding the nature of personality and personality formation. Similarly, all theories of psychotherapy accept the premise that personality is the result of an interplay between the individual's inherited response potentials and the organized limitations on behavior erected by the individual's society or culture. Whereas there is general agreement that personality is expressed in a repetitious pattern of behaviors that enables the inner person to establish need-fulfilling relations with the external world, family treatment differs from the individual therapies on the location of forces that are predominant in determining this pattern.

Although the importance of environmental factors in the shaping of personality is recognized by those conducting individual therapies, they operate on the assumption that internal events and dynamics are dominant among the various forces that determine behavior. This fact is clearly demonstrated in psychoanalysis, both in its highly detailed theory of psychosexual development and in its techniques of treatment, which seek to uncover the conflicts associated with a repressed infantile neurosis under conditions in which, according to Ackerman (1962), "transference is dominant over the existing realities."

Other individual approaches, such as behavior therapy, Gestalt therapy, and client-centered therapy, are founded more in empiricism than in personality theory, but their techniques of treatment demonstrate a primary concern with the manipulation of intrapsychic mechanisms. The fact that the individual therapist structures treatment in such a way that contact with the patient's interpersonal environment is avoided is a logical extension of his belief that treatment ought to change the way the patient handles certain aspects of his own internally organized behavior.

Another facet of the perspective underlying individual treatment is a corollary of the assumption that intrapsychic events determine personality. This is the belief that changes in individual behavior are unopposed by environmental factors or are somehow resistant to external countertherapeutic pressures. These ideas about the controlling nature of intrapsychic forces and the inherent stability of individual change are not compatible with the frame of reference of family therapy.

Personality Development

In family therapy, the dominant forces in personality development are thought to be located externally, in the organized behavioral characteristics of the family by which the family manages and regulates the interpersonal life of its members. Within this perspective the family is viewed as a rule-governed, change-resistant, transactional system with an operational program that has evolved through several generations and that is sustained by its capacity to stimulate system-sustaining conformity within the personalities of family members. According to this thesis the forces of the system operate in all family transactions, and theories of personality that associate personality development with the internalized outcome of a series of dyadic relationships are therefore discounted.

In other words, the early impressions of the external world that are established by the child by means of his weighted contact with his mother are not simply perceptions of that relationship but the child's actual initial contacts with the family system. Thus, the way a mother responds to her infant and his needs will be determined as much by the quality of her relationship with her husband as by the specific characteristics of the child. The adequacy of the mother's response to the needs of her child can be determined by the extent to which her marriage is a primary source of interpersonal need gratification for both parents. If the marital relationship is underdeveloped as the center of parental need-satisfaction, the chances that the parent-child relationship will become overdeveloped are increased.

According to systems concepts, partners in an underdeveloped marital relationship are likely to incorporate in their family lifestyle any behavioral format that serves to justify or conceal the relational deficiencies in the marriage. Therefore, if the child of parents with this kind of marriage displays personality problems associated with an overly intense attachment to a parent or to his place in the family, he has, in systems terms, accepted an externally designed behavioral role thrust upon him by the social organization of his family.

Viewed in this way, the young person's failure to emerge from the parent-child context as an individuated adult is not a reflection of unresolved internal conflicts. Rather, it is the result of a conspiracy of needs in which marital tension between the parents has produced a family unit in which an exaggerated parent-child relationship satisfies the voids in the marital relationship. Since these system characteristics are transgenerational and have the support of grandparents, aunts, and uncles, as well as parents and siblings, their impact on the development of any family member is highly coercive. Applying this perspective to the dynamics of the Freudian oedipal stage of personality development, we could say that the outcome is determined more by the interpersonal behavior of the parents than by the intrapsychic dynamics of the child.

Symptom Formation

Because the individual therapies view personality as a construct built more on internal than on external events, symptoms are perceived as the result of conflict between aspects of the individual's intrapsychic machinery. The environment, social or otherwise, is included as a factor in the process of symptom formation only as the source of stress that serves to activate the opposing aspects of the individual's internal functioning. In psychoanalysis, for example, symptoms are the result of repressed conflicts between the ego and the id or between the conscious and unconscious, brought to the surface by current stresses. In behavior therapy, internal conflict becomes manifest when the patient is unable to tolerate an association with a desired object, person, or situation because of anxiety. The conflict between the desired behavior and the patient's inability to carry out that behavior is the result of unconscious learning or conditioning. In Gestalt therapy, symptoms are the result of interpsychic difficulties that produce conflicts in the patient's efforts to organize his fields of awareness, thereby reducing his capacity for coping with the demands of daily life.

In each of these therapies, the impact of the environment is viewed as contributory; it provides only the external challenge that evokes a symptomatic response because of the presence of internal conflict. Since symptoms are accounted for in terms of conflicts between the component parts of the self, the approach to treatment is understandably aimed at helping the patient remove the disabling areas of inner disharmony.

Family therapy also views symptoms as connected with conflict, but that conflict is viewed as originating outside of the individual. The conflict is located in the transactional interface between the natural developmental strivings of an emerging individual and the distorted relational objectives of a dysfunctional family system. The concept of family dysfunction is derived from the idea that a functional family, rooted in an emotionally secure and stable marriage, provides children with a relationship experience that supports their gradual movement away from the family toward self-sustaining entry into the nonfamily world. A dysfunctional family, therefore, is one whose organizational peculiarities cause it to mismanage those aspects of family interaction associated with individuation, distance, and closeness in such a way that the social maturation of family members is impaired or arrested. This impairment is caused by the presence of culturally dissonant forces that seek to maintain the parent-child relational axis as the principal determinant of family organization.

Under the pressure of dysfunctional social forces, individual attempts at separation are undermined by the excessive emphasis on intergenerational relating, which devalues the independent, peer-level experience necessary to produce an individuated adult. Symptoms—anxiety, depression, or psychosis—are an expression of the conflict between the inherent strivings of the individual to establish himself as an adequate member of his own generation and the opposing pressures generated by a dysfunctional family motivated to maintain the status quo. Symptom formation on the part of the individual attempting to separate is therefore regarded as a consequence of the individual's commitment to a set of socially ineffective interpersonal values and behaviors.

Family therapists have ample experience indicating that dysfunctional families are established by parents who have achieved low levels of separation from their own parents and are poorly prepared to construct an independent marital relationship. Marital partners who experience great difficulty in handling the role of husband or wife may find justification or solace in a family system that promotes the role of parent into a position of emotional priority relative to the role of spouse. This means that some troubled spouses will obscure what Bowen (1969) termed their "emotional divorce" by acting out the idea that the demands of the parent-child relationship leave little time for marital concerns. These parents can then approximate the appearance of a family as long as the responsibilities of responding to children (or grandparents) can be used to justify the lack of closeness in the marriage. Other troubled spouses find it convenient to scapegoat their children as the cause of their marital problems. These parents can continue to behave like a family as long as there is a troublesome or disturbed child to be blamed for the failures of the marriage.

In either type of family, the child is inclined to develop a preoccupation with his role in the problems of his parents. He may be emotionally trapped by the dynamics of the family whether he accepts or rejects the roles designated for him by the family system. Acceptance of the roles and values designed by the family means that the child attempting to leave the family is inadequately prepared for separation and faces a concealed but active opposition. He is therefore likely to experience high levels of anxiety and guilt and to collapse in his efforts at independent living. Rejection of the roles and values of the dysfunctional family may result in a premature breaking away from the protective functions of the family and the child's failure to sustain himself in the outside world. The parents in these families are therefore participants in the conflicts underlying individual symptom formation because they suppress individuation and separation in order to protect the family's triangular, bigenerational base, the loss of which would be destructive to the continuation of the parents' façade of individual and marital health.

The Approach to Therapeutic Change

Because the individual therapist believes the primary forces that shape and maintain personality are a part of the intrapsychic apparatus, he uses an approach that requires only the presence of himself and the patient. Although he is aware that the patient's difficulties have evolved in connection with past or present relationships, the individual therapist feels that the patient's reactions to these relationships or problem situations, as elicited by the therapist, are the best and most available targets for change. As a result, the individual therapist structures treatment in such a way that he alone assists the patient in obtaining the insight, the learning, or the new levels of experience necessary to understand his failures and to make the personal changes needed to obtain relief from his disabling symptoms.

Within the family perspective, the psychodynamic apparatus of the individual is a comparatively weak system when confronted with the multigenerational organization of the family. To the family therapist, any effort to treat individual symptoms ignores the power of the family's commitment to the status quo and its active opposition to any individual changes that would fundamentally alter the established pattern of dysfunctional family relating. The experience of the family therapist has taught him that the family of the patient is an intense opponent of change and, in defense of its organizational integrity, will seek to defeat the efforts of a therapist to produce changes in individual family members. This particular feature of family theory, which the late Don Jackson (1965) termed "homeostatic mechanisms," is accepted by most family therapists as one of the realities of family living, one that must be dealt with in treatment in order to establish permanence of therapeutic change.

The following statement of Jackson's, which includes the concept of homeostasis, achieves a maximum of clarity regarding the fundamental nature of family treatment: "Briefly stated, the major assertion of the theory to be outlined here is that *the family is a rule-governed system:* that its members behave among themselves in an organized, repetitive manner and that this patterning of behaviors can be abstracted as a governing principle of family life" (Jackson, 1965, p. 116).

Using this statement as an expression of one of the most central concepts in family therapy, one can see that the primary objective in this therapy is to isolate for change a pattern of family behaviors that, because of its pathogenic nature, supports the appearance of symptoms in family members. More specifically, family treatment seeks to help the family as a unit to discard interpersonal habits and practices that tend to foster socially deviant or maladaptive responses to commonly encountered, culturally sponsored social situations. Family treatment generally aims at improving the levels of social functioning of the whole family so that no generation maintains a self-serving need to interfere with the successful individuation and separation of an adjacent generation.

To achieve these aims, the therapist meets with the family as a whole to observe firsthand the specific patterns of interaction that are peculiar to it. The therapist seeks to help the family learn about itself as a transactional unit by providing it with a setting in which the dysfunctional aspects of its behavior can be exposed, discussed, and changed under conditions of real social interaction. In this matrix, family members learn directly how they fail each other and what system changes are necessary to support the capacities of each generation to achieve eventual separation and to establish primary emotional bonds with peers.

Comment

The preceding remarks are in no way meant to diminish the value of individual therapies or their theoretical constructs. I have simply tried to clarify some of the conceptual differences between individual and family treatment as contemporary approaches to psychotherapy. Both are valid methods of treatment when applied by skillful practitioners of either persuasion.

References

Ackerman, N. A. (1962), Family psychotherapy and psychoanalysis—the implications of difference. In: *Family Process*, ed. N. A. Ackerman. New York: Basic Books, 1970, pp. 5-18.

Bowen, M. (1969), Family psychotherapy with schizophrenia in the hospital and in private practice. In: *Intensive Family Therapy: Theoretical and Practical Concepts*, ed. I. Boszormenyi-Nagy & J. L. Framo. New York: Harper Medical Books, pp. 213-243.

Jackson, D. D. (1965), The study of the family. In: *Family Process*, ed. N. A. Ackerman. New York: Basic Books, 1970, pp. 111-130.

Multiple Family Therapy has highlighted important new insights. Using a multiple family group, the authors explore one form of interaction behavior between family members and nonmembers, using speech as the level of participation.

The Multiple Family Group as a Small Society: Family Regulation of Interaction with Nonmembers

DAVID REISS and RONALD COSTELL

Direct measurements of interaction behavior between members of the same family have strongly suggested that such behavior is continuously governed by a set of unwritten family rules, conventions, or controls (Condon and Ogston, 1967; Haley, 1967; Ferreira and Winter, 1966; Patterson and Reid, 1970). Indirect evidence from interviews, questionnaires (Elder, 1965; Bell and Zucker, 1968/1969; Edwards et al., 1973), and laboratory models (Reiss, 1967, 1968, 1969, 1970, 1971a, b, c, d; Reiss and Salzman, 1973) has suggested that family rules also govern the interaction between family members and nonmembers. We directly

---

David Reiss, M.D., is Professor and Ronald Costell, M.D., is Assistant Clinical Professor, Center for Family Research, Department of Psychiatry and Behavioral Sciences, George Washington University School of Medicine, 2300 Eye Street, N.W., Washington, D.C. 20037.

This research was funded in part by grant 16-P-5603/3-11 from the Social and Rehabilitation Service, Department of Health, Education, and Welfare, and by the Psychiatric Institute of Washington, D.C. A portion of this study was conducted while the authors were staff members of the Intramural Research Program, National Institute of Mental Health.

Loann Drake and Carole Jones assisted in the analysis of data. Frances Cortan and Lanny Moldauer provided a critique of the data analysis.

measured member/nonmember interaction and provide evidence indicating the operation of this second type of control. These measurements were made on the interaction patterns in groups composed of up to thirteen families at any one time, i.e., multiple family groups. The present report provides data from one of these groups and focuses on one form of interaction behavior: the level of participation or engagement of each individual as measured by the amount he or she talks or is talked to by others.

Method

The multiple family groups were established in family-oriented inpatient adolescent psychiatric programs; each participating family contained two parents, the adolescent inpatient, and, quite often, an adolescent sibling. Informed consent was obtained from each member of each family before the family's participation in any of the research procedures on the inpatient unit.

Multiple family groups tend to duplicate specifically some features of certain social settings or communities. For example, they divide into distinct peer subgroups; an adolescent subgroup, consisting of the adolescent patients and their siblings, and a parent subgroup. This appears to simulate patterns of sociability in ordinary neighborhoods.

The multiple family group reported on in this paper met weekly for 75-minute sessions for 59 weeks. During this period eighteen families participated, entering and leaving the group at different times; as many as thirteen families participated at any one time. All of the families were from social class I, II, or III (Hollingshead and Redlich, 1958), and all were white except for one, which was black.

The clinical research program was designed for nonpsychotic adolescents. The admission diagnosis in all cases was adolescent adjustment reaction. At the time of discharge the diagnoses of two patients had been modified: one patient was found to have an acute schizophrenic reaction, and the other was found to have a seizure disorder. There was no evidence of mental retardation in any patient. The median age of the hospitalized adolescents was 17.5 (range, 15-20).

Two types of data collected during the group sessions are pertinent to this report: seating patterns of group members and patterns of verbal participation in group discussion, i.e., who spoke to whom. At each session a research assistant recorded the seating location of each group member. In order to simplify the scattered and assorted seating locations, each person was assigned to one of five concentric circles in the coding scheme. Although this meant minor relocations from actual positions, a computer program for reconstructing seating positions from the coder's records (and for computing indexes of physical distance between group members) invariably reproduced actual seating locations almost exactly. The coder also recorded who spoke to whom. The unit coded was the "statement," defined as the entire speech of any speaker bounded at the beginning by the speech of the previous speaker and at the end by the speech of the next speaker. Spot checks of the reliability of seating location and who-spoke-to-whom coding judgments yielded values of .90 or over.

Results

The data on seating patterns indicate that the multiple family group did indeed split into peer subgroups. Figure 1 shows the seating patterns of group members during sessions in the initial, middle, and closing phases of the group. In all three phases there was spatial separation into peer subgroups. The pattern seen in the middle and later sessions indicates that this separation was frequently achieved by adolescents sitting in the outer circle of the group and parents sitting more centrally.

Two quantitative analyses document the peer-group split. The first analysis computed the mean physical distance between each individual and every other member of his or her peer group (i.e., for each adolescent, his or her distance from all other adolescents) and from his or her nonpeer group (i.e., for each adolescent, the distance from all parents). The means for these scores were obtained separately for adolescents and for parents in each session. In sessions in which spatial separation into peer groups occurred, we expected the following patterns of scores: adolescent-to-adolescents distance would be less than adolescent-to-parents distance, and parents-to-parents distance would be less than parents-to-adolescents distance. This pattern was seen in 24 of 52 sessions. The probability of obtaining this predicted pattern by chance alone in a single session is .25; thus the probability of obtaining the predicted pattern in as many as 24 of 52 sessions by chance alone is less than .001.

In the second analysis we constructed a contingency table showing the number of parents and adolescents in each of the group's five concentric circles. Chi-square analysis showed a significant separation of parents and adolescents into separate circles in 23 sessions ($p < .10$ in all

FIGURE 1

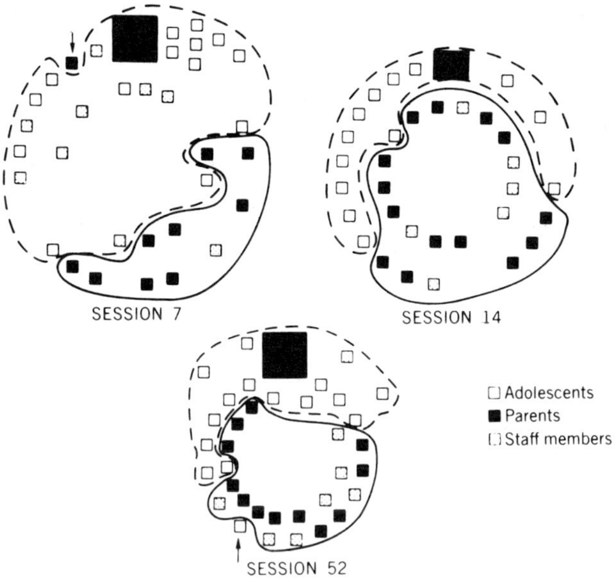

Examples of Seating Patterns of Parents, Adolescents, and Staff Members in the Multiple Family Group*

23 sessions; $p < .01$ in 9 of these). The parents were invariably central in all but 2 of the 38 sessions.

Of the total 52 sessions included in the analyses, 38 showed clear-cut spatial segregation of peer groups by either the distance score or the circle distribution analyses or both. This spatial separation into subgroups was also observed in the overall content of group discussion, which often focused on the adolescents who were perceived to be outside, uninvolved, and separate. Moreover, the adult-adolescent split was indicated by the

*Members sitting away from their peer subgroups are indicated by arrows. Sessions 7 and 52 show clear-cut separation of the subgroups; session 14 shows how the adolescent group often draped itself around the parent group by remaining in the outer circle. Variation in the size of the large dark squares (a post located in the center of the meeting room) gives a visual indication of the moderate distortion introduced by the computerized reconstructive method; such distortions were corrected by the use of rank-order statistics.

relative infrequency in most families of direct talk between adolescents and parents in the same family. The percentage of total statements of adolescents addressed directly to their own parents for the 14 families who attended 2 or more sessions was less than 10% in 7 families; less than 20% in 4; 21% in 1; 25% in 1; and 37% in 1.

Given this overt parent/adolescent split, what evidence is there that the family as a group exerted any control over the participation levels of its individual members? We looked first at the stability of family participation levels; did the family's level of participation remain constant throughout the life of the group in comparison with that of other families? In order to compute stability, the 59 sessions were divided into 4 sections or blocks, each of which included approximately the same number of sessions. The first 4 of the 59 sessions served for pilot testing of observation procedures. The remaining 55 sessions were divided into 4 blocks, approximately equal in size, with boundaries adjusted to maximize the number of families present in every session in the block. Thus block 1 included sessions 5-13 with 7 families present throughout; block 2 included sessions 17-31 with 8 families present throughout; block 3, sessions 32-42 with 10 families; and block 4, sessions 43-59 with 7 families. The inclusion of sessions 14-16 in either block 1 or block 2 would have greatly reduced the number of families in each; they were therefore dropped from analyses requiring blocks. Kendall's coefficient of concordance was computed separately for the family as a whole, the parental pair, and the hospitalized adolescent, producing 12 coefficients (3 segments by 4 blocks).

Despite the shifting membership and focus of topics from week to week, the coefficients are all remarkably high (see Table 1). Moreover, there was a very high correlation between participation levels for parents and adolescents of the same family across all sessions ($r = .62$; $p < .02$).[1] This indicates that parents who were "noisy" with respect to other parents had adolescents who were "noisy" with respect to other adolescents. The same was true for "quiet" parents and adolescents. The stability of these relationships is conveyed by cross-lagged correlations computed for the 10 families who were present for at least 20 sessions. These correlations compared participation levels of parents and adolescents during the first

[1] For this and subsequent correlations we used the rank percentile to correct for inequality in the number of families present at different sessions. The rank percentile for a session is the family's (or parents' or adolescents') rank divided by the number of families (or parents or adolescents) present for that session.

and last 10 sessions the family attended. The correlation for the adolescents' first 10 sessions by the parents' first 10 was .72 ($p < .02$); adolescents' first 10 by parents' last 10 was .80 ($p < .005$); adolescents' last 10 by parents' first 10 was .69 ($p < .05$); and adolescents' last 10 by parents' last 10 was .71 ($p < .02$). Thus, parents' and adolescents' participation levels in the first 10 sessions could be used to predict both parents' and adolescents' participation levels in the last 10 sessions. These data suggest that both parents and adolescents in a family achieve a constant level of participation early in their group experience and maintain it with little variation; in some of the families we studied this was maintained for more than 40 weeks.

Two alternative explanations exist for this stability. One is that each family unit has its own participatory "personality"; that is, during its developmental phase some families may acquire a set of norms characterized as either "noisy" or "quiet" that may operate in virtually any social setting. Each family entering our multiple family group may have simply continued its previous habits or typical reactions. Thus, the division of the group into adolescent and parent subgroups might be expected to have little impact on the family's participation levels because these levels have been established or shaped in all family members months or years before their entry into the group.

A second explanation would posit a constantly active family regulation. This mechanism would also require enduring norms that regulate the participation rate of family members. However, the mechanism concerns small but important variations in such norms from session to session. We know that small changes in participation levels existed in the families we studied because the Kendall's coefficient was substantially less than 1 for all blocks of the sessions.

If the parent in a "noisy" family becomes somewhat less noisy than in the previous session, will the adolescent follow suit? If a child in a "quiet" family becomes more "noisy" than before, will his or her parents do likewise? This form of within-family imitation or regulation would depend on continuous mutual monitoring by members of a family; it could not be explained by a family norm or "personality" established before the family's entry into the group.

Table 2 shows rank-order correlation coefficients computed for each of 10 families who attended at least 20 sessions. The correlations relate the rank percentiles of the parents and the hospitalized adolescent for each session. A positive, significant correlation—obtained here for 8 of

TABLE 1

KENDALL'S COEFFICIENTS OF CONCORDANCE OF STABILITY OF PARTICIPATION LEVELS FOR EACH OF 4 BLOCKS OF SESSIONS, COMPUTED SEPARATELY FOR THE FAMILY AS A WHOLE, THE PARENTAL PAIR, AND THE HOSPITALIZED ADOLESCENT

Block	Number of Families	Family		Parents		Adolescent	
		W	Significance	W	Significance	W	Significance
1	7	.36	$p<.01$	.72	$p<.001$	.21	$p<.01$
2	8	.57	$p<.001$	.46	$p<.001$	.40	$p<.001$
3	10	.62	$p<.001$	.64	$p<.001$	.53	$p<.001$
4	7	.63	$p<.001$	.64	$p<.001$	.52	$p<.001$

TABLE 2
WITHIN-FAMILY RANK-ORDER CORRELATIONS RELATING PARTICIPATION LEVELS OF PARENTS AND ADOLESCENTS IN EACH OF 10 FAMILIES PRESENT FOR 20 OR MORE SESSIONS

Family Number	Number of Sessions	rho	Significance
6	46	+.53	p<.0003
8	34	+.36	p<.04
10	27	+.53	p<.004
11	40	−.01	n.s.
12	44	+.32	p<.03
14	44	+.51	p<.0007
15	40	+.24	p<.13
16	37	+.33	p<.05
17	35	+.49	p<.003
18	23	−.02	n.s.

the 10 families—suggests that if either a parent or an adolescent changed his or her level of participation in the group, the other would very quickly follow suit. This coordination occurred early in the session, at the latest within a few minutes. If the imitative adjustments were not made until the end of the session they would not have been reflected in the total participation score for that session.

Discussion

Taken together, these data present a consistent picture of a family regulatory principle that controls the levels of participation of parents and adolescents alike in the multiple family group on a session-by-session basis. We believe this to be the first clear-cut demonstration of such a family mechanism. Several caveats are in order, however. First, other mechanisms may account for the session-by-session similarities we found between parents and adolescents in participation rates. Brief encounters of family members before the meetings began may have established a tone or stance toward the group that could account for the coordinated session-by-session changes. Alternately, all members of a family may have shifted their participation levels in each session in response to similar shifts in some nonfamily member (e.g., a staff member or the group leader). More data collection and further analysis are under way to examine these possibilities. However, which ever mechanism actually operated—within-family imitation, presession adjustments within the family, or concordant imitation of a nonmember—a significant family-based mechanism appears to have been operating.

A second caveat concerns the limited size of our sample. Although the observations are drawn from 18 families, they are drawn from only one multiple family group. A third caveat is that our assumption that the multiple family group reflects a more general social process may be wrong. The group we studied may have been a very limited or extreme case, especially in light of the fact that it was composed of troubled families and was conducted in a psychiatric hospital. However, we are encouraged by work that has shown the many ways in which the psychiatric hospital is a microcosm of society (Almond, 1974; Stanton and Schwartz, 1954); indeed, the title of this paper is meant, in part, as homage to the late William Caudill, this project's initial consultant, whose first major work was titled *The Psychiatric Hospital as a Small Society* (Caudill, 1973).

References

Almond, R. (1974), *The Healing Community*. New York: Jason Aronson.

Bell, N. W. & Zucker, R. A. (1968/1969), Family-hospital relationships in a state hospital setting: A structural-functional analysis of the hospitalization process. *Internat. J. Soc. Psychiat.*, 15:73-80.

Caudill, W. (1973), *The Psychiatric Hospital as a Small Society*. Cambridge, Mass.: Harvard University Press.

Condon, W. A. & Ogston, W. D. (1967), A segmentation of behavior. *J. Psychiat. Res.*, 5:221-235.

Edwards, J. N., Klemmack, D. L., & Hatos, L. (1973), Social participation patterns among mobile-home and single family dwellers. *Soc. Forces*, 51:485-489.

Elder, G. H. (1965), Family structure and educational attainment: A cross-national analysis. *Amer. Sociol. Rev.*, 30:81-96.

Ferreira, A. J. & Winter, W. (1966), Stability of interactional variables in family decision-making. *Arch. Gen. Psychiat.*, 14:352-355.

Haley, J. (1967), Experiment with abnormal families: Testing done in a restricted communication setting. *Arch. Gen. Psychiat.*, 17:53-63.

Hollingshead, A. B. & Redlich, F. (1958), *Social Class and Mental Illness*. New York: John Wiley.

Patterson, G. R. & Reid, J. B. (1970), Reciprocity and coercion: Two facets of social systems. In: *Behavior Modification in Clinical Psychology*, ed. C. Neuringer & J. Michael. New York: Appleton-Century-Crofts, pp. 133-177.

Reiss, D. (1967), Individual thinking and family interaction: II. A study of pattern recognition and hypothesis testing in families of normals, character disorders and schizophrenics. *J. Psychiat. Res.*, 5:193-211.

——— (1968), Individual thinking and family interaction: III. An experimental study of categorization performance in families of normals, those with character disorders and schizophrenics. *J. Nerv. Ment. Dis.*, 146:384-403.
——— (1969), Individual thinking and family interaction: IV. A study of information exchange in families of normals, those with character disorders and schizophrenics. *J. Nerv. Ment. Dis.*, 149:473-490.
——— (1970), Individual thinking and family interaction: V. Proposals for contrasting character of experiential sensitivity and expressive form in families. *J. Nerv. Ment. Dis.*, 151:187-202.
——— (1971a), Varieties of consensual experience: I. A theory for relating family interaction to individual thinking. *Fam. Proc.*, 10:1-28.
——— (1971b), Varieties of consensual experience: II. Dimensions of a family's experience of its environment. *Fam. Proc.*, 10:28-35.
——— (1971c), Varieties of consensual experience: III. Contrast between families of normals, delinquents and schizophrenics. *J. Nerv. Ment. Dis.*, 152:73-95.
——— (1971d), Intimacy and problem solving: An automated procedure for testing a theory of consensual experience in families. *Arch. Gen. Psychiat.*, 24:442-455.
——— & Salzman, C. (1973), The resilience of family process: Effect of secobarbital. *Arch. Gen. Psychiat.*, 28:425-433.
Stanton, A. H. & Schwartz, M. S. (1954), *The Mental Hospital*. New York: Basic Books.

Family group therapy, as this chapter illustrates, has not only spread horizontally, involving other families to achieve multiple family therapy, but has spread vertically, both into the past and the future, to embrace grandparents, children, and grandchildren.

Ethical and Practical Implications of Intergenerational Family Therapy

IVAN BOSZORMENYI-NAGY

By asking a family therapist to define what psychotherapy is, it appears that the organizers of our Congress have opened the door for radical departures from the traditional definition. In an era which questions the social value of psychotherapy, and in which some believe the traditional family is becoming extinct, it seems appropriate to explore whether the family approach has a new ethical base to offer for re-examining the psychological and societal premises for psychotherapy.

Family System as a Ledger of Accounts

For the purposes of intergenerational family theory, the term family should first be defined as an ongoing social system, not merely a single nuclear family. It is based on an invisible ledger of structured expectations concerning the integrity underlying observable interactions. Because of their existential interwovenness, family members remain personally accountable for both benefits received and injuries inflicted. Ultimately, they cannot avoid facing the balance sheets of fairness of their exchanges.

Ivan Boszormenyi-Nagy, M.D., is Director, Family Psychiatry Division, Eastern Pennsylvania Psychiatric Institute; Clinical Professor of Psychiatry, Hahnemann Medical College, Philadelphia, Pa.

Reprinted from *Psychotherapy and Psychosomatics*, vol. 24, pp. 261-268, 1974.

Such a ledger of transgenerational accountability has been the concern of insightful thinkers ever since the writing of the Hebrew Bible as well as the great playwriting of Ancient Greece. The intergenerationally oriented family therapist has the privilege of witnessing the hidden script of a family's destiny as it emerges from minor denials to tragedies of everyday magnitude. The outcome of the drama can rebalance or further upset the ethical balance of relational accounts. For example, overt or even covert exploitation of a child by its parents, if maintained unilaterally, can undermine the child's base of trust and belief in human justice to such an extent that, upon becoming a parent, the new adult will be "programmed" to start his relationship with his child with an already overencumbered balance sheet. He is actually entitled to make the rest of the world accountable to repay his damages. The invisible script that follows from such a ledger of intergenerational reciprocity sets the stage for many so-called "emotional distortions," manifested in close relationships: projective distortion, parentification, scapegoating, idealization, etc.

It has been customary to view family therapy as merely another method of treatment. The question of specific indications is often raised: Should this schizoid adolescent be treated by individual or family therapy?

Assuming that a more comprehensive knowledge of the patient's relational world can only be helpful, I suggest that the essence of the family or relational approach to psychotherapy lies in the scope of the therapist's responsibility and commitment, rather than in any technical criterion. As the family therapist "contracts" for the care of an entire family, he negotiates from an ethical position entirely different from that of the individual therapist, who forms a confidential alliance with one member while remaining uncommitted and unaccountable to the other members. In contrast, as his contract expects him to refrain from siding with one member or from prejudicially overlooking this member's unfairness to the others, the family therapist is drawn into a role similar to that of a judge who cannot help but consider the balance of reciprocal fairness in human interactions. It is mainly for this reason that the conclusions of this presentation can neither be obtained from nor contradicted through individual practice. The family therapist can temporarily avoid his intrinsic role expectation of "multi-directional partiality" by focusing his attention on the here-and-now, visible interactions and power ploys that fill out the days and hours of any human group. But in so doing, the "interactionalist" family therapist is likely to miss the very dynamic that determines the motivational patterning of long-term, ongoing, multigenerational systems of relationships. How, then, can motivation be defined on a new multiperson, system level?

Ethics and the Therapy of Multiperson Systems

Somewhat paradoxically, the family relational approach poses a serious challenge to the notion that it is psychology that forms the basis of psychotherapeutic intervention. By this I mean, if psychology is defined as the study of the properties of one human mind, or one person's behavior, experience, and underlying motivations, then psychological theory by itself constitutes an incomplete base for understanding the regulatory forces that govern healthy or pathological functioning in individual members. I postulate that the psychological forces themselves are determined rather by the factual nature of balances of justice and injustice in intergenerational family relationships. For example, the actual fact of the exploitation of a child not only affects the child's psychology but it becomes a determinant in the ongoing relationships among family members surrounding the child, including his future children and grandchildren. Their capacity for trust, satisfaction, and reality testing will be affected. The individual's so-called developmental psychology is molded in accordance with the fluctuating balance of human integrity in the dealings of his important others.

It is very important for us to also recognize that the time has come to end the pseudoscientific myth of the desirability of a valueless manner of thinking, as has been customary in contemporary social science and psychotherapy. Furthermore, if psychotherapists are change-agents or catalysts, they cannot deny any longer that they have to define what should be changed. In fact, the family therapist raises the question: Who should change? Very frequently it turns out in the course of therapy that it is one of the "well" members who needs the most help.

I do not believe that every family therapist can adopt the intergenerational approach. Resistance to adopting the approach originates mainly from the intrinsic demand that its practitioner face the embedment of family relations in a context of ethical responsibility. Unprotected by the disguises of an "interactionalist" curiosity for here-and-now events, or unilateral confidential alliance with one individual member for his psychological cure, or alleging to be a valueless agent of behavioral change, the intergenerational family therapist has to face the most difficult aspect of a genuine dialogue: our responsibility for our actions and our responsibility for also holding the others responsible in their dealings with each other and ourselves.

It is true then that the individual is not responsible for, yet bound by, those aspects of the system which derive from the multigenerational ledger of justice. Actually, children can often be devoted to the task of balancing the ledger to the point of placing its cause above their individual goals in life. As Shakespeare states in the prologue to *Romeo and Juliet:* "A pair of star-cross'd lovers take their life; Whose misadventured pitious overthrows, Do with their death bury their parents' strife."

Yet, familial loyalty has its positive, mutually gratifying aspects. A devoted and concerned readiness of small children to volunteer to try to rebalance their parents' unhappiness over their parents' own self-destructive patterns of behavior is one of the most moving observations that family therapists are liable to make. Familial or filial loyalty is thus not based on the power model of enforcement, like a slave's loyalty to the master. It is based, instead, on spontaneous caring and concern and on the fundamental primary obligation of repaying with gratitude those who gave us our lives. Gratitude is a frightening aspect of relationship: it can be used for exploitation. In fact, certain parents do manipulate children's loyalty in such a way that it can far outstrip the extent of benefits the child actually has received from the parents. Real exploitation of children is always based on a manipulation of their loyalty, and almost never on a mere successful power contest.

Symptom and Pathogenic Loyalty

The extension of the dynamics of reciprocal fairness into the question of psychic health and illness underlines the importance of pathogenic loyalty in what leads to individual psychopathology. If we assume that family systems are held together by loyalty, it follows that even self-destructive behavior, like delinquency, drug addiction, psychosis, and other forms of "symptoms," may be maintained in compliance with family loyalty expectations. In fact, I suggest that in understanding the basic dynamic of family systems, one of the principal tasks of the family therapist is to seek out the hidden, invisible loyalty aspects of allegedly objectionable, rejecting, or rejected behavior on the part of family members. He has to ask himself the question repeatedly: in what way may this member's seemingly pathological behavior assure his continued availability for the family of origin?

The spread of focus from individual through marital to intergenerational system levels of problems can be briefly illustrated by a typical marital therapy situation:

A young couple in their mid-twenties came into therapy, essentially upon the initiative of the wife. She was rather desperate, almost suicidally unhappy over the failure of their marriage. She complained that her husband had hardly any sexual interest in her. She described that their personal relationship oscillated between long, painful periods of silence and destructively hostile arguments. She was the only child of intelligent, serious, and overly concerned parents.

The husband readily admitted that there was hardly any sexual activity between him and his wife. He attributed this circumstance to his wife's tendency for having cutting, hostile moods, which would completely demotivate him from sexually approaching her. He claimed that these moods developed as a result of long, daily conversations between her and her mother. These conversations became especially intensified during the past year, during which the couple decided to move to California in the hope of having a "life of their own."

For a number of weeks the wife kept on refusing to acknowledge the importance of the long evening conversations between herself and her mother as having anything to do with the couple's sexual problems. First, she defended the open, emotionally sincere style of communications of her family against the repressive and indirectly expressive style of her husband's family. Gradually, however, she began to talk about the way in which she would get hurt in the long talks with her mother. A recurrent theme of these conversations was that the mother would insist on proving that the daughter had been neglectful of or lacking concern for her parents, for example, by not preparing meals for her sick mother. In one instance, the mother's sickness consisted of a questionable back pain of several days' duration which did not make her bedridden. The well-to-do mother had obviously many options to obtain paid help instead of expecting her married daughter to leave her husband's company in the evening. The young wife added that, as a rule, such quarrels with her mother did not stop until she admitted her guilt as an ungrateful daughter.

Actually, it was a good prognostic sign that this family of an only child handled loyalty expectations with such explicitness, rather than through subtle innuendo and manipulations. In many families the recognition of similar loyalty conflicts is made extremely difficult by complex layers of denial, double messages, and the intensive scapegoating of outside persons. An open confrontation with loyalty expectations was made easier in our case by the fact that this young couple was still childless. In many families children become the most suitable means for avoidance and displacement maneuvers, since the ethical obligation to minister to small children may temporarily silence the conflicting loyalty expectations emanating from the families of origin. The battle of loyalty conflicts then goes underground, so to speak.

It is always risky to try to summarize the complex rationale of a form of therapy in a brief space (Boszormenyi-Nagy and Spark, 1973). The foregoing clinical illustration can be used only to highlight a few aspects of the therapeutic rationale of intergenerational family therapy. First, in contrast to individual psychotherapy, no family therapist would regard the earlier mentioned young woman's psyche as a finite realm of causation, and responsibility as an agent of change. The family therapist would regard her relationship with her parents as an important leverage for change, rather than merely of developmental or historical significance.

Nor will the intergenerational family therapist accept the limited framework of marital couple therapy. In his view the conflict of loyalties is anchored in both families of origin and in the marriage. All three systems should be utilized for maximum benefit in the difficult task of resolving conflicts through rebalancing loyalties. In implementing this strategy, the intergenerational family therapist holds up the grandparents' welfare as part of his primary therapeutic goals. Finding a suitable way of repaying her filial gratitude will not only directly help the young adult, but will also satisfy her parents' legitimate needs for receiving affection from their grown-up child.

Specifically, the intergenerational family therapist will not consider the older generation merely an interfering agent, a tool for helping the young nuclear family, or a source of interference. He will regard the ethical balance of the relationships of all family members from the point of view of his commitment to all of them as his "patients." The intergenerational family therapist will consider the *real* obligations of the emancipating daughter, in our case, to be concerned about the feelings of loss occurring in her parents. The therapist's sympathy will be extended to both the suffering young wife and her painfully grieving parents. He knows that avoidance of the reality of the obligation to repay benefits received will tend to be extremely costly to this young woman. Her loyalties to her family of origin would then go underground and could invisibly pervade and undermine her commitment to both marriage and motherhood.

Therapeutic Rationale

What then is the intergenerational family therapist's therapeutic strategy? First, I would like to state what this strategy is not. The intergenerational therapist is not symptom or behavioral oriented. He does not assume by implication that basic decency and gratitude of children toward their parents is reducible to an error in learning which should be removed by relearning. Nor is he interested in chiefly accomplishing insight into the genetic and remotely conscious areas of the psychology of his patient. Like the young woman referred to earlier, his patients may be conscious of the painful guilt-inducing reality of their not being able to repay gratitude to their parents. One reason for this may lie, for instance, in a mother's inability to accept and receive repayment. What the "patient" may need help with is to enable her mother to receive the repayment and thereby, in turn, to become liberated herself for a warmly loving and giving partnership in her marriage and for a devoted motherhood later. Therapeutic strategy, then, is based on an action design rather than on mere cognitive gains through increased consciousness or on unloading of emotions through increased expressiveness. The suffering subject of a loyalty conflict has to be helped to find appropriate action patterns through which the object of loyalty can be effectively helped or repayed without pathological, self-destructive, symptomatic, or sick patterns of behavior. In distinction from the concept of "working through" in individual psychotherapy or analysis, the welfare of all members is considered in designing the action patterns. Instead of simply trying to eliminate the pathological obligation from his patient's mind, the intergenerational family therapist will help her to face the implications of her realistically unrequited obligations. Such confrontation should never be considered completed until it can be converted into designs for appropriate and successful *relational* strategies, the goal of which is restoration of a balanced reciprocity of fairness. The newly found balance will enable each participant to relinquish substitutive patterns of relational mastery through avoidance.

Many times the real obstacle for such strategy lies in the past of the grandparent. As a carrier of an overencumbered familial ethical ledger, she may be in no position to ever settle the account between herself and her child. Just as the grandparent was kept in arrears regarding the chance of repayment to her parent, she in turn will be inclined to keep her child in arrears. Another obstacle might lie in the parent's justifiable disdain and resentment for his parent. Often it is difficult to maintain an attitude of fairness toward a parent who is persistently manipulative and exploitative through arousal of guilt.

An important strategic leverage for intergenerational therapy lies in the exploration of the grandparent's past. The uncovering of circumstances which used to exploit the grandparent in her own childhood may rearrange her own account and help establish a fair exchange between herself and her child. Subsequently, it will help her child to exonerate his parent through learning about the latter's human dignity and suffering.

In summary, the essence of intergenerational family therapy lies in an ethical or justice orientation. In contrast to individual therapy, it does not offer exclusive alliance with any member at the expense of its concern for other members of the same relationship system. It does not assume that one member can lastingly benefit from effective successful power manipulation through a complete disregard for the other member's interest. Advocacy is thus extended from one individual or a couple to the entire system of relationships. Similarly, expectation of change is also extended to include every member of the relationship system. Whether he comes to family therapy sessions conjointly or remains absent, each member has to be both considered in his own rights and alerted to his responsibilities for improving his side of the balance of reciprocity. However, rather than suggesting a unilaterally giving, self-denying altruism, the intergenerational family therapist suggests a dialectic balance of receiving through giving.

Many observers of the American scene allege that psychodynamic psychotherapy is on its way out. After decades of undeniable contributions, the dynamic individual approach has shown what appears to be its limitations. If it is true, other, currently popular varieties on the theme of individual psychotherapy, such as behavior therapy, encounter and sensitivity programs, and traditional group therapy, are also to face relative disillusionment in the not too distant future. Similarly affected will be the many community mental health programs, most of which are based on a mixture of individual psychodynamic with "valueless" sociological theoretical assumptions.

The systematic thinking through of the implications of intergenerational family therapy should, however, not only help to point up the areas of relative bankruptcy in the individual dynamic model. It should, instead, offer an opportunity for the extension of the therapeutic framework by integrating individual insights with the systemic, intergenerational orientation into a holistic approach. Such an integrated framework holds exciting possibilities for the redefinition of such basic concepts as health, pathology, prevention, as well as individual legal rights and perhaps eventually even of certain basic notions of international relations. Hopefully, the intergenerational family systems approach will contribute to the discovery by governmental, religious, etc., agencies that we can no longer afford the cost of continued dodging of responsibility for preventive planning.

Reference

Boszormenyi-Nagy, I. & Spark, G. M. (1973), *Invisible Loyalties. Reciprocity in Intergenerational Family Therapy*. New York: Harper & Row.

Vector Therapy

Vector therapy is one half of family therapy. This new form of treatment is not a substitute for family psychotherapy (the other half), but is powerful in its own right, and complementary to it. Intrafamily and extrafamily psychic patterns have to be planned anew and realigned in a directed and systematic way to effect a constructive and benevolent change in the family dynamics.

The procedures employed in vector therapy are many. After an overview chapter, a few of the procedures are exemplified—foster-home placement, group foster-homes, adjustment in the school environment, community agencies, and inpatient ward.

This chapter presents a brief overview of vector therapy—its origin, core principle, definition, and application.

Vector Therapy

JOHN G. HOWELLS

Neurosis does not originate within psychotherapeutic interviews. Does it then not follow that if neurosis originates outside the psychotherapeutic interview it is possible that measures taken outside these psychotherapeutic interviews might aid the resolution of neurosis? Vector therapy, a form of psychotherapy which is extrainterview, claims that this is possible. The value of interview psychotherapy is not denied; vector therapy is complementary to it, but it claims that, in certain circumstances, it can be more effective than interview psychotherapy.

Is it conceivable that neurosis can resolve outside psychotherapeutic interviews? As you observe neurotic individuals in society, you will have noticed that their condition fluctuates—sometimes it deteriorates, sometimes it improves, and sometimes it completely resolves. Therefore, the capacity to improve without psychotherapeutic intervention is there. Indeed, one study (Frank, 1961) showed that the neurosis of more than half of patients resolved simply by their appointments' remaining on a clinic's waiting list for one year. What causes this spontaneous improvement? What circumstances are at work outside interview psychotherapy? If we knew the answer to this question, we could utilize the responsible therapeutic factor or factors in treatment. Vector therapy has gone a long way to answering this question and to utilizing the findings in treatment.

Progress often comes from analyzing a mass of apparently disconnected or discordant data and finding an underlying fundamental prin-

---

John G. Howells, M.D., F.R.C.Psych., D.P.M., is Director of the Institute of Family Psychiatry, Ipswich, England.

Presented at VI World Congress of Psychiatry, Honolulu, Hawaii, U.S.A., August 1977.

ciple. It took man, for instance, millions of years to discover, prove, and accept that the world was round or that a stone would always fall toward the center of the earth. Once arrived at, the principles governing these phenomena appear obvious or simple. But they were not obvious before their truth was demonstrated. To overemphasize simplicity can lead to an attitude of mind that is slow to see the potential value of applying the principle in practice. It is necessary to mention this fact because I would not wish you to be led astray by the simplicity of the truths we shall consider into imagining that their application in practice is not complex.

The Morbid Process

We must continue our quest by asking, "What was the morbid process of neurosis which was resolved spontaneously without interview psychotherapy?" The more we can clarify the morbid process, the more we may be able to fashion precise procedures for resolving it. In general terms, we can say that neurosis results from an experience, of short or long duration, whereby an individual's psyche suffers damage by noxious, stressful, emotional forces, which I term vectors, coming from an emotional source—another person.

Let me illustrate a "benevolent vector." A young couple look with admiration at a room full of new furniture. The husband exclaims, "I will always sit on this settee, dear." Wife expresses surprise: "But why on the settee?" The husband replies, "Because then I can always sit next to you, dear." Those few words are a benevolent communication, a benevolent vector, which will cause the wife to glow with emotional and physical pleasure.

We meet the same couple some years later. One night, after intercourse, the wife turns to her husband and says, "I notice that you did not have a climax." He replies, "No. I am keeping that for someone else." These few words are a noxious communication, a noxious vector. The wife is likely to respond with despair and could even be physically sick.

The individual, then, in his daily life is often beset by one or many of such noxious emotional forces, frequently a pattern of forces. Clinical work and experimentation support the belief that the most significant and the most dramatic pattern of forces is that occurring within the family. The time of greatest impact is in the years of personality development, when long-lasting damage can be effected and vulnerabilities to damage later in life can be established. Occasionally, the adverse set of forces arises outside the family—in surrogate families, institutions, schools, work situations, or social milieu.

Family Diagnosis

Can this morbid process in a particular patient or family be explored and described? It can be said that careful assessment of an individual *can* display the pattern of adverse forces that brought and maybe still brings trauma into his life. The main areas of exploration are threefold—the patient's life experience in his preceding family, the patient's life experience in his present family, and the patient's experience outside his family. An invaluable procedure for this exploration is to meet the patient together with his family—either his preceding or present family—a procedure termed Family Group Diagnosis. A particular development is worth mentioning here. Hitherto, the usual procedure in the exploration of the preceding family was to invite an individual patient to remember and relate his experiences in it. How full of errors was this procedure! Far better is to adopt the practice, whenever the preceding family is available, to put it with the patient and observe the adverse process at work. We have found this practice of great value at our Institute.

The morbid process can then be explored and described. Furthermore, the fluctuations in the morbid psychopathological process are often revealed in the material produced in family group diagnosis. Clinical work daily produces examples of spontaneous changes in the neurosis. To quote but a few examples taken from recent meetings with families:

Family 1: The family entering the room consists of father, mother, maternal sister, a young child, and an infant. The infant is the referred patient for his refusal to feed. The infant enters the room crying, held in his mother's arms. The family sits down. The annoyance of the crying increases. Then there is the intervention—maternal sister puts out her arm, takes the infant, and there is an immediate cessation of crying. The infant is responding to a new set of vectors.

Family 2: The family recalls their adolescent son's turbulent life. The parents and boy remember only one period of respite with satisfaction. When the boy was ten, and his parents went abroad for six months, he stayed behind with his parental grandparents. His disturbance seemed to fall away from him, only to recur when he returned to the care of his parents. This boy, too, was responding to a new set of vectors.

Family 3: A husband presents with depression. The whole family meets for treatment. It had hardly begun when the son of 25 is transferred to a post abroad. The family report a sudden improvement in father's depression, which lifts dramatically. It emerges later that he was locked in conflict with his son. Here we had a spontaneous alteration in the pattern of the vector to father's advantage.

The examples are legion.

The Core Principle

What produces these spontaneous changes? If our formulation of psychopathology is correct, it must be that the adverse pattern of forces changes and the change produces an attenuation of the trauma; the degree of change reflects the degree of reduction in trauma. If we can identify ways by which the pattern *spontaneously* changes, could we not *direct* these changes to take place? Creativity through evolution is essentially a repatterning of phenomena in such a way as to allow development through a more harmonious patterning of the phenomena. This applies also to biological phenomena, e.g., the change of position of elements in the composition pattern of a noxious drug can convert that drug into a curative compound. Those new patterns which are in harmony with the environment tend to persist because survival often depends upon them. Vector therapy relies upon our capacity to change patterns of forces, not haphazardly, but in a systematic directed fashion.

Definition and Illustration

A vector denotes a quantity that has direction. Force, including emotional force, is a quantity with direction and therefore can be represented by a vector. Vector therapy identifies the pattern of the vectors inside and outside a family and readjusts the patterns of the emotional forces within the life space to bring improvement to the individual or family within the life space.

Psychotherapy means treatment employing psychic, or emotional, influences. Thus, vector therapy is a psychotherapeutic procedure. But the beneficial psychic influences operate outside the interview; the interview is employed to assess and guide the psychotherapy in progress outside the interview. Vector therapy is thus an extrainterview psychotherapy.

It may be useful to mention a few clinical applications. I will deliberately select simple and therefore clear illustrations; I wish to put the principle starkly before you. Of course, in practice the situations are far from simple and make great demands on the skills of the most experienced of clinicians.

Situation 1: Let me take this simple nuclear family of three—a healthy father, a highly neurotic mother, and a disturbed child. Father's family has taught him that children should be brought up by mothers. The mother and child are locked in an intense, disturbing relationship. Father is concerned, but does not think it right to intervene and moves away to the calm of extrafamily activities. Vector therapy can now intervene. The father is brought into an individual interview, and he learns that fathers can assist in bringing up children. The nuclear family meet and, over a number of interviews, come to accept father as the main parenting agent. The new pattern of vectors brings an immediate improvement in the state of the child. You will notice that it would still be possible for the disturbed young mother to receive psychotherapy.

Situation 2: A young wife presents with anxiety and depression. Exploration of the family situation reveals that the young couple live close to the parental grandparents. The paternal grandmother is a hard, harsh, dominating woman. She sweeps into the house every day and always has something to criticize. The young wife cannot even anticipate at what time of the day this will happen. Her life is full of tension and expectant anxiety. The birth of her child offers more opportunities for criticism from the mother-in-law. Vector therapy intervenes. Over a number of interviews the young couple, the husband in particular, are strengthened to the point where, without precipitating any quarrel with the grandparents, they move some distance away. The husband is also supported to the point where he makes arrangements for his parents to visit infrequently and at expected times. You will notice that, should the situation dictate, it would still be possible for the young wife and her mother-in-law to receive psychotherapy.

Situation 3: An adolescent of fourteen presents with aphonia, anxiety, and insomnia. Exploration reveals overprotective parents unable to support their daughter in meeting the normal trials of everyday life. The girl is quarreling persistently with her school mates. Their retaliation depresses her. Her school work has suffered. Vector therapy intervenes. Family exploration reveals the daughter looks back with pleasure to three months spent with the paternal grandmother, pleasure apparently shared by the elderly widow. The girl is transferred to the care of her grandmother, with an almost immediate relief in her symptomatology and a marked improvement in her school record. You will notice that, should it be required, the adolescent could still receive psychotherapy.

I offer two comments on these examples. First, to say that father must look after his child, that mother-in-law must not visit, and that an adolescent must live with her grandmother is equivalent to saying very forcibly, "This appendix must come out." But you cannot tear a child out of his family any more than you can tear an appendix out of a body. To make a psychiatric, or a surgical, diagnosis calls for experience and understanding of pathology, careful assessment (sometimes over a long period of time), the capacity to evaluate the essentials of a mass of data, the ability to formulate clear advice, an empathic relationship that dissolves the fears of the patient, and, sometimes, the patience to wait until the patient is secure enough to adopt the remedy that offers relief. Vector therapy is an exacting psychotherapeutic procedure. It may call for brave decision-making and sensitive management of the patient, his family, and the many agencies that can assist in the repatterning of the vectors. Second, you will notice that in each of the examples I gave, interview psychotherapy could also be of assistance. Thus, vector therapy and interview psychotherapy are complementary. Indeed, the best results are obtained when they are employed together.

Application

It may be useful to summarize the essential steps in the application of vector therapy. Each step is concerned with assessing psychic factors or effecting psychic changes. The steps are: (1) A careful assessment through family group interviews in order to clarify the pattern of the emotional forces at work in a particular family, i.e., Family Group Diagnosis. (2) To bring understanding of its particular set of forces to the family. (3) To help the family, through a supportive relationship, to accomplish a change in the pattern of its adverse set of forces. (4) When necessary, to put the family in touch with community agencies that can facilitate the change. (5) To create community agencies able to effect changes in family psychic patterns. The agencies bring not material relief, but emotional relief, to the family. This may involve adjusting present community agencies or establishing new agencies.

Vector therapy can be effective when there are no or few facilities for interview psychotherapy. This is a situation common in many countries.

Given limited resources, vector therapy is economical. It demands the same degree of skill in the clinician as interview psychotherapy, but it saves the clinician's time in that it utilizes less interview time because change is produced by monitored therapeutic situations outside the interview. Vector therapy can also be effective when there *are* facilities for interview psychotherapy but they are unlikely to be availing; an example would be the treatment of a hard core or problem family. Again, vector therapy can be utilized when the situation demands an urgent solution, in that someone may be damaged or endangered during the interval before interview psychotherapy becomes effective, e.g., when an infant at risk of being battered in his own home has to be urgently removed to a safer milieu. Given ideal resources, the quickest and best results are obtained by combining interview psychotherapy and vector therapy.

Conclusion

The essential principle of vector therapy is to improve on nature by directing rather than leaving to chance a repatterning of fields of psychic forces. At last we have therapeutic means outside our interview rooms.

References

Frank, J. D. (1961), *Persuasion and Healing. Symptom Relief and Attitude Change*. London: Oxford University Press; Baltimore: The Johns Hopkins Press.

Howells, J. G. (1963), Extra-interview therapy in family psychiatry. *Pub. Health*, 77:368-372.

——— (1975), *Principles of Family Psychiatry*. New York: Brunner/Mazel.

In most circumstances, vector therapy aims to maintain intact the structure of the family, but to change the pattern of the intra- and extrafamily influences. The youngest members of the family spend a large part of their time at school. A benevolent school milieu brings advantage to the child and to the family. This chapter explores school-family interaction.

The Family-School Interview: An Ecostructural Approach

HARRY J. APONTE

A family-school interview includes the child with his family and the personnel of the school who represent the organizational structure of the school. The family is the constellation of people who make up the core of the child's domestic life. The school staff—teachers, counselor, and school principal—have the most to say about the child's activities in the school. The interview is usually handled by cotherapists because of the size and complexity of the group involved.

This form of interview is part of an experimental effort to conduct first interviews at the school with the family and school staff when the school has referred the child to the clinic for treatment and the family sees no problem with the child at home. The intent of the Clinic's staff is to avoid prematurely identifying the child as a patient and to elicit a commitment of the family and the school personnel to a joint problem-solving effort.

The first step in response to the school's referral is to explore the problem where the request for help has originated. Because the pressure for a solution has originated in the school, the therapists have never been

---

Harry J. Aponte, A.C.S.W.T., is Director of the Philadelphia Child Guidance Clinic, Philadelphia, Pennsylvania.

Reprinted from *Family Process*, vol. 15, no. 3, September, 1976.

refused an interview at the school. In the Clinic's experience, the usual sequence begins with a mother calling the Clinic to ask for an appointment for her son or daughter, usually the former. When asked to describe the problem, she explains that the school is complaining about her son, but that he is not a problem at home. The therapist then asks her whether he and the family could meet with the school staff to find out more about the problem. When the mother agrees—and she always has, in our experience—the therapist calls the school counselor to arrange the interview. The counselor is usually willing, but occasionally there is a question of freeing the teacher from class and, more often, the principal's reluctance to take part in the interview. The therapist may call the principal personally, with the explanation that the family can see no problem and that, since the school knows the problem first hand, it would help both the family and the Clinic if all concerned parties could talk together. The Clinic is quite prepared to wait until school personnel can arrange their schedules so that all can attend the interview. We have found that when we compromise and have the first interview with the child and family in the Clinic, we are apt to meet greater resistance to a school interview. Our leverage diminishes as we lose the momentum of the school's initial pressure. This is not to say, however, that such interviews are never held after treatment has begun at the Clinic, but only that they are often more difficult to arrange.

The idea of having school-family interviews has grown naturally from the assumption of family therapists that family problems are best addressed in family sessions. It makes sense to include school personnel when the complaint comes from the school. And, as with the family, we include the key figures in the child's life at school: the counselor, the teacher, and the school principal. In a large institution, the vice-principal occasionally substitutes for the principal. We hold the interview in the school, since it is impractical to expect numerous school staff to come to the Clinic and because, by doing so, the school maintains a primary sense of responsibility with the family to find a solution to the problem.

The family-school interview, as a first session, is intended to serve as an instrument to learn about the presenting problem, the relationships among the people who contributed to the problem, and the ways in which these people can help bring about change. The interview is used principally as a way to find solutions, rather than to dig for causes of trouble. The therapists attempt to make the interview a practical experience in which the family and school staff will recognize the relevance of their roles as agents of positive change. Although an effective diagnostic tool, the interview is built more on a therapeutic than on an exploratory model.

A delicate issue requiring attention from the start is the relationship of the school to the Clinic vis-à-vis the child and his family. The teachers request the Clinic's help with their pupil, but they do not expect to be treated as clients. The prospect of being interviewed with the child and his parents brings into question the school staff's status in relation to their pupil. And yet the therapists are being called on to accomplish something neither the family nor the school could do and thus must lead the three-way effort of family, school, and Clinic to solve the problem. Just as the mother and father must maintain their parental posture in relation to their child, the teachers have their position to uphold in the face of the therapists' assuming direction of the session. This is a difficult spot for the therapists, particularly when the interview is conducted on school grounds, often in the principal's office. But the task is clear. The therapist is not a parent, a teacher, or a principal; he must acknowledge the primacy of each in his or her respective context while at the same time taking leadership of what is essentially a clinical interview. The quest for solutions, not for blame, will call upon the participants as resources, not patients, and this will reinforce rather than undermine their respective roles.

The clinical example we offer is chosen because it contains so many of the dynamics that many of our family-school interviews have presented. The first interview with this family and school is stressed to illustrate the theory that guided the therapists and the techniques employed in the service of our diagnostic hypotheses. The vicissitudes of the ongoing therapy will rarely be cited, since this is not the issue to which we are addressing ourselves.

First, one must conceptualize the child, the family, the school, and the community organization involved in the child's problem as system-interrelated in an ecological complex over a common issue. Their relationships make up the underpinnings of the context, namely, its structure. The transactional patterns that characterize the relationships among the component systems of this complex incorporate the laws by which the parts of these systems function with respect to one another. "It is in terms of these laws that the structure *qua* whole or system is defined" (Piaget, 1970, p. 7).

While each of these systems—child, family, school, and community—has its own internal structure, they all function within, and/or in tandem to the other systems. These systems impinge on one another when a child's problems are dynamically dependent upon his relationships with his family, school, and community. The relationships among these various systems can be referred to as their ecological structure. Clinicians in the mental health field have been addressing themselves to one or another of these component systems, but the challenge is to develop methods for intervening where the systems touch together. Our encounter with a boy named Jerry, his parents, and his school, illustrates our efforts to approach Jerry's school and family problems through a coordinated ecostructural perspective.

Jerry's School Problem

The mother of ten-year-old Jerry called the Clinic to ask for an appointment. She said Jerry was fighting in school and not doing his school work. She denied he was troublesome at home, so we suggested a school interview to include her family and Jerry. She was quite agreeable to our request that she go to the school the next day, but was reluctant to include her husband. She cautioned us that he had a "bad heart" and that his attendance would depend upon how he was feeling. We preferred to have all the children at the interview, but because the mother described more complications involved in bringing the five siblings, we settled for her, Jerry, and the father. We would see the others later if they were needed. We said we would contact the school and ask that Jerry be excused from class for the interview and that representatives of the school join us in the session.

We called the counselor who had urged Jerry's mother to contact us. She thought the participation of the principal, Jerry's three teachers, and the counselor herself was an unusual request. But she was very concerned about Jerry and would try anything. Her main question, however, was whether our purpose was to try to change the school or to help the boy. She said the staff of another mental health center had gone to the school with attempts to treat the school every time it tried to refer a child for treatment. We assured her that we considered the school staff as resources for solutions, not as targets for blame. We wanted to get all concerned with Jerry's school problems to meet together with him to find out just where his difficulties were and how we all, including the Clinic, could work together to solve them. The counselor agreed and called back to say that the principal would arrange coverage for the participating teachers and all school staff would attend.

At the school the following day, with family and school staff assembled, the principal took the initiative by asking us if we knew about the language Jerry had directed at his home-room teacher the previous day. We did not, but we wanted to get to know Jerry better personally before we went into what he had done. My partner from the Clinic, Lynn Hoffman, sat back as I chatted casually with Jerry until he relaxed a bit and could smile when I kidded with him. Lynn then turned to the parents and asked what Jerry was like at home with them. The mother spoke for both parents as she related that he was not easy to handle but was not a serious problem. He was a good athlete, did not talk much, and could be stubborn. He did not pay too much attention to his mother, but was not disrespectful. The mother said that it was her job to take care of the children (there were six) and that the father helped her if she asked. However, the father had not been working since his last heart attack a year ago, and she had not wanted to burden him with worries about the children.

The father spontaneously interjected that he would have gladly helped. He was up to it. As we probed for information about the other children, both parents admitted that it was not just Jerry who was inattentive to his mother. None of the four boys paid much attention to her orders, but this did not cause her to worry because they never did anything seriously wrong. The mother minimized her concern by adding that, if things really got out of hand, she could always turn to the father who, with a word, could get any of the children in line. When queried, Jerry agreed with all they said about him and the rest of the family. Although he spoke infrequently, it was evident that there was affection between him and his parents.

We then turned back to the school staff. Since she did not want to voice them, Jerry's home-room teacher had a written account of the racial slurs he had used against her. (Jerry is white, his teacher black.) The parents knew from the counselor's call the previous day that Jerry had been insulting, but were not aware of what he had said. We were shown what was written, and the parents affirmed that they, too, wanted to see the account of the incident. I passed the teacher's report to them. They became visibly embarrassed and were further startled when, in answer to my question, the teacher replied that Jerry had insulted her on several other occasions. Responding to the parents' surprise, my partner asked the counselor (who is white) about her communications with the parents.

The counselor said she had told them that Jerry was giving his teacher trouble, but had not been specific about what he had done or said. She had been trying to counsel Jerry herself and did not want to worry them too much.

Jerry's home-room teacher said she was offended by the way Jerry had spoken to her. She also complained that Jerry had been fighting with the other children in class and was not doing his school work. While it was evident that she was upset, it was also clear that she had not been firm with Jerry and had tolerated more than she should have. I questioned each of the other two teachers (also black), who said they had had no trouble from Jerry; they liked him. Since these teachers did not mention other children, I asked the size of their classrooms. One was giving Jerry individual tutoring, and the other had him in a small, special make-up class—all part of the counselor's and the principal's effort to give Jerry added help. By this time the home-room teacher had to return to her class. Before she left, I agreed with her about the justice of her complaints. The parents did the same. We thanked her for helping us, and she left.

We then began planning a therapeutic task. Lynn and I communicated aloud to each other that Jerry did indeed have school problems and that the school could well use the father's support. The school staff were pleased with our suggestion that Jerry's family do more to assist the school with his problems. Lynn asked the father if he could help. He was quite willing. He would have done more if he had known how serious the problems were. We suggested to the principal that Jerry be excused from his classes with his home-room teacher for a while and that he do school work at home with his father during those hours. She consented.

We wanted the counselor to be the link between the school and the family and arranged for her to consult daily with the teachers and relay to the father the school assignments he should give Jerry. Since Jerry would be bringing his work home, the father would need to coach him more actively with his school work and to organize his time. The mother, with the father's explicit backing, would make sure the other children did not interfere with the father's activities with Jerry at home. The father was happy with his assignment, and the mother supported him.

The other two teachers would continue their classes with Jerry at school. The principal supported the plan, and Jerry agreed to work with his father at home. We all agreed to meet again at the school in two weeks. As we ended the session, I asked to speak with the principal alone for a moment, while Lynn Hoffman sat with Jerry, his father, and the counselor to detail how they would carry out the home program.

The principal needed no convincing to remove Jerry from his homeroom teacher. There was now too much enmity between them. Race was not the issue. Jerry needed personalized attention and in a classroom under more effective control. The principal was in accord that Jerry's next teacher would need to be a more experienced and forceful person.

Every two weeks for a few sessions we worked on the continued mutual-support program between the school and the family. We also met separately with school personnel to plan their handling of Jerry in school and their communications with the parents about the school work. At the Clinic and in the home, Lynn worked independently with Jerry, his parents, and his siblings to straighten out problems within the family. With Lynn's support, the father worked on becoming more involved with Jerry around his school work and his discipline and behavior at home. The mother also received support from the father in exerting more control over the other boys. Jerry was helped to negotiate with his older brothers for more territory at home. The mother also needed some relief from the life of the harassed housewife. She was encouraged to take care of herself, visit friends, and have some recreation time with her husband. As these changes took place, Jerry's school performance and behavior improved rapidly.

Jerry's Ecological Context

A boy having trouble in school is not having trouble alone. "A child's behavior is caused by many factors. Some are 'inside' the child, like neurons, brains, and glands, as well as memories, motivations, introjections, and drives. 'Outside' the child are factors like his parents, his siblings, his family's socioeconomic status, his house, his school (teacher, peers, and curriculum), his neighborhood, his neighborhood peer group, the hue of his skin, television, and others" (Minuchin, 1970, p. 41). Thus Minuchin ties together various elements in the ecology of a child, from his individual personality to his community. In the example of the family-school interview we have described, the therapists took into consideration these various systems and conceptualized their interaction from an ecological viewpoint. We shall discuss some of the systems in Jerry's ecological context and their structural organization.

The Individual

The boy in our example has internalized ten years of life experiences. Freud describes the inner world of psychological structures in terms of the ego, id, and superego. Fairbairn would talk about internalized objects. Irrespective of our choice of terms, we know that Jerry has a grouping of psychological structures making up a matrix of forces that are at the same time in harmony and at opposites within him. These psychic forces are a vital context in relation to which Jerry will think and act.

In spite of Jerry's bravado, we could see when talking with him that he was shy and awkward in expressing himself. His parents confirmed he was like that most of the time. His teachers had seen it, too, but his home-room teacher had interpreted his behavior as surliness. It seems Jerry always had to fight at home to avoid being overshadowed by his older brothers. At school he apparently fought for a similar reason. When I talked with Jerry in the interview, it was evident that, while he was distrustful, he wanted very much to be liked. His parents and his two minor teachers confirmed that. Evidently, Jerry was a boy who did not believe he was likable and felt he had to fight for recognition. This distrustful, shy, tough, but responsive personality was part of Jerry's personal context. It was useful to see Jerry's vulnerability, and this view of him helped draw a warm and protective reaction from the rest of us during the school interview.

Schools are reluctant to include children in family-school interviews. They want to protect them. But to leave the child out is to assume that we can understand his problems with the school and find solutions for those problems without the child's active involvement.

Jerry needed special attention from the therapist in the very beginning of the family-school interview because he stood accused. He needed to feel and be felt by the rest of us as an individual whose thoughts and feelings were of value and who could influence the process and outcome of the interview.

The Family

Jerry's family is a second context for his being and becoming. The family is not only a collection of complex personalities, but in its own right is a systematic organization with its own rules and dynamics. The family members define who is and who is not a member of the family.

Outsiders reciprocate with their fences. There are boundaries within the family itself, delineating groupings related to the functions of the members within the family organization. Family members may join one another or oppose one another according to the issue or task the family faces at any particular moment. Conclusions are somehow reached about who among them exercises the most power in determining how they carry out family functions. By arriving at these rules about who is included or excluded from an activity, who will join or oppose whom in a task, and who will decide how it is done, the family organizes the structural relationships of its members.

As related earlier in the family-school interview, we talked first with Jerry individually and then addressed ourselves to the family unit. We learned that Jerry's mother could not control him. In fact, we found that she could not effectively handle any of the boys, although she had assumed almost all responsibility for disciplining them. The father did not see child rearing as his job and was being protected by the mother because of his heart condition. As a result, he was not involved with Jerry to the degree Jerry needed him, nor was he providing his wife with the support she needed to discipline the children. We also learned that, within the sibling subsystem, Jerry's being the youngest of four aggressive boys put him very much at a disadvantage, particularly since his mother was powerless to protect him from the older boys and his father was not aware that he needed a patron. However, in spite of all this, the parents got along well in the marital subsystem.

The School Context

Jerry's school is a third social system of which Jerry is a part. That context is made up of the teachers, counselors, and principal, as well as of the students who attend the school. The staff and students are organized in formal and informal structures dictated by a variety of functions that the school must serve for the different subgroups making up that system.

After focusing on the family in the interview, Lynn and I turned our attention to the school as a unit, while simultaneously handling the communication between the family members and the staff. Each of the teachers is in charge of a classroom, a subsystem of the school. The teachers who had Jerry in the smaller classrooms had no trouble with him. The teacher who had him in the larger class could not control him. Jerry could not cope with the competition from his peers in the larger class, especially since he lacked the backing of a strong teacher. The other two teachers could give Jerry the attention he needed. The importance in this interview of having teachers who saw Jerry in different contexts within the school is apparent.

Organizations have sources of power; just as the father is the authority in Jerry's family, so is the principal in the school. As such, the principal needed to participate in the interview. If the school structure is to be changed to resolve a problem, the principal's permission is required. In Jerry's situation, the principal was aware of Jerry's misbehavior with his home-room teacher. Initially, however, the principal did not recognize why Jerry did better with his other teachers and, consequently, saw the family as nonsupporters of the school's efforts with Jerry. Without the principal's understanding and backing of our plans, the changes we suggested in Jerry's school program could not have taken place.

A school counselor is the conduit for communication between family and school. However, in this situation the counselor had adopted a protective and proprietary attitude toward Jerry, screening him from both the teacher and his parents. Her posture stifled communication between the family and the school. With the task we devised in the interview, we attempted to maintain the counselor's centrality in helping Jerry but at the same time to free her to act effectively as a link between parents and school.

The Social Context

Jerry has his personality, his family, and his school, but he also lives in a sociocultural-political context of which everyone else in the interview is a part. This context was relevant to Jerry's problem and to what took place in the interview at the school. Certainly the fact that Jerry is part of a first-generation Italian family who live in an old, closely knit Italian neighborhood had something to do with the sexual role patterns his parents evidenced in their relationship. Sociocultural considerations were also pertinent in the interview when the parents and the two therapists were faced with the fact that Jerry's insults to his teacher, who is black, were racial slurs. That the principal is white, as is the counselor, and that the two other teachers are black added to the dynamics of the interview. One therapist is white and the other Puerto Rican. We can only speculate about how differently the problem and its handling might have been if the racial and ethnic identities were scrambled in different combinations.

Another societal factor we faced was that all school staff relating to Jerry were women. Coupling this with the father's uninvolvement at home left Jerry without adult male support.

However, while all these sociocultural and political factors were relevant to the dynamics of Jerry's situation, they did not play a direct part in his difficulties through any formal community structures. The therapists needed to take these factors into consideration in the interview with the family and the school, but in this instance there was no occasion to include community organizations to represent any of the sociopolitical values and interests that were affecting all of the participants in the interview.

The Goals of the Interview

Jerry's ecological context is his personality, his family, the school, and the community with its sociopolitical character. To briefly summarize his predicament: Jerry is an insecure youngster with a tough exterior. He was in a powerless, somewhat isolated position at home, where his father, whom he respected, was not involved in his care, and his mother, who had little control over him, was responsible for him. His brothers, who are older, out-fought him in the competition for each to have things his own way at home. In the larger class at school, Jerry fought his classmates for similar reasons, which only put him in trouble with his teacher, and, like his mother, this teacher did not have the strength to handle the challenge Jerry presented. The principal sided with the teacher. Jerry's good work with his other teachers was less conspicuous and was not enough to offset the troublemaking reputation he had already earned. In her effort to help Jerry, the counselor overprotected him and prevented the school and his family from working together on Jerry's problems.

The target for the therapists included all of these systems. It was therapeutically economical to have the significant representatives of each of the systems meet face to face. With everyone active in the interview, the therapists had the opportunity to learn how they interacted, and the family and the school staff could see for themselves how their relations with one another affected Jerry. Because the Clinic convened the interview, the therapists had the leverage to assume leadership of the session, a strategically necessary but difficult endeavor when one considers that the family and school staff were confronting each other on the school's turf. That the meeting was conducted under the aegis of the Clinic helped neutralize the area of discussion and made possible the most direct and complete communications these people had experienced to date. The therapists were able actively to affect the flow of communications and the patterns of the transactions in this very real encounter of the people involved in Jerry's problems.

As the interview progressed, the therapists began forming their hypotheses about the nature of the problems and how the structures of the family and school systems were creating the difficulties. They tested their hypotheses by addressing each system as a separate system: first Jerry, then family, then school; and then by checking the communication and relationships among the different systems: Jerry and family, Jerry and school, family and school. With their questions, the therapists looked at: (a) the boundaries of the various groups involved to see who was included and who was excluded from the functions of each group that was relevant to the problems in question; (b) the alignments of people in their cooperative or oppositional efforts vis-à-vis other group members in relation to each system's tasks that affected the boy and his performance in school; and, (c) the distribution of power or force among these people to see who among them most influenced the outcome of the activities of the system to which they belonged, looking not only for sources of problems, but also for the keys to successful change.

The therapists tested the systems by the way they engaged with the members in searching for solutions. For example, the therapists turned to Jerry at the beginning of the interview in reaction to the pressure with which the principal started to tell about the boy's offensive language. Had the principal been allowed to control the transactions and to fix our focus on Jerry's bad behavior, she would have reinforced his delinquent image in the eyes of everyone in the session. The therapists' first hypothesis was based on the principal's first communication. The forcefulness with which the accusation was thrown at the boy alerted the therapists that there could be a pattern of relationship between certain school officials and the boy that made him a ready subject of blame. And if so, was this pattern also duplicated at home?

When the therapists cut off the principal and moved to connect with Jerry in a reassuring way, they were inquiring whether and how the boy himself could grab the opportunity to be treated as good and likable and whether his family and teachers would allow or encourage him to do so. At the same time, their treating him warmly and attentively could be change-producing by possibly triggering a chain of transactions from the others that would coincide with the positive attitude the therapists assumed toward Jerry. This action on the part of the therapists served to search into Jerry's problems with his family and school, while simultaneously attempting to discourage their use of him as a scapegoat for blame and hoping to fortify his own self-image.

The thin hypothesis about his being a ready victim formed a starting point for the development of other hypotheses as the interview progressed. These hypotheses served as the bases for a series of treatment goals: reinvolving the father with Jerry; helping the father to support his wife with the other boys; removing Jerry as the common target of his brothers' aggressiveness; finding a more experienced and forceful homeroom teacher for Jerry with whom he would not have a history of conflict; engaging the counselor as a communication link between home and school; and, eventually, changing Jerry's negative image of himself.

As described in the beginning of this narrative, the therapists set their preliminary goals for treatment during the first interview. In the same interview they began to facilitate interaction within and between the systems that would move everyone toward these goals. The tasks selected at the end of the interview embodied the structural changes suggested by the therapists' initial hypotheses and tentative goals. The work with Jerry, his family, and school lasted several months, and all major objectives were achieved.

Summary

A child with a problem cannot be seen as the sole repository of his problems, nor necessarily should his family. A mental health professional must look at the context of the child with all its ecosystems. A therapist can find the proximate basis for the child's problems, and resources for handling the problems, in the structural organization within and between these systems. The theory and methodology of the ecostructural approach is based on an understanding of the current dynamics of the structure in systems and the ways to bring about reorganization of these structures. An economical and effective instrument for solving some school-related problems for children is the family-school interview herein described.

References

Minuchin, S. (1970), The use of an ecological framework in the treatment of a child. In: *The International Yearbook of Child Psychiatry: The Child in His Family*, ed. E. J. Anthony & C. Koupernik. New York: John Wiley, pp. 41-57.

Piaget, J. (1970), *Structuralism*, ed. & trans. C. Maschler. New York: Basic Books.

Children may be so grossly deprived in their own home, and the home not be modifiable in a reasonable period of time, that a substitute environment becomes necessary for them. This chapter illustrates the tremendous therapeutic potential of one vector-therapy procedure—the foster home.

The Further Development of Twins after Severe and Prolonged Deprivation: A Second Report

JARMILA KOLUCHOVÁ

This is a follow-up to a previous report of severe and prolonged deprivation of twin boys born in 1960 (Koluchová, 1972). The twins, whose mother died shortly after they were born, spent their first eleven months in a children's home. Their father remarried, and they were brought to live with him, his new wife and her two children, and their own two older sisters. Their stepmother abused them, isolating them from the rest of the family and from the outside world. They lived in a small unheated closet, were given no toys, apart from a few building bricks, were fed less than adequately, and were locked up in the cellar for long periods of time. This condition of deprivation lasted from the time they were eighteen months of age until they were in their seventh year. When they were discovered, they could barely walk; they suffered from rickets, were frightened by objects that are normally familiar, and failed to un-

---

Jarmila Koluchová is a member of the Department of Psychology, Palacky University, Olomouc, Czechoslovakia.

The author would like to express her gratitude to Professor A. D. B. Clarke for his interest in her work.

Reprinted from the *Journal of Child Psychology and Psychiatry*, vol. 17, pp. 181-188, 1976.

derstand the meaning or function of pictures. Their IQ's were in the forties. Although their development subsequent to the traumatic period had been surprisingly good, even at the time of the first report, and it was possible to exclude gross damage of their intellect and personality, a number of problems remained which could only be resolved in a long-term study. Clarke (1972) also emphasized the importance of observing the case over a long period.

The twins spent their seventh year in hospital and in a toddler's home; they also went to school for the first time—first to a kindergarten, then to a school for the mentally retarded. Their progress was such, however, that by 1970, when they were nine, they were moved to a normal school. By this time, they had been placed in a foster home consisting of two unmarried middle-aged sisters, one of whom had already adopted a baby girl, slightly younger than the twins.

Having observed the twins ever since their discovery, I wish to record their further development, to mention similar cases, and to arrive at some general conclusions concerning the diagnosis and remediation of severe deprivation.

In the school year 1971-1972, the twins, then between eleven and twelve years old, attended the third grade. Their speech was entirely adequate for their age, both in form and content, despite the pessimistic predictions of speech pathologists and pediatricians. According to the available records of the infants' home, the twins had then been developing adequately for their age. We can assume that, at that time, which is often regarded as a preparatory period for speech and during which a passive knowledge of language is acquired, the children had actively mastered several words and had comprehended the communicative function of speech. They probably retained those abilities during the whole period of deprivation, mostly in a latent form only, because the little speech they heard between eighteen months and seven years did not have a communicative character for them. The basic prerequisite for the development of speech had also been missing, i.e., the individual contact with an adult and the positive stimulation resulting from that contact. But, although the period until their third year, which is often considered the outer limit for generating the ability to speak, had been missed, the twins' speech started to develop, in spite of the fact that they had scarcely spoken at all until the age of seven. The development was most rapid after their ninth year when they came to their foster family, which provided them with all the prerequisites for the development of both speech and the total personality. At school, the boys were agile, gay, and popular; there were no signs of eccentricity or troubles in the social sphere. Until the fourth grade, they did well—they had a grade of two in the Czech language (mother tongue). They were the best pupils of the class in arithmetic (grade 1), which we assume was in compensation for the retardation in intellectual functioning, and by their being two to three years older than their fellow pupils.

They gradually began to feel older in comparison with their schoolmates and to be aware of their late start at school, both these due to the acceleration of their growth and a delayed commencement of prepuberty. Both the teachers and the foster mother supported their natural ambition to master, during the fourth grade, the subject matter of the fifth. They succeeded and were moved up directly from the fourth to the sixth grade. Thus, they found themselves among children closer to their own age, and their self-confidence was reinforced. Their performance fell to the average, but the situation has been gradually improving since then. Both of them like attending school. They love reading; they ride bicycles, can swim and ski, play the piano well, and have both creative and technical talent. Musical ability started to develop at about the age of ten and is now at a good level. In the present school year (1974/1975) the boys attend the seventh grade; their schoolmates are, on the average, one and a half years younger. Because their adolescence began about a year later than is expected, the whole status of their development and interests now corresponds approximately to the standard of their present schoolmates. After finishing basic education (nine grades) they would like to study at a secondary vocational school, for which they show sufficient aptitude.

The development of the twins' intellectual level has been observed continually by means of several methods; to compare previous scores with more recent findings, the author presents here their IQ obtained by means of the WISC: in Table 1.

After the spurt at age seven, the next most rapid development occurred between the ninth and tenth years—the first year of their stay in the foster family and the first year of their school attendance. Judging by the past trend, it is possible that their intelligence scores may continue to show a slight increase. In the nonverbal scale of the WISC and in Raven's Matrices test, the achieved scores are a little higher than in the verbal, which may be explained by the fact that the verbal score is to a certain extent dependent on education, which is still slightly retarded

TABLE 1
WECHSLER INTELLIGENCE TEST SCORES (WISC)

Age	*Twin P.* *IQ*	*Twin J.* *IQ*
8	80	72
9	82	73
10	91	89
11	95	93
12	95	104
13	98	100
14	100	101

(one year) according to their age. The initial differences in their development seem to have leveled out; however, some features of their characters have continued to differ. J. is a little slower than his brother, but he is generally of calmer disposition. P. perceives more quickly, he reacts more promptly, but his attention is rather labile, he is somewhat preoccupied and shows symptoms of autonomic lability.

In the development and forming of the boys' personalities, no psychopathological symptoms or eccentricities appear at present. It is possible to say that there are no consequences of the deprivation remaining which would cause retardation or damage to their development. This does not mean, however, that five years of hardship and ill-treatment have left no traces. The dread of darkness, which persisted for a long time, has already faded, but under oppressive or unusual conditions the boys sometimes show fear and their reaction is neurotic. For example, once they happened to come to a cellar similar to the one in which they had often been imprisoned, which frightened and upset them, and again evoked recollections of past suffering. In the cheerful environment of their new family, and with the help of their foster mother, who is always ready to understand, the boys calm down quite easily.

The twins hate recalling the conditions of their deprivation and are unlikely to speak about it even with each other. However, by occasional remarks and the reactions mentioned above, it is evident that some recollections have remained and will probably be retained forever. The boys' foster mother says that they will tell her something about their cheerless childhood now and then, but always each of them separately in an intimate talk. A comparison between their previous and present recollections makes it clear that there is no tendency to distort or exaggerate their experiences. The boys' recollections of the past are no longer associated with fear of possible recurrence of such living conditions and of losing their new family.

The awareness of the relationship with the family is profound and makes the boys feel safe and assured. Natural emotional bonds with all members of the family have developed; apparently, the relationship with their foster mother, who is in a dominant position in the family, is emotionally deepest. Her sister is an aunt for them. As mentioned in the 1972 paper, the latter had adopted a girl—now sixteen years old, and, in addition, another ten-year-old girl has been staying with the family during the last four years, whose brief history will follow. Thus, there are two foster mothers and their four children, who have very nice sibling relations with each other, although they of course know they are not consanguineous relatives. There is a happy atmosphere in the whole family, full of mutual understanding. Undoubtedly, it is possible to object the fact that the family has no father, whom the boys would need at present in their puberty. The foster mother is aware of this and is trying to compensate for the lack of a man by frequent meetings with her brother and other relatives and friends, who have close relations with the boys.

The fact that has intensified their awareness of firm relationships in this family and has helped to establish the feeling of safety and assurance was the agreed change of surname to that of their foster mother. Even before the change was completed, the boys had been using this surname; they have never uttered their original surname, for it evidently raises negative emotions in them.

Because the most serious deprivation the twins suffered from eighteen months until age seven was almost total social isolation and abuse, especially from their stepmother, the question arises—how has it been reflected in their social relations and behavior?

In the 1972 report, relations of the twins with each other, with other children, and also with adults were described. The situation has been developing as follows: Immediately after they had been removed from the family and placed in the children's home, a strong emotional bond with each other was evident. Apparently, it had developed because it had been the only positive emotion that could have been built up, and, moreover, it had helped them to bear their difficult living conditions. The outer demonstration of their relations, however, corresponded with a much lower age: they used to make themselves understood like toddlers, using mostly mimicry and gestures. Their original shyness with people and reactions of terror disappeared rather quickly, and they reacted positively both to adults and children in a way that is more characteristic of younger children. Mainly, they showed a lesser differentiation of emotional relations and a prevailing interest in adults.

The children's gradual socialization was facilitated by the fact that they had lived for a longer period of time among children approximately three years younger than themselves, which corresponded with their developmental deficit. Starting to attend a school for mentally retarded children at the age of nine, they had access, for the first time, to a larger well-organized group of children, in which they joined successfully. Undoubtedly, the individual attention of their teacher, who had been informed of their history, helped considerably. There were no striking features in their social contacts, they did not show any symptoms of timidity, shyness, or any other abnormality, and they never behaved aggressively either at the school for mentally retarded children or at the normal school later on. The boys have always had close relations with each other—an emotional bond much firmer than is usual with brothers of their age. But, of course, common teasing or petty conflicts are present, as is usual with children in normal families.

Making the boys acquainted with their suffering during the early and preschool age appears to be a relatively difficult educational and psychotherapeutic problem. They can remember that period of time only in fragments and seem unable to comprehend the essentials of the whole event, its circumstances and causes. We consider it advisable to acquaint them with the principal facts concerning their parentage, family, the trial, and further events before their coming to this family, because we think it will help preserve the continuity of their personalities and also as a precaution against possible trauma caused by their hearing about their past later in life. It is necessary to respect their long-standing aversion to reverting to the past, but at the same time their pubescent inquisitiveness and their efforts to know and to evaluate themselves should be recognized. The foster mother is aware of the gravity of this task, and she appears to manage it well.

Regarding the children's general development as highly successful—in contradiction to the original prediction of doctors—it is also necessary to evaluate the therapeutic factors that have contributed to this. As already stated (1972), the children had been treated at an orthopedic and pediatric clinic after their withdrawal from the family and after their rickets had been overcome. At the same time they had been examined in psychiatric and ophthalmological clinics and in a phoniatric ward. Their somatic condition having improved, they were placed in a children's home, where exceptional individual care was bestowed upon them, and their future was discussed and planned carefully. Most important was the favorable prediction consequent to psychological examinations. The present foster family was selected from several interested families. Having been placed in this family, the children were given speech training and they also practiced their pronunciation intensively at home. Consequently, they managed to inhibit their nasal speech and in general to modify their poor articulation. The children have also been carefully looked after by a district pediatrician, who knows all the facts of the case. Another important curative factor is the attitude of their teachers, which is individual and full of sympathy, although they expect the boys to meet reasonable scholastic demands without any preference or special treatment.

Continuing care, carried out during the entire period by the same psychologist (the author), has proved to be fortunate. She acts as an adviser and transmits psychological reports to the school and to other institutions. In the author's opinion, the main advantage of such procedure lies in her detailed knowledge of the whole history, including court reports. Moreover, the twins trust her, which has enabled her to observe the dynamics of their development since their seventh year.

Given all these curative factors, it is necessary to emphasize that the most effective and integrative curative factor is their foster mother and the environment of their family. Although the lady is employed, she devotes all her leisure time to the children with much self-sacrifice; her solicitude for them constitutes the content and purpose of her life; nor does she spoil the children or adopt uncritical attitudes.

The specialists, who had not believed in any possibility of remedying the severe deprivation damage in the twins, later referred to their rapid development as an exception to the rule that states that severe deprivational damage at an early age is irremediable. According to the author's experience, however, there are a number of similar cases, but they are not usually correctly diagnosed or professionally observed and described.

As an example of the importance of a correct diagnosis and the difficulty of remedying severe deprivation, we want to outline a brief history of a girl, L.H., born in 1965, now living in the same family as the twins. This girl was withdrawn legally from her own family at the age of four as a consequence of almost total social isolation and cruel treatment from her psychopathic mother. The child had been hated by her mother; tormented by hunger, she had been constantly kept alone in an unfurnished room, had slept on a straw mattress, and had not acquired the basic habits of body hygiene. All of her mother's seven older children had earlier been withdrawn from her legally. This girl was placed in a children's home, where she behaved anxiously, agitatedly, even aggressively; her language ability was almost totally undeveloped, and she was still incontinent. The schoolmasters in the home considered her ineducable, and it was decided that she should be placed in a mental home. For diagnostic and therapeutic reasons, the child was admitted to a psychiatric hospital and dismissed after a month, with the daignosis of severe mental handicap.

The family with which the twins live happened to hear about this girl. Encouraged by the good development of the twin boys, they decided to adopt the girl in spite of the pessimistic prediction for her development, a prediction based on the assumption that she was intellectually defective. Even though the child was difficult to care for in the family during the first weeks, because of her agitation and anxiety, both women soon understood that she had been damaged by cruelty and isolation and that she had a good intellectual capacity. During our first examination of the child soon after her arrival in the family we were able to eliminate mental subnormality, even though her retardation was considerable and deprivation symptoms conspicuous. The child started learning to speak rather quickly; she was bright, and she began to attend a kindergarten.

On the whole, however, this child has always been an incomparably greater educational problem than the twins. She attends a school for normal children, she can read and write well, and she has an outstanding talent for music, but her attention is very labile, she is not able to take adequate pains while learning, and she shows shortcomings in the functions of memory, which might be due to her having suffered meningitis, caused probably by frequent attacks of otitis media, from which she still suffers. She has continued to have problems in the social sphere, though, thanks to kind-hearted and consistent upbringing, there has been some improvement and rectification even here, which could not have been achieved in a children's home. The girl joins in with other children in her class with great difficulty; sometimes she is aggressive and intolerant with her contemporaries, though she is gentle and kind with younger children.

It is interesting to compare the girl with the twins. The deprivational history of the three children is rather similar; they live in the same family now and are given the same attention. Their different development in the social sphere can be explained by distinct congenital dispositions, but mainly by the fact that the twins, by being twins, had reduced their isolation. The girl's mother is a severely psychopathic person with disorders in character and the social sphere. There are no valid data about her father. On the other hand, the twins' actual mother was quite normal in intelligence and personality structure. The father of the twins was characterized in the 1972 report as passive and of below-average intelligence. According to preserved photographs and to reliable reports, the twins seem to possess their mother's features, both in the somatic and psychological sphere. But their better development in the social sphere should be explained, in the first place, by the fact that they could build up emotional relations with each other, they could stimulate each other to some extent, and thus they did not experience the tormenting feeling of loneliness as intensely and destructively as would a child totally isolated.

We have recorded other cases similar to the twins and the above-mentioned girl, but their detailed history has not yet been obtained and they have been observed only for a shorter period. The author could often confirm, in her work as a clinical psychologist, that children who suffered severe and prolonged deprivation, either coming from inadequate families, often chastised and socially isolated, or living for a long time in a children's-home environment, are misdiagnosed as mentally subnormal by pediatricians, child psychiatrists, and psychologists. The clinical pictures of severe deprivation and mental subnormality are similar, which can lead to a confusion of the two diagnoses when the subjects are only routinely examined, when the test methods are mechanically used or are misinterpreted, and when the history is not known in detail. Both the cases are typical of general retardation of development and speech, social immaturity, and a lowered ability to learn. Especially, the development of children up to the third year may be so profoundly affected as a consequence of all the external and internal conditions of a children's-home environment, that it is rather difficult to differentiate such cases from mental subnormality.

As these children are usually socially forlorn, i.e., their parents cannot or do not want to look after them, it is necessary to solve the problems of their future, and therefore a correct diagnosis is of immense value. The author thinks that in difficult differential diagnosis, psychological findings should always be respected. Only psychological examination can reveal subtle differences between severely deprived and mentally subnormal children. Cursory, nonresidential examination will not do; it is absolutely necessary to carry out a detailed repeated examination by means of both psychometric and nontest methods. Such an examination enables a skilled psychologist to differentiate deprivation from subnormality and to determine the prognosis for its development. Here, the psychological diagnosis is not only a theoretical problem but, above all, a basis for educational, juridical, and therapeutic actions.

In cases of severe deprivation originating at an early age, the therapeutic prognosis has usually been considered poor. But the above-mentioned cases of deprived children, together with others that are still being observed, prove that even gross damage, previously considered to be irreversible, can be remedied. Our experience with the development of speech, too, contradicts the traditional view concerning the critical period for the development of speech. In the twins, as well as in other cases, successful development of speech was observed three to six years after their moving to a stimulating environment, sometimes even later. Thus, the prediction for the retarded development of speech in deprived children seems to be more optimistic if the defect is not organically or genetically conditioned, and when the child is given sufficient professional care and, above all, placed in a favorable family environment.

The view that the effects of severe deprivation were irreparable arose from the fact that for severely deprived children there is difficulty in finding suitable foster care. According to our experience, the environment of a family, stimulating and full of understanding, providing a feeling of safety and firm relationships, is the only effective therapy, although very exacting and time consuming. This conclusion, together with the fact that the family is considered to be the most important educational factor, led to several arrangements for the care of the children living outside their own families in our country, which are designed to prevent deprivation or remedy existing deprivation. There has been a general effort to assimilate a children's-home environment to a family environment, e.g., to integrate a number of children of different ages into so-called "family groups" with unchanging tutors.

Besides the standard children's homes, there have arisen new forms of substitute family care—so-called "children's villages" in which foster mothers with eight to ten children live in separate houses; then, there are so-called "big families," where a married couple looks after a similar number of children. These "big families" are not concentrated in "villages"; they live in normal houses, both in towns and in the country.

"The father" is employed somewhere, like the father of a normal family, and "the mother" looks after the children and is paid by the state on the same basis as "mothers" in "children's villages." There are also cases of paid foster parentage in natural families. Both such families and the people interested in the work either in "children's villages" or in "big families" are carefully selected, including a psychological examination; all the forms of substitute family care are paid for and methodically guided by the state authorities and advisory boards, in which psychologists also work. A special advisory service has also been established with psychologists and pediatricians, and if necessary, other experts can be summoned—for example, child psychiatrists.

Several years' experience with these forms of care indicate the great therapeutic prospects offered by a stimulating family environment. To observe and evaluate them is a task for long-term studies, which might be a valuable contribution to the diagnosis and remediation of deprivation.

Summary

A previous report on the development of twins after severe and prolonged deprivation is followed up, and progress over three further years is described. Intelligence is now average. No psychopathological features or eccentricities in either behavior or social relations can be identified. The boys are sociable, happy and have firm emotional bonds with their foster family; they attend a school for normal children, with good results. A case of a ten-year-old girl with a similar background now living in the same foster family is also described.

The psychological diagnosis of severe deprivation and its remediation are also discussed.

References

Clarke, A. D. B. (1972), Commentary on Koluchová's "Severe deprivation in twins: A case study." *J. Child Psychol. Psychiat.*, 13:103-106.

Koluchová, J. (1972), Severe deprivation in twins: A case study. *J. Child Psychol. Psychiat.*, 13:107-114.

While some would argue that the best substitute new pattern of influences in the life of the child is the foster home, there are situations, as described here, where the group foster home becomes a successful necessity.

Alternative Group Foster Homes: A New Place for Young People to Live

JAMES S. GORDON

A History of Child Placement

Children who leave home or are abandoned by or separated from their parents are an evocative group, the frequent source in myth and legend of heroes, heroines, and monsters, the locus in many societies of strong and often inexplicable fears and concerns, fantasies and hopes. The history of the way they have been treated in the United States, a country which according to Whittaker (1972, p. 56), quoting from the *Proceedings of the Conference on the Care of Dependent Children* (1909), has consistently maintained that the "home is the highest and finest product of civilization," presents a mirror to the development of our society.

The communities of colonial New England were tight theocratic worlds in which the patriarchal family was the primary building block and model of authority (Bremner et al., 1971, pp. 1-63). All people who lived outside families were suspect as potential sources of destruction and discontent; relying on biblical precedent ("God settleth the solitary

---

James S. Gordon, M.D., is Research Psychiatrist and Consultant at the Center for Studies of Child and Family Mental Health, National Institute of Mental Health. He was Director of the Special Study on Alternative Services for the President's Commission on Mental Health.

Reprinted from *Psychiatry*, vol. 39, no. 4, pp. 339—354, November, 1976.

The names of the group foster homes and the residents and counselors who lived and worked in them have been disguised.

in families"—Psalms 68:6), the authorities placed single older people, and orphans and bastards as well, in family settings. The arrangement was economical as well as moral: The community was relieved of the burden of supporting these people, and their labor was available to the families that took them in. When morality and economics clashed—as in the case of a family too poor to support its own children—economics won: The children were "bound out" as apprentices to other families (Bremner et al., 1971, pp. 64-71, 103-184).

An accelerated rate of immigration, the importation of large numbers of young servants, industrialization, and urbanization combined in the late eighteenth and early nineteenth centuries to increase the numbers of American children who could not or did not live with their parents and to decrease the other familial living situations available to them. With cheap servant labor available, children were no longer so useful in homes; in many factories their lack of strength and endurance made them an economic liability. In some communities, children were classified with other paupers and indigents and auctioned off at vendue to whomever could keep them with the least expense. In cities, increasing numbers of them were confined with the poor, the mad, and the chronically ill in almshouses. (The information provided in this historical section stems from Bremner et al., 1971.)

In the first half of the nineteenth century large numbers of special institutions for children were established. These orphanages were usually privately founded and publicly supported. They reflected a rapidly industrializing society's tendency to institutionalize its functions, as well as its growing concern for and recognition of the particular and particularly vulnerable situation of children. The Orphans' Society of Philadelphia, for example, was founded in 1814 "to rescue from ignorance, idleness and in vice, unprotected and helpless children, and to provide for them that support and instruction which may eventually render them valuable members of the community" (Bremner et al., 1971, p. 653).

At the same time "schools of reform" and "houses of refuge" were created for "juvenile offenders" who were "sentenced to imprisonment" or judged "vagrant." In 1837, through the doctrine of "parens patriae" this practice of institutional placement for difficult children was given full legal standing by the Supreme Court of Pennsylvania. The court now could act as "common guardian of the community."

Even as it was gaining ascendancy in the second half of the nineteenth century, there was opposition to the institutional approach. Charles Loring Brace, Secretary of the New York Children's Aid Society, saw institutionalization as debilitating, not reforming: "The longer he is in the asylum, the less likely he is to do well in outside life." Brace believed that "the best of all asylums" was "the farmer's house." Accordingly, he—and those from other states who believed likewise—arranged for thousands of young city dwellers to be transported west. In rural settings their labor would be profitable to farmers, who would in turn instruct them in the virtues of honesty, family life, and hard work.

Progressive reforms of the late nineteenth and early twentieth centuries were designed, in Theodore Roosevelt's words, to promote the "conservation" of children. Through the creation of juvenile courts, child-welfare professionals, and child-labor laws, children were singled out as a group with special needs and interests. Though these reforms sometimes gave rise to more humane living situations, they tended to become regressive as time went on. In appropriating the right to act "in the best interests of the child," the newly created juvenile court often became dictatorial. Probation officers became agents of the juvenile system, which paid them—supervisors of, rather than advocates for the children whom they placed. Child-labor laws were inoperative in rural areas and, for a long time, inefficient in industries where economics dictated the use of children as workers.

During this period, child welfare agencies and juvenile courts collaborated to create group foster homes (Gula, 1964; Scher, 1958; Rabinow, 1964; Herstein, 1964; Fisher, 1952; Wolins and Piliavin, 1964; Whittaker, 1972; Jewett, 1973)—living situations in which several to a dozen young people were placed with foster parents or child-care workers. These group homes represented community-based extensions of institutional care, and an economically advantageous variation on individual foster care. In general they were thought to be particularly suitable for adolescents, for whom they provided a compromise between the intimacy and dependence of family life and the independence of adulthood.

In the first decades of the twentieth century, the developing fields of psychiatry, psychology, and psychoanalysis and their elaboration in the child guidance movement were already influencing procedures and shaping attitudes in every aspect of child placement. According to the early workers in these fields, children were to be understood in the light of their feelings and motives, not simply as the sum of their behaviors—as young people with special needs and as rapidly developing adolescents, not simply as small or irresponsible adults. At its best this perspective helped child guidance workers to train foster parents and child-care workers who were able to "identify with the child despite his behavior," whose "change in attitude" permitted the child to live out the fullness of his own life with them (Bremner et al., 1971, p. 436).

Often, however, psychological understanding degenerated to psychiatric namecalling. Instead of being viewed as a slipped gear in the economic machinery, a public shame or nuisance, children came to be seen as damaged or sick individuals who required diagnosis, treatment, and cure. Though the vocabulary and technology changed, the stigmatization and isolation of earlier institutions remained. In many psychiatric institutions, tranquilizing drugs, electroshock treatment, and the seclusion room have simply replaced beating, repetitive and useless tasks, and solitary confinement. A manipulative group therapy could be used to bring about the same degree of conformity as moral suasion. Nor did high-powered psychological testing and heavily credentialed caseworkers make foster care more loving or intelligent (Whittaker, 1972, pp. 51-61; Mnookin, 1973). Many foster parents are still simply the lowest bidders at the social-welfare vendue.

In recent years a variety of new developments—socioeconomic and political as well as therapeutic and biological—have altered the accepted ideas about adolescents and their placement. Young people come to physiological maturity considerably earlier than they did half a century ago. The increase and spread of affluence and technology have made most of them unnecessary as workers but powerful as consumers. The mass media, particularly television, have provided them with vast amounts of information from which to form their opinions and on which to base their actions. Concurrently, their social and legal status has changed. The 1967 Supreme Court decision *in re Gault* held that children in juvenile court were constitutionally entitled to certain due-process guarantees previously granted only to adults in criminal court (Rodham, 1973). Juvenile correctional officials have begun to dismantle degrading systems of institutional care (Ohlin et al., 1974). The voting age has been lowered to eighteen. Recently, young people, following the example of blacks, women, and old people, have formed liberation groups to insure their civil rights and their right to self-determination.

In this climate of social and political change, increasing numbers of young people and their adult advocates have begun to demand that adolescents be allowed to live autonomously—at or away from home—in settings in which their rights and integrity are respected. And they are beginning to create settings—natural social experiments—where this takes place.

Alternative Services

During the last ten years the need and demands of some young people have begun to be met and articulated by new helpers and new institutions. These people and their projects owe their origins to a "youth culture" and a "counterculture" which are themselves both influences on and heirs to powerful political and social forces: the civil rights movement of the late 1950's and 60's, the antiwar movement, and the women's movement. These workers in "alternative services" affirm the experience of young people in their autonomous integrity, not as a promise of future achievement or reflection of parental or societal ideals.

Among the first of the services they created were runaway houses, refuges for some of the estimated 600,000 to one million young people who each year left their homes or the institutions to which they had been confined (see U.S. Senate, 1972). Runaway houses offered young people a protected alternative to a street life that made them vulnerable to exploitation as well as to arrest and involuntary return home. Since 1967 their numbers have grown from a handful in large cities to well over one hundred in communities of every size (see *National Directory of Runaway Centers*, 1974).

The people who founded the early runaway houses were more likely to be the natural helpers of the "hip" community—ministers, organizers, street people—than those certified by schools of social work, psychology, or criminology. As sympathizers with, if not participants in, both radical politics and the counterculture, they tended to see running away not as a symptom of individual psychopathology or as evidence of criminality, but as a sign of familial disorder and of a society in turmoil. They believed that in a supportive context, running away could become running toward, an act of hope rather than a gesture of petulance or despair.

Once in a runaway house, young people were automatically given the kind of respect that they rarely experienced in the adult world or from its institutions or professional helpers. The workers in the house believed that the young runaways were capable of making the decisions that affected their lives. They tried to listen to the young people, to sympathize without labeling or coercing or trying to "do things for [their] own good."

For those young people whose homes were confusing and disturbing but not intolerable, a few days at a runaway house and some individual and family counseling could provide the support necessary to weather a crisis or understand a particular dilemma; for those who were already all but independent, it was a reassuring way station. But significant numbers of young people left runaway houses after a few days or weeks to return home, only to become embroiled in the same futile destructiveness which had originally forced them to leave. Others, written off by their parents, left home to bum around or live on the street, until they were picked up by the police—to be committed, or recommitted, to mental or penal institutions.

The latter young people returned over and over to runaway houses, often leaving in their wake legal, social-service, and mental health agencies who had made multiple attempts at institutional and foster placement, at counseling and therapy. Between their periodic flights to runaway houses some wrote plaintive letters: "Can I stay at Runaway House for good?" "Isn't there any place I can go?"

Over the last several years, workers in some runaway houses have created group foster homes to answer these dilemmas and needs, to provide more or less permanent places for young people who could or would not stay elsewhere. But in making use of the structure and financing of the group foster homes, workers in alternative services have tried to transform the homes' spirit. They are trying to create real alternatives to institutions and to conventional "agency operated" group homes, as well as to the family situations to which the young people can't or won't return—that is, they are trying to create communal households which will respect the rights of young people to run their own lives, extended families in which power can be democratically distributed and decisions collectively made.

Two Alternative Group Foster Homes

I was a consultant for eighteen months at Markham House and for twenty months at Frye House: a participant observer in weekly "house meetings" of young people and counselors at which "anything" could be discussed; an advisor to the staff; and a confidant—with varying degrees of frequency and intimacy—to individual young people and staff members.

After a brief history of each of the houses and of my introduction to them, I shall discuss several developmental issues which seem to me to be both common and critical to their evolution, the different ways these issues were met in the two houses, and the implications and consequences of their responses for each of the houses. Though the presentation will be roughly chronological, it is important to keep in mind that all of these issues were of some importance throughout my consultation with both houses.

I stopped consulting with Markham eighteen months ago, and with Frye fourteen months ago. I am still in touch with several of the young people who lived in each of the houses and sometimes still visit Frye.

The houses are not precisely comparable, nor do I wish to present them as such. Although both Frye House and Markham House owe their origins to runaway houses, each of them has peculiar characteristics of location, community, ideology, and personality which shaped its development and helped to determine its usefulness to young people.

Frye House: Setting

Frye House opened two years after its parent runaway house several blocks away from it in the integrated hip neighborhood that borders the ghetto and buffers the wealthy white section of the city. The first location was temporary and barnlike, easily large enough for the two counselors and eight young people who, after several months, occupied it. The house was opened with a few dollars borrowed from the runaway house, a small foundation grant, and the promise of "payment for services" from social service departments which were planning to place young people there.

For many months the young paraprofessionals (a man, 23, and a woman, 24) who staffed Frye House groped for some coherent philosophy and structure. Though they had previously worked at the runaway house, they were often overwhelmed by the variety, complexity, and intensity of the problems of the young people who came to live with them. What kind of house and what kind of counseling could accommodate white runaways from middle-class suburban homes, black street kids, tough-talking "delinquents," indifferent "hippies," and spaced-out "flower children"?

The counselors were shaken and pressured by the violent clash of life styles, the noise, the angry discontent, and the disruptive behavior. Neighbors and friends who had volunteered at runaway house sustained them while they weathered some storms, but increasingly they felt compelled to get control over the house. They moved to another building, reduced the number of young people to six (three boys and three girls), and made only fitful attempts to hold onto the most disruptive and alien of their charges. Concurrently, the counselors' political perspective—their vision of the house as a democratic family, of the young people as independent and respected participants—began to erode. Under the influence of a mental health consultant, the young people metamorphosed to patients and children, the counselors to therapists and parents.

Even after this consultant left, the counselors maintained self-consciously therapeutic and conventionally parental roles. Young people who were applying for admission to the house were interviewed first by a new psychiatric consultant, then screened by the counselors. Though house rules were discussed and disputed by the young people, they were promulgated and enforced by the counselors. All of the young people were required "for their own good" to be in school or to work; all of them followed routines for cooking and cleaning established by the counselors; all had to obey rules and regulations considered appropriate to their age—curfews and, in the house, abstention from sex, liquor, and drugs.

When I arrived at Frye there were new counselors: Ann, who had lived in the house for five months, and Fred, who had been there for three. They had asked me to come over because of Tom, a seventeen-year-old boy who had lived in the house for almost a year. We sat in the living room on shabby overstuffed furniture. The house was cool and, except for us, empty and quiet in the late afternoon.

Ann told me that when she first arrived, Tom had been quiet, appealing, and tractable. But over the last few months he had begun to "change." Both she and Fred now thought that he was becoming increasingly "crazy" and maybe "dangerous." He accused them of not caring about him and of wanting to destroy him. In his room, he screamed at unseen tormentors. Questioned about his feelings, he became enraged and abusive.

Something frightening was going on with Tom, and neither Ann nor Fred could figure out how to deal with it. They wondered if I could find another place for him, or see him in therapy, or recommend something.

Ann and Fred went on to tell me about themselves and the house. Ann had earlier been an elementary school teacher, and for eight months had been a counselor at the runaway house. Fred had been an Air Force medic, and then a seminarian. Both of them had been active in the antiwar movement as campaigners for liberal candidates and participants in peace demonstrations. They had both come to Frye because they wanted to live and work with young people in a new way, free from the strictures of conventional child care and social service. They were concerned that, under pressure from the young people, they were falling into disciplinary and parental roles. Their temptation to control and "analyze" Tom's behavior was only the most recent and distressing example.

I told them that I wanted to see Tom not as someone psychiatrically ill but as a member of their home—to understand his behavior, not in the clinical isolation of an interview situation, but in the context of his relationships to those around him. They listened closely, nodding their heads: "Maybe we're too close to really understand what's going on." Their willingness to be self-critical, their openness to my perspective put me more at ease. When I said that the young people would have to agree to my coming to house meetings—that I did not want to be or to seem to be the counselors' agent—they readily agreed. With this consensus, I began my work at Frye.

Markham House: Setting

Markham was opened in 1971 as a runaway house. Located at first in half-a-dozen unused rooms of a local religious mission, it developed over five chaotic months into a group foster home on a quiet street of single family houses in a middle-class residential suburb. Markham's director, Allan, made the changes because he felt overwhelmed by the number of runaways and by the contrary pulls and cumulative pressures of probation officers, young people, and families. The kids—local runaways who found their way to the mission and disruptive teenagers deposited there by the police—had made noise all night, smoked dope, and left just before their probation officers arrived for appointments. Their parents were suspicious, the neighbors furious, and the probation officers dissatisfied.

Allan had recently left his job in the public school system in protest against the oppressiveness of the discipline and the monotony of the curriculum. He had set out to provide a human service for young people, a place where, as he put it, "their personhood would be respected." Working with him were several volunteer counselors, students and recent graduates from local colleges, who seemed both confident and sensitive. But after a while the situation had begun to feel wrong—temporary, unsatisfying, uncontrollable. Allan wanted to provide emergency services to the teenagers in the community, but even more he hoped to establish "a safe, stable, caring environment." He raised a few thousand dollars, found a house, and began to fight for a license to provide foster care.

Markham's first few months in its new location were almost as chaotic as those in the mission. Probation officers appeared at all hours with young runaways in tow, begging Allan to take in "just one more"; kids from nearby towns who "hadn't heard" that the runaway house had become a group foster home came by to "crash." Some neighbors offered food and emotional support; others telephoned the police, complaining of noise, drugs, and degeneracy. An air of crisis—to which the young residents responded alternately with solemnity and secret glee—pervaded the house.

Slowly Allan removed himself from the hour-to-hour operation of Markham. He hired three counselors, who did not live at Markham but slept there several nights a week (there was room only for an office, not a staff bedroom). One was a 22-year-old man who had started as a part-time volunteer and then dropped out of college to become the head counselor. The other two were women volunteers who were hired as full-time counselors. Six young people were accepted as residents. Allan, the three counselors, and several volunteers planned the house's "program," together with a psychiatric social worker who consulted with the staff, a psychologist who saw the young people individually, and a group worker who ran weekly "sensitivity groups" for all the residents.

When I arrived at dinner time, the living-dining room was a jumble of bodies, furniture, and food, of raised voices and rock music. The two-story frame house hardly seemed capable of containing so much activity. The young people ate and nodded hello. Four or five counselors and volunteers were busy tacking down carpets and putting the finishing touches on a coat of paint in the kitchen. Allan explained that neighbors and members of the county council were about to visit; that the house, which had recently been raided by the police "on some trumped-up charge," needed their support to stay open.

Allan wasn't sure exactly how he could use me, only that he wanted me to help. "There are other consultants," he said, "but we can use a psychiatrist—maybe for individual therapy or for court evaluations." Allan began to tell me about some of his "problems." He wanted, he said, to "respect the personhood" of each of the young people, but there was so much confusion, such a great need to "keep up appearances—at least until we're more secure in the neighborhood. I can't have the kids acting like they did at the mission—staying up all night, smoking marijuana.

Here they can't even make noise or swear so anyone can hear them. Some of our neighbors are looking for anything they can to close us. Later the young people can have more freedom; but right now we need some order."

I liked the house: there was something industrious and comforting about the chaos—a group of people working at something together. But I also felt a little uneasy. I guessed that the neighborhood's disapproval would weigh constantly on the house, and I feared that this social pressure might serve as justification—even when it was not compelling—for oppressive policies in the house. Perhaps it was Allan who made me feel that. He seemed at once unsure and self-righteous, too eager for professional help just because it was professional.

I suggested that I spend time around the house, talking with the young people and counselors. I also said that I would like to come to house meetings if they had any. Allan agreed and then asked in passing if I would talk with Bobby, one of the young people in the house. He seemed very "strange," quiet and frightened; he laughed aloud to himself; some of the counselors thought that he might be hearing voices.

Within three weeks I was going to the weekly house meetings that Allan and the counselors found necessary.

At Markham, as at Frye, I attended as a consultant and facilitator, an outside observer who could help unravel the tangled communications and clarify the obscurities of a meeting, someone committed to helping the participants put immediate issues and arguments in the larger context of a group of people—neglected and homeless young people and their counselors—struggling to live and work together in a decent way.

Deviance in Both Houses

Deviance is relative to particular social groups. Decisions about who or what is deviant, and exclusion of people whose behavior or attitudes are so labeled, help to provide groups with a means of defining and organizing themselves (Erikson, 1966, pp. 1-29). From the perspective of the larger society, all of the young people and many of the counselors in both group foster homes were deviant. Within each of the houses there were also people whose behavior and attitudes caused them to be regarded by their fellow residents as deviant. The differing ways of dealing with this perceived deviance were crucial in shaping the development of the two houses.

At Frye House, Tom's "craziness" was allowed and encouraged to emerge in weekly house meetings. (For a more detailed account of Tom's "craziness" and of deviance in Frye House, see Gordon [1973, 1974]). With my help the counselors and other young people came to see his behavior and understand his language as, among other things, indirect and disguised protests against house rules and communal attitudes that seemed contradictory, destructive, and insensitive. By refraining from labeling as delusory his beliefs that they did not care about him and were "destroying him," the counselors could begin to look at the ways in which they were being destructive, at the contradictions between their stated feelings of warmth and sympathy and the content of certain house rules which they enforced. If Tom did not want to go to school or work and they tried to force him to do so, then perhaps they were indeed caring less for him than for their rules. If they said he was free to choose what to do with himself, and simultaneously had a rule that only young people who worked or went to school could stay in the house, that denied his right to choose. If they then denied the contradiction between words and rules, then indeed they were helping—by double-binding him—to "drive him crazy."

The willingness of the counselors to view Tom's behavior as a critique of the social situation rather than simply as deviance from its norms relieved some of the pressure on him. It also provided a precedent for understanding and dealing with all of the young people. The purpose of the house was to include people who had been excluded and isolated, to respect the rights of each one who came there. To judge, regulate, and discipline young people according to the counselors' preconceptions or norms was to reproduce the kind of oppressive social situation that had excluded them in the first place.

In Markham House the tendency to isolate and label the deviant was not modified. Bobby's silent withdrawal was all but ignored in the clamor of group meetings. Both he and Joanne, a sixteen-year-old who had spent time in reform school and several other group homes, were insistently referred for treatment to the house psychologists. Joanne's anger at what she termed "two-faced lies and insults"—which seemed based on the apparent inequity with which privileges were doled out to the young people by one of the counselors—was simply dismissed. In house meetings the counselors said that there were reasons for this, but Joanne just didn't seem to understand. When she persisted, they told her that her constant anger was the reason she had fewer privileges—that, in effect, her protests against the rules justified their use against her.

My comments on this process of exclusion and mystification were not particularly helpful. Allan conceded, in private, that I might be right "in theory, but the time's not right." Admitting the justice of the young peoples' criticisms in a meeting would be opening the house to an "anarchy" it could not afford.

At Frye, the openness to deviance was instrumental in keeping the house an organically evolving entity, in allowing it to change to accommodate the variety of young people who stayed there. This flexibility, in turn, made it possible for a high percentage of the young people to stay for long periods of time, for almost all of them to leave when *they* were ready. In contrast, the counselors and residents at Markham regularly extruded young people—with appropriate psychiatric diagnoses, moral or criminal charges—who were considered "too disruptive."

As far as I was able to tell, there were no appreciable differences among the "kinds" of young people staying at the two houses; sometimes, in fact, the same young person was simultaneously being considered for admission to both houses. At Frye the age range was fourteen to eighteen; at Markham, fourteen to seventeen. The vast majority of them were white and lower-middle class. Virtually all of the young people had run away from their homes and had spent a period of time in detention centers. About a third of the residents in each house had been sent to reform schools, and another third had spent time in mental hospitals. Close to 90 per cent of the young people in both houses had previously been placed in other foster homes; more than half of them had been placed more than once. One person from Frye and one from Markham left the group foster home to return to his or her parents. In each house approximately 15 to 20 per cent of the young people were black.

With these similarities in mind the differences in length of stay are particularly striking: Over an eighteen-month period, nine people stayed at Frye for an average of ten and a half months each; during the same time eighteen lived at Markham for an average of five months each. Many of those who left Markham were asked to do so. Five were sent from Markham directly to institutions.

Power and Rules

At Frye House the distribution of power and the rules which reflected it gradually changed to conform to the spirit of respect and participatory democracy which had originally animated the house's formation.

In the weekly meetings at Frye the young people's challenges to house rules were accepted, not deflected. Social norms which had been adopted unquestioningly—all young people should go to school or work, should wake up and return home at certain hours, etc.—were critically considered and revised to fit the felt needs of the young people.

In the house meetings personal frankness slowly replaced defensiveness. Teenage residents who were not afraid that some privilege would be taken away grew comfortable in criticizing counselors freely and directly, and were able to reveal personal difficulties without fears of arbitrary reprisal. Similarly, the counselors, no longer burdened with moralistic postures, could drop their defensive condescension and be more straightforward about their own annoyances, anxieties, and concerns.

The increased respect of the counselors for the young people provided the basis for new processes of decision-making. Instead of being reserved to the counselors and their consultants, all decisions—regarding household budgets, hiring of new counselors, rules, admission of new people to the house, and overnight guests—began to be made in common. The way the house dealt with drug use is illustrative.

There had always been a counselor-imposed—and collective-wide—rule against drug use in the house: Anyone caught with drugs would be kicked out. In fact, one person had been caught and allowed to stay. Generally, the young people had lied about drugs, claiming that there were none in the house while hiding them from the counselors. Inevitably this drove a wedge between the young people and the counselors. The young people were resentful and guilty, and the counselors were suspicious and self-righteously angry at the betrayal which they knew the young people were perpetrating. In addition, none of the young people felt free to talk about drug-related problems: fears of addiction, the possibility of hepatitis, a bad trip that they had or were having.

Only when group discussions were finally held about drugs in the house, about the real dangers of police arrest and the possible closing down of the house, and only *after* the young people had power over and a stake in the house, did they honestly agree not to have drugs there. It was no longer a "counselors' rule," but a matter of common interest and of group survival.

At Markham House the split between counselors and young people widened. Fears of disorder and an inability to hear young peoples' criticisms, spoken directly or indirectly displayed in angry behavior, led to an increasing concentration of power in the counselors, a proliferation of rules and sanctions. Instead of granting freedom and responsibility together, the counselors insisted that a demonstrated responsibility precede freedom and that they would be the ones who would determine who was responsibile.

A system of levels of privilege was instituted. Several weeks of obedience at one level of freedom (a ten-o'clock curfew, one phone call a night) preceded the granting of greater privileges (a midnight curfew and two phone calls a night). The young people, who resented the levels, disobeyed the rules covertly and conned susceptible counselors into exempting them from sanctions. The counselors (with a circularity of reasoning which took many months for them to understand) justified the need for levels by pointing to the lack of responsibility and honesty that the young people demonstrated in dealing with them.

The counselors always reserved final decision-making power to themselves. Many of them regarded house meetings as simply "a time for the kids to complain, to blow off steam." The real decisions about levels and punishment were to be made by the counselors, away from the meetings. Attempts to make the house more democratic, to share power, turned out actually to be covert systems of manipulation and mystification: Separate orbits of power were designated, one that the young people could control, and a larger, encompassing one that gave the counselors control over the first. These dual orbits were initially welcomed by the young people. When they discovered that they couldn't make substantive changes—hours of curfew, time of clean-up, patterns of phone use—they became more cynical, and the split between them and the counselors widened.

Induction

Freud (1920) has written of powerful forces in all of us which tend to cause us to repeat past patterns of behavior (repetition compulsion) and to act with new people and in novel situations as we have with significant historical, and especially parental, figures and in formative situations (transference) (Freud, 1912). More recently Laing (1973) has described "induction," a transpersonal process by which we induce others to behave toward us as significant historical others once did. In the group foster homes all of these forces and, in particular, induction were continuous, powerful, and pervasive.

Virtually all of the young people in both houses had been, in a variety of ways, rejected, discounted, and nullified by their parents long before they left home. Whatever efforts they made to grow close to the counselors, to make new and better homes for themselves, were inevitably shot through with suspicions and resentments that they transferred from previous settings, attitudes, and actions which tended to induce the counselors to act as their parents and previous caretakers had. Only counselors who were both sensitive to this process and willing to forego the often destructive parental roles for which their own histories prepared them were able to resist induction. Only in a setting in which induction was not easily fulfilled could this take place.

The democratization of Frye House provided a firm basis for resisting a variety of inductions. When they felt victimized, young people could be reminded, truthfully, that they had real power in and over their living situation. Counselors who actively sought the interpersonal meaning of disruptive behavior were predisposed to understand certain of the young peoples' actions as invitations to rejection, to interpret rather than answer them. Still, the struggle was continuous and not always successful.

The counselors were surprisingly capable of dealing with most of the young people. For example, fifteen-year-old Ellen's aggressiveness and self-destructive behavior (stealing, multiple drug use, street fights, temper tantrums) continually invited reprisals, sanctions, and restrictions. The counselors refused either to confine her—as her parents, a succession of foster parents, and reform schools had done—or, when attempts at control proved insufficient, to reject her as they had. For the most part they simply treated her with the respect due someone who was capable of making up her own mind. They confronted her with their response to her disruptive behavior, and tried to stop it when it infringed on them; when she asked for advice, verbally or nonverbally, they tried to dissuade her from actions they thought unwise, to help her think about and find alternative courses. At the same time, they tried to listen to the whys and whens of her actions, to be available to her when depression and loneliness succeeded vengefulness and violence.

The counselors had more difficulty with young people whose early lives seemed to have been characterized by massive indifference and neglect. Two of these young people seemed constantly to drift away from house activities and interactions. They seemed both disdainful and frightened of the participatory possibilities which the openness of the house permitted them. If they took offense, they often refused to admit it; sometimes they seemed to cherish their hurt in secret. Their need for affection well hidden, as well as their anger, they continually slipped further away from engagement with counselors. They were able to find in the counselors' respect for their freedom, its parody, the kind of indifference to which they were accustomed. And in time, the counselors, frustrated and discouraged, did become indifferent to them. Within six months, these young men (who had both previously lived on their own) left the house, vaguely disappointed, to "bum around."

At Markham House the counselors' insistence on concentrating decision-making power in themselves, and their willingness to make rules "for the young people's good" made them particularly vulnerable to inductions. Almost any aspect of behavior could signal the need for an "appropriate" and "effective" response. With bizarre faithfulness, counselors managed to act out an array of contradictory parts in which the young people cast them. At the same time their need to maintain authority made it difficult for them to see this process. Confronted with it, they became defensive and self-righteous, readily willing to blame "the kids."

For example, Allan's relationship with Leslie rapidly became a facsimile of the one she had had with her father: Her good looks, coquettishness, and sweetness immediately attracted him to her, encouraged him to seek her out as a confidante. When she later evaded house rules to be with her boyfriend, Allen seemed to experience it as insult and desertion. He accused her, without any sense of irony, of selfishness, and of not caring, and became bitter, suspicious, and vindictive toward her. A final invasion of her privacy—a public harangue while she was at her job—paralleled exactly her father's jealous intrusiveness on her relations with other young people.

Another counselor (who, in talks with me, admitted his bewilderment) simultaneously acted coolly and condescendingly to one girl, authoritatively and punitively to one boy, and forgivingly to another resident. All the while he spoke in meetings of the need for "consistency in treatment" and of his attempt to be "firm, but fair."

The Group Foster Home and the World

The group foster homes are peculiarly vulnerable to outside influences. Simply to exist, the houses must adhere to strict zoning regulations and obey a variety of sanitary and fire codes that entail substantial expenditures and exact careful compliance. The knowledge that boys and girls live together with young counselors—and the noise that inevitably comes from a place where there are half a dozen adolescents—makes each house a focus of attention for worried and suspicious neighbors. Each of the young people placed in the house is subject to the authority of court-appointed officers; an individual or a house's offenses against a particular probation officer's or social worker's prejudices—as well as actual offenses—may precipitate the removal of a young person. To insure its survival, the group foster home must be cleaner and quieter than its neighbors. The young people who live there must be better behaved than their peers next door, and more careful about what they are seen doing.

There are also more subtle influences of the community on the houses: the economic status of a particular neighborhood, the kind of dwellings, the color of the people who live there, the composition of households, their ages, the community's political climate, the attitude of the police, the quality of the schools, the extent to which there is a self-conscious and supportive network of counterculture services. All of these factors have powerful effects on the group foster home and, to a lesser degree, may be affected by it.

As one of a number of social service projects in a larger, nonhierarchical, collectively run organization, Frye House and the people who lived in it were both responsible to and supported by other counselors and young people. The collective structure of the larger organization provided a model for changes within Frye. Including young people in decision-making was an extension of the franchise, a reaffirmation and deepening of principle by counselors and young people, rather than a departure from it. As a result of these changes in Frye, young people in all the projects were included in collective-wide policy decisions and given a voice in selecting their own counselors.

The structure of the collective and the proximity of a network of alternative services—free clinics, job cooperative, free school, community newspaper, antiprofit businesses—provided a larger world which sustained the democratic and participatory values of the group foster home.

Still, there were aspects of living in a city that were alien and threatening to teenagers who came from suburban schools and neighborhoods. The heavy urban street scene—drugs, prostitution, violence—that existed side by side with the counterculture exerted a powerful and sometimes destructive pull on some of the young people, tugged at the fabric of countercultural vlues. Some young people, though happy in the house, continually hungered for more familiar parental figures, a more settled and conventional life.

In my first months at Frye House the counselors often seemed caught between the young people and the probation officers and caseworkers who supervised their placement. They were defensive with these officials, angry at their intrusions, protectively vague in their responses to questions. Sometimes they transmitted the anxieties they felt to the young people, insisting too loud and long that they "shape up" to protect the house's reputation with the caseworkers. Sometimes the young people complained about the counselors to the caseworkers, and sometimes in frustration the counselors sided with caseworkers against the young people.

With the redistribution of power and the changes in rules, counselors and young people began to present a united front to the supervisory forces. At first this was largely protective, with each "covering" for the other's derelictions from court policy. But, as the house grew more confident about its policies, it was able, in a relatively unintimidated and undefensive manner, to advance its own beliefs about the young people's right to make their own decisions. There was evidence in Frye's favor: Young people who were labeled incorrigible, who had never been able to stay anywhere else, were able to live at Frye House; some of those whom counselors had refused to force to work or go to school had later, on their own, chosen to do so; young people considered irresponsible, delinquent, and psychotic were taking part in running a functioning household.

The counselors saw no reason for caseworkers to impose conventional but arbitrary standards of conduct and morals on the young people who lived in the house. Impressed by the counselors' assurances, respecting the house's success, knowing there was no other place for many of their most difficult young people, many caseworkers relented: some even seemed converted.

The isolation of Markham in its community contributed greatly to its increasing obedience to the norms of the surrounding suburban community and to its institutionalization in rules and relationships between staff and residents.

Many property holders and politicians opposed Markham as an unwholesome and dangerous addition to the community. In public meetings, Allan and his staff again and again had to overcome their objections. These neighbors spurred police to make raids for runaways and complained to them of minor annoyances; to politicians they spoke of drug use, sexual activity, delinquent behavior, and noise. As allies, the director had a few neighbors and probation officers, people who were for the most part no more committed to the house's survival than they were to traditional and somewhat condescending ideas of child care.

Allan transmitted the constant pressure on him to counselors and young people directly, through strict and detailed rules designed to appease the community and "keep things cool," and indirectly, by self-righteous accusations in the genre of "Look at all I'm doing for you. Why don't you act more grateful?" Some of the counselors shared Allan's approach and his angers; others, painfully sensitive to the young people's reactions but not able to oppose Allan, tended to apologize for him.

The young people banded together with the counselors for special efforts: cleaning the house and the yard before a county council site visit; practicing speeches for a zoning commission meeting. But afterward they were resentful. The arbitrariness of the rules and their lack of flexibility made the young people feel that they were more the instrument for than the purpose of the house's survival. The director's "guilt tripping" was often a hurtful reminder of attitudes prevalent in their own homes.

Under outside pressure, without the mediation of an extended "alternative" community, hierarchical, male-dominated structures tended to perpetuate themselves. A male director—the only fund raiser and administrator—appointed a male head counselor. Both supervised the work of female counselors. Among the young people in the house, stronger males pushed weaker ones around; and both were ascendant over females. Girls tended to be assigned to cooking and cleaning, boys to garage and yard work. The basic hierarchy between rule-making counselors and rule-obeying (or disobeying) kids was further subdivided in terms of levels of more or less privileged young people.

The counselors tended to go for their emotional, intellectual, and political support to a relatively small group of people in the surrounding community. This helped make the house more a part of the community, a place where neighbors, probation officers, and consultants felt comfortable dropping in. But it also had a conservatizing and confining effect. All house members were under constant if informal and well-intentioned scrutiny. The director felt compelled to accede to the wishes of the probation officers who supported his program. At virtually any hour he would accept "referrals" from them, regardless of the objections of the young people in the house.

The young people feared the closeness of the counselors and probation officers for other reasons. Perhaps secrets told to counselors would be revealed to the probation officers, who could return them to detention centers and reform schools. More generally, the expectations and standards of educated middle-class white counselors and probation officers, and of their neighbors and advisors, were inappropriate for or intimidating to poor and/or black young people.

Leaving

Leaving is a constant issue in group foster homes for adolescents. Only the youngest of teenagers does not feel the pressure or the pull of the "some day" when he or she will be "on my own." In my experience, only the newest of counselors or the most settled of couples does not wonder "what's next for me?"

For the most part, young people left Frye when they were ready or felt ready. The right to leave was as important and as respected by counselors as any other right. Generally, their purpose was to understand and facilitate the young person's choice, not oppose or influence it. When they disagreed with a decision they tried simply to say so and explain why. For young people who wanted to leave before they were eighteen, the counselors simultaneously worked both for legal emancipation and a kind of trial separation: They wanted the young person to be free to go, but for at least a month they tried to keep a place open in the house in case he or she decided to return.

The same philosophy of respect for the young person's rights and wishes made it reasonable for the counselors to fight to keep young people who felt they needed to stay beyond their eighteenth birthday. Sympathetic caseworkers and probation officers facilitated continued financial support in some instances; where this was not forthcoming, the counselors and the young person tried together to raise the necessary funds.

Young people who were neither forced out nor bound to the group foster home had both the time and the freedom to work through some of the conflicts that beset separation. Ellen, for instance, was able to "decide to leave" half a dozen times. She rejected the counselors in word—"The only reason you want me to stay is because of the money"—and deed, taking off several times for a night or a week, and discovered that she was not rejected. In house meetings she expressed harsh rigidity in her own ideas about separation ("People who leave," she said, "shouldn't be allowed to just drop over to eat") and heard them mitigated by others—counselors and young people—who wished to provide continuing emotional support to former residents. In the daily attention the house and the larger collective paid to former residents—allowing them to come to eat, to attend group meetings, or to stay overnight, asking them to act as volunteers or paid workers in the runaway house or job cooperative—Ellen was able to see that the rejection she advocated (and perhaps feared) would not be visited on her. When she did leave at seventeen and a half, after three years, Ellen *knew* she could depend on Frye House's support.

This continued feeling of a connection which supersedes and evolves beyond separation was also present among counselors and consultants. My own experience is perhaps illustrative. During the time I was there I was intensely involved with the house as a whole and the people in it. I was at once facilitator of group meetings and a friend and advisor to individuals. After group meetings I ate dinner at the house, sometimes went for a walk or to a movie with individual members. Sometimes on weekends, house members would come to visit me. When I asked two friends of mine to take my place as consultant, I had the feeling I was "inviting them into the family" as much as I was asking them to do a piece of work.

For a while after I left, I kept in touch with individual house members but stayed away from the house itself. I felt a little strange, unsettled in my relationship to it. I was accustomed to a certain dependency in the house's relationship to me and, I realized, a position of authority. How, I wondered, could I fit in without being so central? After a few months I began to relax into a new role, as an avuncular member of an extended family, someone who is "there" for the house, a part of its growth and, if needed, a present support—a reminder of its history, and a promise of continuity.

Markham House's tendency to extrude deviants who wanted to stay was cruelly caricatured in its difficulty in letting go of those who wanted to leave. The fitful behavior that preceded or accompanied a decision to leave was often met with renewed attempts to control the young person. Unless he or she was peculiarly careful or shrewd or patient, the young person fell victim to a kind of "Catch 22": The more the young person asserted independence, the more likely he or she was to lose privileges and be restricted. Finally, when the young person—furious and disillusioned—rebelled against the whole system of authority and control and committed "a very serious violation," he or she was kicked out.

Lacking the proper emancipation papers, labeled as "irresponsible," some of the young people were remanded to still more confining situations. The counselors, meanwhile, were depressed, bewildered, and resentful. What could they have done differently? Why did the young person act that way? They had lost the control they thought so necessary to helpfulness and were left only with the bitterness of blame.

For some, this final disappointment colored the whole experience of having been at Markham. Even if the young person had concluded that much of the time spent there was helpful, the resentment—sometimes embarrassment—that characterized his or her departure made it virtually impossible to use the home as a support in the months of uncertainty that followed leaving. Some came to depend on individual counselors or professionals (including me) whom they'd met while in the home. Many more, among them some of the most troubled and despairing, withdrew in disillusionment from contact with any "helping" people.

Conclusion

Alternative group foster homes are both heir to a tradition of child placement and a challenge to it. They are providing places for young people who have not been able to live with their parents or foster parents, who would otherwise be—and often have been—institutionalized in mental hospitals and reform schools. Instead of helping them to adjust to a social structure which had already defined them as deviant, counselors in these homes are trying to discover, and to create with the young people, a new microsocial structure.

My experience at Frye and Markham has helped me to understand the variety of factors that facilitate or retard this process: the political and moral climate of the surrounding community; the support of other workers engaged in a similar enterprise; the organizational structure of the group home itself; the real commitment of counselors to the rights of young people; and the integrity and courage with which they persist, against the odds of overwork, abuse, anxiety, and convention, in respecting each of them.

If they are able to resist the false promises and restricting bonds of parent-child or therapist-client relationships, counselors in these homes can provide the emotional support of respectful mutuality. Understanding that they cannot have "the answers," they may be able to live and work with—and learn from—young people in a way which helps all of them to value and make sense of their common experience.

References

Bremner, R. H. et al., eds. (1971), *Children and Youth in America: A Documentary History*, 2 vols. Cambridge, Mass.: Harvard University Press.

Erikson, K. T. (1966), *Wayward Puritans*. New York: John Wiley.

Fisher, F. M. (1952), *The Group Home: An Innovation in Child Placement*. New York: Child Welfare League of America.

Freud, S. (1912), The dynamics of transference. *Standard Edition*, 12:99-108. London: Hogarth Press, 1958.

—— (1920), Beyond the pleasure principle. *Standard Edition*, 18:3-64. London: Hogarth Press, 1955.

Gordon, J. S. (1973), The uses of madness. *Soc. Policy*, 4:31-43.

——— (1974), Coming together: Consultation with young people. *Soc. Policy*, 5:40-52.

Gula M. (1964), Group homes—new and differentiated tools in child welfare, delinquency and mental health. *Child Welfare*, 44:393-402.

Herstein, N. (1964), What is a group home? *Child Welfare*, 44:403-414.

Jewett, D. (1973), The group home. *Children Today*, 2:16-20.

Laing, R. D. (1973), *The Politics of the Family*. New York: Pantheon.

Mnookin, R. (1973), Foster care: In whose best interest? *Harvard Educ. Rev.*, 43:596-638.

National Directory of Runaway Centers (1974), Washington, D.C.: Natl. Youth Alternative Project.

Ohlin, L. E. et al. (1974), Radical correctional reform: A case study of Massachusetts youth correctional system. *Harvard Educ. Rev.*, 44:74-111.

Proceedings of the Conference on the Care of Dependent Children (1909), Washington, D.C.: U.S. Government Printing Office.

Rabinow, I. (1964), Agency-operated group homes. *Child Welfare*, 44:415-422.

Rodham, H. (1973), Children under the law. *Harvard Educ. Rev.*, 43:487-514.

Scher, B. (1958), Specialized group care for adolescents. *Child Welfare*, 37:12-17.

U.S. Senate (1972), *Hearings on S.2829 ("Runaway Youth"), Before the Subcommittee to Investigate Juvenile Delinquency of the Senate Committee on the Judiciary*. Washington, D.C.: Congressional Record.

Whittaker, J. K. (1972), Group care for children: Guidelines for planning. *Soc. Wk.*, 17:51-61.

Wolins, M. & Piliavin, I. (1964), *Institution or Foster Family: A Century of Debate*. New York: Child Welfare League of America.

The most testing family to treat is the hard-core, multiproblem family. Family group therapy, the author argues, is not enough, and a pattern of community agencies have to be encouraged to bear upon the family.

Producing Effective Change in Impoverished, Disorganized Families: Is Family Therapy Enough?

GERALD FLEISCHER

In working with disorganized families, Minuchin et al. (1967) describe a characteristic mode of relating in which the parents are too demoralized to be able to provide a sense of continuity or consistency in the transactions through which the family performs household chores, enforces discipline, or communicates one member with the other. The result is that the family members do not develop a sense of the world as a stable place with consistent rules. It is extremely difficult for the child growing up in such a chaotic environment to internalize a set of rules of personal conduct. Instead, he learns to attend to the shifting moods of those around him and to take advantage of opportunities when they arise. Delaying present gratification for future gains is senseless in such a family, because there is no reason to believe that future gains will be forthcoming.

The structural treatment of such families usually involves subtle but active efforts by the therapist to restructure and solidify generational and sexual roles, model and encourage the parents to provide consistent limits

---

Gerald Fleischer, Ph.D., is from the Department of Psychology and Sociology, Drexel University, Philadelphia, Penn. 19104.

Reprinted from *Family Therapy*, vol. 2, no. 3, 1975.

and controls, and provide a basis from which family members can learn to communicate feelings and thoughts while simultaneously gaining the expectation that others will respond appropriately.

The following case history represents an extreme example of such an impoverished, disorganized family, the treatment of which was handicapped by the reluctance of two significant family members to attend therapy, and by treatment having come about as a judicial order rather than a voluntary contract.

What was most striking about working with this family was the irrelevance of the usual goals of family therapy to the needs of the family, as well as the ineffectuality of the usual techniques in producing change. The inability of the therapist to rely on previous experience and guidelines resulted in much trial and error and improvisation on his part. Effective intervention occurred only after the therapist changed his perception of the family. In a very real sense, it was the therapist who changed rather than the family, and to a degree sufficient to substantially alter his subsequent approaches to family intervention.

In the following account of the course of treatment, the therapist will attempt to describe both his efforts at intervention and his changing perceptions of the family in the time sequences they occurred, so that the reader may share his changing experiences.

The Steele Family

The Steeles were a black family, consisting of a mother (Mabel), her husband (Sylvester) of two years, her six children (by previous fathers) who were living at home (ranging in age from sixteen to five), and Roy (age one and a half,) the only child of the present union. They were referred to the Family Intervention Program of the Delaware County (Pa.) Juvenile Court by the judge and were seen a total of five times.

The referral followed the adjudication of the two eldest boys (Charles, sixteen and Calvin, fifteen) for assaulting their stepfather. The two youths had physically beaten him on several occasions. The most recent attack, which had led to court intervention, had been a severe one in which the two boys had kicked, punched, and beaten Sylvester with bed slats. There had also been a previous court referral in which Calvin had been involved in minor theft and truancy.

First Meeting

Sylvester sat with Roy in his lap, opposite Calvin and Charles. Mabel sat separated from her husband and midway between him and the two older boys. The older children tended to sit next to Charles and Calvin, while the little ones clustered around their mother and Sylvester.

The initial meeting with the family produced the following additional information: Prior to his marriage to the mother, the stepfather (age 51) had been living in the home for several years, ostensibly as a boarder, but in actuality, as everyone recognised, he was the mother's lover. Surprisingly, this arrangement had not produced any serious conflicts. It was only when the mother (age 52) and Sylvester had married that the violent assaults had begun. In fact, the first attack on Sylvester had occurred the night he and his wife announced that they had secretly been married.

The sons' violent reaction to the marriage initially suggested to the therapist that the "legalization" of Sylvester's relationship with the mother was perceived as a threat to their own status in the family. This preliminary explanation, while consistent with the classical concept of oedipal rivalry and thus providing some structure for the therapist's own comfort, did not provide him with any ready means of intervention into the family system.

In both the family's verbal accounts and in their verbal and nonverbal interactions, it became clear that Sylvester was regarded with contempt by the two oldest sons. Everyone also agreed that Sylvester was not the aggressor, and no one could provide any instance of his instigating the attacks. Furthermore, he did appear passive in the meeting, and gave the impression that he would be ineffectual in controlling the boys' aggression against him. There seemed to be a clear reversal of generational roles operating. It seemed equally clear that Charles and Calvin had no intention of giving up their aggressive control of the situation. Their reactions to the therapist also consisted of barely concealed contempt.

The mother and the other children were harder to evaluate. The younger children seemed to deny any involvement in the situation. One had the impression they felt too vulnerable to risk taking sides. Clyde, the next oldest boy (age twelve), seemed to be cautiously moving toward aligning himself with his older brothers, although he had not as yet participated in any of the assaults.

The mother appeared to side with Sylvester and was a cocomplainant in the petition against the boys. However, it was not clear how much support she gives her husband when the boys actually threaten to attack him. Furthermore, the boys justify their assaults on Sylvester by stating that they feel that he takes advantage of their mother. Further clarification of this claim focused on their resentment of the fact that Sylvester seldom is employed and most of the time lives off the family welfare check. Mother acknowledges that she is resentful of Sylvester's failure to bring in money. Thus, the possibility exists that mother may be covertly egging the boys on in their assaults.

The therapist then attempted to focus on the relationship between the parents, operating on the working hypothesis that if he could improve the relationship between the parents enough so that they would support each other in dealing with the boys, then much of the assaultiveness could be controlled. A secondary goal of improving the relationship between Sylvester and the boys was also considered. The implementation of these two goals became the work of the remainder of the initial meeting and most of the second meeting.

Second Meeting

In retrospect, it appears that the therapist was fairly successful in improving the relationship between the parents, but not in improving the relationship between Sylvester and the boys. In fact, at the third meeting we found out that the parents had succeeded in presenting a united front to the boys, with the result that this time both parents had been assaulted. It looked as if the therapist, in winning a victory, was losing the war.

During the second meeting, when the therapist attempted to work with the relationship between Sylvester and the boys by encouraging them to negotiate an agreement, Calvin defiantly made it clear that his goal was to drive Sylvester out of the home. When asked to state under what conditions he would accept Sylvester, he stated that when Sylvester worked and brought in money, then there was never any "trouble." The therapist, at that time, viewed this as an example of the reversal of the generational roles, but regarded the statement itself as a self-justifying rationalization.

Third Meeting

The third meeting was very discouraging to the therapist, who was left with considering the possibility that the only means of avoiding family mayhem was either to terminate treatment and recommend placement for the two boys, or to support Sylvester in moving out of the house, a plan which he reported himself considering.

The meeting was attended by the two parents, and by the younger children, but both Charles and Calvin had "disappeared" shortly before they were to leave for the meeting. The conclusion was inescapable that the boys had beaten the therapist to the gun in terminating.

Two items of interest were reported during the third meeting. First, the fight in which the two boys had attacked both parents occurred when the parents, without consulting the boys, had rented one of the rooms in the house to a boarder. When the boys found out, they had ejected the boarder and attacked the parents when they attempted to intervene. There was also some intimation that the parents had been drinking when the fight occurred. If drinking was a problem for the parents, as it did appear to be, then it might very well underlie the contempt the boys held for Sylvester and, increasingly, for their mother.

Second, the mother reported the presence of another child who may have been a significant factor in the family transaction; Ruth (age nineteen) was totally overlooked by the therapist because, although present in the records, they indicated that she was out of the home and living in her own apartment with her two-year-old daughter. In addition, there were two other older children in their twenties with homes and families of their own who were not considered part of the immediate nuclear family. Mrs. Steele reported that Ruth actually instigated this latest assault, and further informed the therapist that, while Ruth does have her own apartment, her man had left her, so that for the past six months Ruth spent much of her time with the Steeles. This had not been mentioned previously, and it may well have been the mother's desperation which prompted this revelation.

Home Visit—Fourth Meeting

Although the therapist was feeling quite discouraged, he decided to set up a home visit in lieu of another meeting at the court, hoping that he could thus engage Charles and Calvin, and also Ruth.

Actually, the home visit was only partially successful in this aim. The therapist did meet Ruth, and this meeting was highly significant, but both Charles and Calvin again "disappeared" before the meeting and did not attend.

The home visit revealed to the therapist the true extent of the impoverished conditions under which the family lived. The family lived in and behind a boarded-up store in an extremely run-down neighborhood. While the home was fairly clean, the furniture was very shabby, and the living area extremely crowded. Until the therapist had seen the home, the economic aspects of the family problem had had little impact upon him, but once enveloped by the incredibly depressing atmosphere of the home, he could not help but be impressed with the tremendous sense of apathy and helplessness that seemed to pervade the family. This, in turn, led him into exploring the family's economic situation more carefully than he had. Thus, he learned that while both parents were on welfare, they occasionally worked as migrant farm laborers, harvesting crops on farms in a neighboring state for which they were paid $12 a day. This required a trip of 40 miles each way which cost them $5 each. The work itself required twelve hours of exhausting labor, plus three hours of traveling, after which each would return with a net gain of $7. Even this exploitive and back-breaking work was available only on a sporadic basis.

Previously, when Calvin had remarked that the boys resented Sylvester because he was not bringing in money, this explanation was disregarded as a rationalization by the therapist. However, with his greater empathy for the family's economic problems, this explanation made much more sense to him. He then learned that Sylvester as a boarder had generally contributed money to the household, and that the marriage between Sylvester and Mabel had coincided with Sylvester's becoming more dependent upon the family for support.

The home visit made the therapist aware of other, almost overwhelming, problems the family was facing. Charles was reported to have an active case of tuberculosis, but would not go to the hospital to have it treated or even to have the seriousness of the condition assessed. Robert, age four, had a hernia which required surgery but which had been neglected.

As the home visits persisted, the therapist became aware of the importance of Ruth to the family situation, and also of the problems which were affecting her. As mentioned, Ruth did appear to be able to provoke

Charles and Calvin in their assaults upon Sylvester. In a very real sense, she was the dominant family member. Ruth also had the best potential for breaking out of the snare of poverty that the family was in. Ruth had received training in secretarial skills from the Federal Job Corps, and had the ability to support herself and establish an independent life away from her family, or to help the family economically by contributing part of her income to it. However, she was doing neither. Instead, she spent much of her time at home, fighting for control with the ineffectual and apathetic parents.

Ruth showed no interest in seeking employment, and for an apparently good reason: Ruth's appearance was strikingly marred by the absence of all her front teeth. This impairment made her appear so deviant and bizarre that she could not obtain any positions, let alone a secretarial job.

It also became apparent that this had important psychological implications, as well as economic and cosmetic ones. In retrospect, the most significant and effective intervention the therapist made during the entire course of therapy was when he dealt with Ruth's feelings about her sense of loss and impairment in relation to her teeth. Until then, Ruth had been silent and sullen and had behaved similarly to her brothers when they attended the first two meetings. Somewhat in desperation, the therapist made a risky intervention by saying, "It's a shame about your teeth. You would be an attractive girl, but they ruin your appearance." This had an immediate and striking impact upon Ruth, who burst into tears.

The therapist was afraid that she would become so hurt that she would refuse to cooperate any further. Instead, the tears were followed by a cathartic release of a torrent of feelings and events associated with her loss. The teeth had been knocked out almost two years earlier by her boyfriend. It had a profound effect upon the self-image and self-esteem of what appeared to have been a vivacious and assertive teenager. It severely curtailed her social life. Her feelings of humiliation and isolation forced her to retreat to and remain dependent upon her family, which became her sole remaining source of emotional support. Indeed, it might be reasoned that her feelings of loss were in part responsible for her resentment against her stepfather, whose passivity and chronic unemployment she blamed for her own plight.

Furthermore, the loss robbed her of all confidence and initiative. She no longer had hopes of finding a job. Except for the anger displayed within the family, her way of relating to the world had become largely apathetic, as if she no longer harbored any hope of obtaining any satisfaction. Even such a basic move as going to the welfare-supported dental clinic was too much for her, so that for almost two years her condition remained unchanged.

Final Meeting

Having established a relationship with Ruth, the therapist was able to work with her in dealing with some of her problems. The therapist was able to get Ruth to agree to set up an appointment at the Welfare Dental Clinic. While this sounds like a simple matter, it certainly was not. First, it generally took about six months between setting up an appointment and actually being able to see a dentist. Second, Ruth had not set up an appointment earlier because she was afraid of the pain she anticipated from the experience. This, combined with the state of dependency and apathy she had sunk into, virtually paralyzed her so that she could not mobilize the resources to take the necessary steps to improve her situation. At any rate, with considerable support from the therapist, Ruth was able to agree, at least in principle, to go to the dentist.

In addition, other plans were raised and discussed. The possibilities of Ruth getting help in obtaining employment were discussed, as was the possibility of her getting additional vocational training. As the session continued, Ruth seemed to become more motivated and hopeful.

Both Charles and Calvin had again refused to attend the meeting. However, the parents reported that there had been no assaults since the last meeting. The attending family members discussed the problem of the boys in their absence. Ruth gave the impression that she had separated herself from the boys, and was no longer involved in their attacks. She agreed that, together with her parents, she would attempt to get Charles into the hospital to have his tuberculosis looked after. During this meeting, the therapist had the satisfying feeling that, perhaps for the first time, he was engaging the family, and that it was now actively working with him. The predominant air of apathy and helplessness had been temporarily conquered. The family was now acting in an integrated manner to improve the situation, although in the absence of the two boys.

Aftermath

While the therapist did not meet with the family again, therapy may be said to have continued through the intervention of other individuals.

This was done by the therapist working with the probation officer, who, in turn, was able to mobilize other community resources. Thus, while Ruth had called for a dental appointment, it was feared that if she had to wait six months in order to get help, whatever tenuous motivation and hope she had would be destroyed. The probation officer was able to contact the welfare agency and to obtain an appointment for Ruth in two months time. Furthermore, it was decided that in view of Ruth's apprehension about the dental appointment, it would be desirable if someone could support her when she had to face the ordeal. Eventually, it was decided the welfare worker would drive Ruth to the clinic and remain with her throughout the appointment.

Ruth, with some support from her parents, was able to convince Charles to go to the hospital to have his tuberculosis treated. Fortunately, the condition was found to be inactive, so that no hospitalization was needed.

In the past year and a half, there have been no major assaults by the boys against Sylvester, although there have been arguments which approached the danger point. The parents report the situation improved, although Calvin did receive a court petition for theft. Ruth has a set of dentures, and finally has found a job in a department store. The parents' drinking has increased considerably, and the probation officer has expressed the fear that the younger children may well experience serious problems as they reach the dangerous years of adolescence, particularly as the neighborhood that their family lives in is known for its high crime rate, its gangs, and its deteriorated conditions.

Discussion

While generalizing from one case is open to question, the family seems typical enough of impoverished, disorganized families to raise some important questions.

General Effectiveness of Traditional Techniques

The usual techniques and principles of family intervention did not work with this family. The exceptions to the above statement are noteworthy, however. First, the importance of the "absent member" (Sonne et al., 1962) was confirmed in the case of Ruth. On the other hand, therapy was able to proceed and, indeed, was effective, even when the two sons absented themselves from the therapy.

The family-intervention model which, in retrospect, seemed most useful to the therapist was the one developed by Bowen (1961), particularly with regard to his emphasis on working with the family member most likely to produce changes in the family system. Recognizing and working with Ruth was an example of that principle.

Inappropriate Goals

Most of the goals usually listed by family therapists as occurring in successful family therapy were not reached here, and yet the therapist regards working with the Steeles a highly satisfying and successful experience. The parents, while more supportive of each other, remained ineffective, apathetic people who continued to drink heavily. The children, especially Ruth, remained the dominant family force, with the therapist's support. In effect, generational roles continued in a deviant pattern from the dominant cultural mode.[1] The children continued to run the family but, it may be said, in a less chaotic and less brutal manner than before.

Generally, family therapists expect the family to take responsibility for changing their life situation. However, in the case of the Steele family, though Ruth was fairly well motivated to remedy the dental problem which had virtually imprisoned her in the home, it was our judgment that she was not strong enough to take this responsibility entirely on her own, nor could we depend upon the family to provide the support and encouragement for her to get to the dental clinic. Therefore, it became necessary to mobilize community resources to assist her.

Pathology or Adaptive Behavior?

It is certainly possible to regard the Steele family pattern as grossly pathological: the parents appear to have drinking problems; they are almost totally ineffectual as disciplinarians, as breadwinners, and as positive role models for the children; generational roles are strikingly reversed, with the added twist that the dominant children seem to be

[1] But not necessarily from the low-status black family. Much has been written about the matriarchal black family, in which the paternal figure is not able to provide an adequate image as an individual worthy of admiration and emulation (Moynihan, 1965).

brutally utilizing Sylvester as a scapegoat in order to avoid facing their own problems and responsibilities; growth, differentiation, and individuation seem seriously impaired.

On the other hand, the Steeles seemingly bizarre behavior may be viewed as attempts to adapt to an extremely stressful situation that few family therapists have experienced or understood. The parents' apathy appears to be a typical response to a hopeless situation. They have come to feel that there is little or nothing they can do to overcome the pervasive poverty in their lives. Seligman (1975) has clearly demonstrated that apathy and passivity, and ultimately death, are frequent reactions in both humans and animals when they are made to feel that situational outcomes are totally independent of their own actions.

In contrast to the parents, the children appear to be attempting to reject and rebel against the pervasive apathy in the family. Indeed, the physical assaults may be viewed as desperate attempts to ward off feelings of helplessness. It is as if they are saying to the parents, "Look! I am not like you. I can have an impact on my environment. When I threaten you, you flee. I am the master and not the victim." Unfortunately, the children were exercising their need for mastery upon the parents because this was the only relationship where they could have an impact. Outside the family, they were falling into the same pit of helplessness as the parents, with the result (at least in the case of Ruth) of regression into further dependency upon the family.

It is important to note that the conditions which resulted in the family's drifting into apathy were still present. The family was black, had little education, few marketable vocational skills, and lived in a generally impoverished community with extremely high unemployment, and with few social and financial resources to support its residents. While Ruth and the community made some tentative steps to free her from the sense of helplessness, the rest of the family were still very much trapped in the same situation. These conditions limit the effectiveness of any therapeutic effort that does not also attempt to deal with the prevailing conditions outside the family which affect and perpetuate family conditions.

Therapist-Patient Differences in Attribution of Causality

As a rule, therapists tend to perceive the locus of problems to lie within the patient (Batson, 1975). In contrast, social-psychological research generally indicates that individuals who are experiencing problems generally perceive the locus of the problems as residing outside themselves, within the situation. While family therapists perceive the locus of the problem within the family rather than the individual, they tend to treat the family as if it were an individual, and hold it "responsible" for its problems and for the problems of individuals within the family. To some degree, it is necessary for a therapist to maintain such a perception, because if he does not see the problems as residing within the individual or family, but rather in the situation, then he is himself likely to feel helpless in effecting any change. On the other hand, if he goes too far in perceiving all responsibility as residing within the family, he is likely to be insensitive to very real stresses that families and individuals experience, and to be perceived as condemning and uncaring.

In the case of the Steeles, it was only when the therapist could understand and empathize with the family's sense of hopelessness as expressed and depicted by Ruth that any effective changes could be attempted. Furthermore, the interventions that were undertaken involved both changes within the family (e.g., getting Ruth to go to the dentist), and without (e.g., getting the welfare clinic to give Ruth an earlier appointment). Both types of intervention are needed. Rather than representing two incompatible approaches to change, they complement and strengthen each other.

Particularly in the case of impoverished families, there are almost certain to be strong external pressures and stresses acting on the family, and to ignore them and act on the assumption that all problems lie within the family is likely to squander therapeutic effort.

Assuming the opposite, namely, that all problems lie outside the family, is also likely to be ineffective in that it is apt to overwhelm the therapist with difficulties involved in changing the system, and thus produce a social reformer rather than a therapist. The obvious need is for a therapist who can be sensitive to both external pressures and to the family's mode of dealing with those pressures. He must be able to determine how the family can be mobilized to respond more effectively to both external and internal problems. However, he also must be able to determine when the family is indeed helpless, either because nothing can be done or, as in the case of the Steeles, because the psychological result of chronic poverty is the family sense of helplessness. At such times, he must be able to mobilize community support. He must, in a very concrete sense, provide "hope" for the family.

New Roles for the Family Therapist

Most family therapists have evolved out of the traditional mental health professions, namely, psychiatry, clinical psychology, and psychiatric social work. Because of their traditional training, family therapists tend to assume that the problem lies within the *family*, that it is the *family* that must change, and that failure to respond to therapeutic efforts results from either defensive resistance or lack of cooperation from the *family*. Both the family's problems and the failure of the family to respond to treatment are treated as resulting from the family's "sickness." However, at least in the case of severely impoverished families, this assumption may be untenable and counterproductive. The psychological effects of very real problems are likely to be considerable.

In addition to the traditional therapeutic role, the family therapist needs to assume the role of the urban anthropologist, whose function it is to observe the family *in vivo*. In contrast to the therapeutic role, the anthropologist does not attempt to intervene within the group being observed. Instead, he at first attempts to gain sufficient acceptance so that the observed group can continue its everyday existence without being affected by the presence of the observer. Secondly, he attempts to understand how the observed unique group is attempting to deal with the problems of human existence. Only then can he hope to intervene effectively.

In addition, the therapist may also find it necessary to function as a community-resources specialist. Thus, the mobilization of community resources, as well as family resources, becomes critical in the effective treatment of impoverished families.

While it would be desirable for the family therapist to wear at least three hats (anthropologist, traditional family therapist, and community specialist), these three roles can also be met by the use of teams. In his role as anthropologist as well as therapist, the family therapist(s) would of course have direct contact with the family, while the community specialist would act as a resource person for the therapeutic team. Ideally, such an approach could be undertaken under the aegis of a community mental health center, rather than a juvenile court. More important, the case described above points out the need for greater interdependency among various social service providers within a given community, as well as the need for coordination of joint efforts. In the case of the Steeles, services were needed from such diverse professions as various medical specialists, dental surgeons and technicians, vocational counselors, rehabilitation counselors, visiting nurses, and perhaps others. The family therapist, with his understanding of the family needs and limitations, is in the best position to serve as an ombudsman, who helps the impoverished family to reach out to appropriate community resources.

References

Batson, C. D. (1975), Attribution as a mediator of bias in helping. *J. Pers. & Soc. Psychol.*, 32:455-466.

Bowen, M. (1961), Family psychotherapy, from the family as a unit of study and treatment. *Amer. J. Orthopsychiat.*, 31:40-60.

Minuchin, S., Montalvo, B., Guerney, B. C., Jr., Rosman, B. L., & Schumer, F. (1967), *Families of the Slums*. New York: Basic Books.

Moynihan, D. O. (1965), *The Negro Family: The Case for National Action* (The Moynihan Report). Washington, D.C.: U.S. Dept. of Labor, Office of Policy Planning & Research.

Seligman, M. E. (1975), *Helplessness: On Depression, Development and Death*. San Francisco: W. H. Freeman.

Sonne, J., Speck, R., & Jungreis, J. (1962), The absent member maneuver as a resistance in family therapy of schizophrenia. *Fam. Proc.*, 1:44-62.

Family members may need the escape to and the respite of the hospital with its, usually, more harmonious set of influences. This chapter explores the subsequent interaction between the family and the ward staff.

Family Intervention with Severely Disturbed Inpatients

CAROL M. ANDERSON

Since the early 1950's, various attempts have been made to study the interplay between family interaction and individual symptomatology. Some investigations aimed at identifying the etiology of schizophrenia (Bateson, et al., 1956; Bowen, 1960; Lidz and Fleck, 1960; Mishler and Waxler, 1966; Reiss, 1967; Wynne, 1972); others attempted to measure the level of family stress and its individual ramifications (Coe et al., 1969; Davis et al., 1957; Kreisman and Joy, 1974; O'Brien and Azrin, 1973; Rose, 1959; Welldon, 1971). Although theories and results vary, these studies have led to an increased appreciation of the impact families have on the fate of their individual members. Much of what has been learned is particularly relevant to the issue of recidivism among psychiatric inpatients, since the length of hospitalization and frequency of readmission seem related to the behavior, circumstances, and attitudes of the patient's family (Yarrow et al., 1955; Angrist et al., 1961; Barrett et al., 1972; Brown et al., 1972; Esterson, 1965; Evans et al., 1961; Fleck, 1963; Lorei, 1967; Peretti, 1974).

Interestingly, however, few inpatient psychiatric settings have treatment programs that successfully involve families. Problems often arise when staff who are untrained in techniques of family intervention are

Carol M. Anderson, M.S.W., is from the Department of Psychiatry, School of Medicine, University of Pittsburgh.

Reprinted from the *Archives of General Psychiatry*, vol. 34, June, 1977.

confronted with families who become resistant out of fear, discomfort, and misunderstanding. The resultant chaos and alienation produces unnecessary stress for both families and staff. Regrettably, the family therapy literature is not particularly helpful to those working on inpatient units; such concepts as "defining the family as the patient" (Richter, 1974) tend to alienate both the medical staff of an institution and the already overwhelmed and guilt-ridden families. The polarized approaches of family therapists, who generally operate on a "systems" model which overemphasizes interactional variables, and psychiatrists, who generally operate on a "medical" model which overemphasizes individual variables, disregard the complex and complementary interplay of biological, psychodynamic, and interactional factors.

A Collaborative Family-Staff Relationship

A collaborative relationship between families and the hospital staff could be developed by the establishment of treatment contracts that combine these two models, accepting the patient's illness as the focus *while* recognizing the importance of family variables. This article will attempt to delineate the problems of the family and the hospital staff as the patient is admitted, and briefly describe administrative and clinical techniques that will increase the likelihood of a contact for successful family participation.

The Family

When a patient is hospitalized, it is usually after a time of turmoil and decreased ability to function (Wood et al., 1960). Whatever attempts the family has made to cope with the patient, and possibly with other family members or problems, have failed. Whether the cause of the illness is biological or interactional, the patient and family have begun to relate to one another in ways that tend to be destructive for all concerned. At best, this is a temporary family crisis; at worse, it can spiral into habitually negative relationships. Because families feel responsible and stigmatized (Rabkin, 1974), they arrive at a hospital burdened by a sense of failure, guilt, and shame.

On admission, most hospital systems ask the family for information about the patient. This information-gathering process too often assumes an accusatory air, augmenting the family's guilt. At the other extreme, the hospital staff may simply send the family home to worry about what they have done wrong and what part they have played in the patient's crisis. In either case, little attempt is made to deal with the family's needs and anxieties or to use this opportunity to begin to work with them for the sake of the patient (Appleton, 1974; Maxmen et al., 1974).

Once the patient has settled into the hospital, the family members may be allowed to visit, but they tend to be viewed as outsiders and made to feel as though they are intruders interfering with the care system. The staff, quickly identified with the problems and pains of the hospitalized patient, form alliances against the family. They acknowledge that the patient is sick, but regard the family as both sick *and* destructive. This attitude further polarizes all issues without helping either patient or family.

The net result is that the family withdraws from a hostile situation and protects itself in whatever ways are available (Myers, 1968; Myers, 1959; Fleck et al., 1957). They may deny, project, retaliate, or just disappear. If repeated hospitalizations occur (and without family participation they are more likely), families commonly invoke the tactic of angrily rejecting the patient altogether because they can no longer cope with the despair caused by the unexplained recurrent hospitalizations (Swingle, 1965).

The Staff

The staff of a psychiatric ward are busy and overworked. Upset patients are admitted at inconvenient times, and the family's questions and concerns are just one more burden. Families may be able to give some helpful information, but, on the other hand, they may not even be available. In either case, they are usually upset, sometimes obnoxious, and require more energy than staff have to give. Families take time. It becomes almost a relief if they won't come in, since when they do, they cause "trouble." The patient is almost always more upset when the family visits. The family challenges the competence of the clinicians and the plans of the staff. If "family therapy" is started, even the most experienced clinician can grow to feel de-skilled in the face of escalating conflictual interactions. At times (particularly when staff have had similar dynamics in their own families), the manner in which the family relates to the patient stirs up memories of unfinished family business for a staff member and, as a result, it becomes hard to be supportive to these families.

Hostilities accumulate over time, and difficulties increase as each side becomes more negative and alienated.

Techniques for Involving Resistant Families

There are ways in which a hospital system can be structured and ways in which clinicians can behave in order to minimize these problems. The following procedures are especially useful: (1) establish immediate contact, (2) require involvement, (3) structure availability, (4) create a good working climate, (5) appoint a family representative, (6) conduct controlled family therapy meetings, (7) provide a variety of treatment formats, and (8) plan adequate aftercare.

Immediate Contact

The chances of involving a resistant family are better if the first family contact occurs at the time of admission or very close to it. Ideally, the family should be seen when the patient is brought to the hospital. If the patient arrives without family members, or if a clinician is not available, a contact should be made within 24 hours. An overwhelmed family that is upset, concerned about the patient, and worried about the treatment facility is more likely to be receptive to a helpful contact. If the staff can be responsive to the family's need for support and information, the climate created at this first encounter may set the foundation for a collaborative, rather than an adversary, relationship. For this reason, it is particularly important that the meeting *not* be limited to gathering information about the patient. Questioning merely puts the family on the defensive, ignores their needs, and establishes a totally patient-oriented contract. Some attention must be given to what they have been going through, other current stresses in their lives, and their feelings about the patient and the hospital.

Required Involvement

A second technique for enlisting the cooperation of resistant families is to stress the importance of their participation, communicating to the family that they are an integral part of the treatment process, not a liability to the patient or an imposition on the hospital system. Respecting their power is an essential step toward establishing a workable treatment contract. They have knowledge of what has already been tried, how successful it was, what went wrong. They have strengths and things to give, or the power to undo in five minutes months of therapeutic work.

Considering the stereotypes of mental hospitals (many of which are true), few families originally *want* to be involved in the patient's treatment. Because staff often empathize with this position and do not fully accept the idea of the family as a cause of mental illness, many hospital systems do not insist on family involvement. However, it is necessary to accept neither a causal relationship nor a systems approach to see the importance of family work in a time of stress. The family can be mobilized around their own needs and the needs of the patient. A quotation from the civil rights movement comes to mind: "If you are not a part of the solution, you are a part of the problem." Everyone must be a part of the solution.

Even if a hospital makes a commitment to require family involvement, trouble frequently arises. As the families begin to come, staff, which remain ambivalent about family involvement, communicate this to the family in a way that sabotages their continued attendance. These negative communications occur in a number of ways: requested information and feedback are not given, the family's complaints are not heard, and sometimes the staff do not adhere to even the most elementary rules of courtesy.

Sensing staff ambivalence, families will push to be the "exception" to the rule of required involvement. Distance, illness, work schedules, etc., will be raised as reasons that prevent participation. Therefore, the level of family involvement depends a good deal on the convictions of the staff. In our setting, initially resistant families eventually drove four hours to attend weekly meetings. Businessmen have been able to rearrange work schedules to attend daytime sessions. The staff, however, *must* communicate the importance of attendance, whatever difficulties arise. This is not a power struggle, but an integral part of treatment.

Structuring Availability

If families are fearful and ambivalent, they may initially be unwilling to take work time to attend family sessions. Once committed to the treatment program, some families can be asked to come during daytime hours. For many others, however, daytime appointments represent a very real hardship. It should not follow that those who cannot be seen during the day cannot receive help. The staff should be available for meetings and telephone calls to answer a family's questions on at least some evenings or weekends.

Creating a Good Working Climate

The family's perception of the treatment team can be influenced by any member of the hospital staff. The most important person to a family is the one who is there when needed. Creating a good climate begins during the admission of the patient. Responding to the family's anxieties, answering questions, or providing information can set the tone, as does a friendly social gesture such as offering a cup of coffee. Furthermore, family members should be made to feel welcome and relevant at each contact. This does not mean they should never be confronted with their behavior or the problems they create. To the contrary, when caring is emphasized, family members become receptive to direct and critical statements about their behavior.

Appointing a Family Representative

Since the staff's tendency to identify with the patient is so strong on an inpatient service, a more balanced view of the presenting problems can be achieved by having someone specifically appointed to be aware of and responsive to the needs of the family. The role may be played by a social worker, nurse, or resident psychiatrist so long as both staff and family understand whose responsibility this is. The person so identified should be the one to conduct the initial required meetings and to establish a good relationship with the family. The following techniques are particularly useful in the initial stages of this relationship.

One to Three Meetings Held Without the Identified Patient

It is often advisable to postpone joint meetings between the patient and his family. Initially, the family tend to be reluctant to express negative feelings in front of the patient, and these are often times when the patient is too confused and upset to participate productively. To insist on a "whole family" orientation at such times increases anxiety and decreases future cooperation. It is far better to use this opportunity to prime the family, to identify issues, to prepare them for the family therapy to be conducted later in the hospitalization, and to encourage them to bring their concerns to the meetings. These first few sessions are particularly geared toward allowing the family to decompress their sense of guilt, anger, concern, and stigmatization about the patient and the hospitalization. Although the expression of empathy is important while these feelings are discussed, it is even more crucial that the clinician structure the conversation by limiting rambling, ruminations, and the spilling of family secrets. If too much is said or said too prematurely, families regret it later and withdraw. These sessions should have as goals the reduction of tensions and the provision of specifically useful techniques that will help to cope with whatever is bothering the family most.

For instance, the family frequently has questions about what to discuss with the patient and how to discuss it. Families who ask how to react to the patient's psychotic or obnoxious behavior, who feel unable to set limits because of the patient's supposed "fragility" or their own anxiety about taking a stand, may need permission to cut their visits short if the patient becomes withdrawn, hostile, or disorganized in his thinking. Those families who are unable to leave without compounding their guilt should be assisted by the staff in limiting the duration or frequency of upsetting visits. In so doing, the staff may actually role-model appropriate limit-setting behaviors for the family.

Families may also request help in dealing with the social impact of psychiatric hospitalization and with deciding what information should be shared and with whom. Since stigma about mental illness remains a factor, negative ramifications are possible whatever choice is made. The clinician may be of greatest assistance by helping the family to review alternative explanations and to choose one with which they are comfortable.

Finally, some family members are upset enough to require an unusual amount of support or even medication. Since it is not uncommon that other family members are at least as disturbed or anxious as the identified patient, another useful function of the family representative is to recognize and care for the needs of these individuals.

Preparation for Treatment

Once the family's anxieties begin to diminish, they are more receptive to information and are better able to assimilate it. This is a good time to prepare them for what is going to happen over the course of treatment, a process that in itself can reduce anxiety, dependency, and a family's fear of the unknown. It is important to share information about the hospital system, the types of therapy given, the requirements of the family, and even something as simple as a list of visiting hours. The anticipated course of the patient's illness and its treatment should also be discussed. However, since the family is likely to misunderstand or not remember much of this, it is advisable to stress the clinician's availability to answer questions when they arise.

Confronting Questions of Competence

It is almost a universal fact that family members question the role and competence of the person assigned to them in the course of the first meetings. The competence is challenged of not only nurses, social workers, and psychologists who do not have a medical degree, but also of residents and even senior physicians. In any case, the more directly the clinician can deal with these challenges, the more comfortable the family will be in bringing issues to meetings. By acknowledging and making explicit the family concerns and their right to worry, the clinician communicates a secure and unthreatened stance that in turn enables the family to use him or her more extensively.

Use of Written Records and Forms

Since a hospital setting inevitably requires a good deal of information from the family and since meeting time is limited, detailed information should be collected whenever possible from past records or written forms that the family can fill out unassisted. This technique can free the clinician's time to interact with and relate to family members, and help avoid creating the climate of interrogation that occurs when limited time forces the collection of information too quickly. Finally, clinicians should avoid pushing for family secrets or unnecessary information not directly related to diagnosis or treatment planning. The need for help should not require total and immediate abdication of the right to privacy.

Facilitating Medical Treatments

Most patients and families have many questions about psychological reactions to what they have heard about the cause and course of the illness, and methods of treatment. Since many myths and misconceptions exist, the family representative can have an enormous impact, positive or negative, on the level of cooperation with treatments prescribed by the medical staff. For these reasons, the family representative must be well informed about current theories of mental illness, the biology of disease, and the possible impact of psychotropic medications and other treatments. It becomes his or her role to help the family to understand and to demythologize the issues by facilitating open communication with medical personnel. This in itself will encourage both the proper use of drugs, as well as feedback about adverse side effects or other undesirable responses to treatments. Although patients are clearly more responsive to family meetings when their overt psychotic reactions or severe depressions have been mitigated by psychotropic medication, the tendency of the family clinician often is to focus only on psychodynamic explanations for behavior. With severely disturbed patients, this is a danger that could lead to polarization or competition between staff members about who is actually helping the patient. It is far better if mutual respect can be developed with each professional supporting all the treatment modalities being used.

Conveying Hope

Finally, the family should be given hope. Using the clinician's own power and experience as an "expert," the message can be sent that the problem, though currently overwhelming, is surmountable. The timing of this communication is very important. If such reassurance is given too soon, it seems false and serves to cut off the expression of legitimate concerns. If it is given too late, the family will feel rushed into "relevant issues" and into making a commitment before their own needs have been met. The message must be given that the clinician appreciates the complexities of the family's difficulties but is not overpowered by them.

Conducting Controlled Family Therapy Sessions

Once the family representative has formed a relationship with the family and the acute phase of the illness has passed, meetings should be scheduled with the entire family. Most often the family representative and the patient's individual therapist become cotherapists in the family meetings. While cotherapy raises its own problems, it is well worth its liabilities on an inpatient ward, for this technique is useful in diminishing the family defensiveness caused by a single clinician's overidentification with either the patient or a particular family member.

The purpose of these meetings is to facilitate the rapid return of the patient and his family to effective functioning outside the hospital (whether it be together or separately) and to connect them with outpatient therapy. For this purpose, family meetings in psychiatric hospitals should have a concrete focus on specific, attainable, and mutual goals. To paraphrase *Alice in Wonderland*, "How do you know when you get there, if you don't know where you are going?" In order to formulate realistic goals with a family, the following questions may be helpful: (1) What behaviors prevent the family and the patient from working together without hospital support? (2) What behaviors and attitudes are most upsetting to each person? (3) What does each person want to see changed?

As these concerns and goals emerge in discussions with the family, the clinician clarifies, organizes, and helps family members to establish priorities. It is the responsibility of the clinician to assist the family to specify their needs and desires, since such goals as "better communication" or a "happier life" are too general to be helpful in giving direction to treatment. The clinician must also help them to eliminate inappropriate goals, choosing those that can reasonably be accomplished in the time available and postponing those that are more suitable to outpatient therapy. The clinician should share his or her own perceptions and additional recommendations for goals with the family, thus facilitating the establishment of mutually agreeable treatment goals.

It is particularly helpful to both therapist and family to re-evaluate progress toward these goals frequently, since it is easy to get lost in the multitude of issues that come up for discussion. Re-evaluations around specific goals and issues also diminish chaos and, with it, the feelings of powerlessness in both family and therapist. Since supportive and adaptive family behavior is the short-term goal, meetings should not seek to uncover conflicts, search for insight, or determine meanings of behaviors. Such a focus tends to increase the length of hospitalization, which in turn complicates the patient's life in other ways. If too much anxiety is raised, the family will be less likely to cooperate in outpatient treatment. These issues, if dealt with at all, should be explored only after the patient is functioning well in the outside world for a reasonable period and without the explicit or implicit promise that this will prevent relapse. Furthermore, since fears of loss of control are central in families of severely disturbed patients, under no circumstances should psychotic behavior be encouraged or ignored. If any member ceases to make sense in a family meeting, this should be noted and explicitly discouraged. If this intervention does not prove effective in limiting bizarre behavior, it should be explained that inasmuch as the meeting does not seem to be helpful it will be discontinued and rescheduled at a convenient time. Family meetings should be limited to a tolerable length. The therapist who ignores or supports disorganized or otherwise maladaptive behavior is a poor role model for the family by futher confusing their ideas about what is right and reasonable and encouraging the continuance of patient-type behaviors.

A family can best be supportive of a disorganized patient by setting limits, and not tolerating behavior that will get him or her into trouble or decrease the chances of adjusting to the society outside the hospital. The family's belief about what is supportive and helpful may need to be repeatedly challenged. While we are focusing on the patient, such behavior may also be demonstrated by other family members. The same procedure should be followed no matter who demonstrates inappropriate behavior, since the overall goal is to maximize everyone's ability to function without the help of the hospital.

Structure may be provided for the meetings and the time in between meetings by having an action orientation. Rather than dealing with feelings and conflict at great length, the therapist should give tasks that deal specifically with the conflict. If a father has not been involved with his son, it is better to plan things they can do together rather than to discuss the dynamics behind their estrangement. The use of specific helpful cues and instructions and more positive ways of dealing with controversial issues must be practiced in the meetings through role-playing. Finally, families who are overwhelmed with anxiety may also find it helpful to be assigned tasks to complete between interviews. The focus of something to do (contact an agency, prepare a patient's room for his return) diminishes guilt and anxiety.

Providing a Variety of Treatment Formats

Families, like patients, may respond differently to various types of treatment. We have already discussed family meetings with and without the patient. Two other particularly useful types of therapy may also be used: a general multifamily group meeting, and a task-oriented multifamily group meeting.

Multifamily Group

A multiple family group, described in detail elsewhere (Barcai, 1967; Berman, 1972; Detre, et al., 1961; Harrow et al., 1967; Hes and Handler, 1961; Laqueur et al., 1964; Levin, 1966; Tucker and Maxmen, 1972), can decrease the family's sense of aloneness and isolation during a major crisis; many families are too embarrassed to share their problems with relatives and friends. It is also initially easier to see what others are doing "wrong" in their family relationships than to examine one's own family. In such groups, many family members stop in the middle of a comment to someone in another family, saying "Why, I do that, too. I never really saw myself before."

Varying compositions of such groups have been tried. One successful grouping comprises all the family and patients of a particular clinician. Another very helpful criteria for grouping is to separate two-generational family systems and spouse systems. For instance, all patients who are adolescents or young adults may be placed in one group with their parents and siblings, and all patients who are adults and who have spouses in another. Themes of responsibility for illness and fears of recurrence, of course, pervade both groups. However, this is a natural composition in terms of such issues as emancipation, individuation, intimacy, dependency, compromise, etc.

Task-Oriented Groups

Families also can be helped by short-term groups with a specific focus. These task-oriented groups, which may actually teach adaptational skills, are constructed around needs of the population. Some specific topics might be "The Impact of Depression on Marriage," "Family Communication Skills," "Adolescence," "Male-Female Roles in Marriage," and "Socialization Techniques." One particularly helpful task-oriented group focuses on "Preparation for Discharge and Living Together Again." In such a group, family readjustment problems can be anticipated, alternative coping mechanisms discussed, and the importance of establishing outpatient treatment and the need for continuity of care emphasized. Using the techniques of role-playing and role-reversal, new attitudes and behavior can be encouraged for families.

Adequate Aftercare Planning

The first three to six months after hospitalization have been noted to be the most difficult (Bachmann, 1971; Michaux et al., 1969; Zolik et al., 1968; Peretti, 1974). The patient and the family must deal with the impact of the "illness," and the impact of having been in a mental hospital, as well as all the other normal life stresses that may come their way. They must adjust to outpatient therapy and relearn to relate to one another in a world that is less protected and structured than the hospital. For these reasons, the family is less resistant if a number of graduated steps are taken to insure a more comfortable and smooth transition from hospital to home.

Realistic Plans

Building on the importance of activity and structure, the clinician should work with the family and the patient to insure that the plans are neither too ambitious nor too cautious (Freeman and Simmons, 1963). It will not help for a family to decide to return an adolescent to a very demanding academic program if the patient's drug regimen causes drowsiness or impairment of his vision. A husband who attempts to do all the housekeeping and child-care tasks, so that his wife will have no demands on her time, may overburden himself and rob his wife of important role activities and a needed structure for her day.

When dealing with families of adolescents or young adults who have been psychotic, it is particularly important to be realistic about the issue of separation. Such families are often enmeshed and unable to deal with the developmental process of emancipation-individuation. There is no one-way causal relationship for these separation difficulties: both parents and children contribute to keeping these families together. Many clinicians evaluating families recognize their "craziness" or fragility and encourage patients to make an immeidate move away from home (long-term residential treatment, boarding school, an apartment, etc.). These precipitous separations rarely hold. The process of separation should be respected as one that must be worked through carefully over time and even then cannot always be accomplished successfully. To prevent the sabotage of treatment and aftercare planning, very limited goals should be set during hospitalization; rarely should a separation be pushed unless all family members are at least verbally committed to the plan. Long-term family therapy is indicated in these families, and thus the primary goal of inpatient family therapy becomes their acceptance of a commitment to outpatient family treatment.

Home Visits of Gradually Increasing Duration

Because a certain amount of awkwardness is inevitable after a hospitalization (Wolfe, 1969), and because small units of time in upsetting situations are easier to handle, a series of gradually lengthening visits with the family is indicated. A few hours over lunch or dinner are a good beginning; then, using the feedback from the patient and the family, visits may be increased to weekend passes. Some families are comfortable almost immediately, while others find this period filled with anxiety and fears of recurrence. Staff responsiveness to a family's feedback is crucial for the maintenance of in-hospital gains.

Teaching the Reading of Danger Signals

Because acute emotional or psychotic reactions may recur, it is essential to teach the family to read the danger signals and seek help before a problem reaches crisis proportions (Astrachan and Detre, 1968). Reviewing the beginning signs of the past episodes and the problems that emerged does much to raise the awareness of the family. Giving information that will prepare them for future problems may help them to react less catastrophically. It may be helpful, for instance, to mention the possibility of a postpsychotic depression before it occurs. For certain families, a written list of agreed-on "warning signs" may help them to use professionals appropriately without overresponding to day-to-day fluctuations in behavior. The general theme is to encourage a realistic appraisal of the situation and their resources, clarifying both pitfalls and opportunities.

Summary

One method of involving the families of hospitalized psychiatric patients has been described. This approach stresses the importance of meeting the needs of the family by providing information, structure, and control in a time of chaos and crisis. Special attention is given to the importance of appointing a family representative to counterbalance staff tendencies to identify with the patient and to insure that the needs of the family are taken into consideration in treatment planning.

References

Angrist, S., Lefton, M., Dinitz, S., et al. (1961), Aftercare: Tolerance of deviant behavior, posthospital performance levels, and rehospitalization. In: *Proceedings of the Third World Congress of Psychiatry*, Vol. 1. Montreal: University of Toronto and McGill University Press, pp. 237-241.

Appleton, W. S. (1974), Mistreatment of patients' families by psychiatrists. *Amer. J. Psychiat.*, 131:655-657.

Astrachan, B. M. & Detre, T. P. (1968), Post-hospital treatment of the psychotic patient. *Compr. Psychiat.*, 9:71-80.

Bachmann, B. J. (1971), Re-entering the community: A former patient's view. *Hosp. Commun. Psychiat.*, 22:119-122.

Barcai, A. (1967), An adventure in multiple family therapy. *Fam. Proc.*, 6:185-192.

Barrett, J., Kuriansky, J., & Gurland, B. (1972), Community tenure following emergency discharge. *Amer. J. Psychiat.*, 128:958-964.

Bateson, G., Jackson, D. D., Haley, J., et al. (1956), Toward a theory of schizophrenia. *Behav. Sci.*, 1:251-264.

Berman, K. (1972), Multiple family therapy: Its possibilities in preventing readmission. In: *Family Therapy: An Introduction to Theory and Practice*, ed. G. D. Erickson & T. P. Hogan. Monterey, Calif.: Brooks-Cole.

Bowen, M. (1960), A family concept of schizophrenia. In: *The Etiology of Schizophrenia*, ed. D. D. Jackson. New York: Basic Books, pp. 346-372.

Brown, G. W., Birley, J. L. T., & Wing, J. K. (1972), Influence of family life on the course of schizophrenic disorders: A replication. *Brit. J. Psychiat.*, 121:241-258.

Coe, W. C., Curry, A. E., & Kessler, D. R. (1969), Family interactions of psychiatric inpatients. *Fam. Proc.*, 8:119-130.

Davis, J. A., Freeman, H. E., & Simmons, O. G. (1957), Rehospitalization and performance level among former mental patients. *Soc. Probl.*, 5:37-44.

Detre, T., Sayers, J., Norton, N. M., et al. (1961), An experimental approach to the treatment of the acutely ill psychiatric patient in the general hospital. *Conn. Med.*, 25:613-619.

Esterson, A. (1965), Results of family orientated therapy with hospitalized schizophrenics. *Brit. Med. J.*, 2:1462-1465.

Evans, A., Bullard, P., & Solomon, M. (1961), The family as a potential resource in the rehabilitation of the chronic schizophrenic patient. *Amer. J. Psychiat.*, 117:1075-1083.

Fleck, S. (1963), Psychiatric hospitalization as a family experience. *Acta Psychiatr. Scand.*, 39(suppl. 169):1-24.

——— Cornelison, A. R., Norton, N., et al. (1957), Interaction between hospital staff and families. *Psychiat.*, 20:343-350.

Freeman, H. & Simmons, O. (1963), *The Mental Patient Comes Home*. New York: John Wiley.

Harrow, M., Astrachan, B. M., Becker, R. E., et al. (1967), An investigation into the nature of the patient-family therapy group. *Amer. J. Orthopsychiat.*, 37:888-899.

Hes, J. P. & Handler, S. L. (1961), Multidimensional group psychotherapy. *Arch. Gen. Psychiat.*, 5:70-75.

Kreisman, D. E. & Joy, F. D. (1974), Family response to the mental illness of a relative: A review of the literature. *Schiz. Bull.*, 10:34-57.

Laqueur, H. P., LaBart, H. A., & Morony, E. (1964), Multiple family therapy. *Curr. Psychiat. Ther.*, 4:150-154.

Levin, E. C. (1966), Therapeutic multiple family groups. *Internat. J. Group Psychother.*, 16:203-208.

Lidz, T. & Fleck, S. (1960), Schizophrenia, human integration and the role of the family. In: *The Etiology of Schizophrenia*, ed. D. D. Jackson. New York: Basic Books, pp.323-345.

Lorei, T. W. (1967), Prediction of community stay and employment for released psychiatric patients. *J. Consult. Psychol.*, 31:349-357.

Maxmen, J. S., Tucker, G. J., & LeBow, J. (1974), *Rational Hospital Psychiatry*. New York: Brunner/Mazel.

Michaux, W., Katz, M., Kurland, A., et al. (1969), *The First Year Out: Mental Patients After Hospitalization*. Baltimore: Johns Hopkins University Press.

Mishler, E. & Waxler, N. (1966), Family interaction and schizophrenia. *Arch. Gen. Psychiat.*, 15:64-74.

Myers, B. (1968), *A Decade Later: A Follow-up of Social Class and Mental Illness*. New York: John Wiley.

Myers, R. (1959), *Family and Class Dynamics in Mental Illness*. New York: John Wiley.

O'Brien, F. & Azrin, N.H. (1973), Interaction-priming: A method of reinstating patient-family relationships. *Behav. Res. Ther.*, 11:133-136.

Peretti, P. O. (1974), Precipitating factors of readmission of psychiatric patients. *Commun. Ment. Hlth J.*, 10:89-92.

Rabkin, J. (1974), Public attitudes toward mental illness: A review of the literature. *Schiz. Bull.*, 10:1-33.

Reiss, D. (1967), Individual thinking and family interaction. *Arch. Gen. Psychiat.*, 16:80-93.

Richter, H. E. (1974), *The Family as Patient*. New York: Farrar, Straus, & Giroux.

Rose, C. L. (1959), Relatives' attitudes and mental hospitalization. *Ment. Hyg.*, 43:194-203.

Swingle, P. G. (1965), Relatives' concepts of mental patients. *Ment. Hyg.*, 49:461-465.

Tucker, G. J. & Maxmen, J. S. (1972), Multiple family group therapy in a psychiatric hospital. *J. Psychoanal. Groups*, 4:27-34.

Welldon, R. M. C. (1971), The "shadow of death" and its implications in four families, each with a hospitalized schizophrenic member. *Fam. Proc.*, 10:281-302.

Wolfe, E. (1969), *Aftershock*. New York: Putnam's Sons, p.125.

Wood, E. C., Rakusin, J. M. & Morse, E. (1960), Interpersonal aspects of psychiatric hospitalization. *Arch. Gen. Psychiat.*, 3:632-641.

Wynne, L. C. (1972), Family research on the pathogenesis of schizophrenia: Intermediate variables in the study of families at high risk. In: *Progress in Group and Family Therapy*, ed. C. J. Sager & H. S. Kaplan. New York: Brunner/Mazel, pp.659-676.

Yarrow, M. R., Schwartz, C. G., Murphy, H. S., et al. (1955), The psychological meaning of mental illness in the family. *J. Soc. Issues*, 11:12-24.

Zolik, E. S., Lantz, E. M., & Sommers, R. (1968), Hospital return rates and prerelease referrals. *Arch. Gen. Psychiat.*, 18:712-717.

NAME INDEX

SUBJECT INDEX